STUDY GUIDE

FUNDAMENTALS OF GENERAL, ORGANIC, AND BIOLOGICAL CHEMISTRY

FIFTH EDITION

JOHN R. HOLUM
Augsberg College

JOHN WILEY & SONS, INC.
New York Chichester Brisbane Toronto Singapore

ISBN 0-471-59879-8

Printed in the United States of America

10 9 8 7 6 5 4 3 2 1

Contents

Contents

1
GOALS, METHODS, AND MEASUREMENTS

STRATEGY FOR STUDY

A world of difference exists between understanding and knowing. Understanding is only the first step to knowing and the *knowing* of chemistry is our goal.

What counts in your courses to come as well as in your professional life is *remembered chemistry*. "Understood chemistry" is of itself almost never "remembered chemistry." "Understood chemistry" taken alone is chemistry very soon forgotten; chemistry that can seldom, if ever, be applied. It's like a house stopped at the foundation. On the other hand, "rote-memorized chemistry" is almost never "remembered chemistry," either. It is like a house without a foundation and will soon collapse. A complete house requires both a foundation and a superstructure.

The text, lectures, and outside help are your chief aids to understanding. This **Study Guide** will help you get from the understanding to the knowing stage. The **Study Guide** also has examples of worked problems. Definitions of important terms are given. Drill exercises (with answers) are provided as well as self-test questions. As a final check, use the list of objectives for the chapter being studied and see if you can do each of them.

Very broadly, the two main steps for mastering chemistry are these.

First comes understanding.

Study the material until it is understood, until you can say to yourself "that makes sense," or "now I get it," or something similar. With easy material, one reading will get you this far. With the more difficult, you'll need the text, class lectures and discussions, and sometimes extra help. But first get understanding.

Second comes knowing.

Drill yourself on the understood material until you know it. This means memorizing the definitions of new words. It means working problems and answering thought questions.

Step 1. Read the chapter in the text, if possible, once *before* class. Put a pencil mark in the margin near any part you have trouble understanding.[1]

Step 2. Use the lecture period to clear up what you didn't understand in the reading. Erase each check mark as understanding moves in and puzzlement moves out. If the lecture leaves any points still unclear, see your instructor or a teaching assistant about them as soon as you can. Often another classmate can help you.

Step 3. After reaching the understanding stage, begin the knowing stage. Learn the definitions of the important terms. They appear in boldface in the text and are defined in the glossaries of each chapter in this **Study Guide**.

Step 4. Rework any "worked examples." Be sure to do the Practice Exercises. Do all of the other exercises for which answers are provided. The **Study Guide** has many additional problems for you to solve. This step is very important.

Step 5. Test yourself with the Self-Testing Questions in this **Study Guide**. All of the answers are given, and in many instances explanations are also provided. If you do not do very well, take it as a sign that you need to do more studying. But you're really on the verge of knowing the chemistry, so stick with it.

Step 6. As a final test, check the list of objectives for the chapter as given in this **Study Guide**. Be sure you can write out a correct response for each objective.

PROBLEM SOLVING, CALCULATIONS, AND "CHEM ANXIETY"

There is probably nothing that gives students more anxiety about taking chemistry than the thought of having to work problems involving mathematics. The trouble is *not* how to multiply, divide, add, or subtract. Inexpensive, hand-held calculators make these operations particularly easy. Rather, the difficulty is *when to apply the math skills you already know*. Calculating is not the barrier; the problem-solving that *precedes* calculating is the stumbling block.

That's right; the essential work of problem-solving is not the same as doing the calculations. The difference is the same as that encountered daily by a physician. Someone comes in with "a strange pain" in the stomach. The *problem* is "what's causing this pain?" It's a *problem* (and not a mere drill exercise) because the answer is not immediately obvious. This problem has to be solved *before* the physician even thinks about a treatment.

Your use of a calculating skill in working a chemistry problem is like a physician's selection of a treatment in medicine. It's done *after* the problem has been analyzed and solved to the point where the specific calculations or steps in treatment actually are obvious! In chemistry, these steps are often simple mathematical operations but sometimes they are the application of a set of rules (e.g., in naming a chemical compound) or the use of a special source of information (e.g., the periodic table of the elements).

---

[1] I owe the formulation of this step and the next to S. Paul Steed of American River College, Sacramento, California. *Journal of Chemical Education*, December 1976, p. 745.

By means of careful explanations and copious worked examples, we have taken great pains in the text to show you how to analyze a problem and get to the point where you know what calculating skills are applicable. At the end of many worked examples there is a "Check" paragraph that asks, "Does the answer make sense?" It's a way of rethinking the analysis by asking, "Is the result far too large or far to small or about right?"

We have placed a special **icon** in the text margin to identify each calculating skill that is somewhat unique to chemistry and that can easily be mastered. *Be sure that you master these skills.* A physician working on the solution to a medical problem might know that the patient's blood pressure would be useful information. Precisely at this moment a special (but easily mastered) skill is necessary. Always remember, problem solving is not the same as doing the calculations. Problem solving is the creative part; doing the calculations is applying a simple skill. The better you have learned the skills the more smoothly will the problem solving occur.

"Chem anxiety" is handled in many ways. You already have the calculating skills; the text and this Study Guide will help you learn *when* to use them. Don't get behind. Chemistry cannot be learned by cramming before an exam. Take time each day to do some studying, and if you get into this habit you'll be surprised at the difference it makes.

OBJECTIVES

After you have studied this chapter and have worked the exercises in it, you should be able to do the following. (Other objectives may also be assigned.)

1. State what is meant by a "reproducible fact."
2. Describe the relationships among facts, hypotheses, and theories.
3. Distinguish between a number and a physical quantity.
4. Describe in general terms the difference between a physical and a chemical property.
5. Distinguish between a base quantity, a base unit, a standard of measurement, and a derived unit.
6. Give the present name (in the English translation) and the official abbreviation for the successor to the metric system.
7. Name, define, and give the symbols of the SI base units of length, mass, temperature, and time and the derived unit for volume.
8. Describe the advantage of the use of base-10 in the SI.
9. Use the conventions for writing figures and symbols for SI units.
10. Use the prefixes kilo-, centi-, milli-, and micro- with SI units.
11. Convert back and forth between kilograms, grams, milligrams, and micrograms.
12. Convert back and forth between liters, milliliters, and microliters.
13. Use the factor label method and conversion factors to change from one system to another.
14. Tell how many significant figures a number has.
15. Correctly round off numbers obtained by arithmetic operations on physical quantities.
16. State the differences among "accuracy," "error," "uncertainty," and "precision."
17. Tell what is meant by an exact number.
18. Convert between the Fahrenheit, Celsius, and Kelvin scales.
19. Do calculations involving densities.
20. Define each term listed in the Glossary.

GLOSSARY

Accuracy. In science, the degree of conformity to some accepted standard or reference; freedom from error or mistake; correctness.

Base Quantity. A fundamental quantity of physical measurement such as mass, length, and time; a quantity used to define derived quantities such as mass/volume for density.

Base Unit. A fundamental unit of measurement for a base quantity — such as the kilogram for mass, the meter for length, the second for time, the kelvin for temperature degree, and the mole for quantity of chemical substance; a unit to which derived units are related.

Centimeter (cm). A length equal to one-hundredth of the meter. 1 cm = 0.01 m = 0.394 in.

Chemical Property. Any chemical reaction that a substance can undergo and the ability to undergo such a reaction.

Chemical Reaction. A property of substances observed when they change into other substances.

Chemistry. The study of that part of nature bearing on substances, their composition and structures.

Conversion Factor. A fraction that expresses a relationship between quantities that have different units, such as 2.54 cm/in.

Degree Celsius. One-hundredth (1/100) of the interval on a thermometer between the freezing point and the boiling point of water.

Degree Fahrenheit. One-one hundred and eightieth (1/180) of the interval on a thermometer between the freezing point and the boiling point of water.

Density. The ratio of the mass of an object to its volume; the mass per unit volume. Density = mass/volume (usually expressed in g/mL).

Derived Quantity. A quantity based on a relationship that involves one or more base quantities of measurement such as volume (length^3) or density (mass/volume).

Error. The difference between the experimental value and the correct value.

Extensive Property. Any property whose value is directly proportional to the size of the sample; for example, the volume or the mass of a sample.

Factor-Label Method. A strategy for solving computational problems that uses conversion factors and the cancellation of the units of physical quantities as an aid in working toward the solution.

Gram (g). A mass equal to one-thousandth of the kilogram mass, the SI standard mass. 1 g = 0.001 kg = 1000 mg; 1 lb = 454 g.

Hypothesis. A conjecture, subject to being disproved, that explains a set of facts in terms of a common cause and that serves as the basis for the design of additional tests or experiments.

Inertia. The resistance of an object to a change in its position or its motion.

Intensive Property. Any property whose value is independent of the size of the sample, such as temperature and density.

International System of Units (SI). The successor to the metric system with new reference standards for the base units but with the same names for the units and the same decimal relationships.

Kelvin. The SI unit of temperature degree and equal to 1/100th of the interval between the freezing point and the boiling point of water when measured under standard conditions.

Kelvin Scale. The scale of absolute temperatures expressed in kelvins beginning with 0 K for the coldest temperature attainable.

Kilogram (kg). The SI base unit of mass; 1000 g; 2.205 lb.

Length. The base quantity for expressing distances or how long a thing is.

Liter (L). A volume equal to 1000 cm³ or 1000 mL or 1.057 liquid quart.

Mass. A quantitative measure of inertia based on an artifact at Sèvres, France, called the standard kilogram mass; a measure of the quantity of matter in an object relative to this reference standard.

Measurement. An operation whereby we compare an unknown physical quantity such as length or mass with a known physical quantity such as a meter stick or a gram mass.

Meter (m). The base unit of length in the International System of Measurements (SI). 1 m = 100 cm = 39.37 in. = 3.280 ft = 1.093 yd

Microgram (μg). A mass equal to one-thousandth of a milligram. 1 μg = 0.001 mg = 1×10^{-6} g

Microliter (μL). A volume equal to one-thousandth of a milliliter. 1 μL = 0.001 mL = 1×10^{-6} L

Milligram (mg). A mass equal to one-thousandth of a gram. 1 mg = 0.001 g; 1000 mg = 1 g

Milliliter (mL). A volume equal to one-thousandth of a liter. 1 mL = 0.001 L = 1 cm³; 1 liquid ounce = 29.57 mL; 1 liquid quart = 946.4 mL.

Millimeter (mm). A length equal to one-thousandth of a meter. 1 mm = 0.001 m = 0.0394 in.

Physical Property. Any observable characteristic of a substance other than a chemical property, such as color, density, melting point, boiling point, temperature, and quantity.

Physical Quantity. A property of something to which we assign both a numerical value and a unit, such as mass, volume, or temperature; physical quantity = number × unit.

Precision. The fineness of a measurement or the degree to which successive measurements agree with each other when several are taken one after the other. (See also *Accuracy.*)

Property. A characteristic of something by means of which we can identify it.

Reference Standard. A physical description or embodiment of a base unit of measurement, such as the standard meter or the standard kilogram mass.

Scientific Method. A method of solving a problem that uses facts to devise a hypothesis to explain the facts and to suggest further tests or experiments designed to discover if the hypothesis is true or false.

Scientific Notation. The method of writing a number as the product of two numbers, one being 10^x where x is some positive or negative whole number.

Second (s). The SI unit of time; 1/60th minute.

Significant Figures. The number of digits in a numerical measurement or in the result of a calculation that are known with certainty to be accurate plus the first digit whose value is uncertain.

Specific Gravity. The ratio of the density of an object to the density of water.

Temperature. The measure of the hotness or coldness of an object. *Degrees* of temperature, such as those of the Celsius, Fahrenheit, or Kelvin scales, are intervals of equal separation on the thermometer.

Theory. An explanation for a large number of facts, observations, and hypotheses in terms of one or a few fundamental assumptions of what the world (or some small part of the world) is like.

Time. A period during which something endures, exists, or continues.

Uncertainty. The estimate of how finely a number can be read from a measuring instrument.

Volume. The capacity of an object to occupy space.

Weight. The gravitational force of attraction on an object as compared to that of some reference.

MULTIPLES AND SUBMULTIPLES BY MOVING A DECIMAL POINT

The purpose here is to become skilled in changing a number by units of 10, 100, 1000, or more or by 0.1, 0.01, 0.001, etc., simply by moving the decimal point. We shall practice applying this skill to a set of problems that involves specific quantities stated in metric or SI units.

The most common metric or SI conversions are made by moving the decimal point either three places or multiples of three places. The prefix used indicates the type of change to be made. Consider those prefixes most commonly encountered in the life sciences and in chemistry:

Prefix	Exponential Equivalent
kilo-	10^3
REFERENCE	1 (or 10^0)
milli-	10^{-3}
micro-	10^{-6}

To change a quantity expressed in the unit of the reference (e.g., liters) to the equivalent expressed by the next smaller unit in this list (e.g., milliliter), we simply move the decimal three places to the right.

Example: 3 liters = 3000 milliliters

Remember, to go from a larger to a smaller unit we always move the decimal point to the right.

To change a physical quantity from a smaller to a larger unit, we move the decimal point to the left.

Example: 2000 millimeters = 2 meters

2000.0 millimeters becomes 2 . 0 . 0 . 0 . 0 meters

3 2 1 ← left

Note that "milli-" means "a thousandth"; thus, the meter is a larger unit than the millimeter.

DRILL EXERCISES

I.   EXERCISES IN METRIC UNITS

The purpose of these exercises is to help you become very skillful in converting from a quantity to one of its multiples or submultiples. Every conversion in these exercises involves nothing more than moving the decimal point. Fill in the blanks of the second column with a number that, together with its unit, is equivalent to the quantity in the first column. Another purpose of the exercises is to learn the accepted abbreviations of the various SI units (consult the table in the text for these).

	Quantity	Equivalent
Examples:	0.001 m	1 m
	1000 m	1.000 km
	1654 g	1.654 kg

1. 0.01 m _____ cm

2. 0.10 m _____ cm

3. 2985 m _____ km

11. 0.547 mg _____ µg

12. 0.120 mL _____ µL

13. 15 mm _____ cm

4. 1564 mg _____ g

5. 156.4 mg _____ g

6. 15.64 mg _____ g

7. 1640 mL _____ L

8. 0.002 L _____ mL

9. 454 g _____ kg

10. 150 mL _____ L

14. 15 cm _____ m

15. 0.98 m _____ cm

16. 1.620 g _____ mg

17. 0.101 L_____ mL

18. 0.067 g _____ mg

19. 250 mL_____ L

20. 0.0001 mL _____ µL

II. EXERCISES IN SCIENTIFIC NOTATION

The purpose of these problems is to help you become skilled in converting back and forth between numbers expressed in the usual way and their equivalents in scientific notation.

SET A. Change each number to the form it has in scientific notation.

1. 1,062,457 _____

2. 0.00543 _____

3. 111.6 _____

4. 0.00000521_____

5. 5.025 _____

SET B. Change each number given in scientific notation to its equivalent stated in the usual way.

1. 6.150×10^{3}_____

2. 5.362×10^{2}_____

3. 2.35×10^{-2}_____

4. 8.79×10^{-5}_____

5. 6.542001×10^{6}_____

III. EXERCISES IN SIGNIFICANT FIGURES

Rule 1.   Zeros sandwiched between nonzero digits are always significant.

Rule 2.   Zeros that do no more than set off the decimal point on their *left* are never counted as significant figures.

Rule 3.   Trailing zeros to the *right* of the decimal point are always significant.

Rule 4.   Trailing zeros are counted as significant when they occur before the decimal point (which is how we treat them in the text and this Study Guide).

Rule 5.   Exact numbers are treated as having an infinite number of significant figures.

Examples: 4.0054   5   (Rule 1)

4540   4   (Rule 4)

0.000454   3   (Rule 2)

4.5400   5   (Rule 3)

1. 60,500 _____   2. 6.0500 _____

3. 0.605 _____   4. 0.6050 _____

5. 0.000605_____   6. 0.0006050 _____

7. 1.0098 _____   8. 1.9800×10^{10} _____

9. 46000 _____ 10. 60510 _____

IV. EXERCISES IN THE FACTOR–LABEL METHOD FOR CONVERTING FROM ONE SYSTEM OF UNITS TO ANOTHER

The factor-label method is *not* a method for solving a problem but a strategy for guiding the use of your calculating skills. You have to analyze the problem first to decide what factor-labels should be used. The "method" is then a way of using the units (labels) to help you know when to multiply or divide. The method involves two key elements, a key idea and a key strategy.

The key idea: Fix in your mind the final unit you want, and work to make your answer be in that unit.

The key strategy: Set up multiplications or divisions to get all unwanted units to cancel. If they don't, you know you have set up the solution to the problem incorrectly.

We'll study and learn to do this by means of examples.

Sample Problem 1: Change 10.0 inches into centimeters.

Analysis   We need the relationship between inches and centimeters. (Once we know this, we let the units guide the calculation.)

Solution   A table of conversion factors (e.g., Table 1.1 in the text) tells us that there are 2.54 cm in 1 inch (exactly).

We can write this basic relationship in either of two equivalent ways. Both state the same relationship between the inch and the centimeter. One is simply the inverse, or the reciprocal, of the other.

$$\frac{2.54\,\text{cm}}{1\,\text{in.}} \quad \text{or} \quad \frac{1\,\text{in.}}{2.54\,\text{cm}}$$

The divisor line is read as "per." The first ratio says "2.54 cm per 1 in." The second says "1 in. per 2.54 cm."

We want our answer to be in centimeters. We must, therefore, use the ratio that will give us this answer. This is the "key idea" for this problem.

Step 1.   Write down the given.
            (be sure to include the unit.)   10.0 in.
Step 2.   Multiply the given by the right conversion factor.

Do we write it as   (A) $10.0 \text{ in.} \times \dfrac{2.54\,\text{cm}}{1\,\text{in.}}$?

            or

Do we write it as   (B) $10.0 \text{ in.} \times \dfrac{1\,\text{in.}}{2.54\,\text{cm}}$?

In other words, which way do we use the relation between inches and centimeters? In

(B), the units will not properly cancel to leave the answer solely in "cm." In (A), the units do cancel correctly,

$$(A) \qquad 10.0 \ \cancel{\text{in.}} \times \frac{2.54 \ \boxed{\text{cm}}}{1 \ \cancel{\text{in.}}}$$

Step 3.   Do the arithmetic. Do whatever multiplications or divisions of numbers that there are left to do.

$$10.0 \times 2.54 \ \text{cm} = 25.4 \ \text{cm}$$

Check   Does the answer make sense? Should the *size* of the number (25.4) be larger than the number of inches? Yes, because we know that the number of centimeters is always greater than the corresponding number for inches.

SET A. Before continuing, work enough of the following until you are sure you understand and can set up conversion factors in either of two ways

1.   There are 5280 feet in a mile. _____

2.   There are 2.20 pounds in a kilogram. _____

3.   There are 454 grams in a pound. _____

4.   There are 36.4 inches in a yard. _____

5.   There are 1000 milligrams in a gram. _____

6.   There are 1000 meters in a kilometer. _____

7.   There are 29.6 milliliters in a fluid ounce._____

8.   There are 7000 grains in 454 grams._____

9.   There are 1000 kilograms in a metric ton._____

10.   There are 1000 grams in a kilogram. _____

Sample Problem 2:   How many inches are there in 127 centimeters?

Step 1.   Write down the given.   127 cm
Step 2.   Multiply the given by the right conversion factor.

Do we write it   (C) $127 \ \text{cm} \times \dfrac{2.54 \ \text{cm.}}{1 \ \text{in.}}$?

Or do we write it   (D) $127 \ \text{cm} \times \dfrac{1 \ \text{in.}}{2.54 \ \text{cm}}$?

Only (D) lets us cancel units in a way that leaves the answer in the unit called for in the problem.   (Draw the cancel lenes yourself.)

$$127\,\text{cm} \times \frac{1\ \text{in.}}{2.54\ \text{cm}} = \frac{127}{2.54}\ \text{in.} = 50.0\ \text{in.}$$

The units for (C) would be $\dfrac{(\text{cm})(\text{cm})}{\text{in.}}$ or $\dfrac{\text{cm}^2}{\text{in.}}$!

Step 3.   Do the arithmetic.

SET B. Work the following problems using the conversion factors stated in Set A.

1. How many feet are there in 0.5000 mile? _____

2. How many miles are there in 15,000 feet? _____

3. How many yards are there in 100 inches? _____

4. How many milligrams are there in 0.100 gram? _____

5. How many grams are there in 5.0 grains? _____

These problems were actually quite simple. The real power of the factor-label method comes when you don't have a single conversion factor to use to work a problem and you have to improvise from two or more factors. Using the conversion factors given in Set A, let us see how this works by studying examples.

Sample Problem 3: How many metric tons are there in 1000 pounds?

We don't have a factor to convert pounds to metric tons directly. We have to improvise. We do have a factor relating metric tons to kilograms (No. 9 in Set A).

$$\frac{1000\ \text{kilograms}}{1\ \text{metric ton}} \quad \text{or} \quad \frac{1\ \text{metric ton}}{1000\ \text{kilograms}}$$

We also have a factor relating kilograms to pounds (No. 2 in Set A).

$$\frac{2.20\ \text{pounds}}{1\ \text{kilogram}} \quad \text{or} \quad \frac{1\ \text{kilogram}}{2.20\ \text{pounds}}$$

Following our steps, we have:

Step 1.   Write down the given: 1000 pounds
Step 2.   Pick a factor that allows you to cancel "pounds."

$$1000\ \cancel{\text{pounds}} \times \frac{1\ \boxed{\text{kilogram}}}{2.20\ \cancel{\text{pounds}}}$$

Multiply all this by another factor that allows you to cancel kilograms.

$$1000\ \cancel{\text{pounds}} \times \frac{1\ \cancel{\text{kilogram}}}{2.20\ \cancel{\text{pounds}}} \times \frac{1\ \boxed{\text{metric ton}}}{1000\ \cancel{\text{kilograms}}}$$

(In principle, you would keep doing this, picking additional conversion factors that let you cancel unwanted units, until only the desired unit(s) remains. As you can see, we are through using conversion factors in this sample problem.)

Step 3.   Do the arithmetic.

$$1000 \times \frac{1}{2.20} \times \frac{1}{1000} \text{ metric tons} = 0.455 \text{ metric ton}$$

The advantage of leaving all the arithmetic to the end is that one can often cancel some of the numbers too.

Sample Problem 4: How many milligrams are there in 1.00 grain?

(The needed units are given in Set A.) Here is how the final solution will look before the arithmetic is done.

$$1.00 \text{ grain} \times \frac{454 \text{ grams}}{7000 \text{ grains}} \times \frac{1000 \text{ milligram}}{1 \text{ gram}}$$

Final answer: 64.9 milligrams per grain

SET C. Practice what you have learned from Sample Problems 3 and 4 by working the following.

1.   How many grains are there in 1.00 kilogram? _____

2.   How many pounds are there in 2.0 metric tons? _____

3.   How many milligrams are there in 0.5 kilogram? _____

SELF-TESTING QUESTIONS

COMPLETION. Fill in the blanks with the words or phrases that best complete each statement or answer the question.

1.   The operation by which we compare an unknown physical quantity with a known quantity such as a reference standard is called _____ .

2.   Properties that we can measure without changing a substance into some other substance are called _____ properties.

3.   The inertia of an object is its ability to _____ .

4.   The quantitative measure of an object's inertia is called its _____ .

5.   Which of these are base units and which are derived?
     (a)   volume _____   (c)   area _____
     (b)   mass _____ (d)   length _____

6.   The successor to the metric system is the _____ .

7.   The physical embodiment of a base unit is called a reference_____ .

8.   The base unit of length in the metric system is the_____ .

9.   The base unit of length in the successor to the metric system is the _____ .

10.   The reference standard for the measurement of length in the metric system is _____
      _____ .

11.   Is this also the reference standard for the measurement of length in the successor to the metric system? _____

12.   If not, how do the two differ in length?_____

13. The base unit of mass in the metric system is the _____ .

14. The base unit of mass in the successor to the metric system is _____ .

15. Scientists would like to have a reference standard for mass that is not an artifact (not a manufactured object) because _____ .

16. The base unit of time in the SI is the _____ .

17. The base unit for the temperature degree in the SI is the _____ .

18. The degree _____ was formerly called the degree Centigrade.

19. There are _____ degree divisions between the freezing point and the boiling point of water on the Fahrenheit scale.

20. The meter is a little longer than _____ feet.

21. Half an inch would be _____ than 1 centimeter.
                              (shorter or longer)

22. In 1.0 milliliter of water there are about 16 drops. One drop is therefore _____ microliters.

23. One kilogram of water occupies one _____ of volume (in SI terms), and this volume is roughly one _____ in the "English" system.

24. To change 0.00056 to scientific notation we move the decimal point 4 places to the _____ and use an exponent of _____ for the 10 part of the expression; e.g., 5.6×10^{-4}.

25. Express these numbers in scientific notation in which the first part of the number is between 1 and 10.
     (a) 156 _____
     (b) 4,360,890,000,000 _____
     (c) 0.00000043 _____
     (d) 0.10004 _____

26. Complete the following conversions of the first numbers given to alternative expressions in scientific notation in which the exponents are numbers divisible by 3.
     (a) $94,500,000 = 94.5 \times 10^{-}$
     (b) $0.000896 = 896 \times 10^{-}$ or $0.896 \times 10^{-}$

27. Write the accepted SI abbreviations for each unit.
     (a) milligram _____   (c) deciliter _____
     (b) microliter _____   (d) milliliter _____

28. Reexpress these quantities using the SI prefix supplied.
     (a) 1500 g = _____ kg
     (b) 0.0000080 L = _____ μL
     (c) 0.0045 mL = _____ μL
     (d) 4502 mg = _____ g
     (e) 0.015 kg = _____ g

29. If the correct value of the mass of an object is 14.5068 g and someone found it to be 14.5069 g, we'd say that the reported measurement is very _____ .
                                          (precise or accurate)

30. Using one weighing balance, an object was found to have a mass of 16.1 g. Using a different balance, the mass was found to be 16.11 g. What is the advantage of the second balance, less *error* or less *uncertainty?* _____

31. State how many significant figures are in each physical quantity.
(a) 1.00050 g _____
(b) 1.000 × 10⁴ L _____
(c) 0.0105 mL _____

32. The inch is legally defined as 2.54 cm, exactly. In doing calculations, how many significant figures can be assumed are in 2.54 cm when it occurs in the conversion factor:

$\dfrac{2.54 \text{ cm}}{1 \text{ in.}}$? _____

33. When we subtract 24.567 mL from 482.4 mL, how do we round off the difference and how is the difference correctly expressed? _____ (The calculator answer is 457.833.)

34. If we subtract 0.458 m from 362 m, how is the difference correctly expressed? _____ (The calculator answer is 361.542.)

35. In multiplying 2.3 in. times $\dfrac{2.54 \text{ cm}}{1 \text{ in.}}$, how is the product correctly expressed? _____
(The calculator answer is 5.842.)

36. If we multiply 3.678 cm by the conversion factor $\dfrac{1 \text{ in.}}{2.54 \text{ cm}}$, the answer is correctly expressed as
_____ . (The calculator answer is 1.4480314.)

37. If we multiply 13.97 cm by the conversion factor $\dfrac{1 \text{ in.}}{2.54 \text{ cm}}$, the answer is correctly expressed as
_____ . (The calculator answer is 5.5.)

38. The relationship 1 liter = 1.057 quart can be expressed by means of what two ratios that we can use as conversion factors? _____   _____

39. If 1 gram = 15.43 grain and 1 dram = 60 grains (exactly), then how many drams are in 425 gram?
_____

40. What is 75 °F in °C? _____   In K? _____

41. The mass of a sample of water is an example of an _____ property.
(extensive or intensive)

42. The weight of an object divided by its volume equals its _____ .

43. An organic liquid that cannot dissolve in water has a specific gravity of 1.5. Will this liquid sink or float in water? _____

44. At the same temperature, object A has a density of 1.6 g/mL and object B has a density of 1.1 g/mL. Suppose a sample of A and a sample of B weigh the same. Which would occupy the larger volume?_____

45. Suppose someone invented a new temperature scale—call it the X scale — and arbitrarily (a) set 200-degree intervals between the freezing point and the boiling point of water, and (b) set the freezing point of water at +10° X on the new scale. What would be the equation for converting from degrees X to degrees Celsius? (Check your equation by doing the conversions at known values for the freezing point and the boiling point of water in degrees Celsius.) _____

46. (Special Topic 1.1) The density of mercury at room temperature is (rounded) 13.5 g/mL. The density of water at room temperature (again rounded) is 1.0 g/mL. What is the specific gravity of mercury at room temperature? _____

MULTIPLE–CHOICE. For each of the following select all of the correct answers found among the choices (in some questions two or more choices will correctly answer the question).

1.   An example of a chemical property is
     (a)   the melting of ice
     (b)   the digestion of a slice of bread
     (c)   the golden luster of polished brass
     (d)   the evaporation of water

2.   When properly expressed in scientific notation, the quantity 0.01205 liter becomes
     (a)   12.05 mL   (c) 1.205×10^{3} L
     (b) 12.05×10^{3} L   (d) 1.205×10^{-2} L

3.   A distance of 100 cm is the same as
     (a) 1.00 meter   (b) 10 cc   (c) 1.00×10^{3} mm   (d)   0.00100 kilometer

4.   A temperature of 60 °C is the same as
     (a) 15.6 °   (b) 213 K   (c) 108 °   (d) 140 °F

5.   A length of 25.4 mm is the same as
     (a) 1 in. (exactly)   (b) 10 in.   (c) 2.54 cm   (d) 0.0254 meter

6.   A measurement reported as 1.5050×10^{-3} g has how many significant figures?
     (a) 4   (b) 5   (c) 7   (d) 8

7.   A substance that is denser than water might have a density of
     (a)   1000 grams per liter
     (b)   0.50
     (c)   18 micrograms per microliter
     (d)   1.0

8.   One milliliter is the same as
     (a)   0.001 deciliter
     (b)   1000 microliters
     (c)   1 mm
     (d)   0.001 liter

9.   Which unit is closest in size to 500 grams?
     (a) ounce   (b) 500 mL   (c) pound   (d) kilogram

10. A temperature of 27 °C is the same as
     (a) 246 K   (b) –27 K   (c) 300 K   (d) 27 K

11. A volume of 145 mL is the same as
     (a) 0.145 L   (b) 0.145 kL   (c) 1450 mL   (d) 1.45 L

12. A mass of 0.203 g is the same as
     (a) 2.03 kg   (b) 0.0203 kg   (c) 20.3 mg   (d) 203 mg

13. A mass of 5,000,000 µg is the same as
     (a) 5000.000 mg   (b) 5 kg   (c) 5.000000 g   (d) 0.5 g

14. How many meters are in 1.00 bolt of cloth, if
          1 bolt = 120 feet (exactly), and
          1 foot = 0.3048 meter (exactly)?

(a) 36.6 m   (b) 394 m   (c) 0.00254 m   (d) 40.0 m

15.   How many furlongs are in 5.00 mile if

      1 furlong = 220 yards (exactly)

      1 yard = 3 feet (exactly) and

      1 mile = 5280 feet (exactly) ?

(a)   360 furlong   (c) 1.29×10^{-4} furlong

(b) 1.94×10^{6} furlong   (d) 40.0 furlong

16.   The density of liquid water at 20°C may be accurately given in any one of these ways. Which has the least uncertainty?

(a) 1 g/mL   (c) 0.999 g/mL

(b) 1.0 g/mL   (d) 0.99862 g/mL

17.   A sample of a mineral has a volume of 4.50 mL and a mass of 13.5 grams. What is its density?

(a) 3.00 g/mL   (c) 0.333 g/mL

(b) 0.33 mL/g   (d) 3.00 mL/g

18.   Benzene boils at 80°C. What is its boiling point in degrees F?

(a) 27°F   (b) 176°F   (c) 353°F   (d) 160°F

ANSWERS

ANSWERS TO DRILL EXERCISES

I.   Exercises In Metric Units

1.	1 cm	11.	547 µg
2.	10 cm	12.	120 µL
3.	2.985 km	13.	1.5 cm
4.	1.564 g	14.	0.15 m
5.	0.1564 g	15.	98 cm
6.	0.01564 g	16.	1620 mg
7.	1.640 L	17.	101 mL
8.	2 mL	18.	67 mg
9.	0.454 kg	19.	0.250 L
10.	0.150 L	20.	0.1 µL

II.   Exercises in Exponential Notation

Set A.   1. 1.062457×10^{6} Set B. 1. 6150

      2. 5.43×10^{-3} 2. 536.2

      3. 1.116×10^{2} 3. 0.0235

      4. 5.21×10^{-6} 4. 0.0000879

      5.   5.025 (not 5.025×10^{0};   5. 6,542,001

      this is not done.)

III.   Exercises in Significant Figures

1. 5 (Rule 1, Rule 4)

2. 5 (Rules 1 and 3)

3. 3 (Rule 1)

4. 4 (Rules 1 and 3)

5. 3 (Rules 1 and 2)

6. 4 (Rules 1, 2, and 3)

7. 5 (Rule 1)

8. 5 (Rule 3)

9. 5 (Rule 4)

10. 5 (Rules 1 and 4)

IV.   Exercises in the Cancel-Unit Method for Converting from One System of Units to Another

Set A.

1. $\dfrac{5280 \text{ feet}}{1 \text{ mile}}$ or $\dfrac{1 \text{ mile}}{5280 \text{ feet}}$

2. $\dfrac{2.20 \text{ pounds}}{1 \text{ kilogram}}$ or $\dfrac{1 \text{ kilogram}}{2.20 \text{ pounds}}$

3. $\dfrac{454 \text{ grams}}{1 \text{ pound}}$ or $\dfrac{1 \text{ pound}}{454 \text{ grams}}$

4. $\dfrac{36.4 \text{ inches}}{1 \text{ yard}}$ or $\dfrac{1 \text{ yard}}{36.4 \text{ inches}}$

5. $\dfrac{1000 \text{ mg}}{1 \text{ g}}$ or $\dfrac{1 \text{ g}}{1000 \text{ mg}}$

6. $\dfrac{1000 \text{ m}}{1 \text{ km}}$ or $\dfrac{1 \text{ km}}{1000 \text{ m}}$

7. $\dfrac{29.6 \text{ mL}}{1 \text{ fl oz}}$ or $\dfrac{1 \text{ fl oz}}{29.6 \text{ mL}}$

8. $\dfrac{7000 \text{ grains}}{454 \text{ grams}}$ or $\dfrac{454 \text{ grams}}{7000 \text{ grains}}$

9. $\dfrac{1000 \text{ kg}}{1 \text{ ton}}$ or $\dfrac{1 \text{ ton}}{1000 \text{ kg}}$

10. $\dfrac{1000 \text{ g}}{1 \text{ kg}}$ or $\dfrac{1 \text{ kg}}{1000 \text{ g}}$

Set B   1. $0.5000 \text{ mile} \times \dfrac{5280 \text{ feet}}{1 \text{ mile}} = 2640 \text{ feet}$

2. $15000 \text{ feet} \times \dfrac{1 \text{ mile}}{5280 \text{ feet}} = 2.841 \text{ miles}$

3. $100 \text{ inches} \times \dfrac{1 \text{ yard}}{36.4 \text{ inches}} = 2.75 \text{ yards}$

4. $0.1 \text{ gram} \times \dfrac{1000 \text{ mg}}{1 \text{ g}} = 100 \text{ mg}$

5. $5.0 \text{ grains} \times \dfrac{454 \text{ grams}}{7000 \text{ grains}} = 0.32 \text{ gram}$

Set C   1. $1.00 \text{ kg} \times \dfrac{1000 \text{ grams}}{1 \text{ kg}} \times \dfrac{7000 \text{ grains}}{454 \text{ grams}} = 1.54 \times 10^4 \text{ grains}$
(The pocket calculator result, 15,418.5022, has to be rounded to 3 significant figures.)

2. $2.0 \text{ metric ton} \times \dfrac{1000 \text{ kilogram}}{1 \text{ metric ton}} \times \dfrac{2.2 \text{ pounds}}{1 \text{ kilogram}} =$
$4.4 \times 10^3 \text{ pounds}$

3. $0.5 \text{ kg} \times \dfrac{1000 \text{ grams}}{1 \text{ kg}} \times \dfrac{1000 \text{ milligrams}}{1 \text{ gram}} =$
$5 \times 10^5 \text{ milligrams}$

ANSWERS TO SELF–TESTING QUESTIONS

Completion

1. measurement
2. physical
3. resist a change in motion
4. mass
5. (a) derived   (b) base   (c) derived   (d) base
6. SI (International System of Units)
7. standard
8. meter
9. meter
10. the distance between two scratches on a bar of platinum-iridium alloy kept at Sèvres, France)
11. No
12. They do not differ at all in length.
13. kilogram mass (at Sèvres, France)
14. the same kilogram mass

15. manufactured artifacts are subject to corrosion and possibly to theft or loss through natural disaster

16. second

17. kelvin

18. Celsius

19. 180

20. 3

21. longer

22. 63 microliters. Using the   factor-label method it works out like this: $\dfrac{1.0 \ \cancel{mL}}{16 \text{ drops}} \times \dfrac{1000 \text{ microliters}}{1 \ \cancel{mL}} = 63 \ \dfrac{\text{microliters}}{\text{drop}}$

23. liter, quart (liquid, U.S.)

24. right; −4; 5.6×10^{-4}

25. (a) 1.56×10^{2} (b) 4.36089×10^{12}
    (c) 4.3×10^{-7} (d) 1.0004×10^{-1}

26. (a) 6   (b) −6; −3

27. (a) mg   (b) μL   (c) dL   (d) mL

28. (a) 1.500 kg   (b) 8.0 μL   (c) 4.5 μL   (d) 4.502 g   (e) 15 g

29. accurate

30. less uncertainty

31. (a) 6 (b) 4 (c) 3

32. an infinite number

33. 457.8 mL

34. 362 m

35. 5.8 cm

36. 1.448 in.

37. 5.500 in.

38. $\dfrac{1 \text{ liter}}{1.057 \text{ quart}}$ or $\dfrac{1.057 \text{ quart}}{1 \text{ liter}}$

39. 109 dram

40. 24 °C; 297 K

41. extensive

42. density

43. sink

44. Object B. Being less dense, it needs more room to have the same mass as the more dense A.

45. $2°C = °X − 10$ or $C = \dfrac{1}{2}(°X − 5)$

46. 13.5

Multiple–Choice

1. b	2. d	3. a, c, and d
4. d	5. a, c, and d	6. b
7. c	8. b and d	9. c
10. c	11. a	12. d
13. a and c	14. a	15. d
16. d	17. a	18. b

2

MATTER AND ENERGY

The kinds of matter and the states of matter are described in this chapter in only general terms. More about the nature of matter will be presented later, but first we encounter the laws of chemical combination here.

Because matter changes in important ways when energy is either given to it or taken from it, the broad topic of energy dominates Chapter Two. Energy can cause changes in physical state, and it can cause chemical reactions. Energy can also be produced by changes of state and by chemical reactions. No matter where energy goes or how it is transformed, however, it is always conserved.

When we add or remove energy, we need units for describing quantities involved. The units we use are the calorie and the kilocalorie. They are particularly important in chemistry as applied to the life sciences.

Our physical well-being depends upon our keeping a steady body temperature in the face of internal chemical changes that constantly release heat. Because water, the main body fluid, helps us to do just that, we take a thorough look at the thermal properties of water.

These particular aspects of Chapter Two and the important terms should be given your best attention.

OBJECTIVES

After you have studied this chapter and have worked the exercises in it, you should be able to do the following. (Other objectives may also be assigned.)

1. Define "matter," give its three states, and name and define its three kinds.
2. State the key differences among elements, compounds and mixtures.

3. Be able to tell from a chemical equation what are the symbols of the reactants and the products.
4. Write the names and symbols of common elements listed in Table 2.1 of the text.
5. State the following laws of nature: the law of conservation of energy, the law of conservation of mass, the law of definite proportions, and the law of multiple proportions.
6. Give the five main postulates of Dalton's atomic theory and explain how they fit the three laws of chemical combination.
7. Define "energy" and give the names for six forms of energy.
8. Define "joule" and "kilojoule" as well as "calorie," "kilocalorie," and "large calorie (Calorie)."
9. Do calculations involving specific heats, heats of fusion, and heats of vaporization.
10. Explain how the specific heat and the latent heat of water make it especially fit as the body fluid.
11. Explain what is meant by exothermic and endothermic.
12. Define all of the terms listed in the Glossary.

GLOSSARY

Alloy. An intimate mixture of one or more metals in each other made by mixing the metals in their molten forms and then cooling the mixture.

Atom. The smallest particle of a given element that bears the chemical properties of the element.

Atomic Symbol. The one- or two-letters used instead of names of atoms in equations and formulas.

Boiling Point. The temperature at which a liquid boils.

Calorie. The amount of heat that raises the temperature of 1 g of water by 1 degree Celsius from 14.5°C to 15.5°C.

Chemical Energy. The potential energy that substances have because their arrangements of electrons and atomic nuclei are not as stable as are alternative arrangements that become possible in chemical reactions.

Coefficients. Numbers placed before formulas in chemical equations to specify the proportions of the formula units involved in a reaction.

Compound. A substance made from the atoms of two or more elements that are present in a definite proportion by mass and by atoms.

Condensation. The physical change of a substance from its gaseous state to its liquid state.

Dalton's Atomic Theory. A theory that accounts for the laws of chemical combination by postulating that matter consists of indestructible atoms; that all atoms of the same element are identical in mass and other properties; that the atoms of different elements are different in mass and other properties; and that in the formation of a compound, atoms join together in definite, whole-number ratios.

Element. A substance that cannot be broken down into anything that is both stable and more simple.

Endothermic. Describing a change that needs a constant supply of energy to happen.

Energy. A capacity to cause a change that can, in principle, be harnessed for useful work.

Equation, Balanced. A chemical equation in which all atoms that appear among the reactants are found among the products.

Equation, Chemical. A shorthand representation of a chemical reaction that uses formulas instead of names for reactants and products; that separates reactant formulas from product formulas by an arrow; that separates formulas on either side of the arrow by plus signs; and that expresses the proportions of the chemicals (in terms of formula units) by simple numbers (coefficients) placed before the formulas.

Evaporation. The conversion of a substance from its liquid to its vapor state.

Exothermic. Describing a change by which heat energy is released from the system.

Formula, Chemical. A symbol for a chemical substance that uses atomic symbols and subscripts to describe the ratio of atoms in one formula unit of the substance.

Formula, Empirical. A chemical symbol for a compound that gives only the ratios of the atoms and not necessarily the composition of a complete molecule.

Formula Unit. A single particle that has the composition shown by the chemical formula of the substance.

Gas. Any substance that must be contained in a wholly closed space and whose shape and volume is determined entirely by the shape and volume of its container; a state of matter.

Heat. The form of energy that transfers between two objects in contact that have initially different temperatures.

Heat Capacity. The quantity of heat that a given object can absorb (or release) per degree Celsius change in temperature.

$$\text{Heat capacity} = \text{heat}/\Delta t \text{ where } \Delta t \text{ is the change in temperature.}$$

Heat of Fusion. The quantity of heat that one gram of a substance absorbs when it changes from its solid to its liquid state at its melting point.

Heat of Vaporization. The quantity of heat that one gram of a substance absorbs when it changes from its liquid to its gaseous state.

Joule (J). The SI derived unit of energy. 4.184 J = 1 cal (exactly)

Kilocalorie (kcal). The quantity of heat equal to 1000 calories.

Kilojoule (kJ). 1000 joules.

Kinetic Energy. The energy of an object by virtue of its motion.

$$\text{Kinetic Energy} = (\frac{1}{2})(\text{mass})(\text{velocity})^2$$

Law of Conservation of Energy. Energy can be neither created nor destroyed but only transformed from one form to another.

Law of Conservation of Mass. Matter is neither created nor destroyed in chemical reactions; the masses of all products equal the masses of all reactants.

Law of Definite Proportions. The elements in a compound occur in definite proportions by mass.

Law of Multiple Proportions. When two elements can combine to form more than one compound, the different masses of the first that can combine with the same mass of the second are in the ratio of small whole numbers.

Liquid. A fluid state of matter in which a substance's volume but not its shape is independent of the shape of its container.

Matter. Anything that occupies space and has mass.

Melting Point. The temperature at which a solid changes into its liquid form.

Metabolism. The sum total of all of the chemical reactions that occur in an organism.

Metal. Any element that is shiny, conducts electricity well, and (if a solid) can be hammered into sheets and drawn into wires.

Mixture. One of the three kinds of matter (together with elements and compounds); any substance made up of two or more elements or compounds combined physically in no particular proportion by mass and separable into its component parts by physical means.

Nonmetal. Any element that is not a metal. (See *Metal.*)

Photosynthesis. The synthesis in plants of complex compounds from carbon dioxide, water, and minerals with the aid of sunlight captured by the plant's green pigment, chlorophyll.

Potential Energy. Stored or inactive energy.

Product. A substance that forms in a chemical reaction.

Radioactivity. The property of unstable atomic nuclei whereby they emit alpha, beta, or gamma rays.

Reactant. One of the substances that reacts in a chemical reaction.

Reaction, Chemical. Any event in which substances change into different chemical substances.

Solid. A state of matter in which the visible particles of the substance have both definite shapes and definite volumes.

Specific Heat. The amount of heat that one gram of a substance can absorb per degree Celsius increase in temperature.

$$\text{Heat capacity} = \frac{\text{heat}}{g\Delta t}$$ where Δt = the change in temperature. (The unit of heat is usually the calorie, but kilocalorie, joule, or kilojoule can be used.)

States of Matter. The three possible physical conditions of aggregation of matter—solid, liquid, and gas.

Substances, Chemical. The materials of which matter consists.

Substances, Pure. Elements and compounds, not mixtures.

Vaporization. The change of a liquid into its vapor.

SELF-TESTING QUESTIONS

COMPLETION

1. The general name we give to anything that occupies space and has mass is _____ .
2. The three states of matter are , _____ , _____ and _____ .
3. The three kinds of matter are, _____ , _____ and _____ . Which are called "pure substances?"

   _____

4. Two classes of matter that are organized around such physical properties as their abilities to conduct electricity or to be hammered into sheets are _____ and _____ .
5. In the chemical equation: Mg + S → MgS the symbol(s) of the reactant(s) is(are)_____ _____ and of the product(s): _____ .
6. Referring to the equation of question 5, which is the more elementary substance, Mg or MgS?

   _____

7. Write the symbols of the following elements.
   (a) calcium _____ (b) oxygen _____
   (c) sodium _____ (d) phosphorus _____

(e) potassium _____ (f) iron _____

(g) chlorine _____ (h) nitrogen _____

(i) magnesium _____ (j) manganese _____

(k) lead _____ (l) copper _____

(m) lithium _____ (n) sulfur _____

8. Write the names of the following elements.

(a) Ag _____ (b) H _____

(c) I _____ (d) Hg _____

(e) Ba _____ (f) Br _____

(g) Zn _____ (h) Na _____

(i) K _____ (j) Mg _____

9. Which two kinds of matter, by definition, obey the law of definite proportions?

_____ and _____

10. Examples that illustrate the law of multiple proportions are limited to which kind of matter?

_____

11. Element A and element B, both colorless, odorless gases, are mixed to give a colorless, odorless gas that, when cooled sufficiently, changes to a liquid identified as the liquid form of A with a gas above it identified as B. The mixing of A and B is an example of a _____ change.

12. Element X and element Y, both colorless gases that can be kept in glass containers are mixed. A great deal of heat is generated, and, after cooling, the mixture, still a colorless gas, slowly dissolves the glass container. The mixing of X and Y is an example of a _____ change.

13. If the separate masses of elements X and Y (question 12) are 2 grams each, then according to the law of _____ the mass of the result of mixing X and Y would be _____.

14. The five main postulates of Dalton's Atomic Theory are

(a) _____

(b) _____

(c) _____

(d) _____

(e) _____

15. If atoms are indestructible, then the ratios of the atoms present in a compound can be expressed only in _____ numbers.

16. If atoms are present in a compound in a definite ratio by atoms, and if atoms are indestructible, then the atoms must also be present in a definite ratio by _____ .

17. In the formula Na_2SO_4, the 4 is called a _____ , and the ratio of sulfur atoms to sodium atoms is 1 to _____ .

18. A car in motion, by virtue of this motion, possesses _____ energy.

19. If a bar of metal warmed to 40 °C is placed in physical contact with a solid object and the temperature of the metal falls, then the solid object either experiences an increase in its temperature or some of it (or all of it) _____

20. If a bar of metal warmed to 40 °C is placed in physical contact with a solid object and the temperature of the metal remains the same, then the solid object has the same _____ as the metal.

21. When a substance changes from its liquid state to its vapor state, we call this in general, a _____ change; the specific name for this change is _____ .

22. To change a specified quantity of a substance from its liquid to its vapor state requires a certain amount of heat; the amount of heat required per gram is called the _____ of the liquid.

23. If one gram of water at 100 °C is changed to its vapor at 100 °C _____ calories are absorbed by the water and are present in the water vapor.

24. What happens to the heat in water vapor when the vapor changes back into a liquid at the same temperature?

    _____

25. The amount of heat that one gram of an object must absorb in order to change its temperature by one degree Celsius is called the _____ of that object, and it has common units of

    _____ .

26. The amount of heat absorbed by an object in changing only its physical state but not its temperature is called the object's _____ of fusion or _____ of vaporization, and it usually has units of _____ .

27. Ice at 0 °C is better for making a cold pack than water at 0 °C because the ice can absorb heat by the physical change of _____ , which requires _____ calories per gram, whereas the liquid water can absorb heat only by the physical change of _____ , which requires only _____ cal/g °C.

28. The amount of heat that a specific object or a specific mass of a substance can absorb while changing temperature by one degree Celsius is called that substance's _____ .

29. The temperature at which a substance boils is called its _____ .

30. The capacity of an object to transfer heat to its surroundings or take heat from its surroundings without changing its own temperature is called that object's _____ of fusion or vaporization.

31. The burning of coal is a _____ change that, thermally, would be described as

    _____ .

32. The name of the process in plants that converts simple substances into complex substances is

    _____ .

    The energy for this process comes from the _____ .

MULTIPLE–CHOICE

1. One of the states of matter is
   (a) a mixture   (b) liquid   (c) element   (d) the atom

2. One of the kinds of matter is
   (a) a mixture   (b) liquid   (c) solid   (d) gas

3. One of the "building blocks" of matter is
   (a) a mixture   (b) liquid   (c) calorie   (d) the atom

4. The correct symbols for calcium, carbon, copper, and chlorine, in this order are:
   (a) C, Cl, Ca, Cu   (c) Ca, Cb, Cr, Ch
   (b) Cl, Cu, Ca, C   (d) Ca, C, Cu, Cl

5. The names that correspond to the following symbols for elements N, Na, K, Ag are, in the order given:
   (a) silver, sulfur, nitrogen, potassium

(b) nitrogen, sodium, potassium, silver

(c) sodium, nitrogen, mercury, aluminum

(d) neon, iron, phosphorus, argon

6. Water from any source in the world always has hydrogen and oxygen combined in the ratio of 11.1 g of hydrogen to 89.9 g of oxygen. This fact illustrates the law of

(a) definite proportions   (c) conservation of mass

(b) multiple proportions   (d) conservation of energy

7. Substances that obey the law of definite proportions include all

(a) elements   (b) compounds   (c) mixtures   (d) both a and b

8. Most of the elements are

(a) metals   (b) nonmetals   (c) liquids   (d) gases

9. One formula unit of Al_2O_3 is made of

(a) 2 aluminum atoms and 6 oxygen atoms

(b) 3 aluminum atoms and 2 oxygen atoms

(c) 6 atoms of all kinds

(d) 2 aluminum atoms and 3 oxygen atoms

10. One of the forms of energy is

(a) temperature   (b) hypothermia   (c) heat   (d) convection

11. When liquid water at 0 °C changes to ice at 0 °C, the water will give up to the surroundings its

(a) specific heat   (c) heat of fusion

(b) heat of vaporization   (d) specific gravity

12. When liquid water at 0 °C changes to ice at 0 °C, the water gives up to the surroundings

(a) 80 cal/g   (b) 80 kcal/g   (c) 540 cal/g   (d) 540 kcal/g

13. When ethyl chloride is sprayed on the skin to cool it, the heat drawn from the skin goes mostly to the ethyl chloride to

(a) warm it   (b) evaporate it   (c) sublime it   (d) condense it

14. Ice is a better coolant than water (even when the water is at 0 °C) because ice has a relatively large

(a) specific heat   (c) heat of vaporization

(b) heat capacity   (d) heat of fusion

15. When the body allows the evaporation of water to carry away body heat, it takes advantage of water's relatively large

(a) specific heat   (c) heat of vaporization

(b) heat capacity   (d) heat of fusion

16. Metabolism is described best by which (one) word:

(a) basal   (b) exothermic   (c) endergonic   (d) endothermic

17. The ability of a given mass of a substance to absorb heat while undergoing a change in temperature is called its

(a) latent heat   (c) exothermic capacity

(b) heat capacity   (d) kinetic energy

18. If atoms of A and of B chemically combine in a ratio of 1:1 by atoms but a ratio of 2:1 by mass, then compared to the atoms of B those of A are

(a) half as heavy   (c) twice as heavy

(b) equal in mass   (d) three times as heavy

19. If 50 g of water underwent a temperature change from 15 °C to 25 °C, the water
    (a) absorbed 500 calories   (c) released 500 calories
    (b) absorbed 500 kcal   (d) released 500 kcal

20. Dalton's theory proposed that matter is made of particles called
    (a) elements   (b) atoms   (c) mixtures   (d) compounds

21. Hot steam at 100 °C is more dangerous to exposed skin than hot water at 100 °C because the steam contains the water's
    (a) heat of vaporization   (c) kinetic energy
    (b) specific heat   (d) sensible heat

22. To change one gram of steam at 100 °C to one gram of ice at 0 °C, one would have to remove how many calories from the water?
    (a) 640 cal   (b) 180 cal   (c) 720 cal   (d) 100 cal

23. How much heat does it take to warm a 500-g piece of granite from 15.5 °C to 37.0 °C? The specific heat of granite is 0.192 $\frac{cal}{g\,°C}$.
    (a) 21.5 cal   (c) 4.66 cal
    (b) 2.06×10^3 cal   (d) 1.08×10^4 cal

24. When 3.0 g of benzene freezes, how much heat is released to the surroundings? The heat of fusion of benzene is 30 cal/g.
    (a) 10 cal   (b) 0.10 cal   (c) 3.0 cal   (d) 90 cal

ANSWERS

ANSWERS TO SELF–TESTING QUESTIONS

Completion

1. matter
2. solid, liquid, and gas
3. elements, compounds, and mixtures. Elements and compounds are pure substances.
4. metals and nonmetals
5. Mg and S; MgS
6. Mg
7. (a) Ca   (b) O   (c) Na
   (d) P   (e) K   (f) Fe
   (g) Cl   (h) N   (i) Mg
   (j) Mn   (k) Pb   (l) Cu
   (m) Li   (n) S
8. (a) silver   (b) hydrogen
   (c) iodine   (d) mercury
   (e) barium   (f) bromine

(g) zinc   (h) sodium

(i) potassium   (j) magnesium

9. elements and compounds
10. compounds
11. physical
12. chemical
13. conservation of mass; 4 grams
14. (a) Matter consists of atoms.

(b) Atoms are indestructible. (Even in chemical changes they only rearrange.)

(c) Atoms of the same element are identical, particularly in mass.

(d) Atoms of different elements differ in mass.

(e) In compounds, atoms occur in definite ratios or proportions.

15. whole
16. mass
17. subscript; 2
18. kinetic
19. melts
20. temperature
21. physical; evaporation (or vaporization)
22. heat of vaporization
23. 540 (rounded from 539.6)
24. The heat is released to the surrounding air.
25. specific heat; calories per gram per degree (or calories per degree per gram)
26. heat; heat; calories per gram
27. melting; 80 (rounded from 79.6); an increase in temperature; 1.0
28. heat capacity
29. boiling point
30. heat
31. chemical; exothermic
32. photosynthesis; sun

Multiple–Choice

1. b	2. a	3. d
4. d	5. b	6. a
7. d	8. a	9. d
10. c	11. c	12. a
13. b (Note 1)	14. d (Note 2)	15. c
16. b	17. b	18. c
19. a	20. b	21. a (Note 3)
22. c (Note 4)	23. b (Note 5)	24. d (Note 6)

NOTES

1. Some warming (choice a) also occurs, but heats of vaporization are generally much greater than specific heats. Only the specific heat of ethyl chloride is involved in warming; the heat of vaporization is involved in evaporation.

2. Ice can cool an object in contact with it simply by drawing heat from the object in order to melt, and ice's heat of fusion is much larger than liquid water's specific heat.

3. Both forms, of course, are very dangerous. However, cooler skin in contact with the steam would make some of the steam condense, releasing the heat of vaporization which is relatively large. This extra heat could then cause more injury.

4.

heat of vaporization	540 cal/g
cooling liquid water by 100 degrees at 1 cal/deg/g	100 cal/g
heat of fusion	80 cal/g
Total	720 cal/g

5. $\Delta t = (37.0 - 15.5)°C = 21.5°C$. Then,

$$0.192 \frac{cal}{°C \cdot g} \times 500 \, g \times 21.5 \, °C = 2064 \text{ cal, which}$$

has to be rounded and expressed to show 3 significant figures.

6. $30 \frac{cal}{g} \times 3 \, g = 90 \text{ cal}$

3

QUANTITATIVE RELATIONSHIPS IN CHEMICAL REACTIONS

If a chemist were asked to name the single most important concept in all of *chemistry*, a concept at the very heart of understanding how things work at the molecular level of anything, including life, the *mole concept* would be named. The concepts of energy and of atoms, of course, are also vital, but the mole concept most uniquely "belongs" to the field of chemistry. The mole concept illuminates the proportions in which substances naturally combine or form; substances combine in definite ratios by moles. As minimum goals for this chapter, learn the definition of the *mole*, see it as both a "counting number" and as a weighing unit for lab work, be able to calculate moles from grams and grams from moles, and be able to use the mole concept with a balanced equation.

OBJECTIVES

After you have studied this chapter and worked the assigned exercises, you should be able to do the following.

1. Understand a chemical formula as representing a *formula unit*—an atom, a molecule, or an ion group—that enters into a reaction as a unit irrespective of its actual mass.
2. Give the name and value of the number that chemists use as a standard counting number for formula units.
3. Explain why a "counting number" for a pure substance must be translated into a certain mass in order to do lab work.
4. Give the names of the three subatomic particles and identify the two that contribute significantly to an atom's actual mass.

5. Explain how two isotopes of the same element differ in composition.
6. Explain the relationship between naturally occurring carbon and carbon-12.
7. Define the *mole* in terms of a certain mass of carbon-12 (the SI definition) and in terms of the chemist's "counting number."
8. Calculate a formula mass from a chemical formula.
9. Set up the two possible conversion factors that the formula mass of a substance provides.
10. Calculate how many grams a sample must weigh, given its chemical formula, if the sample is known to contain Avogadro's number of formula units.
11. Calculate how many formula units are in a sample of a substance when you know the mass of the sample and the formula mass.
12. Calculate how many moles of a substance are in a given mass of a sample.
13. Calculate how many grams of a substance are in a given number of moles.
14. Describe the two aspects of *stoichiometry*, its concerns about ratios by atoms within formula units and about ratios by whole formula units within balanced chemical equations.
15. Examine any chemical equation and tell if it is balanced.
16. For those equations that can be balanced by the procedures developed in this chapter, balance such equations, given the formulas of the reactants and products.
17. Explain what the coefficients in a chemical equation represent and contrast this meaning with the information given by the subscripts within formulas.
18. Given a balanced chemical equation, calculate how many moles of one substance in the reaction are required if a certain number of moles of any other substance in the reaction is given.
19. Given a balanced equation, calculate how many grams of one substance must be involved if a certain number of grams of any other substance is involved.
20. Describe the relationships among the terms: solution, solute, and solvent.
21. Know how and when to use the qualitative descriptions of concentration such as dilute, concentrated, unsaturated, saturated, and supersaturated.
22. Describe what occurs when we say that something precipitates from a solution.
23. Define "molar concentration" and attach specific units to the numerical value of the molarity of a solution.
24. Set up the two possible conversion factors that the molarity of a solution provides.
25. Calculate the grams of a solute that must be measured to prepare a solution that has a given volume and molarity.
26. Calculate how many milliliters of a solution of known molarity must be measured to obtain a given number of moles of the solute.
27. Do stoichiometric calculations that involve solutions of known molarity whose solutes participate in a given reaction.
28. Do the calculations needed to prepare a dilute solution of known molarity from a more concentrated solution.

GLOSSARY

Atom. The formula unit of most metallic elements. The smallest particle of an element that has the chemical properties of the element.

Atomic Mass. The average mass, in atomic mass units (u), of the atoms of the isotopes of a given element as they occur naturally.

Atomic Number. The number of protons in one atom of an element.

Avogadro's Number. 6.02×10^{23}. The number of formula units in one mole of any element or compound.

Coefficients. Numbers placed before formulas in chemical equations to indicate the mole proportions of reactants and products.

Concentration. The quantity of some component of a mixture in a unit of volume or a unit of mass of the mixture; the ratio of quantity of solute to quantity of solvent or quantity of solution.

Equation, Balanced. A chemical equation in which all of the atoms represented in the formulas of the reactants are present in identical numbers among the products, and in which any net electrical charge provided by the reactants equals the same charge indicated by the products. (See also *Chemical Equation.*)

Dalton (D) A unit for formula mass; one atomic mass unit.

Formula Mass. The sum of the atomic masses of the atoms represented in a chemical formula.

Isotope. One of the components of a sample of an element in which all of the atoms are identical in atomic number and mass number.

Limiting Reactant. The reactant that is completely consumed in a reaction while one or more other reactants are not used up.

Mass Number. The sum of the number of protons and the number of neutrons contained within one atom of an isotope of an element.

Molar Concentration (M). A solution's concentration in units of moles of solute per liter of solution; molarity.

Molarity. (See *Molar Concentration.*)

Mole (mol). A mass of a compound or of an element that equals its formula mass in grams; Avogadro's number of a substance's formula units.

Molecule. Small particles capable of independent existence and made up from two or more atoms.

Molecular Mass. The formula mass of a substance.

Precipitate. A solid that separates from a solution as the result of a chemical reaction (or of cooling off).

Precipitation. The formation and separation of a precipitate.

Solubility. The extent to which a substance dissolves in a fixed quantity of solvent at a given temperature.

Solute. The component of a solution that is understood to be dissolved in or dispersed in a continuous solvent.

Solution. A homogeneous mixture of two or more substances that are at the smallest levels of their states of subdivision—at the ion, atom, or molecule level.

Solution, Aqueous. A solution in which water is the solvent.

Solution, Concentrated. A solution with a high ratio of quantity of solute to that of solvent.

Solution, Dilute. A solution with a low ratio of solute to solvent.

Solution, Saturated. A solution into which no more solute can be dissolved at the given temperature.

Solution, Supersaturated. An unstable solution that has a higher concentration of solute than that of the saturated solution.

Solution, Unsaturated. A solution into which more solute could be dissolved without changing the temperature.

Solvent. That component of a solution into which the solutes are considered to have dissolved; the component that is present as a continuous phase.

Stoichiometry. A branch of chemistry dealing with the ratios by atoms of the elements in a formula unit or with the mole proportions of reacting chemicals.

DRILL EXERCISES

We provide you here with additional drill exercises for the important calculating skills studied in this chapter. These skills are necessary *after your analysis of a problem shows you that the problem is one in stoichiometry.* Remember, the solution of any chemical problem starts with analyzing what kind it is and only then applying the recognized calculating skills.

I. EXERCISES IN CALCULATING FORMULA MASSES

Calculate the formula masses of the following substances. Round atomic masses to their first decimal place before using them in these calculations (except use 1.01 for the atomic mass of hydrogen), and round the answers to the first decimal place. Then write the two conversion factors made possible for each substance by its formula mass. The answers will be used in later drill exercises.

1. NH_3 _____ Conversion factors:

2. H_2O _____ Conversion factors:

3. SO_3 _____ Conversion factors:

4. NO_2 _____ Conversion factors:

5. $MgCl_2$ _____ Conversion factors:

6. I_2 _____ Conversion factors:

7. NaOH _____ Conversion factors:

8. H_2SO_4 _____ Conversion factors:

9. KNO_3 _____ Conversion factors:

10. $C_{12}H_{22}O_{11}$ _____ Conversion factors:

II. EXERCISES IN CALCULATING GRAMS FROM MOLES

Calculate the number of grams in the following samples. The conversion factors were prepared in the previous exercise. Show the full setup for the solution and make the correct cancel lines. (Notice that the mole quantities that are specified limit each answer to three significant figures.)

1. 3.00 mol of NH_3 _____ g NH_3

2. 9.00 mol of H_2O _____ g H_2O

3. 0.200 mol of SO_3 _____ g SO_3

4. 0.0100 mol of NO_2 _____ g NO_2

5. 6.00 mol of $MgCl_2$ _____ g $MgCl_2$

6. 0.300 mol of I_2 _____ g I_2

7. 0.0500 mol of NaOH _____ g NaOH

8. 0.300 mol of H_2SO_4 _____ g H_2SO_4

9. 1.50 mol of KNO_3 _____ g KNO_3

10. 0.100 mol of $C_{12}H_{22}O_{11}$ _____ g $C_{12}H_{22}O_{11}$

III. EXERCISES IN CALCULATING MOLES FROM GRAMS

Calculate the number of moles in the following samples. The conversion factors were prepared in Drill Exercise I. Show the full setup for the solution and make the correct cancel lines. Include the right unit with the answer, and leave only the correct number of significant figures.

1. 34.0 g of NH_3 _____

2. 54.0 g of H_2O _____

3. 400 g of SO_3 _____

4. 4.60 g of NO_2 _____

5. 0.950 g of MgCl _____

6. 12.7 g of I_2 _____

7. 8.00 g of NaOH _____

8. 5.65 g of H_2SO_4 _____

9. 32.0 g of KNO_3 _____

10. 28.4 g of $C_{12}H_{22}O_{11}$ _____

IV. EXERCISES IN BALANCING CHEMICAL EQUATIONS

Convert the following sentences into balanced chemical equations. Always remember that once you've set down the correct formula for a substance you are not allowed to alter the formula to balance the equation. All you can alter are the coefficients. Also remember that many nonmetals occur as diatomic molecules, for example, O_2, H_2, N_2, Cl_2, etc.

1. Magnesium reacts with oxygen to form magnesium oxide.
2. Calcium reacts with oxygen to form calcium oxide.
3. Sulfur reacts with oxygen to form sulfur dioxide (SO_2).
4. Sulfur reacts with oxygen to form sulfur trioxide (SO_3).
5. Hydrogen reacts with chlorine to form hydrogen chloride.
6. Hydrogen reacts with oxygen to form water.
7. Carbon reacts with oxygen to form carbon dioxide (CO_2).

V. EXERCISES IN MASS-RELATION PROBLEMS INVOLVING BALANCED EQUATIONS

We can summarize the basic steps for working these problems as follows.

Step 1.   Be sure you are working with a balanced equation.
Step 2.   Calculate the formula masses and set them off to one side for reference.
Step 3.   Beneath the formulas of the balanced equation, draw two rows of blank lines, the upper row representing the "mole level" and the lower the "gram level." For example:

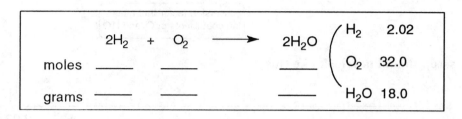

Step 4.   Write in the "given" on the proper line. For example, let the question be as follows: If you start with 64.0 grams of oxygen, how much hydrogen can be consumed and how much water will be produced (both in grams)? If the given is in a mass, convert it at once to moles and write in the answer on the proper line.
To convert the given into moles:

$$64.0 \; g \; O_2 \times \frac{1 \; mol \; O_2}{32.0 \; g \; O_2} = 2.00 \; mol \; O_2$$

Here is how the setup should now look:

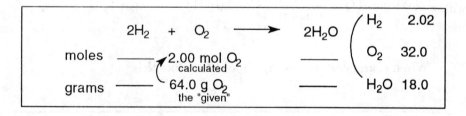

This step illustrates the most important rule in mass relation problems: SOLVE THE PROBLEM AT THE MOLE LEVEL; THEN GO BACK TO THE GRAM LEVEL AS NEEDED.
Step 5.   Use the coefficients of the equation to construct conversion factors that are used in calculating the numbers of moles of anything else requested. This step fills in the blanks at the mole-level of the answer. For example, to find out how many moles of hydrogen are needed for a reaction with 2.00 mol of oxygen:

$$2.00 \; mol \; O_2 \times \frac{2 \; mol \; H_2}{1 \; mol \; O_2} = 4.00 \; mol \; H_2$$

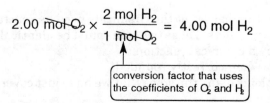

conversion factor that uses the coefficients of O_2 and H_2

To find the number of moles of water made by the reaction of 2.00 mol of O_2:

$$2.00 \text{ mol } O_2 \times \frac{2 \text{ mol } H_2O}{1 \text{ mol } O_2} = 4.00 \text{ mol } H_2O$$

conversion factor that uses the coefficients of O_2 and H_2O

The setup should now look like this:

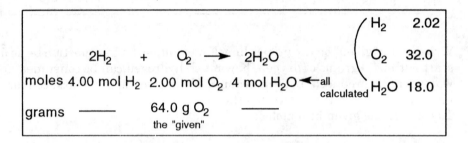

Step 6.   Convert moles into grams for the final answers to the original question. (Insert the cancel lines yourself.)

For hydrogen: $4.00 \text{ mol } H_2 \times \dfrac{2.01 \text{ g } H_2}{1 \text{ mol } H_2} = 8.04 \text{ g } H_2O$

For water: $4.00 \text{ mol } H_2O \times \dfrac{18.0 \text{ g } H_2O}{1 \text{ mol } H_2O} = 72.0 \text{ g } H_2O$

When completed, the setup should look like this:

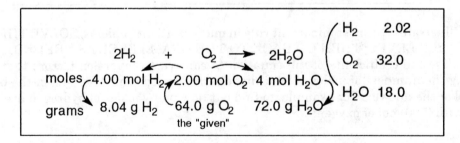

As a final check, add up the masses of the chemicals used as reactants. Then add up the masses of the chemicals made as products. These two sums must be identical. Remember: matter is neither created nor destroyed by a chemical reaction.
8.04 g + 64.0 g = 72.0 g (when correctly rounded)
Work the following problems using the steps that we have just covered. Check your answers at the end of the chapter.

Problem A

The combustion of methane is shown by the following equation:

$$CH_4 \quad + \quad 2O_2 \quad \rightarrow \quad CO_2 \quad + \quad 2H_2O$$

methane   oxygen   carbon dioxide   water

If 48.0 grams methane are burned in this way, how much oxygen is needed and how much carbon dioxide and water are produced? State your answer both in moles and in grams.

Problem B

The combustion of ethane is shown by the following equation:

$$2C_2H_6 + 7O_2 \rightarrow 4CO_2 + 6H_2O$$

ethane

If 15.0 grams of ethane are burned this way, how much oxygen is needed and how much carbon dioxide and water are produced? State your answer both in moles and in grams.

SELF-TESTING QUESTIONS

COMPLETION

1. *Stoichiometry* deals with the ratio by *atoms* in _____ and the ratio by *formula units* in _____ .

2. What is the name given to the *kind* of small particle that is the formula unit in gold, Au?
_____

3. What is the name of the *kind* of small particle that makes up a sample of oxygen, O_2.
_____

4. Another name for the formula unit in potassium bromide, KBr, an ionic compound, is
_____ .

5. The chemist's reference number for formula units is called _____ and (to three significant figures) its value is _____ .

6. To have one mole of atoms of gold, how many atoms are needed? _____

7. The mass of any given atom is provided almost entirely by which of its smaller (subatomic) particles? _____ . The masses of which of an atom's smaller (subatomic) particles are ignored?_____

8. An atom with 10 protons and 11 neutrons has an atomic number of _____ and a mass number of _____ .

9. An atom with a mass number of 35 and an atomic number of 17 has _____ neutrons and _____ protons.

10. An amount of carbon containing Avogadro's number of carbon atoms has a mass of _____ grams.

11. We must refer to an *atomic mass* of an element as an *average* mass because elements nearly always consist of mixtures of _____ .

12. The atomic mass of copper is 63.546. Therefore a sample of copper containing Avogadro's number of copper atoms has what mass? _____ A sample of copper containing 1.00 mol of copper has what mass? _____

13. The formula mass of carbon dioxide (CO_2) is 44.0. Therefore, one mole of carbon dioxide has a mass of _____ grams, and 0.500 mole has a mass of _____ .

14. A sample of water containing 6.02×10^{23} molecules has a mass of _____ (include the unit); this amount of water is one standard reacting unit of water or, to use the scientific term, one_____.

15. A sample of sodium chloride containing 6.02×10^{23} of these formula units has a mass of _____ (include the unit); this amount is one standard reacting unit of sodium chloride, or one _____.

16. If you have a relatively large sample of any pure substance — an element or a compound — that consists of 6.02×10^{23} particles of its own particular smallest representative sample, then you would have one _____ of it.

17. Compounds X, Y, and Z have the following formula masses: X = 50.0; Y = 100; and Z = 150. We shall assume they are all covalent compounds and therefore consist of molecules.

    (a) Suppose you had 50.0 g of X, 100 g of Y, and 150 g of Z in separate containers. What would each of these samples have in common? _____

    (b) Suppose you had 100 g of Y and 100 g of X in separate containers. Which container would have the greater number of molecules? _____

    (c) Suppose that X and Y react to produce Z and that you elect to use 50.0 g of X in a particular experiment. How much of Y (in grams) would you have to use (assuming you want a "clean" reaction, one in which nothing of X or Y was left over)? _____. The equation or the reaction is X + Y → Z.

    (d) An individual molecule of Z has a mass that is _____ times as much as the mass of a molecule of X; one billion molecules of Z would have a mass that is_____ times as much as one billion molecules of X.

    (e) If you wanted to prepare 300 g of Z, how many moles of X and Y would you need?
    _____ moles X, _____ moles Y. How many grams?
    _____ g X, _____ g Y.

18. How many moles of water are in 250 g of water (about one cup)? _____

19. If one drop of water has a mass of about 6.3×10^{-2} g, it therefore consists of _____ mol of water and it contains _____ molecules of water.

20. A chemistry experiment calls for 0.134 mol of aluminum. This can be obtained in the lab by measuring out how much aluminum (in the usual lab unit)? _____

21. Sulfur reacts with fluorine (F_2) to give sulfur hexafluoride (SF_6), an important insulating oil used in electrical transformers. Suppose that 175 g of SF_6 is needed. The question is "how much sulfur is required to make 175 g of SF_6?

    (a) By "how much?" is generally meant how many _____ of sulfur must be weighed out?

    (b) To solve this problem we need the equation for the reaction, which is: _____

    (c) The equation is essential to give us what relationship that relates to the stated question?
    _____

    (d) How many moles of SF_6 are in 175 g of SF_6? _____

    (e) How many moles of S are needed to make 175 g of SF_6? _____

    (f) How many grams of S are needed to make 175 g of SF_6? _____

    (g) How many grams of F_2 are needed to make 175 g of SF_6? _____

22. To prepare 250 mL of 0.150 M H_2SO_4 requires that we dissolve _____ mol of H_2SO_4 or _____ g of H_2SO_4 in enough water to make the final volume _____ mL.

23. If one took 175 mL of 0.250 M NaOH, the sample would contain _____ mol of NaOH and _____ g of NaOH.

24. If 80.0 mL of a 0.500 M solution are diluted with water to a final volume of 400 mL, the final concentration will be _____ .

25. How many milliliters of 0.250 M H_2SO_4 are needed to react with 5.46 g of $NaHCO_3$ according to the given equation? _____

$$2NaHCO_3(s) + H_2SO_4(aq) \rightarrow Na_2SO_4(aq) + 2CO_2(g) + 2H_2O(l)$$

MULTIPLE–CHOICE

1. When the following equation is balanced, which term(s) will appear?

    ____ Na_3PO_4 ____ $CaCl_2$ → ____ $Ca_3(PO_4)_2$ ____ $NaCl$

    (a) $2Na_3PO_4$ (c) $Ca_3(PO_4)_2$
    (b) $2CaCl_2$ (d) $6NaCl$

2. In the reaction, $CaCl_2 + 2AgNO_3 \rightarrow Ca(NO_3)_2 + 2AgCl$, if one mole of $AgNO_3$ is to be consumed, then

    (a) one mole of AgCl will form
    (b) one-half mole of $CaCl_2$ will be needed
    (c) one mole of $Ca(NO_3)_2$ will also be produced
    (d) one-half mole of calcium will also be produced

3. Suppose that the formula mass of X is 30 and that of Y is 60. Which of the following statements are correct?

    (a) X weighs 30 g and Y weighs 60 g
    (b) 30 g of X will have the same number of molecules as 60 g of Y
    (c) 60 g of X will have the same number of molecules as 120 g of Y
    (d) Molecules of Y are twice as heavy as molecules of X
    (e) Molecules of Y weigh five times as much as atoms of carbon-12

4. A 40-g sample of substance X is known to contain the same number of molecules as a 120-g sample of substance Y. Therefore the formula mass of X is related to the formula mass of Y in which way(s)? The formula mass of X is

    (a) equal to the formula mass of Y
    (b) one-third the formula mass of Y
    (c) three times the formula mass of Y
    (d) 4.8 times the formula mass of Y

5. The atoms of element X are one-third as heavy as the atoms of carbon-12. The formula mass of X is

    (a) 36   (b) 3   (c) 4   (d) 12

6. An important unit of concentration in chemistry is the

    (a) molar unit   (c) molecule unit
    (b) mole unit   (d) molecular mass unit

7. Compound X, whose solubility in water at 50 °C is 60 g per 100 mL, is available as a 6% solution. This solution is

    (a) concentrated   (c) dilute
    (b) supersaturated   (d) isotonic

8. A 0.50 M solution of compound Y is known to contain 50 g Y per liter. The formula mass of Y is

    (a) 50   (b) 25   (c) 0.50   (d) 100

9. To prepare 250 mL of 0.0400 M glucose ($C_6H_{12}O_6$) we would have to obtain a sample of glucose with a mass of how many grams?

    (a) 0.180 g glucose   (c) 18.0 g glucose
    (b) 1.80 g glucose   (d) 10.0 g glucose

10. If we obtained 125 mL of 0.0450 M NaCl, the sample would contain how much solute?

    (a) 0.329 g NaCl   (c) 0.0450 g NaCl
    (b) 0.00231 mol NaCl   (d) 0.0112 g NaCl

11. How many milliliters of 1.25 M HCl would it take to react completely with 2.56 g of magnesium hydroxide according to the equation?

$$Mg(OH)_2(s) + 2HCl(aq) \rightarrow MgCl_2(aq) + H_2O$$

    (a) 35.3 mL   (b) 18,200 mL   (c) 1.25 mL   (d) 70.3 mL

12. When 10.5 mL of 0.150 M HCl are diluted to a final volume of 100 mL, the concentration of the resulting solution is

    (a) 1.43 M HCl   (c) 0.00150 M HCl
    (b) 0.0158 M HCl   (d) 10.5 M HCl

ANSWERS

ANSWERS TO DRILL EXERCISES

I.   Exercises in Calculating Formula Masses

1. $\dfrac{17.0 \text{ grams } NH_3}{1 \text{ mole } NH_3}$ or $\dfrac{1 \text{ mole } NH_3}{17.0 \text{ grams } NH_3}$

2. $\dfrac{18.0 \text{ grams } H_2O}{1 \text{ mole } H_2O}$ or $\dfrac{1 \text{ mole } H_2O}{18.0 \text{ grams } H_2O}$

3. $\dfrac{80.1 \text{ grams } SO_3}{1 \text{ mole } SO_3}$ or $\dfrac{1 \text{ mole } SO_3}{80.1 \text{ grams } SO_3}$

4. $\dfrac{46.0 \text{ grams } NO_2}{1 \text{ mole } NO_2}$ or $\dfrac{1 \text{ mole } NO_2}{46.0 \text{ grams } NO_2}$

5. $\dfrac{95.3 \text{ grams } MgCl_2}{1 \text{ mole } MgCl_2}$ or $\dfrac{1 \text{ mole } MgCl_2}{95.3 \text{ grams } MgCl_2}$

6. $\dfrac{253.8 \text{ grams } l_2}{1 \text{ mole } l_2}$ or $\dfrac{1 \text{ mole } l_2}{253.8 \text{ grams } l_2}$

7. $\dfrac{40.0 \text{ grams } NaOH}{1 \text{ mole } NaOH}$ or $\dfrac{1 \text{ mole } NaOH}{40.0 \text{ grams } NaOH}$

8. $\dfrac{98.1 \text{ grams } H_2SO_4}{1 \text{ mole } H_2SO_4}$ or $\dfrac{1 \text{ mole } H_2SO_4}{98.1 \text{ grams } H_2SO_4}$

9. $\dfrac{101.1 \text{ grams } KNO_3}{1 \text{ mole } KNO_3}$ or $\dfrac{1 \text{ mole } KNO_3}{101.1 \text{ grams } KNO_3}$

10. $\dfrac{342 \text{ grams } C_{12}H_{22}O_{11}}{1 \text{ mole } C_{12}H_{22}O_{11}}$ or $\dfrac{1 \text{ mole } C_{12}H_{22}O_{11}}{342 \text{ grams } C_{12}H_{22}O_{11}}$

II. Exercises in Calculating Grams from Moles

1. 51.0 g NH_3 From: $3.00 \text{ mol } NH_3 \times \dfrac{17.0 \text{ g } NH_3}{1 \text{ mol } NH_3}$

2. 162 g H_2O　　　　　3. 16.0 g SO_3

4. 0.460 g NO_2　　　　5. 572 g $MgCl_2$

6. 76.2 g I_2　　　　　　7. 2.00 g NaOH

8. 29.4 H_2SO_4　　　　9. 152 g KNO_3

10. 34.2 g $C_{12}H_{22}O_{11}$

III. Exercises in Calculating Moles from Grams

1. $2.00 \text{ mol } NH_3$ From: $3.00 \text{ mol } NH_3 \times \dfrac{17.0 \text{ g } NH_3}{1 \text{ mol } NH_3}$

2. 3.00 mol H_2O　　　　3. 4.99 mol SO_3

4. 0.100 mol NO_2　　　5. 0.00997 mol $MgCl_2$

6. 0.0500 mol I_2　　　　7. 0.200 mol NaOH

8. 0.0576 mol H_2SO_4　　9. 0.317 mol KNO_3

10. 0.0830 mol $C_{12}H_{22}O_{11}$

IV. Exercises in Balancing Chemical Equations

1. $2Mg + O_2 \rightarrow 2MgO$

2. $2Ca + O_2 \rightarrow 2CaO$

3. $S + O_2 \rightarrow SO_2$

4. $2S + 3O_2 \rightarrow 2SO_3$

5. $H_2 + Cl_2 \rightarrow 2HCl$

6. $2H_2 + O_2 \rightarrow 2H_2O$

7. $C + O_2 \rightarrow CO_2$

V.   Exercises in Mass-Relation Problems Involving Balanced Equations

Problem A. When completed the setup should look like this.

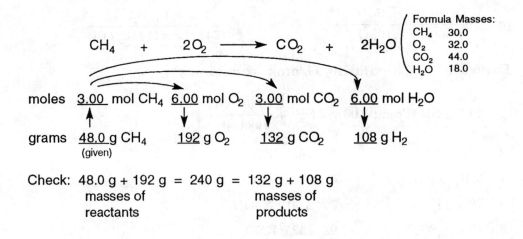

Formula Masses:
CH₄   30.0
O₂   32.0
CO₂   44.0
H₂O   18.0

$$CH_4 \quad + \quad 2O_2 \longrightarrow CO_2 \quad + \quad 2H_2O$$

moles   3.00 mol CH₄ 6.00 mol O₂ 3.00 mol CO₂ 6.00 mol H₂O

grams   48.0 g CH₄   192 g O₂   132 g CO₂   108 g H₂
        (given)

Check: 48.0 g + 192 g = 240 g = 132 g + 108 g
        masses of   masses of
        reactants   products

Problem B. When completed the setup should look like this.

Formula Masses:
C₂H₆ 30.0
O₂   32.0
CO₂   44.0
H₂O   18.0

$$2C_2H_6 \quad + \quad 7O_2 \longrightarrow 4CO_2 \quad + \quad 6H_2O$$

moles   0.500 mol C₂H₆ 1.75 mol O₂ 1.00 mol CO₂ 1.50 mol H₂O

grams   15.0 g C₂H₆   56.0 g O₂   44.0 g CO₂   27.0 g H₂
        (given)

Check: 15.0 g + 56.0 g = 71.0 g = 44.0 g + 27.0 g
        masses of   masses of
        reactants   products

ANSWERS TO SELF–TESTING QUESTIONS

Completion

1. compounds; chemical reactions
2. an atom
3. a diatomic molecule
4. ion group
5. Avogadro's number; 6.02×10^{23}
6. 6.02×10^{23}
7. neutrons and protons
8. 10; 21
9. 18; 17
10. 12.0
11. isotopes
12. 63.546 g of copper; 63.546 g of copper
13. 44.0 g; 22.0 g
14. 18.0 g; mole
15. 58.5 g; mole
16. mole
17. (a) Each would consist of 1.00 mole of that substance (or each would contain Avogadro's number — 6.02×10^{23} — of molecules).
    (b) X (Since each molecule of X is lighter by half than each molecule of Y, you get twice as many X molecules as Y in the same mass of samples.)
    (c) 100 g
    (d) three; three
    (e) 2.00, 2.00; 100, 200
18. 13.9 mol of water
19. 3.5×10^{-3} mole of water; 2.1×10^{21} molecules of water
20. 3.62 g of aluminum
21. (a) grams
    (b) $S + 3F_2 \rightarrow SF_6$
    (c) 1 mol S $\Leftrightarrow$ 1 mol SF_6
    (d) 1.20 mol SF_6
    (e) 1.20 mol S
    (f) 38.5 g S
    (g) 137 g F_2

21. 0.0375 mol H_2SO_4; 3.68 g H_2SO_4; 250 mL
22. 0.0438 mol NaOH; 1.75 g NaOH
23. 0.100 M.
24. 130 mL

Multiple–Choice

1. a, c, and d	2. a and b	3. b, c, d, and e
4. b	5. c	6. a
7. c	8. d	9. b
10. a	11. d	12. b

4

ATOMIC THEORY AND THE PERIODIC SYSTEM OF THE ELEMENTS

Mastering the contents of this chapter is of vital importance in understanding the information presented in the rest of the book.

The specific objectives of this chapter can be classified under three main objectives.

1. Learn how the elements can be sorted into families having somewhat similar properties. The Periodic Table will be a helpful aid in correlating the properties of the elements as we proceed to later chapters.

2. Learn how to write the electron configuration for an atom of any element with atomic number from 1 to 20. We need a thorough knowledge of electron configurations in order to be able to understand how these elements form various kinds of chemical bonds and chemical compounds.

3. Continue to accumulate the basic vocabulary of chemistry. Most of the terms in the glossary will be used again and again throughout the course, particularly in the next chapter. They must be mastered.

OBJECTIVES

After studying this chapter and working all of the assigned exercises, you should be able to do the following.

1. Describe the general property of the chemical elements that makes possible their particular arrangement in the periodic table.

2. State the periodic law and give at least one illustration of this law for a physical property and a chemical property of the elements.

3. Use the periodic table to identify the representative elements and to look up the symbols, atomic numbers, and atomic masses of the members of any given family of such elements.

4. Locate the metals, metalloids, and nonmetals in the periodic table.

5. Locate the transition and the inner transition elements in the periodic table.

6. In general terms, describe what acids and bases are and how they behave toward each other.

7. Name and give the relative masses and electric charges for the three subatomic particles of interest to chemists.

8. Give Rutherford's contribution to atomic theory.

9. State Bohr's two fundamental postulates and describe his atomic model.

10. Define and distinguish between: (a) atom and element; (b) orbit and orbital; (c) period and group; (d) atomic number and atomic mass; (e) the Bohr model and the orbital model; and (f) an atom and its isotope.

11. Use atomic numbers and mass numbers to find the charge on the nucleus, the numbers of electrons, protons, and neutrons in one atom of any given isotope, and to write the correct symbol for the isotope.

12. Use the atomic number and atomic mass to construct an electron configuration, including the composition of the nucleus, for an atom of any element from 1 through 20, showing the distribution among the orbitals.

13. Repeat objective twelve for an atom that would reasonably be an isotope of any given atom having an atomic number of 1 through 20.

14. Illustrate the application of Pauli's Principle and Hund's Rule.

15. Given only the atomic number of an element (among the first 20), write the electron configuration of the element occurring next to it, on either side, in the Periodic Table.

16. Define all of the terms in the Glossary.

GLOSSARY

Acid. A substance that can destroy or neutralize the caustic properties of alkali metal hydroxides or bases.

Alkali Metals. The elements of Group IA of the Periodic Table — lithium, sodium, potassium, rubidium, cesium, and francium.

Alkaline Earth Metals. The elements of Group IIA of the Periodic Table — beryllium, magnesium, calcium, strontium, barium, and radium.

Atomic Number. The positive charge on an atom's nucleus; the number of protons in an atom's nucleus.

Atomic Orbital. A region in space close to an atom's nucleus in which one or two electrons can reside.

Aufbau Principle. In constructing electron configurations, as each additional proton is located into an atomic nucleus, an electron enters whichever of the available orbitals corresponds to the lowest energy (Hund's rule and the Pauli exclusion principle applying).

Base. A substance that can neutralize an acid.

Binary Compound. A compound made from just two elements.

Bohr Model of the Atom. The solar system model of the structure of an atom, proposed by Niels Bohr, that pictures the electrons circling the nucleus in discrete energy states called orbits.

Boron Family. The Group IIIA elements in the Periodic Table— boron, aluminum, gallium, indium, and thallium.

Carbon Family. The Group IVA elements in the Periodic Table — carbon, silicon, germanium, tin, and lead.

Electron. A subatomic particle that bears one unit of negative charge and has a mass that is 1/1836 the mass of a proton.

Electron Cloud. A mental model that views the one or two rapidly moving electrons of an orbital as creating a cloud-like distribution of negative charge.

Electron Configuration. The most stable arrangement (that is, the arrangement of lowest energy) of the electrons of an atom, ion, or molecule.

Electron Shell. An alternative name for *principal energy level.*

Element. A substance that cannot be broken down into anything that is both stable and more simple; a substance in which all of the atoms have the same atomic number and the same electron configuration; one of the three broad kinds of matter, the others being compounds and mixtures.

Group. A vertical column in the Periodic Table; a family of elements.

Halogens. The elements of Group VIIA of the Periodic Table — fluorine, chlorine, bromine, iodine, and astatine.

Heisenberg Uncertainty Principle. It is impossible simultaneously to determine with precision and accuracy both the position and the velocity of an electron.

Hund's Rule. Electrons become distributed among *different* orbitals of the same general energy level insofar as there is room.

Inner Transition Elements. The elements of the lanthanide and actinide series of the Periodic Table.

Isotope. A substance in which all of the atoms are identical in atomic number, mass number, and electron configuration.

Metalloids. Elements that have some metallic and some nonmetallic properties.

Model, Scientific. A mental construction, often involving pictures or diagrams, that is used to explain a number of facts.

Neutralization. A reaction between an acid and a base.

Neutron. An electrically neutral subatomic particle with a mass of 1 u.

Nitrogen Family. The elements of Group VA of the Periodic Table—nitrogen, phosphorus, arsenic, antimony, and bismuth.

Noble Gases. The elements of Group 0 of the Periodic Table—helium, neon, argon, krypton, xenon, and radon.

Nucleus. In chemistry and physics, the subatomic particle that serves as the core of an atom and that is made up of protons and neutrons.

Orbital. (See *Atomic Orbital.*)

Outside Shell Electrons. The electrons occupying any of the available orbitals at the highest occupied principal energy level.

Oxygen Family. The elements in Group VIA of the Periodic Table—oxygen, sulfur, selenium, tellurium, and polonium.

Pauli Exclusion Principle. No more than two electrons can occupy the same orbital at the same time, and two can be present only if they have opposite spin.

Period. A horizontal row in the Periodic Table.

Periodic Law. Many properties of the elements are periodic functions of their atomic numbers.

Periodic Table. A display of the elements that emphasizes the family relationships.

Photon. A package of energy released when an electron in an atom moves from a higher to a lower energy state; a unit of light energy.

Principal Energy Level. A space near an atomic nucleus where there are one or more sublevels and orbitals in which electrons can reside; an electron shell.

Proton. A subatomic particle that bears one unit of positive charge and has a mass of 1 u.

Quantum. A quantity of energy possessed by a photon.

Representative Element. Any element in any A-group of the Periodic Table; any element in Groups IA – VIIA and those in Group 0.

Subatomic Particle. An electron, a proton, or a neutron; the atomic nucleus as a whole is also a subatomic particle.

Subshell. A region that makes up part (sometimes all) of a principal energy level and that can itself be subdivided into individual orbitals.

Transition Elements. The elements between those of Group IIA and Group IIIA in the long periods of the Periodic Table; a metallic element other than one in Group IA or IIA or in the actinide or lanthanide families.

SELF-TESTING QUESTIONS

COMPLETION. Some of the sentences in these exercises may well be completed by various answers. If you have picked an answer not given at the end of this chapter, remember that the sentence as completed by the answer given is meant to give you a new slant on the concept. Let it work that way for you. The object is not to get a score of 100. The object is to understand and then to know.

1. The scientist given the most credit for recognizing the periodic relations among the elements was _____

2. Metallic elements generally have _____ , _____ or _____ electrons in their outside levels.

3. Elements whose outside levels all have seven electrons are in Group _____ .

4. As one crosses from left to right in the second main period of the Periodic Table, energy level number _____ is filling.

5. The periodic law states that _____ .

6. The representative elements in Group IA are called _____ ; those in VIIA are _____ ; those in IIA are the _____ .

7. Referring to the Periodic Table, the symbols of the elements in the carbon family are, in order _____ .

8. The atoms of the oxygen family all have _____ electrons in their highest occupied main energy levels.

9. A very large group of elements occurring roughly in the center of the Periodic Table are called _____ elements.

10. Referring to the Periodic Table, the element of atomic number 79 is likely a metal or a nonmetal? _____

11. The formula of calcium oxide is CaO. Considering the Periodic Table, the formula of magnesium oxide is likely _____ .

12. Sodium hydroxide is a *base*, meaning that it can neutralize an _____ .

13. The names of the three subatomic particles are _____ , _____ , and _____ .

14. A larger subatomic particle present in all atoms and discovered by Rutherford is the

    _____ .

15. A substance whose atomic nuclei all have the same amount of electric charge is called

    _____ .

16. In atomic mass units (u), the mass of the proton is _____ , of the neutron is _____ , and of the electron is _____ .

17. Which number can be used to determine how many electrons must be arranged in writing an electron configuration, the atomic number or the mass number? _____

18. The two fundamental postulates made by Niels Bohr concerning electron configurations and atomic structure were:

    (a) _____

    (b) _____

19. Of the terms, orbit and orbital, which describes a region of space in the vicinity of a nucleus? _____ Which describes a particular path around the nucleus?

    _____

20. When one electron jumps from a higher energy level to a lower energy level it emits one

    _____ .

21. According to the Heisenberg principle, it is not possible to determine with precision and accuracy both the _____ and the _____ of an electron simultaneously.

22. Complete the following table by writing in the numbers of the different kinds of sublevels and the total number of atomic orbitals at each given principal or main level.

Main Level	Number of Different Kinds of Sublevels	Total Number of Atomic Orbitals
1	_____	_____
2	_____	_____
3	_____	_____

23. A p-type sublevel consists of how many orbitals? _____

24. According to the Pauli exclusion principle, an orbital can hold a maximum of how many electrons? _____ What must be true about the electrons corresponding to this maximum if they actually are in the same orbital? _____

25. If the electron configuration of an atom is $1s^2 2s^2 2p_x^2 2p_y^2 2p_z^1$, then its atomic number is _____ .

26. The total number of electrons in the outside level of the atom whose electron configuration was given in question 16 is _____ .

27. Using both the normal and the abbreviated forms, write the electron configuration of an element of atomic number

    (a) 14 _____   _____

    (b) 19 _____   _____

28. Write the electron configuration of the element with the lowest atomic number that illustrates Hund's rule. _____

MULTIPLE–CHOICE

1. Lord Rutherford's contribution to our understanding of atomic structure was that atoms

    (a) are like solar systems   (c) have dense inner cores

    (b) contain electrons   (d) have neutrons

2. Bohr postulated that electrons occur in atoms

    (a) in discrete orbitals

    (b) in discrete energy states

    (c) in a condition of constant shifting between states

    (d) in hard, dense, inner cores

3. An atom with 20 protons would have

    (a) a nuclear charge of 20+

    (b) a nuclear charge of 20–

    (c) 20 electrons

    (d) 40 neutrons

4. An element whose atoms have 10 protons, 10 neutrons, and 10 electrons would have an atomic number of

    (a) 10   (b) 20   (c) 30   (d) 40

5. All of the atoms of any naturally occurring element will have identical numbers of

    (a) protons   (b) nuclei   (c) neutrons   (d) electrons

    Problems 6 through 10 should be answered without reference to tables or charts.

6. An element of atomic number 19 consists of atoms having how many electrons in their outside levels?

    (a) eight   (b) nine   (c) one   (d) 19

7. An element of atomic number 14 is probably

    (a) a metal   (c) a transition element

    (b) a nonmetal   (d) a noble gas

8. Standing immediately to the left of the element of atomic number 17 in the Periodic Table is an element with

    (a) a charge of 16+ on its nuclei

    (b) a charge of 18+ on its nuclei

    (c) a charge of 17+ on its nuclei

    (d) a charge of 9+ on its nuclei

9. Standing immediately below the element of atomic number 17 in the Periodic Table is an element with

    (a) 17 electrons in its outside level

    (b) 7 electrons in its outside level

(c)   17 protons in its nuclei

(d)   7 protons in its nuclei

10.   If element X is a gas, then the element immediately above it in the Periodic Table is most likely a

(a)   metal   (b)   nonmetal   (c)   gas   (d)   transition element

11.   An element whose atoms have one, two, or three electrons in their outside levels is probably

(a)   a nonmetal   (b)   a gas   (c)   a liquid   (d)   a metal

12.   An element whose atoms have 7 or 8 electrons in their outside levels is probably

(a)   a nonmetal   (c)   a transition element

(b)   a solid   (d)   a metal

13.   If an element of atomic number 20 has two isotopes and one isotope has 20 neutrons while the other has 22 neutrons, and if these isotopes are present in a 50:50 ratio, what would be the atomic mass of the element as determined chemically?

(a)   20.5   (b)   21   (c)   40.5   (d)   41

14.   The $3s$ orbital of the element of atomic number 20 has how many electrons?

(a)   0   (b)   1   (c)   2   (d)   10

ANSWERS

ANSWERS TO SELF–TESTING QUESTIONS

Completion

1.   Dimitri Mendeleev
2.   one, two, three
3.   VIIA
4.   two
5.   the properties of the elements are a periodic function of their atomic numbers.
6.   the alkali metals; the halogens; the alkaline earth metals
7.   C, Si, Ge, Sn, Pb
8.   6
9.   transition
10.   metal
11.   MgO
12.   acid
13.   electrons, protons, and neutrons
14.   nucleus
15.   an element
16.   1 u; 1 u; 1/1836 u
17.   atomic number
18.   (a)   Electrons may be in an atom only in certain allowed energy states.

(b)   An atom neither absorbs nor radiates energy so long as its electrons remain in their energy states.

19.   orbital, orbit

20.   quantum of energy (1 photon)

21.   position, velocity

22.   1   1   1
        2   2   4
        3   3   9

23.   three

24.   two; they must have opposite spin.

25.   9

26.   7

27.   (a) $1s^2 2s^2 2p_x^2 2p_y^2 2p_z^2 3s^2 3p_x^1 3p_y^1$ $[Ne]\, 3s^2 3p_x^1 3p_y^1$
        (b) $1s^2 2s^2 2p^6 3s^2 3p^6 4s^1$ $[Ar]\, 4s^1$

28. $1s^2 2s^2 2p_x^1 2p_y^1$

Multiple–Choice

1.   c   2.   b   3.   a and c

4.   a   5.   a, b, and d   6.   c (Note)

7.   b (Note)   8.   a   9.   b

10.   b and c   11.   d   12.   a

13.   d   14.   c

NOTE. Problems 6 and 7 illustrate problems that are solved by first writing an electron configuration (main levels only) and then applying the rules that correlate the number of electrons in the outside level with particular properties.

5

CHEMICAL COMPOUNDS AND CHEMICAL BONDS

We complete in this chapter our basic introduction to the *structure* of matter. In the last chapter, we learned what holds subatomic particles together in atoms. In this chapter, we consider the following questions: What holds atoms together in compounds? What determines the ratios in which atoms of different elements join together? Why do only certain specific ratios occur and not others?

Broadly speaking, the main topics in this chapter are chemical bonds (ionic and covalent) and types of compounds (ionic and molecular). The ideas and the vocabulary introduced are basic. Terms such as ion, molecule, polar molecule, molecular compound, and ionic compound will be used frequently in succeeding chapters. We cannot speak of a molecular basis of life without knowing what a molecule is.

OBJECTIVES

After you have studied this chapter and worked the exercises in it, you should be able to do the following.

1. Name two kinds of compounds and describe the kinds of particles that make up each type.
2. Define and explain the difference between (a) an atom, an ion, and a molecule and (b) an ionic bond and a covalent bond.
3. Give the electrical charges of all the ions in Tables 5.1 and 5.3. For the representative elements, use the Periodic Table to tell what charges their ions have.
4. Write formulas from names and names from formulas for ionic compounds (limiting this skill to the information in Tables 5.1 and 5.3).

5.   For monatomic ions, describe how ionic sizes relate to atomic radii and give reasons for the variations.

6.   For monatomic ions, describe the relationship between oxidation numbers and ionic charges.

7.   Tell whether a given change in oxidation number is an oxidation or a reduction.

8.   Analyze a redox reaction to tell what is the oxidizing agent, what is the reducing agent, and what species are oxidized and reduced.

9.   Use the Periodic Table to write Lewis electron-dot structures for the representative elements.

10.   Use Lewis structures to tell if an atom can form covalent bonds, and predict how many such bonds can form.

11.   Represent a reaction in electron-dot symbolism.

12.   Use the octet rule and electron-dot symbolism to figure out a structural formula, even when it might involve double or triple bonds.

13.   Explain the difference between a covalent bond and a coordinate covalent bond, and give examples of each.

14.   Describe how a covalent bond and a coordinate covalent bond are alike.

15.   Write the structures (structural formulas) of the following species, using lines for shared electron pairs and dots for unshared pairs (if any): H_2, HCl, HBr, H_2O, NH_3, NH_4^+, CH_4, CO_2, H_2CO_3, HCO_3^-, CO_3^{2-}, H_2SO_4, HSO_4^-, SO_4^{2-}.

16.   Describe the general properties of acids and why acids share these properties.

17.   Describe how the VSEPR theory explains the geometry of the molecules of CH_4, NH_3, and H_2O.

18.   Define "electronegativity" and use its values, when supplied, to predict if given bonds will be polar or nonpolar.

19.   Explain how molecules can sometimes stick to each other even though they are electrically neutral.

20.   Describe the F—F bond in F_2 and the S—H bond in H_2S in the molecular orbital terms of the overlapping of atomic orbitals.

21.   Describe how an sp^3 hybrid atomic orbital forms from simple atomic orbitals.

22.   Describe the covalent bonds in CH_4, NH_3, and H_2O in molecular orbital terms.

23.   Describe how an sp^2 hybrid atomic orbital forms.

24.   Explain how each of the two bonds in the double bond of ethylene forms.

25.   Describe how a sigma bond and a pi bond differ.

26.   Define the Glossary terms.

GLOSSARY

Acid. Any substance that makes H⁺ available in water.

Anion. A negatively charged ion.

Base. A compound that provides the hydroxide ion.

Bond, Chemical. A net electrical force of attraction that holds atomic nuclei near each other within compounds.

Bond Angle. The angle formed by two bonds from the same atom.

Cation. A positively charged ion.

Coordinate Covalent Bond. A covalent bond in which both of the electrons of the shared pair originated from one of the atoms involved in the bond.

Covalence Number. The number of covalent bonds that an atom can have in a molecule.

Covalent Bond. The net force of attraction that arises as two atomic nuclei share a pair of electrons. One pair is shared in a single bond, two pair in a double bond, and three electron pairs are shared in a triple bond.

Diatomic Molecule. A molecule made of two atoms.

Dipole, Electrical. A pair of equal but opposite (and usually partial) electrical charges separated by a small distance in a molecule.

Double Bond. Two electron-pair covalent bonds, such as in $H_2C=CH_2$.

Electrolyte. Any substance whose solution in water conducts electricity; or the solution itself of such a substance.

Electron Dot Structure. A Lewis structure of a molecule in which all valence shell electrons, whether shared or unshared, are shown either by dots or by lines (bonds).

Electronegativity. The ability of an atom joined to another by a covalent bond to attract the electrons of the bond toward itself.

Electron Sharing. The joint attraction of two atomic nuclei toward a pair of electrons situated between the nuclei and between which, therefore, a covalent bond exists.

Formula, Empirical. A chemical symbol for a compound that gives just the ratios of the atoms and not necessarily the composition of a complete molecule.

Formula, Molecular. A chemical symbol for a substance that gives the composition of a complete molecule.

Formula, Structural. A chemical symbol for a substance that uses atomic symbols and lines to describe the pattern in which the atoms are joined together in a molecule.

Hybrid Orbital. An atomic orbital obtained by mixing two or more pure orbitals (those of the s, p, d, or f types).

Ion. An electrically charged, atomic or molecular-sized particle; a particle that has one or a few atomic nuclei and either one or two (seldom, three) too many or too few electrons to render the particle electrically neutral.

Ionic Bond. The force of attraction between oppositely charged ions in an ionic compound.

Ionic Compound. A compound that consists of an orderly aggregation of oppositely charged ions that assemble in whatever ratio ensures overall electrical neutrality.

Lewis Structure. An electron-dot structure in which electrons of valence shells are represented by electron-dots.

Molecular Compound. A compound whose smallest representative particle is a molecule; a covalent compound.

Molecular Orbital. A region in the space that envelopes two (or sometimes more) atomic nuclei where a shared pair of electrons of a covalent bond resides.

Molecule. An electrically neutral (but often polar) particle made up of the nuclei and electrons of two or more atoms and held together by covalent bonds; the smallest representative sample of a molecular compound.

Monatomic Ion. An ion with only one atomic nucleus.

Neutralization, Acid-Base. A reaction between an acid and a base.

Noble Gas Rule. The octet rule.

Octet, Outer. A condition of an atom or ion in which its highest occupied energy level has eight electrons — a condition of stability.

Octet Rule. The atoms of a reactive element tend to undergo those chemical reactions that most directly give them the electron configuration of the noble gas that stands nearest the element in the Periodic Table (all but one of which have outer octets).

Orbital Hybridization. The mixing of two or more ordinary atomic orbitals to give an equal number of modified atomic orbitals, called *hybrid orbitals*, each of which possesses some of the characteristics of the originals.

Orbital Overlap. The interpenetration of one atomic orbital by another from an adjacent atom to form a molecular orbital.

Oxidation. A reaction in which an oxidation number becomes more positive or less negative, often by the loss of one or more electrons from an atom, molecule, or ion.

Oxidation Number. For simple monatomic ions, the quantity and sign of the electrical charge on the ion.

Oxidation-Reduction Reaction. A reaction in which oxidation numbers change.

Oxidizing Agent. A substance that can cause an oxidation.

Pi Bond. A covalent bond formed when two electrons fill a molecular orbital created by the side-to-side overlap of two *p* orbitals.

Polar Bond. A bond at which we can write $\delta+$ at one end and $\delta-$ at the other end, the end that has the more electronegative atom.

Polar Molecule. A molecule that has sites of partial positive and partial negative charge and therefore a permanent electrical dipole.

Polyatomic Ion. Any ion made from two or more atoms, such as OH^-, SO_4^{2-}, and CO_3^{2-}.

Redox Reaction. Abbreviation of *reduction-oxidation reaction*; a reaction in which oxidation numbers change.

Reducing Agent. A substance that can cause another to be reduced.

Reduction. A reaction that makes an oxidation number become less positive or more negative often by the gain of one or more electrons by an atom, ion, or molecule.

Salt. Any crystalline compound that consists of oppositely charge ions (other than H^+, OH^-, or O^{2-}).

Sigma Bond. A covalent bond associated with a molecular orbital whose shape is symmetrical about the bonding axis.

Single Bond. One electron-pair covalent bond, such as in H—H.

sp^2 Hybrid Orbital. A hybrid orbital made by mixing one *s* orbital and two *p* orbitals to form three new, identical orbitals whose axes are in one plane and point to the corners of an equilateral triangle.

sp^3 Hybrid Orbital. One of four equivalent hybrid orbitals formed by the mixing of one *s* and three *p* orbitals and whose axes point to the corners of a regular tetrahedron.

Structure. Synonym for structural formula.

Subscripts. Numbers placed to the right and a half space below the atomic symbols in a chemical formula.

Tetrahedral. The array of bonds having bond angles of 109.5°.

Triple Bond. Three electron-pair covalent bonds, such as in N≡N.

Unshared Pairs. Valence-shell electrons not involved in covalent bonds.

Valence Shell. The outside shell of a neutral atom.

Valence-Shell Electron-Pair Repulsion Theory (VSEPR Theory). Bond angles at a central atom are caused by the repulsions of the electron clouds of valence-shell electron-pairs.

SELF-TESTING QUESTIONS

COMPLETION

1. The fundamental physical force that is responsible for all kinds of chemical bonds is an _____ force.

2. A small particle with one or a few atomic nuclei but bearing a net negative or positive charge is called _____ .

3. A compound consisting of an orderly aggregation of oppositely charged ions is classified as _____ .

4. The formula unit of a molecular compound is called _____ .

5. When the nuclei and electrons of atoms are reorganized to form particles of opposite electrical charge, the product is classified as _____ compound.

6. The net force of attraction that operates in an ionic compound to keep the ions from flying apart has the special name of_____ .

7. The reaction of lithium with chlorine, $2Li + Cl_2 \rightarrow 2LiCl$, changes the lithium atom (Li) to the _____ , which has the symbol _____ . It changes the chlorine atom (in Cl_2) into _____ , for which the symbol is _____ . In this oxidation-reduction reaction, the lithium atom is_____ (reduced or oxidized) and the chlorine atom is_____ . The oxidizing agent is_____ (name). Its symbol is _____ . The reducing agent is _____ (name) and its symbol is_____ .

8. The formula unit of an ionic compound consists of a pair or a small cluster of _____ .

9. The ions Al^{3+} and SO_4^{2-} would aggregate in a ratio of_____ions of Al^{3+} to_____ ions of SO_4^{2-}.

10. They must aggregate in that ratio because chemical compounds are, in general, electrically _____.

11. Test how well you have learned the names and formulas for the ions in Tables 5.1 and 5.3 in the text by completing the following. Give the formula for each ion; for example,

    sulfite SO_3^{2-}

    (You must include the electric charge, for instance, SO_3 by itself is the symbol of sulfur trioxide, an air pollutant.)

    (a) chloride ion   _____

    (b) sodium ion   _____

    (c) magnesium ion   _____

    (d) hydroxide ion   _____

    (e) sulfate ion   _____

    (f) potassium ion   _____

    (g) iodide ion   _____

(h) calcium ion   _____

(i) hydronium ion   _____

(j) nitrate ion   _____

(k) hydrogen sulfate ion   _____

(l) permanganate ion   _____

(m) bromide ion   _____

(n) nitrite ion   _____

(o) ammonium ion   _____

(p) dihydrogen phosphate ion

12. Using your knowledge of the names and formulas of ions, write formulas for each of the following ionic compounds.

(a) sodium iodide   _____

(b) sodium sulfate   _____

(c) sodium phosphate   _____

(d) sodium nitrate   _____

(e) magnesium sulfate   _____

(f) calcium sulfate   _____

(g) potassium sulfate   _____

(h) aluminum sulfate   _____

(i) ammonium nitrate   _____

(j) ammonium sulfate   _____

(k) calcium phosphate   _____

(l) sodium monohydrogen phosphate   _____

(m) potassium nitrite   _____

(n) silver nitrate   _____

(o) potassium permanganate   _____

(p) iron(III) oxide   _____

13. Write the name of each of the following compounds.

(a) $NaBr$ _____

(b) Na_2SO_4 _____

(c) $NaNO_3$ _____

(d) Na_2CO_3 _____

(e) $NaMnO_4$ _____

(f) Na_3PO_4 _____

(g) $NaHSO_4$ _____

(h) KH_2PO_4 _____

(i) KCl _____

(j) $KHCO_3$ _____

(k) KNO_2 _____

(l) $MgCl_2$ _____

(m) $MgHPO_4$ _____

(n) $Ca(NO_3)_2$ _____

(o) $CaSO_4$ _____

(p) $(NH_4)_2SO_4$ _____

(q) NH_4Cl _____

(r) NH_4NO_3 _____

(s) $FeCl_3$ _____

(t) $HgCl_2$ _____

(u) $AgCl$ _____

(v) $FeCl_2$ _____

(w) $HgCl$ _____

(x) K_2CO_3 _____

(y) $CaCO_3$ _____

(z) $MgCO_3$ _____

(aa) $NaHCO_3$ _____

(bb) $LiHCO_3$ _____

(cc) $Ca(HCO_3)_2$ _____

(dd) $Al_2(SO_4)_3$ _____

14. Being guided by the locations of the following elements in the Periodic Table, write the correct symbols for the most reasonable ions these elements could form. Be sure to show the electrical charge. If an ionic existence is highly unlikely, write "no ion." The numbers in parentheses are the atomic numbers of the elements.

(a) Cs (55) _____

(b) I (53) _____

(c) Sr (38) _____

(d) Xe (54) _____

15. Each of the following formulas represents an ionic compound, and you should know the electrical charge on one of the ions involved. Using this knowledge, figure out the electrical charge on the ion specified. Write the correct symbol of the ion.

(a) Rb_2SO_4 — Rb ion _____

(b) $Pb(NO_3)_2$ — Pb ion _____

(c) $Cd_3(PO_4)_2$ — Cd ion _____

(d) $NiCO_3$ — Ni ion _____

16. The radius of a potassium atom is 227 pm. The radius of the potassium ion will be _____ (larger or smaller) than this.

17. A reaction in which K changes to K^+ represents a change in oxidation number for potassium from _____ to _____ , and this called an _____.

18. In one reaction, a molecule of bromine, Br_2, is changed to two bromide ions, Br^-. The oxidation number of bromine changes from_____ to_____ in this reaction, and such a change is called a_____ .

19. Consider the following reaction,

$Mg + Cl_2 \rightarrow MgCl_2$

This is a redox reaction because _____

Write the symbols of the species in each case.

(a) The species that is oxidized _____

(b) The species that is reduced   _____

(c) The reducing agent   _____

(d) The oxidizing agent   _____

20. The particle that results when two or more atoms have their nuclei and electrons reorganized so that some electrons are shared between the nuclei is called _____ .

21. A small particle having two or more nuclei that is capable of isolated existence and that is electrically neutral is called _____ .

22. A small particle that is the smallest representative sample of a molecular compound is called
_____ .

23. The net electrical force of attraction that operates in molecules to keep their nuclei from flying apart has the special name of _____ .

24. Complete the following table according to the pattern provided by the example. Write the electron configuration (main levels only) of the atom whose atomic number is given. Deduce if the atom can form an ion; if so, write the formula of the ion using just the general symbol X for the atom in each case. Deduce next if the atom can participate in covalent bond formation; if so, give the most reasonable number of covalent bonds it will have on the basis of the octet theory.

	Atomic Number	Electron Configuration (Main Levels)[a]	Symbol of Ion (if any)	Number of Covalent Bonds
Example	16	2 8 6	X^{2-}	2
(a)	9	_____.	_____.	_____.
(b)	20	_____.	_____.	_____.
(c)	5	_____.	_____.	_____.
(d)	17	_____.	_____.	_____.
(e)	8	_____.	_____.	_____.
(f)	13	_____.	_____.	_____.

[a]In order, left to right, of level 1, level 2, etc.

25. Write the electron-dot symbols for the atoms of group IA in the Periodic Table.

_____

26. Write the electron-dot symbols for the atoms of period (row) 2 in the Periodic Table.

_____

27. Write the electron-dot symbol for lead (Pb), atomic number 82. _____

28. Represent the formation of CaS by electron-dot symbolism.

_____

29. Using electron-dot symbolism show how the electron pairs in the bonds of CH_4, NH_3, and H_2O originate from the separated atoms. (Use small x's to represent electrons provided by H atoms,

and small dots for other electrons. Ignore bond angle considerations. Do not omit unshared electrons of valence shells.)

CH_4 _____ NH_3 _____ H_2O _____

30. Using the octet rule and electron-dot structures, figure out the structures of the following.
(a) H_2Se _____ (b) AsH_3 _____

31. Hydrogen cyanide, HCN, has a triple bond. Write its structural formula. _____

32. Formaldehyde, H_2CO, has a double bond. Write its structural formula. _____

33. The following reaction illustrates the formation of what kind of bond?_____

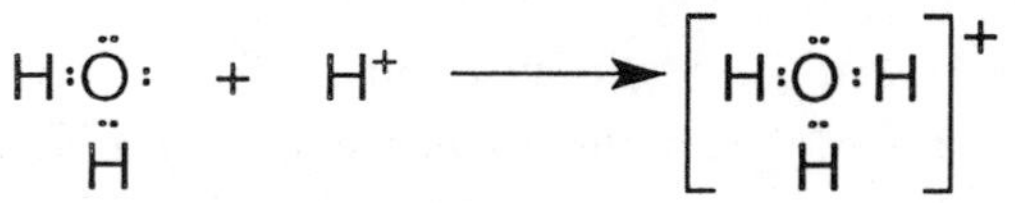

$$H\!:\!\ddot{O}\!: \; + \; H^+ \longrightarrow \left[H\!:\!\ddot{O}\!:\!H \right]^+$$
$$\overset{}{\underset{H}{|}} \qquad\qquad \overset{}{\underset{H}{|}}$$

Once it forms, how does the third bond in H_3O^+ differ (if at all) from the original two? _____

34. Acids are all sources of _____, and substances that can neutralize acids are called _____.

35. What is the *skeletal* structure of nitrous acid, HNO_2? _____

36. What is the Lewis structure of nitrous acid, HNO_2? _____

37. What is the name of the theory that correctly predicts the bond angles in methane, ammonia, and water molecules? _____

State the essential idea of this theory.

_____

38. If two electrically neutral molecules can still attract each other, they must be _____.

39. Using their atomic symbols, arrange these elements in order of their relative electronegativities: carbon, oxygen, nitrogen, and hydrogen.

_____

least electronegative   most electronegative

40. If element X has a relative electronegativity of 3.5 and that of Y is 2.5, then in the molecule X—Y, the δ+ will be close to _____ (X or Y) and the δ– will be close to _____.

41. The electron configuration of an isolated atom of carbon is _____.

42. When a carbon atom forms four single bonds, a mixing of some of the orbitals of the isolated carbon atom takes place to give _____ (1, 2, 3, or 4) new, hybrid atomic orbitals called _____ hybrid orbitals. The original orbitals that mix are the _____ orbital and the three _____ orbitals. Each hybrid orbital has _____ lobes, one larger than the other.

43. The individual axes of the hybrid orbitals (question 42) point to the corners of a _____ and these axes make angles of _____ with each other.

44. The electron configuration of an atom of nitrogen when it is forming _____ (1, 2, or 3) single bonds is _____ _____ .

45.   In ammonia, one valence level hybrid orbital of nitrogen does not form a bond to hydrogen, but it holds _____ electrons.

46.   In the water molecule, there are _____ (1, 2, or 3) valence level hybrid orbitals that are not involved in bonds to hydrogen but that contain _____ electrons each.

MULTIPLE–CHOICE

1.   If an atom, X, can accept two electrons from another atom in the process of changing into a relatively stable ion, then an atom of X
   (a)   has two protons in its nuclei
   (b)   is a metal
   (c)   will be in Group IIA in the Periodic Table.
   (d)   is also capable of forming a molecule of the formula H_2X.

2.   Atoms of elements with atomic numbers 20 and 17 are known to combine. If X is the symbol of element 20 and Y is the symbol of element 17, the correct formula for the most stable compound between these two elements is
   (a) X_2Y (b) XY_2 (c) YX_2 (d) XY

3.   Pure substances classified as molecular are characterized as being
   (a)   mixtures
   (b)   made of oppositely charged ions
   (c)   aggregations of molecules
   (d)   metallic

4.   The type of bonding found in sodium bromide is
   (a) ionic   (b) covalent   (c) coordinate   (d) nonpolar

5.   A particle having eleven protons and ten electrons would bear a charge of
   (a) 1–   (b) 0   (c) 1+   (d) 11+

6.   If elements X and Y are in the same family and X forms the compound Na_2X, then one of the compounds of Y would be
   (a) K_2Y (b) CaY (c) Na_2Y (d) Al_2Y_3

7.   If X just precedes Y in a horizontal row of the Periodic Table (i.e., the atomic number of X is one less than that of Y), and if X forms the compound HX, then a compound of Y would be
   (a)   HY
   (b) H_2Y
   (c) H_3Y
   (d)   Y is a noble gas; therefore it will form no compound.

8.   Each formula unit of $Mg(H_2PO_4)_2$ contains a total of how many atomic nuclei?
   (a)   sixteen   (b) fifteen   (c) eight   (d) fourteen

9.   In the equation, $2Na + Cl_2 \rightarrow 2NaCl$, the number just to the right of Cl is called a
   (a)   subscript   (c) multiplier
   (b)   superscript   (d) coefficient

10.   The symbol Fe is the symbol for
   (a)   an iron atom   (c) an iron molecule
   (b)   an iron ion   (d) the element iron

11. The symbol $3Cl_2$ is the symbol for
     (a) three molecules of chlorine
     (b) three atoms of chlorine
     (c) three grams of chlorine
     (d) six molecules of chlorine

12. In the equation, $Zn + 2AgNO_3 \rightarrow Zn(NO_3)_2 + 2Ag$
     (a) the equation is balanced
     (b) the equation is not balanced
     (c) Zn is oxidized
     (d) Ag^+ is reduced

13. In the equation of problem 12,
     (a) Zn is an oxidizing agent
     (b) Zn is a reducing agent
     (c) Ag^+ is an oxidizing agent
     (d) Ag^+ is a reducing agent

14. The substance calcium chloride, $CaCl_2$, is an aggregation of which particles?
     (a) calcium atoms and chlorine molecules (Cl_2)
     (b) calcium atoms and chlorine atoms
     (c) calcium ions and chlorine molecules
     (d) calcium ions and chloride ions

15. The formula of sodium hydroxide is
     (a) SOH   (b) SoOH   (c) $Na(OH)_2$ (d) NaOH

16. The name of $Mg_3(PO_4)_2$ is
     (a) magnesium phosphonate
     (b) magnesium phosphate
     (c) manganese phosphate
     (d) none of the above

17. The electron-dot symbol of Ca, group IIA, is

     (a) Ca·   (b) Ca: (c) ·Ca·   (d) :Ca·

18. The electron-dot symbol of hydrogen peroxide, H_2O_2 is

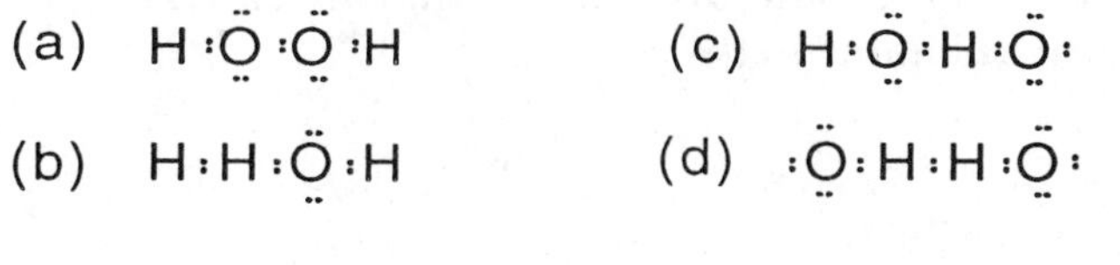

     (a) H:Ö:Ö:H   (c) H:Ö:H:Ö:

     (b) H:H:Ö:H   (d) :Ö:H:H:Ö:

19. A substance that most likely could neutralize a base is
     (a) NaOH   (b) H_2 (c) H_2O (d) H^+

20. In the water molecule there are four pairs of electrons in the outside level of the oxygen atom. According to the VSEPR theory, what should be the bond angle?
     (a) 90°   (b) 109.5°   (c) 120°   (d) 180°

21. In the boron trifluoride molecule, BF_3, there are only *three* pairs of the electrons in the valence shell of boron. Each pair is part of a covalent bond to a fluorine atom. The VSEPR theory would enable one to predict that the three fluorine atoms are

   (a) at three of the four corners of a tetrahedron and make bond angles of 109.5°

   (b) at the three corners of a regular triangle and make bond angles of 120°

   (c) make bond angles of 90°

   (d) make bond angles of 60°

22. On the basis of electronegativities, the bonds in the molecule NH_3 are in which state of polarity?

   (a) $\overset{\delta+}{N}$ — $\overset{\delta-}{H}$ (b) $\overset{+}{N}$ — $\overset{-}{H}$ (c) $\overset{\delta-}{N}$ — $\overset{\delta+}{H}$ (d) $\overset{-}{N}$ — $\overset{+}{H}$

23. If element A has a relative electronegativity of 3.7 and that of B is 2.7, and the molecule whose formula is A_2B is nonpolar, then the structure of A_2B is most likely

   (a) A—A—B   (b) A—A   (c) B   (d) A—B—A
                           \   / \
                           B   A   A

24. A substance, Z, consists of molecules. Z is a gas at room temperature and remains a gas even at −140 °C. The molecules of Z, therefore, are most likely

   (a) very polar

   (b) made of oppositely charged ions

   (c) relatively nonpolar

   (d) negative ions

25. The orbitals used by carbon in forming the bonds in CH_4 are

   (a) $2s^2$ and $2p_x^2$

   (b) $2s^2$, $2p_x^1$ and $2p_y^1$

   (c) $1s^1$, $2s^1$, sp_x^1 and $2p_y^1$

   (d) $2(sp^3)^1$, $2(sp^3)^1$, $2(sp^3)^1$, and $2(sp^3)^1$

26. Using hybrid orbitals, instead of the half-filled $2p$ orbitals, of nitrogen to form the bonds to the three hydrogen atoms in NH_3 results in stronger bonds because

   (a) the large lobe of the hybrid orbital extends farther and can overlap better with hydrogen's $1s$ orbital.

   (b) the hybrid orbitals have two pair of electrons instead of only one, and thus they can form stronger bonds with half-filled $1s$ orbitals of hydrogen atoms.

   (c) the hybrid orbitals permit the N—H bonds to have axes that are closer to each other than they can be in any alternative bonding network.

   (d) none of the above

ANSWERS

ANSWERS TO SELF–TESTING QUESTIONS

Completion

1. electrical
2. an ion
3. an ionic compound
4. a molecule
5. an ionic
6. the ionic bond
7. lithium ion, Li^+; chloride ions, Cl^-; oxidized, reduced; chlorine, Cl_2; lithium, Li
8. oppositely charged ions
9. two, three
10. neutral
11. (a) Cl^- (b) Na^+ (c) Mg^{2+} (d) OH^-
    (e) SO_4^{2-} (f) K^+ (g) I^- (h) Ca^{2+}
    (i) H_3O^+ (j) NO_3^- (k) HSO_4^- (l) MnO_4^-
    (m) Br^- (n) NO_2^- (o) NH_4^+ (p) $H_2PO_4^-$
12. (a) NaI (b) Na_2SO_4 (c) Na_3PO_4
    (d) $NaNO_3$ (e) $MgSO_4$ (f) $CaSO_4$
    (g) K_2SO_4 (h) $Al_2(SO_4)_3$ (i) NH_4NO_3
    (j) $(NH_4)_2SO_4$ (k) $Ca_3(PO_4)_2$ (l) Na_2HPO_4
    (m) KNO_2 (n) $AgNO_3$ (o) $KMnO_4$
    (p) Fe_2O_3
13. (a) sodium bromide
    (b) sodium sulfate
    (c) sodium nitrate
    (d) sodium carbonate
    (e) sodium permanganate
    (f) sodium phosphate
    (g) sodium hydrogen sulfate
    (h) potassium dihydrogen phosphate

    (i) potassium chloride
    (j) potassium bicarbonate
    (k) potassium nitrite
    (l) magnesium chloride
   (m) magnesium monohydrogen phosphate
    (n) calcium nitrate
    (o) calcium sulfate
    (p) ammonium sulfate
    (q) ammonium chloride
    (r) ammonium nitrate
    (s) iron(III) chloride [ferric chloride]
    (t) mercury(II) chloride [mercuric chloride]
    (u) silver chloride
    (v) iron(II) chloride [ferrous chloride]
   (w) mercury(I) chloride [mercurous chloride]
    (x) potassium carbonate
    (y) calcium carbonate
    (z) magnesium carbonate
  (aa) sodium bicarbonate
  (bb) lithium bicarbonate
  (cc) calcium bicarbonate
  (dd) aluminum sulfate

14. (a) Cs^+ (b) I^- (c) Sr^{2+} (d) no ion

15. (a) Rb^+ (b) Pb^{2+} (c) Cd^{2+} (d) Ni^{2+}

16. smaller

17. 0, +1, oxidation

18. 0, −1, reduction

19. oxidation numbers change
    (a) Mg   (b) Cl_2 (c) Mg   (d) Cl_2

20. a molecule

21. a molecule

22. a molecule

23. covalent bond

24.

	Atomic Number	Electronic Configuration			Symbol of Ion	Number of Covalent Bonds
(a)	9	2	7		X^-	1
(b)	20	2	8	8 2	X^{2+}	none
(c)	5	2	3		X^{3+}	none
(d)	17	2	8	7	X^-	1
(e)	8	2	6		X^{2-}	2
(f)	13	2	8	3	X^{3+}	none

25. Li·   Na·   K·   Rb·   Cs·   Fr·

26. Li·   ·Be·   ·Ḃ·   ·Ċ·   ·Ṅ·   ·Ö·   :Ḟ·

27. ·Pḃ·

28. ·Ca· + ·S̈· $\longrightarrow$ Ca^{2+} + $\left[:\ddot{\underset{..}{S}}: \right]^{2-}$

29.
$$
\begin{array}{c}
\text{H} \\
\text{H×C×H} \\
\text{H}
\end{array}
\qquad
\begin{array}{c}
\text{H×N̈×H} \\
\text{H}
\end{array}
\qquad
\begin{array}{c}
\text{H×Ö×H} \\
\text{H}
\end{array}
$$

30. (a) H:S̈e:H   (b) H:Äs:H
                            H

31. H—C≡N:

32.
$$
\begin{array}{c}
:\!O\!: \\
\| \\
\text{H—C—H}
\end{array}
$$

33. Coordinate covalent bond; no difference
34. hydrogen ions; bases
35. H O N O

36. H :Ö:N̈::Ö:

37. Valence-shell electron-pair repulsion theory
    Electron clouds of valence electrons, whether shared or unshared, repel each other.
38. polar
39. H < C < N < O
40. Y, X (since X is more electronegative than Y)
41. $1s^2 2s^2 2p_x^{1} 2p_y^{1}$
42. 4; sp^3; $2s$; $2p$; two
43. regular tetrahedron; 109.5°
44. 3; $1s^2 2(sp^3)^2 2(sp^3)^1 2(sp^3)^1 2(sp^3)^1$
45. two
46. 2; two

Multiple–Choice

1. d (X has six electrons in its outer level and therefore can also form two covalent bonds.)
2. b
3. c
4. a
5. c $[(11+) + (10-) = 1+]$
6. a, b, c, and d (an ion of X must have a charge of 2–; therefore, the charge on an ion of Y must be 2–, also.)
7. d
8. b
9. a
10. a and d
11. a

12. a, c, and d	17. c	22. c
13. b and c	18. a	23. d
14. d	19. d	24. c
15. d	20. b	25. d
16. b	21. b	26. a

6

STATES OF MATTER AND THE KINETIC THEORY

The chief topics of this chapter are the laws governing the behavior of gases, the kinetic theory that explains these laws, and the physical properties of liquids (particularly water) and solids. This chapter also introduces London forces, dipole-dipole attractions, and the hydrogen bond, the most important weak forces involved in the structure and physical states of matter.

OBJECTIVES

After you have studied this chapter and worked the exercises, you should be able to do the following.

1. Name, define, and give the normally used units for four properties of a gas that are used to describe its physical state.
2. Know when to use Boyle's law, Charles' law, Gay-Lussac's law, the combined gas law, and the ideal gas law to calculate how a fixed amount of a gas will change in pressure, volume, or temperature when others of these variables change.
3. Use Dalton's law of partial pressures to convert between total pressure and partial pressures.
4. Compute the total pressure of gases over water on a dry basis when water vapor is present.
5. State the volume-mole relationship for gases compared at the same pressure and temperature.
6. Give the values of STP.
7. Define an "ideal gas" and contrast it with a "real gas."
8. Give the postulates of the kinetic theory of gases.
9. Relate the temperature of a gas to kinetic theory in general terms.
10. Explain how dipole-dipole attractions and London forces arise and how they affect the ability of a given substance to be in a particular physical state.

11. Describe (in general terms only) how the kinetic model of a gas applies (a) to the liquid and the solid states and (b) to the phenomena of melting, boiling, and vapor pressure.
12. Know when to use such terms as "volatile" and "nonvolatile" when describing a liquid.
13. Use an example such as a change of physical state to explain what is involved (in general terms) in a dynamic equilibrium.
14. Write equations (using words) for the equilibria between a liquid and its vapor, or between a solid and its liquid form, equations that include a heat term, and explain how these equilibria shift when heat is added or removed from the system.
15. Know how and when to use such terms associated with equilibria as Le Châtelier's principle, forward and reverse changes, upsetting or shifting an equilibrium, and favored and unfavored reactions.
16. Be able to tell from a structural formula if hydrogen bonds can exist between the molecules of a substance.
17. Explain how surface tension arises and how it is responsible for the beading of water on a waxy surface.
18. Describe the effect of a surfactant and cite two examples in which surfactants are vital to our lives.
19. Describe the solid state and the equilibrium at the melting point of a solid.
25. Define each of the terms in the Glossary.

GLOSSARY

Absolute Zero. The coldest temperature attainable; 0 K (-273.15 °C)

Atmosphere, Standard (atm). The pressure that supports a column of mercury 760 mm high when the mercury has a temperature of 0 °C.

Avogadro's Principle. Equal volumes of gases contain equal numbers of moles when they are compared at identical temperatures and pressures.

Barometer. An instrument for measuring atmospheric pressure.

Boiling. The turbulent behavior in a liquid when its vapor pressure equals the atmospheric pressure and when the liquid absorbs heat while experiencing no rise in temperature.

Boiling Point, Normal. The temperature at which a substance boils when the atmospheric pressure is 760 mm Hg (1 atm).

Boyle's Law. The volume of a gas is inversely proportional to its pressure when the temperature is constant.

Charles' Law. The volume of a gas is directly proportional to its Kelvin temperature when the pressure is kept constant.

Combined Gas Law. For a fixed amount of a gas,

$$\frac{P_1 V_1}{T_1} = \frac{P_2 V_2}{T_2}$$

Condensation. The physical change of a substance from its gaseous state to its liquid state.

Dalton's Law of Partial Pressures. The total pressure of a mixture of gases is the sum of their individual partial pressures.

Diffusion. A physical process whereby particles, by random motions, intermingle and spread out so as to erase concentration gradients.

Dipole-Dipole Attraction. The electrical force of attraction between δ+ and δ- sites of polar molecules.

Endothermic. Describing a change that needs a constant supply of heat energy to happen.

Equilibrium, Dynamic. A situation in which two opposing events occur at identical rates so that no net change happens.

Equilibrium Equation. An equation in which oppositely pointing arrows separate reactants and products that are in equilibrium.

Evaporation. The conversion of a substance from its liquid to its vapor state.

Exothermic. Describing a change by which heat energy is released from a system.

Forward Reaction. In an equilibrium equation, that particular reaction by which substances to the left of the double arrows change into substances to the right.

Gas Constant, Universal (R). The ration of PV to nT for a gas, where P = the gas pressure, V = volume, n = number of moles, and T = the Kelvin temperature. When P is in atm and V is in L, $R = 0.0821$ L atm/mol K. When P is in mm Hg and V is in mL, $R = 6.23 \times 10^4$ mm Hg mL/mol K.

Gay-Lussac's Law. The pressure of a gas is directly proportional to its Kelvin temperature when the gas volume is constant.

Heat of Reaction. The net energy difference between the reactants and the products of a reaction.

Hydrogen Bond. The force of attraction between a δ+ on a hydrogen held by a covalent bond to oxygen or nitrogen (or fluorine) and a δ- on a nearby atom of oxygen or nitrogen (or fluorine).

Ideal Gas. A hypothetical gas that obeys the gas laws exactly.

Ideal Gas Law. $PV = nRT$

Kinetic Theory of Gases. A set of postulates about the nature of an ideal gas: that it consists of a large number of very small particles in constant, random motion; that in the collisions the particles lose no frictional energy; that between collisions the particles neither attract nor repel each other; and that the motions and collisions of the particles obey all the laws of physics.

Le Châtelier's Principle. If a system is in equilibrium and a change is made in its conditions, the system will change in whichever way most directly restores equilibrium.

London Force. A net force between molecules that arises from temporary polarities induced in the molecules by collisions or near-collisions with neighboring molecules.

Manometer. A device for measuring gas pressure.

Melting Point. The temperature at which a solid changes into its liquid form; the temperature at which equilibrium exists between the solid and liquid forms of a substance.

Millimeter of Mercury (mm Hg). A unit of pressure equal to 1/760 atm.

Molar Volume, Standard. The volume of one mole of a gas at STP; 22.4 L.

Nonvolatile Liquid. Any liquid with a very low vapor pressure at room temperature and that does not readily evaporate.

Partial Pressure. The pressure contributed by an individual gas in a mixture of gases.

Pascal (Pa). The SI unit of pressure. 1 atm = 101,325 Pa

Pressure. Force per unit area.

Pressure-Temperature Law. (See *Gay-Lussac's Law*).

Pressure-Volume Law. (See *Boyle's Law*).

Reverse Reaction. The reaction in an equilibrium that undoes the effect of the forward reaction. (See *Forward Reaction.*)

Standard Conditions of Temperature and Pressure (STP). 0°C (or 273 K) and 1 atm (or 760 mm Hg).

Sublimation. A change of state from the solid state directly to the gaseous state.

Surface Active Agent. A substance, such as a detergent, that reduces the surface tension of water.

Surfactant. (See *Surface Active Agent.*)

Temperature-Volume Law. (See *Charles' Law*).

Torr. A unit of pressure; 1 torr = 1 mm Hg; 1 atm = 760 torr.

Vacuum. An enclosed space in which there is no matter.

Vapor Pressure. The pressure exerted by the vapor that is in equilibrium with its liquid state at a given temperature.

Volatile Liquid. A liquid that has a high vapor pressure and readily evaporates at room temperature.

HOW TO STUDY THE GAS LAWS

The properties of gases are described by various laws. What is important here are the properties of gases, not the names of the laws. Even after you forget which law is Boyle's and which is Charles' or Gay-Lussac's, you should remember the basic properties of gases.

Start by learning the list of variables used in the gas laws. These variables are the properties of a sample of gas that can be measured and that can be varied or adjusted by the experimenter. They are:

Pressure	P	Temperature	T (in kelvins)
Volume	V	Quantity	n (in moles)

Often the subscripts 1 and 2 are used to designate the two different states of the gas. Usually, a fixed quantity of a gas is involved, which means that n, the number of moles of the gas, is a constant. This leaves just three variables: P, V, and T. Always remember that T must be in kelvins (kelvins = degrees Celsius + 273).

If a question involves changes in all three variables — P, V, and T — then the ideal gas law is generally used:

$$PV = nRT$$

where R is the universal gas constant whose numerical value depends upon the units selected for P and V. Thus, when P is in atm and V is in L, $R = 0.0821$ L atm/mol K. When P is in mm Hg and V is in mL, $R = 6.23 \times 10^4$ mm Hg mL/mol K.

If you forget the value of R or if a reference containing it is not handy, then you can use the combined gas law (provided that the amount of gas is fixed):

$$\frac{P_1 V_1}{T_1} = \frac{P_2 V_2}{T_2}$$

This equation is perhaps the best single equation to memorize. From it, if needed, Boyle's, Charles', and Gay-Lussac's equations can be readily derived.

Boyle's law is the pressure-volume law: both n and T are fixed. If $T_1 = T_2$, then they cancel in the basic equation and we have the equation: $P_1 V_1 = P_2 V_2$

Charles' law is the temperature-volume law; both n and P are fixed. If $P_1 = P_2$, then they cancel in the basic equation and we have:

$$\frac{V_1}{T_1} = \frac{V_2}{T_2}$$

Gay-Lussac's law is the temperature-pressure law, both n and V are fixed. If $V_1 = V_2$, they cancel in the basic equation, and we have:

$$\frac{P_1}{T_1} = \frac{P_2}{T_2}$$

Since the relations among the variables are more important than the names of the laws, be sure you learn these basic relations.

1. Pressure varies inversely with volume (T and n are fixed).
    Increase the pressure → reduce the volume
    Decrease the pressure → increase the volume
2. Volume varies directly with Kelvin temperature (P and n are fixed).
    Increase the temperature → increase the volume
    Decrease the temperature → decrease the volume
3. Pressure varies directly with Kelvin temperature (V and n are fixed).
    Increase the temperature → increase the pressure
    Decrease the temperature → decrease the pressure

We are also concerned with Dalton's law and Avogadro's principle. Be especially certain to understand and learn Dalton's law of partial pressure.

The kinetic theory of gases is particularly helpful in its explanation of the gas laws; it gives something of a "molecule's-eye view" of gases. It is also a beautiful illustration of the interplay between experimental work and theoretical concepts. The theory tells us that the pressure of a gas is proportional to the mean kinetic energy of the gas particles. Likewise, it tells us that the temperature of a gas is proportional to the mean kinetic energy of the gas particles. If we raise the temperature of a gas, we increase its mean kinetic energy; if we raise the temperature of a confined gas, we also raise its pressure.

The kinetic theory also gives us a "molecule's-eye view" of the motion or vibration of atoms and molecules in liquids and solids. Concentrate on learning the vocabulary in Sections 6.6 through 6.9.

The effects of weak forces of attraction — those weaker than ionic or covalent bonds — on the physical state of a sample of matter will appear repeatedly in our study of the molecular basis of life. The hydrogen bond, for example, is involved in the structures of both proteins and nucleic acids (the chemicals of heredity). Be sure that you can tell from a structure if such molecules can have hydrogen bonds between them, or other dipole-dipole attractions, or London forces.

SELF-TESTING QUESTIONS

COMPLETION

1. The atmosphere at sea level presses down with a force of _____ lb/in.^{2} and will hold up a column of mercury that is _____ mm in height.
2. Another name for 1 mm Hg is _____ .
3. Robert Boyle discovered the relation between the pressure and the _____ of a fixed amount of gas when its _____ is constant.

4.   Boyle found that this relation appears to be true for all _____ .

5.   Using symbols of P_1, P_2, V_1, and V_2, Boyle's law may be written in mathematical form as: _____ .

6.   In a general way, Boyle's law tells us that if greater pressure is placed on a gas (without changing its temperature), the volume of the gas will _____.

7.   Alternatively, if the pressure on a gas is reduced, its volume will _____, assuming no change in T.

8.   If the pressure on a gas is reduced by one-half, its volume will _____, assuming no change in T.

9.   When it is possible to heat a gas without causing a change in its pressure, the volume of the gas _____ in accordance with _____ law.

10.   In order to double the volume of a fixed amount of gas without changing the gas pressure, what new value of temperature must the gas be given if the initial temperature is 25°C? _____

11.   When the temperature of a fixed amount of gas in a rigid container is doubled, the gas pressure _____, according to _____ law.

12.   The gas law to use in a calculation involving a fixed amount (n) of gas that undergoes changes in two or three of the variables, P, V, or T, has what name? _____

13.   At 745 mm Hg and 24.0°C, a 345-mL glass bottle can hold how many moles and how many grams of O_2? _____

14.   If a mixture of gases is made up of three individual gases, A, B, and C, and the total pressure on the gas mixture is 760 mm Hg, what is the partial pressure of C if the partial pressures of A and B are each 350 mm Hg? _____

15.   Comparing inhaled air with exhaled air, the partial pressure of _____ is less in exhaled air partly because it has been consumed during chemical reactions in the body.

16.   A sample of oxygen was collected at 22°C over water. The volume of this wet oxygen was 475 mL at a pressure of 742 mm Hg. What volume would the oxygen occupy if completely dry at 742 mm Hg? The vapor pressure of water at 22 °C is 19.8 mm Hg. _____

17.   The standard conditions of temperature and pressure are _____ K and _____ atm.

18.   At STP, one mole of oxygen occupies _____ liters, one mole of hydrogen occupies _____ liters, and one mole of nitrogen occupies _____ liters.

19.   Hydrogen and oxygen combine to form water:
$$2H_2 + O_2 \rightarrow 2H_2O$$
For a complete reaction, one liter of oxygen at STP would require _____ liters of hydrogen also at STP, because according to Avogadro's law, "when measured at the same T and P, equal volumes of gases contain equal numbers of _____."

20.   The basic postulates of the kinetic theory of gases that describe an ideal gas are:

(a) _____

(b) _____

(c) _____

(d) _____

21.   If somehow the average kinetic energy of all the particles in a sample of helium gas contained in a tight flask is made to increase, then both the _____ and the _____ of the helium will increase.

22.   Ionic compounds are solids, not liquids or gases, at room temperature because the force of attraction between _____ is much stronger than the force that can normally exist between _____ of molecular compounds.

23. The names given to the three forces of attraction that we have studied and that are at work within a sample of a liquid to retain it in the liquid state are

_____

_____

_____

24. Between polar molecules there exist _____ forces of attraction.

25. Between nonpolar molecules, _____ forces arise because temporary _____ are created when _____ become distorted during collisions between molecules.

26. What important physical constant of a liquid will likely have a relatively low value if the liquid is considered to be very volatile?

27. Consider the following physical equilibrium:

$$\text{liquid} \rightleftharpoons \text{solid} + \text{heat}$$

(a) As this expression is written, which is the forward change? (Write the equation for just this change.)

_____

(b) What could be done to the temperature to shift this equilibrium to the left?

_____

(c) Is the reverse change in this equilibrium endothermic or exothermic?_____

(d) Describe a stress that could be put on this equilibrium to make it shift to the left?_____

(e) The responses of equilibria to stresses are predictable by applying a general principle called

_____ .

28. The hydrogen bond is a special case of a _____ .

29. Hydrogen bonds do not exist between molecules of CH_4 because H is not attached to an atom with a high enough _____ .

30. Hydrogen bonds can exist between molecules that have H attached to X if X is an atom of

_____ .

31. In terms of the net *electrical* charge for the whole molecule, the water molecule is _____ .

32. However, the water molecule is _____ , because the center of density of all its _____ charges (contributed by its atomic nuclei) does not coincide with the center of density of all its _____ charges (contributed by its _____).

33. Write the structure of two water molecules, orienting them in a manner we would expect because they can attract each other. _____

34. The net force of attraction between water molecules is called the _____. It extends from a site of δ+ associated with the _____(H or O) of one molecule to a site of δ− associated with the _____(H or O) end of the other molecule.

35. If water forms tight beads on the surface of a plastic bottle, the molecules in the plastic must be _____(polar or nonpolar).

36. The surface tension of water would be enough to collapse the lungs by collapsing the _____ in the lungs if the water in the lungs did not contain some _____.

37. The equilibrium equation (including a heat term) for which the forward reaction corresponds to sublimation is _____ .

38. The temperature at which a solid is in equilibrium with its liquid form is called the solid's

_____ .

MULTIPLE-CHOICE

1. The two gases important in respiration are
   (a) nitrogen   (c) oxygen
   (b) carbon dioxide   (d) water vapor

2. Pressure is the same as
   (a) force   (c) force per unit distance
   (b) force per unit volume   (d) force per unit area

3. One atmosphere of pressure may be expressed as
   (a) 1 atm   (b) 760 mm Hg   (c) 760 torr   (d) 20 lb/in^2

4. If 1.00 L of a gas at 20°C is made to change its pressure from 1 atm to 2 atm, the new volume will be
   (a) 2.00 L   (b) 1.00 L   (c) 0.500 L   (d) 0.100 L

5. If 1.00 L of a gas at 50°C is made to change its temperature to 100°C under conditions where it is allowed to freely expand in order to maintain a constant pressure, the new volume of the gas will be
   (a) 2.00 L   (b) 0.500 L   (c) 4.00 L   (d) 1.15 L

6. If a gas mixture consists of 1 mol of helium and 1 mol of argon at STP, the partial pressure of helium will be
   (a) 1 atm   (b) 0.5 atm   (c) 2 atm (d)   1.15 atm

7. A sample of an unknown gas occupies 22.4 L at STP and the sample has a mass of 32.0 grams. The formula mass of the gas is, therefore,
   (a) 22.4   (b) 32.0   (c) 11.2   (d) 16.0

8. The postulate of the kinetic theory stating that the molecules of a gas move in straight lines, not curved lines, between collisions is another way of postulating that between the molecules
   (a) no forces of attraction exist
   (b) no forces of repulsion exist
   (c) balanced forces of attraction and repulsion exist
   (d) collisions are perfectly elastic

9. If the molecules of a gas confined within a sealed container are somehow made to have a lower average velocity but still remain in the gaseous state,
   (a) the density of the gas will decrease
   (b) the pressure of the gas will decrease
   (c) the temperature of the gas will decrease
   (d) the volume of the gas will decrease

10. The temperature of a substance is a measure of
    (a) the average kinetic energy of its formula units
    (b) the number of its formula units present
    (c) the gram-formula weight
    (d) the chemical energy of the formula units

11. The opposite of condensation is
    (a) melting   (b) boiling   (c) freezing   (d) evaporation

12. The curved arrow points to what kind of bond?

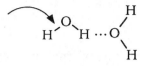

(a) covalent   (c) hydrogen bond

(b) ionic   (d) nonpolar

13. The dotted line in the structure of question 12 points to

(a) a covalent bond   (c) a hydrogen bond

(b) an ionic bond   (d) a London force bond

14. Which hydrogen bond does not exist?

(a) C—H·····C—H   (c) N—H·····O—H

(b) O—H·····O—H   (d) N—H·····N—H

15. Hydrogen bonds between molecules will be the strongest for which substance?

(a) NH_3 (b) CH_4 (c) H_2O (d) H—H

16. If water tends to spread out and form a very thin film on a surface, then the molecules in that surface are very likely

(a) nonpolar   (b) polar   (c) dense   (d) mobile

ANSWERS

ANSWERS TO SELF–TESTING QUESTIONS

Completion

1. 14.7; 760
2. torr
3. volume, temperature
4. gases
5. $P_1V_1 = P_2V_2$
6. decrease
7. increase
8. double
9. increases; Charles'
10. 596 K or 323°C. (The *absolute* temperature must be doubled, not the temperature in °C.)
11. doubles; Gay-Lussac's
12. combined gas law
13. 1.39×10^{-2} mol O_2; 0.445 g O_2
14. 60 mm Hg (350 + 350 +*60* = 760; Dalton's law)
15. oxygen

16. 462 mL
17. 273; 1
18. 22.4, 22.4, 22.4
19. two, moles
20. (a) Gases consist of large numbers of small particles in **random motion.**
    (b) These particles are very hard and collide in frictionless collisions.
    (c) These particles neither attract nor repel each other.
    (d) The motions of these particles obey the laws of physics.
21. pressure, temperature
22. ions; molecules
23. dipole-dipole attractions, London forces, and hydrogen bonds
24. dipole-dipole
25. London; dipoles; electron clouds
26. boiling point
27. (a) liquid → solid + heat
    (b) raise the temperature
    (c) endothermic
    (d) add heat
    (e) Le Châtelier's principle
28. dipole-dipole attraction
29. electronegativity
30. F, O, or N
31. electrically neutral
32. polar; positive; negative; electrons

33.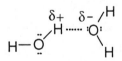

34. hydrogen bond; H; O
35. nonpolar
36. air sacs; surfactant
37. solid + heat ⇌ vapor
38. melting point

Multiple–Choice

1.	b and c	2.	d
3.	a, b, and c	4.	c
5.	d	6.	b
7.	b	8.	a and b
9.	b and c	10.	a
11.	d	12.	a
13.	c	14.	a
15.	c	16.	a

7

SOLUTIONS AND COLLOIDS

The topics in this chapter that are most important for an understanding of the molecular basis of life are:

1. How water can dissolve some substances well and others poorly

   Because water is the fluid of cells and blood.

2. Dialysis

   Because the principles of dialysis permit us to predict the directions of the net movements of certain solutes across cell membranes.

3. Ways to express concentrations other than in units of moles per liter.

   Because these are often used to describe numbers of fluids found in living systems as well as systems in environmental studies, agriculture, and medicine.

OBJECTIVES

After you have studied this chapter and worked the exercises in it, you should be able to do the following.

1. Compare and contrast true solutions, colloidal dispersions, and suspensions with respect to particle sizes and four physical properties.

2. Explain the Tyndall effect and the Brownian movement.

3. Explain how the high polarity of water helps it to function as a solvent.

4. Explain why hydrates are called *compounds*, not mixtures, and give formulas for plaster of paris and gypsum.

5. Use Le Châtelier's principle to explain how temperature affects solubility.

6. Describe the dependence of the solubility of a gas in water on (a) the temperature and (b) the pressure of the gas over the solution.

7. Use Henry's law (the pressure-solubility law) to calculate the solubility of a gas in water.

8. Explain how chemical reactions enable carbon dioxide, sulfur dioxide, and ammonia to be much more soluble in water than gases such as oxygen or nitrogen.

9. Describe how changes in the oxygen tension and the carbon dioxide tension of blood and cell fluids help deliver these gases in the body.

10. Do the calculations required for the preparation and use of solutions of known percent concentrations (a) from pure solutes and solvents and (b) from more concentrated solutions.

11. In general terms, describe the colligative properties of solutions and how they are affected if solutes are molecular or ionic.

12. Give the circumstances necessary for osmosis or dialysis.

13. Predict the direction in which water will flow in osmosis or dialysis, given the concentrations of solutes expressed as molarities or osmolarities.

14. Define each of the terms in the Glossary.

GLOSSARY

Active Transport. The movement of a substance through a biological membrane against a concentration gradient and caused by energy-consuming chemical changes that involve parts of the membrane.

Anhydrous Form. A substance without any water of hydration.

Brownian Movement. The random, chaotic movements of particles in a colloidal dispersion that can be seen with a microscope.

Colligative Property. A property of a solution that depends only on the concentrations of the solute and the solvent and not on their chemical identities (e.g., osmotic pressure).

Colloidal Dispersion. A relatively stable, uniform distribution in some dispersing medium of colloidal particles — those with at least one dimension between 1 and 1000 nm.

Colloidal Osmotic Pressure. The contribution made to the osmotic pressure of a solution by substances colloidally dispersed in it.

Crenation. The shrinkage of red blood cells in contact with a hypertonic solution.

Deliquescence. The ability of a substance to attract water vapor to itself to form a concentrated solution.

Desiccant. A substance that combines with water vapor to form a hydrate and thereby reduces the concentration of water vapor in the air space around the substance.

Dialysis. The passage through a dialyzing membrane of water and particles in solution, but not of particles that have colloidal size.

Dialyzing Membrane. A membrane permeable to solvent and small solute ions or molecules but impermeable to colloidal sized particles.

Dissociation. The separation of preexisting ions from one another as an ionic compound dissolves or melts.

Emulsion. A colloidal dispersion of tiny microdroplets of one liquid in another liquid.

Gas Tension. The partial pressure of a gas over its solution in some liquid when the system is in equilibrium.

Gel. A colloidal dispersion of a solid in a liquid that has adopted a semisolid form.

Gradient. The presence of a change in value of some physical quantity with distance, as in a *concentration* gradient in which the concentration of a solute is different in different parts of the system.

Hemolysis. The bursting of a red blood cell.

Henry's Law. The concentration of a gas in a liquid at any given temperature is directly proportional to the partial pressure of the gas on the solution.

Heterogeneous Mixture. A mixture in which the composition of one small portion is not identical with that of another.

Homogeneous Mixture. A mixture in which the composition and properties are uniform throughout.

Hydrate. A compound in which intact molecules of water are held in a definite molar proportion to the other components.

Hydrated Ion. An ion around which molecules of water have been drawn by ion-dipole attractions.

Hydration. The association of water molecules with dissolved ions or polar molecules.

Hygroscopic. Describing a substance that can reduce the concentration of water vapor in the surrounding air by forming a hydrate.

Hypertonic. Having an osmotic pressure greater than some reference; having a total concentration of all solute particles higher than that of some reference.

Hypotonic. Having an osmotic pressure less than some reference; having a total concentration of dissolved solute particles less than that of some reference.

Ion-Dipole Attraction. The electrical force of attraction between an ion and a polar molecule.

Isotonic. Having an osmotic pressure identical to that of a reference; having a concentration equivalent to the reference with respect to the ability to undergo osmosis.

Macromolecule. Any molecule with a very high formula mass — generally several thousand or more.

Milligram Percent. The number of milligrams of solute in 100 mL of the solution.

Osmolarity. The molar concentration of all osmotically active solute particles in a solution.

Osmosis. The passage of water only, without any solute, from a less concentrated solution (or pure water) to a more concentrated solution when the two solutions are separated by a semipermeable membrane.

Osmotic Membrane. A semipermeable membrane that permits only osmosis, not dialysis.

Osmotic Pressure. The pressure that would have to be applied to a solution to prevent osmosis if the solution were separated from water by an osmotic membrane.

Parts per Billion (ppb). The number of parts in a billion parts. (Two drops of water in a railway tank car that holds 34,000 gallons of water correspond roughly to 1 ppb.)

Parts per Million (ppm). The number of parts in a million parts. (Two drops of water in a large, 32-gallon trash can correspond roughly to 1 ppm.)

Percent (%). A measure of concentration.

Volume/volume percent: The number of volumes of solute in 100 volumes of solution.

Weight/weight percent: The number of grams of solute in 100 g of the solution.

Weight/volume percent: The number of grams of solute in 100 mL of the solution.

Milligram percent: The number of milligrams of the solute in 100 mL of the solution.

Physiological Saline Solution. A solution of sodium chloride with an osmotic pressure equal to that of blood.

Pressure-Solubility Law. (See *Henry's Law*.)

Reagent. Any mixture of chemicals, usually a solution, that is used to carry out a chemical test.

Saturated Solution. A solution into which no more solute can be dissolved at the given temperature; a solution in which dynamic equilibrium exists between the dissolved and the undissolved solute.

Semipermeable. Descriptive of a membrane that permits only certain kinds of molecules to pass through and not others.

Solution. A homogeneous mixture of two or more substances that are at the smallest levels of their states of subdivision — at the ion, atom, or molecule level.

Suspension. A homogeneous mixture in which the particles of at least one component have average diameters greater than 1000 nm.

Tyndall Effect. The scattering of light by colloidal sized particles in a colloidal dispersion.

Water of Hydration. Water molecules held in a hydrate in some definite mole ratio to the rest of the compound.

SELF-TESTING QUESTIONS

COMPLETION

1. If water contains a dispersion of particles larger than simple ions or molecules but not heavy enough to be forced by gravity to settle or otherwise coagulate, this mixture is called a _____.

2. If you direct a light beam through this mixture (question 1), you will observe the _____ effect.

3. A colloidal dispersion of one liquid in another is called an _____ .

4. The motions of colloidal dispersed particles in a fluid are called the _____ .

5. Potassium chloride is similar in structure to sodium chloride. At 20 °C the solubility of KCl in water is 24.7 g/100 mL solution.

   (a) What particles make up the formula unit of KCl? (Give both their names and their symbols.)
   _____ whose symbol is _____, and _____ whose symbol is _____.

   (b) What particles separate from the crystal of KCl as it goes into the solution in water? (Formulas only)
   _____ and _____

   (c) What happens to them as they enter the solution (something involving the water molecules)?
   _____

   (d) In the crystal of KCl, the potassium ions were generally surrounded by what electron-rich particles? (Name) _____

   (e) By going into solution, have the potassium ions given up being surrounded by an electron-rich envelope? _____

What electron-rich substance surrounds each K^+ ion in the solution? _____

(f) As for the chloride ions in KCl, they are surrounded by what relatively electron-poor particles?

_____   _____
(Give name)   (Formula)

(g) When the chloride ions go into solution in water, what is it that is relatively electron-poor that crowds around them? (Be specific; it is not just the particle's name we seek but also a particular part of it.)

_____

6. Le Châtelier's principle enables us to predict that the following equilibrium will shift to the _____ if it is cooled.

     (left or right)

$$heat + CuSO_4(s) \rightleftharpoons Cu^{2+}(aq) + SO_4^{2-}(aq)$$
                    water

(The symbol (s) stands for the solid substance and (aq) for the dissolved particles.)

7. Le Châtelier's principle helps us to predict that the gas tension of carbon dioxide over water will _____ if the mixture of the following equilibrium is heated.

     (increase or decrease)

$$CO_2(aq) + heat \rightleftharpoons CO_2(g)$$

The symbol (g) stands for the gaseous state, and (aq) means the aqueous solution.

8. We would use _____ law to predict the solubility of oxygen in water at 640 mm Hg if we knew its solubility at 760 mm Hg (at the same temperature).

9. The solubility of oxygen in water at 20 °C and 760 mm Hg is 4.30 mg/dL. What is its solubility at a pressure of 270 mm Hg? _____

10. Suppose you have a solution of KCl at 20 °C with a concentration of 34.7 g KCl/100 g water. This is also the solubility of KCl in water at 20 °C.

(a) What qualitative expression describes this solution most accurately? _____

(b) What is the percent of concentration (w/w)? _____

(c) What would you see if you added some crystals of KCl to this solution? _____

(d) If you separated this solution from pure water by a semipermeable membrane, _____ would occur and the volume of this solution would _____ (increase or decrease) and its concentration would _____ (increase or decrease).

11. To prepare 500 mL of a 10% (v/v) solution of ethanol in water, you have to mix _____ mL of ethanol with _____ mL of water (assuming that these volumes, when mixed actually give 500 mL of solution).

12. In 100 mL of 5% (w/v) of salt in water there is _____ g of salt.

13. Three colligative properties of solutions containing nonvolatile solutes are

(a) _____

(b) _____

(c) _____

14. Which solution will have the lower freezing point, a solution with 1 mole of KCl in 1 kg of water or a solution with 1 mole of $MgCl_2$ in 1 kg of water? _____
Explain.

15. Which of the two solutions in the previous question would have the higher osmotic pressure? _____

16. If pure water were fed intravenously, a patient's red blood cells would tend to _____ (shrink or burst); technically, this is called _____.

17. A compound with the formula $Na_3PO_4 \cdot 12H_2O$ is an example of a _____.

18. If this compound (in question 17) were heated intensely, it would lose its water of _____ and be changed into its _____ form.

19. Calcium chloride, $CaCl_2$, will take water vapor from humid air and change to $CaCl_2 \cdot 6H_2O$. What would this product be called? _____

20. Because anhydrous calcium chloride will do this, it is called a _____.

MULTIPLE–CHOICE

1. When water molecules in liquid water are attracted to and crowd around solute ions (or molecules), the phenomenon is called (one choice)
    (a) hydrolysis   (c) hydration
    (b) solvation   (d) hydrogenation

2. One property a colloidal dispersion has that a solution does not is
    (a) homogeneity   (c) the Tyndall effect
    (b) filterability   (d) osmotic pressure

3. The dispersion of oil droplets in water is called
    (a) a smoke   (c) a sol
    (b) an emulsion   (d) a gel

4. In a dilute solution of sugar in water, water is the
    (a) solute   (c) emulsifying agent
    (b) solvent   (d) desiccant

5. An aqueous solution whose concentration effectively matches the concentration of blood is said to be
    (a) isotopic   (c) isotonic
    (b) isobaric   (d) isoelectronic

6. To prepare 50.0 g of 1% (w/w) $AgNO_3$, you would need to weigh out how many grams of $AgNO_3$?
    (a) 0.0500 g   (b) 0.500 g   (c) 5.00 g   (d) 50.0 g

7. To prepare 500 g of 2.00% (w/w) NaCl from 5.00% (w/w) NaCl, how many grams of the more concentrated solution would you have to weigh out and dilute?
    (a) 2.00 g   (b) 20.0 g   (c) 200 g   (d) 50.0 g

8. In 500 mL of 2.00% (mg/vol) of glucose in water there is how much glucose?
    (a) 10.0 mg   (b) 1.00 mg   (c) 10.0 g   (d) 1.00 g

9. To make 300 mL of a 4.00% (w/v) solution of sugar we need to weigh out
    (a) 4.00 g of sugar
    (b) 40.0 g of sugar
    (c) 12.0 g of sugar
    (d) We need to know the formula mass of sugar before calculating an answer.

10. If a bag made of a dialyzing material and containing a mixture of water, dissolved salt, and

colloidally dispersed protein were placed in a beaker of pure water, the water would eventually contain

(a) dissolved salt   (c) both salt and protein

(b) protein   (d) no additional material

11.   The weak force of attraction acting between water molecules is called

(a) a hydrogen to oxygen covalent bond

(b) a hydrogen bond

(c) an ionic bond

(d) a hydration bond

12.   In the substance whose formula is $Na_2CO_3 \cdot 10H_2O$, for every five formula units of Na_2CO_3 there are how many water molecules?

(a) 50   (b) 2   (c) 10   (d) 100

ANSWERS

ANSWERS TO SELF–TESTING QUESTIONS

Completion

1. colloidal dispersion

2. Tyndall

3. emulsion

4. Brownian movement

5. (a) the potassium ion, K^+, the chloride ion, Cl^-

(b) K^+ and Cl^-

(c) They become hydrated

(d) chloride ions

(e) No, they have not; water molecules

(f) potassium ions, K^+

(g) the hydrogen ends of water molecules

6. left

7. increase

8. Henry's law (the pressure-solubility law)

9. 1.53 mg O_2/dL H_2O

10. (a) saturated. (It is also concentrated.)

(b) 25.8% (w/w). $[34.7/(34.7 + 100)] \times 100$

(c) The crystals sink to the bottom and do not dissolve.

(d) osmosis, increase, decrease

11. 50 mL of ethanol and 450 mL of water

12. 5 g

13. (a) lowering of the freezing point of the solvent
    (b) raising of the boiling point of the solvent
    (c) osmotic pressure of the solution
14. The $MgCl_2$ solution; 1 mol $MgCl_2$ will provide 3 mol of ions (1 of Mg^{2+} and 2 of Cl^-) whereas 1 mol KCl will provide only 2 mol of ions (1 of K^+ and 1 of Cl^-) when the solutes are fully dissolved.
15. The $MgCl_2$ solution; it has the higher concentration of solute particles.
16. burst; hemolysis
17. hydrate
18. hydration, anhydrous
19. a hydrate (calcium chloride hexahydrate)
20. desiccant

Multiple–Choice

1. c	2. c	3. b	4. b	5. c
6. b	7. c	8. a	9. c	10. a
11. b	12. a			

8

ACIDS, BASES, AND IONIC COMPOUNDS

In our study of the molecular basis of life, we need to be familiar with the major topics of this chapter for several reasons.

1. Acid-base theories and acid-base equilibria. — Because acids and bases (particularly as viewed in the Brønsted theory) are involved in most reactions of metabolism.

2. Net ionic equations. — Because from now on we shall use them almost exclusively to describe reactions that involve ions.

3. The reactions of ions. — Because we need to know how to tell which ions can remain unaffected in the presence of others in body fluids and which cannot,

If only one goal were to be stated for this chapter, it would be to learn the chief chemical properties of ions and ion-producing substances—acids, bases, and salts.

Before you attempt any problems or exercises, you should commit to memory the names and formulas for the five strong acids plus phosphoric acid listed in Table 8.1 and the strong bases listed in Table 8.2. These are short lists, and we make the important assumption that any acids or bases not on the lists of the strong acids or bases will be weak. Also commit to memory the solubility rules for salts. Then you have automatically learned what the insoluble salts are—any salts not mentioned in the solubility rules.

Next learn the properties of acids and bases in water and the reactions of strong acids with ammonia, and with active metals and their hydroxides, carbonates, and bicarbonates. Practice writing both full and net ionic equations. Acquiring skill now in these matters will make later studying that much easier. The summary of the circumstances in which the various ions react with one another, given in section 8.5, is very important.

OBJECTIVES

After studying this chapter and working the exercises in it, you should be able to do the following.

1. Distinguish between ionization and dissociation and give examples of reactions that illustrate them.

2. Define and give examples of electrolytes and be able to use the terms cation and anion correctly in connection with ions.

3. Explain how an aqueous electrolyte, like $CuBr_2(aq)$ conducts a current of electricity.

4. Describe an electrolyte as weak or strong and explain what these terms mean.

5. Give the names and formulas of the two ions that form when water self-ionizes.

6. Define acidic, basic, and neutral solutions in terms of the relative concentrations of hydronium and hydroxide ions.

7. Describe how litmus is used.

8. Give the main points in the Brønsted theory.

9. Write the names and formulas of five strong acids and two strong highly soluble bases and explain why they are classified as "strong."

10. Given the formula of an acid or base, tell whether it is strong or weak.

11. Give the formulas of the following acids and *all* their ions: acetic acid, phosphoric acid, sulfuric acid, and carbonic acid.

12. Convert molecular equations into net ionic equations.

13. Write equations, molecular and net ionic, for the reactions of strong aqueous acids with active metals and their hydroxides, bicarbonates, and carbonates.

14. Write net ionic equations involving proton transfers between (a) the ammonia molecule and the hydronium ion and (b) the ammonium ion and the hydroxide ion.

15. Describe what it means when a metal is high in the activity series.

16. Recognize and write formulas of conjugate acid-base pairs.

17. Tell if the conjugate base of an acid is a weak or strong base.

18. Tell if the conjugate acid of a base is weak or strong.

19. Explain why the strongest acid that can exist in water is H_3O^+.

20. Explain why the strongest base that can exist in water is OH^-.

21. Qualitatively predict positions of equilibria in acid-base equilibria.

22. Recognize from a formula if a compound is a salt and if it is, write equations for making that salt in four different ways using a strong acid.

23. Use the solubility rules to predict double replacements.

24. Summarize the three circumstances under which ions usually react, giving the equations of two specific examples for each.

25. Explain how the common ion effect is an example of Le Châtelier's principle, giving a specific example.

26. Calculate the mass of one equivalent and one milliequivalent of an ion.

27. Define (and, where substances are involved, illustrate) all of the terms listed in the Glossary.

GLOSSARY

Acid. Any substance that makes the molar concentration of hydronium ions greater than that of hydroxide ions.

Acid, Brønsted Theory. Any substance that can donate a proton (H^+).

Acid-Base Indicator. A compound whose color is different in acid than in base.

Acid-Base Neutralization. The reaction of an acid with a base.

Acidic Solution. A solution in which the molar concentration of hydronium ions is greater than that of hydroxide ions.

Activity Series. A list of elements (or other substances) in the order of the ease with which they release electrons under standard conditions and become oxidized.

Anion. A negatively charged ion.

Anode. The positive electrode to which negatively charged ions—anions—are attracted during electrolysis.

Base. Any substance that makes the molar concentration of hydronium ions less than that of hydroxide ions.

Base, Brønsted Theory. A proton-acceptor; a compound that neutralizes hydrogen ions.

Basic Solution. A solution in which the molar concentration of hydroxide ions is greater than that of hydronium ions.

Brønsted Theory. An acid is a proton-donor and a base is a proton-acceptor.

Cathode. The negative electrode to which positively charged ions—cations—are attracted during electrolysis.

Cation. A positively charged ion.

Common Ion Effect. The reduction in the solubility of a salt in some solution by the addition of another solute that furnishes one of the ions of this salt.

Conjugate Acid-Base Pair. Two particles whose formulas differ by only one H^+, such as NH_4^+ and NH_3, or HCl and Cl^-.

Diprotic Acid. An acid with two protons available per molecule to neutralize a base, e.g., H_2SO_4.

Dissociation. The separation of pre-existing ions as a salt dissolves in water.

Double Replacement. A reaction in which a compound is made by the exchange of partner-ions between two salts.

Electrical Balance. The condition of a net ionic equation wherein the algebraic sum of the positive and negative charges of the reactants equals that of the products.

Electrode. A metal object, usually a wire, suspended in an electrically conducting medium through which electricity passes to or from an external circuit.

Electrolysis. A procedure in which an electrical current is passed through a solution that contains ions, or through a molten salt, for the purpose of bringing about a chemical change.

Electrolyte. Any substance whose solution in water conducts electricity; or the solution itself of such a substance.

Equivalent (eq). The number of grams of an ion that carries 1 mol of electrical charge. 1 eq = 1000 meq

Hydronium Ion. H_3O^+

Hydroxide Ion. OH^-

Inorganic Compound. Any compound that is not an organic compound.

Ionic Equation. A chemical equation that explicitly shows all of the particles—ions, atoms, or molecules—that are involved in a reaction even if some are only spectator particles. (See also *Net Ionic Equation*; *Equation, Balanced*.)

Ionization. A change, usually involving solvent molecules, whereby molecules break apart into ions.

Material Balance. The condition of a chemical equation in which all of the atoms present among the reactants are also found in the products.

Milliequivalent (meq). See *Equivalent*.

Molecular Equation. An equation that shows the complete formulas of all of the substances present in a mixture undergoing a reaction. (See also *Net Ionic Equation*; *Equation, Balanced*.)

Monoprotic Acid. An acid with one proton per molecule that can neutralize a base.

Net Ionic Equation. A chemical equation in which all spectator particles are omitted so that only the particles that participate directly are represented.

Neutral Solution. A solution in which the molar concentration of hydronium ions exactly equals the molar concentration of hydroxide ions.

Nonelectrolyte. Any substance that cannot furnish ions when dissolved in water or when melted.

Organic Compounds. Compounds of carbon other than those related to carbonic acid and its salts, or to the oxides of carbon, or to the cyanides.

Salt. Any crystalline compound that consists of oppositely charged ions (other than H^+, OH^-, or O^{2-}).

Simple Salt. A salt that consists of just one kind of cation and one kind of anion.

Strong Acid. An acid with a high percentage ionization.

Strong Base. A metal hydroxide with a high percentage ionization in solution.

Strong Brønsted Acid. Any species, molecule or ion, that has a strong tendency to donate a proton to some acceptor.

Strong Brønsted Base. Any species, molecule or ion, that binds an accepted proton strongly.

Strong Electrolyte. Any substance that has a high percentage ionization in solution.

Triprotic Acid. An acid that can supply three protons per molecule.

Weak Acid. An acid with a low percentage ionization in solution.

Weak Base. A metal hydroxide with a low percentage ionization in solution.

Weak Brønsted Acid. Any species, molecule or ion, that has a weak tendency to donate a proton and poorly serves as a proton donor.

Weak Brønsted Base. Any species, molecule or ion, that weakly holds an accepted proton and poorly serves as a proton-acceptor.

Weak Electrolyte. Any electrolyte that has a low percentage ionization in solution.

SELF-TESTING QUESTIONS

COMPLETION

1. Substances whose aqueous solutions are able to conduct a current of electricity are

   _____ .

2. When an ionic compound, like sodium chloride, dissolves in water, its _____ separate, and this change is called _____ .

3. When a molecular compound, like HCl gas, dissolves in water to give a solution that readily conducts electricity, the event that happens during the dissolving action is called _____ .

4. In an electrolysis experiment, the metal surfaces that dip into the electrolytic solution have the general name of _____ . Negative ions are called _____ , and during electrolysis, they will migrate toward a metal surface, called specifically the _____ .

5. Positive ions are called _____ , and they migrate toward the electrode called the _____ .

6. During the electrolysis of $CuBr_2$, the cation has the formula _____ , and when this cation reaches the cathode it _____ (takes or gives) electrons and changes into a particle with the formula _____ . This cation thereby is _____ (reduced or oxidized).

7. When 10.0 g of compound X was dissolved in 100 mL of water, the solution only faintly conducted electricity. Compound X is, therefore, a _____ electrolyte.

8. The self-ionization of water can be written by what equilibrium equation?

9. The three broad classes of substances that can liberate ions in water are _____ , _____ and _____ .

10. The hydronium ion has the formula _____ ; the hydrogen ion has the formula

    _____ .

11. When water is the solvent and its molecules react with molecules of hydrogen chloride to form hydronium ions and chloride ions, water molecules are acting as Brønsted _____ and hydrogen chloride molecules are acting as Brønsted _____ .

12. After dissolving 100 g of the covalent compound HX in a liter of water, an average of 10% of the HX molecules were always in their intact molecular form and an average of 90% were split up into the ions X^- and H^+ (actually, H_3O^+). HX may be classified as a _____ (strong or weak) _____ (acid, base, or salt). What kind of an electrolyte is it? _____

13. Give the chemical formulas for:

    (a) sulfuric acid _____

    (b) carbonic acid _____

    (c) nitric acid _____

    (d) phosphoric acid _____

    (e) hydrochloric acid _____

    (f) ammonia _____

    (g) acetic acid _____

14.   Write the names and formulas of the strong acids and bases.

Strong Acids

Name   *Formula*

_____   _____

_____   _____

_____   _____

_____   _____

_____   _____

Strong Bases

Name   *Formula*

_____   _____

_____   _____

_____   _____

_____   _____

15.   Give the formulas and names of the anions that the following acids can give.

Formula of acid	*Formulas of anions*	*Names of anions*
H_2SO_4	_____	_____
	_____	_____
H_2CO_3	_____	_____
	_____	_____
H_3PO_4	_____	_____
	_____	_____
	_____	_____

16.   Write the net ionic equation for the reaction (if any) of
   (a) calcium with nitric acid

   _____

   (b) potassium hydroxide with hydrochloric acid

   _____

   (c) sodium chloride with sulfuric acid

   _____

   (d) sodium bicarbonate with hydrochloric acid

   _____

17. When metals are arranged in an order corresponding to their relative tendencies to become ionic, we call this series the _____.

18. The most reactive metals are in Group _____ of the periodic table.

19. If HCl is a strong Brønsted acid, this must mean that the ion Cl^- is a _____ (good or poor) binder of a proton and that Cl^- is therefore a _____ (weak or strong) Brønsted base.

20. We can generalize from this. The conjugate base obtainable from any strong will be a relatively _____ Brønsted base. The conjugate base obtainable from any weak acid will be a relatively _____ Brønsted base.

21. The conjugate base of the water molecule is named the_____ and has the formula _____ . It is a _____ (strong or weak) Brønsted base.

22. Suppose we contrive to make a neutral particle, B, take a proton to form BH. What will be the net electrical charge on BH, if any? _____

23. If B holds the proton very weakly, would we classify HB^+, the conjugate acid, as weak or strong?
_____

24. Which is the stronger Brønsted base in each pair?
PO_4^{3-} or $H_2PO_4^-$ _____; NH_3 or NH_4^+ _____

25. Test your knowledge of the solubility rules for the salts given in the text by predicting whether each of the following would be soluble in water. (Use a plus sign if soluble, a minus sign if insoluble.)

(a) sodium carbonate _____   (b) calcium bromide _____

(c) potassium nitrate _____   (d) lead nitrate _____

(e) magnesium nitrate _____   (f) nickel sulfite _____

(g) copper(II) arsenate _____   (h) ammonium sulfate _____

(i) lead chloride _____   (j) sodium sulfide _____

26. Test your knowledge of the solubility rules, of the typical reactions of acids and bases, and of which acids and bases are strong by predicting the chemical reactions (if any) that would occur if you mixed together aqueous solutions of the following pairs. Write net ionic equations for reactions you predict. (If there is no reaction, write "none.")

(a) LiCl and $AgNO_3$ _____

(b) $NaNO_3$ and $CaCl_2$ _____

(c) KOH and H_2SO_4 _____

(d) $Pb(NO_3)_2$ and NaCl   _____

(e) K_2S and $CuSO_4$ _____

(f) Na_2CO_3 and HBr   _____

27. If concentrated hydrobromic acid, HBr(aq), is added to a saturated solution of NaBr in water, in which direction will the following equilibrium shift (if any)?

$$NaBr(s) \rightleftharpoons Na^+(aq) + Br^-(aq)$$

This equilibrium will shift to the _____ (left or right), and you will be able to see what happen? _____

This experiment illustrates what effect? _____

28. The atomic mass of potassium is 39.1. What is the mass of 1.00 eq of K^+? _____

29. The atomic mass of sulfur is 32.1. What is the mass of 1.00 eq of S^{2-}? _____

30. How many milliequivalents are there in 0.0345 eq of Na^+? _____

MULTIPLE-CHOICE

1. When nitric acid reacts with sodium bicarbonate, which of the following is not formed?
   (a) $NaNO_3$ (b) CO_2 (c) Na   (d) H_2O

2. Which equation represents the neutralization of hydrochloric acid?
   (a) $HCl(aq) + AgNO_3 \rightarrow AgCl + HNO_3$
   (b) $HCl(aq) + NaBr \rightarrow NaCl + HBr$
   (c) $2HCl(aq) + Ca(NO_3)_2 \rightarrow CaCl_2 + 2HNO_3$
   (d) $HCl(aq) + NaHCO_3 \rightarrow NaCl + H_2O + CO_2$

3. What is the net ionic equation for the following?
   $Mg(s) + 2HBr(aq) \rightarrow MgBr_2(aq) + H_2(g)$
   (a) $Mg^{2+}(aq) + 2H^+(aq) \rightarrow Mg(s) + H_2(g)$
   (b) $Mg(s) + 2H^+(aq) \rightarrow Mg^{2+}(aq) + H_2(g)$
   (c) $Mg(s) + 2HBr(aq) \rightarrow MgBr_2(aq) + 2H^+(aq)$
   (d) $Mg(s) + 2HBr(aq) \rightarrow Mg^{2+}(aq) + Br_2(aq) + H_2(g)$

4. After a solution of potassium hydroxide has been carefully neutralized by hydrochloric acid, the solution will contain (besides water)
   (a) K^+ and Cl^- (c) K^+ and OH^-
   (b) K and Cl   (d) K^-, H^+, and Cl_2

5. The covalent substance HA was soluble enough in water to make a very concentrated solution; however, whether concentrated or dilute, the percentage of ionization of HA into A^- and H^+ (actually H_3O^+) was less than 5%. Another covalent substance, HB, was virtually insoluble in water, but what did dissolve ionized by about 95% into B^- and H^+. Which would be classified as the stronger acid?
   (a) the concentrated solution of HA
   (b) the dilute solution of HA
   (c) simply HA
   (d) HB

6. The conjugate acid of PO_4^{3-} is
   (a) HPO_4^{2-} (b) $H_2PO_4^-$ (c) H_3PO_4 (d) $H_4PO_4^+$

7. The strongest base among the following is
   (a) NO_3^- (b) HSO_4^- (c) CO_3^{2-} (d) I^-

8. Which of the following substances could be added to aqueous hydrobromic acid to reduce the concentration of hydronium ions?
   (a) silver nitrate   (c) ammonium chloride
   (b) ammonia   (d) potassium nitrate

9. An example of a weak acid is
   (a) HBr   (b) HNO_3 (c) H_2SO_4 (d) HNO_2

10. If you mixed a solution of sodium bicarbonate with a solution of sulfuric acid, which particles would interact to form new products?
    (a) SO_4^{2-} and Na^+ (c) Na^+ and H_3O^+
    (b) HCO_3^- and SO_4^{2-} (d) H_3O^+ and HCO_3^-

11. If you mixed a solution of hydrochloric acid with ammonia water, which particles would be involved in the primary chemical change?

   (a) NH_3 and Cl^- (c) NH_3 and H_2O

   (b) NH_3 and H_3O^+ (d) NH_3 and HCl (molecules)

12. The hydronium ion would readily transfer a proton to which of the following?

   (a) PO_4^{3-} (b) CO_3^{2-} (c) OH^- (d) NO_3^-

13. The reaction of hydrochloric acid with sodium hydroxide is called

   (a) hydrolysis   (c) neutralization

   (b) crenation   (d) proton transfer

14. Reactions involving acids, bases, or salts can be predicted to take place if there is the possibility of forming

   (a) an insoluble precipitate

   (b) a strong acid

   (c) a gas

   (d) an un-ionized (but soluble) substance

15. Consider the equilibrium between solid potassium chloride and its ions in the dissolved state in a saturated solution:

$$\text{Heat} + KCl(solid) \rightleftharpoons K^+(aq) + Cl^-(aq)$$

   If somehow the equilibrium "shifts to the left," then more solid KCl will

   (a) dissolve   (b) form   (c) vaporize   (d) melt

16. The equilibrium (of question 15) could be shifted to the right by adding

   (a) solid KCl   (b) HCl(aq)   (c) NaBr(solid)   (d) heat

17. The equilibrium (of question 15) would be shifted to the left by adding

   (a) solid KCl   (b) HCl(aq)   (c) NaBr(solid)   (d) heat

ANSWERS

ANSWERS TO SELF-TESTING QUESTIONS

Completion

1. electrolytes
2. ions, dissociation
3. ionization
4. electrodes, anions, anode
5. cations, cathode
6. Cu^{2+}, takes, Cu, reduced
7. weak
8. $2H_2O \rightleftharpoons H_3O^+(aq) + OH^-(aq)$
9. acids, bases, salts (any order)

10. H_3O^+, H^+

11. bases, acids

12. strong acid; strong electrolyte

13. (a) H_2SO_4 (b) H_2CO_3 (c) HNO_3

     (d) H_3PO_4 (e) HCl   (f) NH_3 (g) $HC_2H_3O_2$

14.

Strong Acids		*Strong Bases*	
hydrochloric acid	HCl	sodium hydroxide	NaOH
hydrobromic acid	HBr	potassium hydroxide	KOH
hydriodic acid	HI	magnesium hydroxide	$Mg(OH)_2$
nitric acid	HNO_3	calcium hydroxide	$Ca(OH)_2$
sulfuric acid	H_2SO_4		

15.
HSO_4^-	hydrogen sulfate ion
SO_4^{2-}	sulfate ion
HCO_3^-	bicarbonate ion
CO_3^{2-}	carbonate ion
$H_2PO_4^-$	dihydrogen phosphate ion
HPO_4^{2-}	monohydrogen phosphate ion
PO_4^{3-}	phosphate ion

16. (a) $Ca(s) + 2H^+(aq) \rightarrow Ca^{2+}(aq) + H_2(g)$

     [or $Ca(s) + 2H_3O^+(aq) \rightarrow Ca^{2+}(aq) + H_2(g) + 2H_2O$]

    (b) $OH^-(aq) + H^+(aq) \rightarrow H_2O$

     [or $OH^-(aq) + H_3O^+(aq) \rightarrow 2H_2O$]

    (c) none

    (d) $HCO_3^-(aq) + H^+(aq) \rightarrow H_2O + CO_2(g)$

     [or $HCO_3^-(aq) + H_3O^+(aq) \rightarrow 2H_2O + CO_2(g)$]

17. activity series

18. IA

19. poor, weak

20. weak; strong

21. hydroxide ion, OH^-; strong

22. +1 (as in BH^+)

23. strong

24. PO_4^{3-}; NH_3

25. (a) +   (b) +   (c) +   (d) +   (e)   +

     (f) −   (g) −   (h) +   (i) −   (j)   +

26. (a) $Cl^-(aq) + Ag^+(aq) \rightarrow AgCl(s)$

    (b) none

    (c) $OH^-(aq) + H^+(aq) \rightarrow H_2O$

    (d) $Pb^{2+}(aq) + 2Cl^-(aq) \rightarrow PbCl_2(s)$

    (e) $S^{2-}(aq) + Cu^{2+}(aq) \rightarrow CuS(s)$

    (f) $CO_3^{2-}(aq) + 2H^+(aq) \rightarrow H_2O + CO_2(g)$

27.   left. Crystals of NaBr will precipitate.
      common ion effect
28.   39.1 g
29.   16.1 g
30.   34.5 meq of Na^+

Multiple–Choice

1.   c
2.   d (in the other three choices the concentration of hydronium ions does not change. Therefore, regardless of the fate of the chloride ion the acid has not been neutralized.)

3. b	4. a	5. d
6. a	7. c	8. b
9. d	10. d	11. b
12. a, b, and c	13. c and d	14. a, c, and d
15. b	16. d	17. b

9

REACTION KINETICS AND CHEMICAL EQUILIBRIA. ACID-BASE EQUILIBRIA

The most important topics in this chapter are:

1. The factors that affect the rates of reactions and how they do so.

   Because these factors— reactants, physical states, concentration, temperature, and catalysts —repeatedly figure in rates of metabolism

2. The concept of an equilibrium law.

   Because it enables us to think more clearly about the position of an equilibrium

3. The pH concept

   Because we use pH to describe the relative acidities of aqueous fluids, including those of living systems.

4. Buffers

   Because they are vital to the control of the pH of aqueous fluids in living systems.

5. The carbonate buffer

   Because it is at the heart of the acid-base status of the blood.

The most important calculating skills that should be mastered are the following.

1. pH from $[H^+]$ and $[H^+]$ from pH
2. Buffer calculations, particularly those involving the carbonate buffer in blood. (This skill thus requires an understanding of the concept of pK_a.)
3. Acid-base titration calculations.

OBJECTIVES

After you have studied this chapter and have worked the Practice Exercises and Review Exercises, you should be able to do the following.

1. Explain and illustrate the influences of reactants, physical states, concentration, temperature, and catalysis on rates of reactions.

2. Use collision theory to explain how the various factors work that influence a reaction rate.

3. Explain the relationship between a collision between two reactant, particles and the energy of activation for the reaction.

4. Interpret a progress of reaction diagram for a reaction and indicate which features of the diagram represent the energy of activation, the heat of reaction, the reactants, and the products.

5. Describe how a catalyst affects the energy of activation of a reaction, the energy of the reaction, and the rate of the reaction.

6. Describe how an increase in the temperature of a mixture of reactants affects exothermic and endothermic reactions.

7. Write the equation that constitutes the equilibrium law for the ionization of an acid (or a base).

8. Describe how the size of the equilibrium constant relates to the position of an equilibrium.

9. Describe the effect of adding more of one component in an equilibrium on the equilibrium constant for the system.

10. Write the equation of K_w and use it to calculate a value of $[H^+]$ from a value of $[OH^-]$ or vice versa.

11. Relate $[H^+]$ to pH by two equations (9.4 and 9.5 in the text).

12. Give the relationship between pH and pOH at room temperature.

13. Explain why the pH in a solution of a weak acid does not represent the total capacity of the solution to neutralize a strong base, like NaOH

14. Calculate the pH and the pOH of a dilute solution of a strong acid (or a strong base) given only the molarity of the solution.

15. State the range of pH values that corresponds to an acidic solution and the range that corresponds to a basic solution.

16. Describe the purpose of an indicator.

17. Give the color of litmus in an acid and in a base. (Do the same for any other indicators that may be assigned.)

18. Write the expression for K_a for the ionization of any weak, monoprotic acid.

19. Judge from the K_a value of an acid whether it is a strong, moderate or a weak acid.

20. Write the equilibrium equation for the ionization of the ammonium ion as a weak acid.

21. Briefly explain how salts of transition metal cations can form solutions that have pH values less than 7.

22. Write the expression for K_b for the reaction of any weak base with water.

23. Use the K_b value of a base to judge the strength of the base.

24. Judge if a given anion will tend to make an aqueous solution test basic.

25. Use the facts of which acids and bases are strong to predict whether an aqueous solution of a given salt will test acidic, basic, or neutral.

26. Calculate pK_a from K_a, and calculate pK_b from K_b.

27. Tell from the pK_a values of two acids which is stronger.

28. Tell from the pK_b values of two bases which is weaker.

29. Use the pK_a value of an acid to calculate the pK_b of its conjugate base.
30. Use the terms *acidosis* and *alkalosis* in discussions of the acid-base status of the blood.
31. Explain what is meant by a statement such as "This solution is buffered."
32. Write the net ionic equations that describe how the phosphate and the carbonate buffers work to control pH.
32. Explain how ventilation cooperates with the carbonate buffer to control the pH of the blood.
33. Explain how the slight basicity of blood enables it to carry much larger concentrations of carbon dioxide than it could if it were slightly acidic.
34. Describe the role of carbonic anhydrase when the blood circulates in the lungs.
35. Give the Henderson-Hasselbalch equation and use it to find the pH of a buffered solution.
36. Describe the two factors that govern the pH of a buffered solution.
37. Give the form of the Henderson-Hasselbalch equation when used for the carbonate buffer in the blood at body pH.
38. Describe the role of the kidneys in stabilizing the pH of the blood.
39. Describe the purpose of a titration and how it is carried out.
40. Describe the difference between "end point" and "equivalence point."
41. Calculate molar concentrations from titration data.
42. Define all of the terms listed in the Glossary.

GLOSSARY

Acidic Solution. A solution in which the molar concentration of hydronium ions is greater than that of hydroxide ions; a solution in which the pH is less than 7.00 (at 25 °C).

Acid Ionization Constant, (K_a). A modified equilibrium constant for the following equilibrium:

$$HA + H_2O \rightleftharpoons H_3O^+ + A^- \qquad K_a = \frac{[H_3O^+][A^-]}{HA}$$

Acidosis. A condition in which the pH of the blood is below normal.

Alkalosis. A condition in which the pH of the blood is above normal.

Base Ionization Constant, (K_b). For the equilibrium (where B is some base)

$$B + H_2O \rightleftharpoons BH^+ + OH^- \qquad K_b = \frac{[BH^+][OH^-]}{[B]}$$

Basic Solution. A solution in which the molar concentration of hydroxide ions is greater than the molar concentration of hydronium ions; a solution in which the pH is greater than 7.00 (at 25 °C).

Buffer. A combination of solutes that holds the pH of a solution relatively constant even if small amounts of acids or bases are added.

Carbonate Buffer. A mixture or a solution that includes bicarbonate ions and dissolved carbon dioxide in which the bicarbonate ion can neutralize added acid and carbon dioxide can neutralize added base.

Catalysis. The phenomenon of an increase in the rate of a chemical reaction brought about by a relatively small amount of a chemical—the catalyst—that is not permanently changed by the reaction.

Catalyst. A substance that is able, in relatively low concentrations, to accelerate the rate of a chemical reaction without itself being permanently changed. (In living systems, the catalysts are called enzymes.)

Collision Theory. A theory about the rates of chemical reactions that postulates collisions between reacting particles.

End Point. The stage in a titration when the operation is stopped.

Energy of Activation. The minimum energy that must be provided by the collision between reactant particles to initiate the rearrangement of electrons relative to nuclei that must happen if the reaction is to occur.

Enzyme. A catalyst in a living system.

Equivalence Point. The stage in a titration when the reactants have been mixed in the exact molar proportions represented by the balanced equation; in an acid-base titration, the stage when the moles of hydrogen ions furnished by the acid match the moles of hydroxide ions (or other proton acceptor) supplied by the base.

Equilibrium Constant, (K_{eq}). The value that the mass action expression has when a chemical system is at equilibrium.

Equilibrium Law (Law of Mass Action). The molar proportions of the interacting substances in a chemical equilibrium are related by the following equation (in which the ratio on the left is called the *mass action expression* for the system).

$$\frac{[C]^c \, [D]^d}{[A]^a \, [B]^b} = K_{eq}$$

The symbols refer to the following generalized equilibrium:

$$aA + bB \rightleftharpoons cC + dD$$

and the brackets, [ ], denote molar concentrations. (When an equilibrium involves additional substances, the equation for the equilibrium constant is adjusted accordingly.)

Heat of Reaction. The net energy difference, expressed in units of heat, between the reactants and the products of a reaction.

Henderson-Hasselbalch Equation. An equation used in buffer calculations,

$$pH = pK_a + \log \frac{[\text{anion}]}{[\text{acid}]}$$

Hydrolysis of Anions. Reactions in which anions (other than OH^-) react with water and increase the pH of a solution.

Hydrolysis of Cations. Reactions in which cations (other than H_3O^+) react with water and decrease the pH of the solution.

Hyperventilation. Breathing considerably faster and deeper than normal.

Hypoventilation. Breathing more slowly and less deeply than normal; shallow breathing.

Indicator. A dye that, in solution, has one color below a measured pH range and a different color above this range.

Ion Product Constant of Water (K_w). The product of the molar concentrations of hydrogen ions and hydroxide ions in water at a given temperature.

$K_w = [H^+][OH^-] = 1.0 \times 10^{-14}$ (at 25 °C)

K_a. (See *Acid Ionization Constant*.)

K_b. (See *Base Ionization Constant*.)

K_{eq}. (See *Equilibrium Constant*; *Equilibrium Law*.)

K_w. (See *Ion Product Constant of Water*.)

Kinetics. The field of chemistry that deals with the rates of chemical reactions.

Law of Mass Action. (See *Equilibrium Law*.)

Moderate Acid. An acid with a K_a in the range of 1 to 10^{-3}.

Neutralizing Capacity. The capacity of a solution or a substance to neutralize an acid or a base— expressed as a molar concentration.

Neutral Solution. A solution in which the molar concentration of hydronium ions exactly equals the molar concentration of hydroxide ions.

pH. The negative power to which the base 10 must be raised to express the molar concentration of hydrogen ions in an aqueous solution.

$$[H^+] = 1 \times 10^{-pH}$$
$$-\log [H^+] = pH$$

pK_a $pK_a = -\log K_a$

pK_b $pK_b = -\log K_b$

Phosphate Buffer. Usually a mixture or a solution that contains dihydrogen phosphate ions ($H_2PO_4^-$) to neutralize OH^- and monohydrogen phosphate ions (HPO_4^{2-}) to neutralize H^+. The principal buffer inside living cells.

pOH. The negative power to which the base 10 must be raised to express the concentration of hydroxide ions in an aqueous solution in mol/L.

$$[OH^-] = 1 \times 10^{-pOH}$$

At 25 °C,   pH + pOH = 14.00

Rate of Reaction. The number of successful (product-forming) collisions that happen each second in each unit of volume of the reacting mixture.

Respiration. The intake and chemical use of oxygen by the body and the release of carbon dioxide.

Standard Solution. Any solution for which the concentration is accurately known.

Standardization. The experimental procedures used to determine the concentration of a standard solution.

Strong Acid. An acid with a K_a value greater than 1. An acid that is essentially 100% ionized.

Strong Base. A base that has essentially 100% dissociated in water.

Titration. An analytical procedure that carefully combines a solution of unknown concentration with a standard solution until an indicator changes color or some other signal shows that equivalent quantities have reacted. One solution is usually added from a buret.

Ventilation. The movement of air into and out of the lungs by breathing.

Weak Acid. An acid with a K_a value less than 1×10^{-3}.

Weak Base. A base with a K_b value less than 1×10^{-3}.

SELF-TESTING QUESTIONS

Assume that the temperature of any aqueous solution used in any questions is 25 °C, unless otherwise specified.

COMPLETION

1. List five factors affecting the rates of chemical reactions.

   _____

   _____

   _____

   _____

   _____

2. Which of the factors in question 1 best explains why substances burn more vigorously in pure oxygen than in air? _____

3. Which of the factors in question 1 has the greatest influence on how rapidly reactions proceed in living things? _____

4. Classify the following reactions as *heterogeneous* or *homogeneous*.
   (a) The reaction (combustion) of methane gas with the oxygen of the air._____
   (b) The reaction (combustion) of wood with the oxygen of the air. _____
   (c) The rusting of iron, a combination of iron with oxygen._____
   (d) The digestion of table sugar. _____
   (e) The digestion of butter fat. _____

5. The minimum collision energy of two reacting particles above which all collisions of the proper orientation will produce products is called the _____.

6. If a reaction has a high energy of activation, it probably will proceed _____ (slowly or rapidly).

7. Increasing the concentration of the reactants increases the rates of most reactions because higher concentrations mean higher frequencies of _____ between the reactants.

8. Raising the temperature of a reacting mixture increases the rate of reaction largely by increasing the _____ of the collisions.

9. Introducing a catalyst into a reacting mixture increases the rate of the reaction by altering the way by which a reaction takes place so that there is a lowering of the reaction's _____.

10. The catalysts found in living things are called _____.

11. The combustion of coal in air is an example of an energy-releasing or _____ event.

12. A reaction normally requiring a high temperature in order to take place is an energy-consuming or _____ event.

13. Consider the following chemical equilibrium:

$$H_2 + I_2 \rightleftharpoons 2HI$$

   (a) An increase in the initial concentration of H_2 would favor a shift in which direction for this equilibrium? _____
   (b) If the forward reaction is endothermic, in which direction will this equilibrium shift if the temperature is lowered? _____
   (c) If a catalyst were found for this equilibrium system, what would the catalyst do to the position of equilibrium? _____

14. Write the equilibrium law for the following equilibrium.

$$2NO \rightleftharpoons N_2O_4$$

_____

15. For the equilibrium: $2NO(g) + O_2(g) \rightleftharpoons 2NO_2(g)$
the value of K_{eq} is 3.4×10^{13}. At equilibrium which side is favored, the reactants or the products?
_____

16. Notice the location of the heat term in the following equilibrium.

$$N_2(g) + 3H_2(g) \rightleftharpoons 2NH_3(g) + heat$$

Considering Le Châtelier's principle, if heat is added to a gaseous mixture of N_2, H_2, and NH_3 at equilibrium by this equation,
(a) In which direction will this equilibrium shift, to the left or to the right?_____
(b) Will the equilibrium constant change if heat is added to this equilibrium?_____
(c) Will the equilibrium constant change if the concentration of N_2 is increased?
_____

17. What special name and symbol does the constant in the following expression have?
constant = $[H^+][OH^-]$

_____

18. In a solution in which $[H^+] = 4.0 \times 10^{-8}$ mol/L, what is the value of $[OH^-]$?_____
19. The pH in a solution that is 0.040 M HCl is _____.
20. The pH of a solution for which $[H^+] = 1.0 \times 10^{-5}$ mol/L is_____ .
21. A solution with a pH of 6.50 is _____.
(acidic, basic, neutral)
22. The concentration of hydroxide ions in pure water is (in moles per liter) _____.
23. If the pH of a solution is 7.42, then the concentration of hydrogen ions (in moles per liter) is between 1.0×10^{-7} and $1.0 \times$_____.
24. If $[OH^-] = 4.0 \times 10^{-9}$ mol/L, the solution is _____.
(acidic or basic)
25. A sample of orange juice had a pH of 3.80. What is $[H^+]$?_____
26. A sample of aqueous Na_2CO_3 solution had a pOH of 2.35. What are the values of pH and $[H^+]$ for this solution?

_____

27. Write the expression for K_a for the ionization of HCN (hydrocyanic acid) as a monoprotic acid.

_____

28. For HCN (previous question), $K_a = 6.2 \times 10^{-10}$. Is HCN a weak, moderate, or strong acid?
_____

29. In what equilibrium does the ammonium ion participate when a solution of aqueous ammonium chloride is prepared?
(Write the equation.) _____

30. Will an aqueous solution of $Cu(NO_3)_2$ have a pH less, equal to, or more than 7? _____ How can you tell?

_____

31. Write the equilibrium in which NH_3 molecules participate in aqueous ammonia. _____

32. Write the K_b expression for the equilibrium of question 31.

    _____

33. The base ionization constant for NO_2^- is 1.4×10^{-11} and that for the HCO_3^- ions is 2.6×10^{-8}. Which ion is the stronger base?_____

34. If K_2CO_3 were added to water:
    (a) Which ions would it liberate in the solution? (Formulas)
        _____ and _____
    (b) Could either ion react with water to give some OH^-?
        _____ If yes, which ion? (Formula) _____
    (c) Could either ion react with water to produce some H^+?
        _____ If yes, which ion? (Formula) _____
    (d) In what way will K_2CO_3 change the pH—leave it the same, lower it, or raise it?

        _____

35. Will the addition of Na_3PO_4 to water make the solution basic, acidic, or will it not affect the pH?
    _____

36. The K_a for hydrofluoric acid, $HF(aq)$, is 6.8×10^{-4}. What is its pK_a?_____

37. The pK_a for HCO_3^- is 10.33 and that for HPO_4^{-2} is 12.35. Which ion is the stronger acid?
    _____

38. The pK_a for $HCN(aq)$ is 9.21. What is pK_b for CN^-, its conjugate base? _____ What is K_b for CN^-? _____

39. The pH of the blood of a patient was found to be 7.25. This is a condition of _____.

40. At a considerable sacrifice in accuracy, parts (a) through (d) ignore the fact that the following equilibrium and many others exist in the solution described in part (a):

    $$PO_4^{3-} + H_2PO_4^- \rightleftharpoons 2HPO_4^{2-}$$

    (a) If you had a solution that contained both NaH_2PO_4 and Na_3PO_4 as solutes, would the pH of that solution be less than or greater than 7? _____
    (b) Whatever the pH is, would the solution of part (a) be buffered? _____
    (c) If so, what ionic equation represents the reaction that will occur if some acid is added to the solution of part (a)?_____
    (d) If so, what ionic equation represents the reaction that will occur if some alkali is added to the solution of part (a)?_____

41. Write the net ion equations for the following.
    (a) The carbonate buffer in blood neutralizes hydroxide ion. _____
    (b) The carbonate buffer in blood neutralizes hydrogen ion. _____

42. What is the name of the enzyme that brings about the extremely rapid equilibration between $CO_2(aq) + OH^-(aq)$ and the product, $HCO_3^-(aq)$? _____

43. A person whose rate of breathing is moving CO_2 out of the body at a slower than normal rate is experiencing what kind of ventilation? _____

44. A person whose lung system is unable to remove CO_2 at a rapid enough rate will experience what kind of change in blood pH, acidosis or alkalosis? _____

45. Normally, if the rate of metabolism generates CO_2 at a faster rate, what will be the ventilation response? _____

46. The body works to prevent acidosis by what two normal mechanisms?

_____   _____

_____

47. Write the Henderson-Hasselbalch equation for a buffer system that involves a weak acid and its conjugate base.

_____

48. Calculate the pH of a buffer solution made up of 0.014 M potassium acetate and 0.11 M acetic acid. (The pK_a of acetic acid is 4.74.) _____

49. The K_a for acid HX is 1.0×10^{-5} and the K_a for acid HY is 1.0×10^{-8}. If your task is to prepare a buffer for a pH of 4.95, which acid, HX or HY, would you pick? _____
Why?_____

50. Write the modified Henderson-Hasselbalch equation used when working with the carbonate buffer as it occurs in the blood stream at body temperature.

_____

51. What value is used for pK_a (that is, for pK') in the equation of the previous question?_____

52. In human arterial blood under normal conditions, [HCO_3^-] =_____ (include units), and [CO_2] =_____ (include units). Using these values, the normal pH of arterial blood calculates to be _____ .

53. If arterial blood were suddenly to receive hydrochloric acid in the amount of 5.0 mmol/L, what would be the new value of [HCO_3^-]?_____ (include units). What would then be the new value of [CO_2], assuming no loss by ventilation? _____ (include the units). If no CO_2 loss could occur, what would be the new value of the pH of the blood? _____ But if the extra load of CO_2 were removed, then what would be the new pH? _____

54. The kidneys are able to manufacture which component of the carbonate buffer of the blood? (Give its formula.)_____

55. If you titrate acetic acid with sodium hydroxide, what salt is present at the equivalence point? (Name) _____

56. Would the pH of this solution (question 55) be less than 7, greater than 7, or exactly equal to 7?_____

57. A student titrated 20.0 mL of NaOH solution with standard hydrochloric acid. It took 18.4 mL of 0.112 M HCl to neutralize the base. What was the molarity of the base? _____

58. It took 12.4 mL of 0.104 M H_2SO_4 to neutralize 25.0 mL of KOH solution. What was the molarity of the KOH solution? _____

MULTIPLE–CHOICE

1. Which units can be used the describe the *rate* at which a reactant undergoes a chemical change?

(a) $\dfrac{mol}{s}$

(c) $\dfrac{L/mol}{s}$

(b) $\dfrac{mol/L}{s}$

(d) $\dfrac{s}{mol}$

2.   Which of the following changes could cause a reaction to occur at a slower rate?
      (a)   warming the mixture
      (b)   introducing a catalyst
      (c)   increasing a collision frequency
      (d)   decreasing the concentration of a reactant

3.   A chemical reaction that is extremely rapid at room temperature
      (a)   is probably highly endothermic
      (b)   probably has a very low energy of activation
      (c)   very likely has an unusually high energy of activation
      (d)   may have the benefit of a catalyst

4.   The following equilibrium would be shifted in which direction by increasing the temperature?

$$C_2H_4 + H_2 \rightleftharpoons C_2H_6 + heat$$

      (a)   to the left   (c)   both directions equally
      (b)   to the right   (d)   in neither direction at all

5.   In the equilibrium law for the equilibrium:

$$2H_2(g) + O_2(g) \rightleftharpoons 2H_2O(g) + heat$$

      the concentration of $H_2O(g)$ will appear in
      (a)   the denominator with a coefficient of 2.
      (b)   the numerator with an exponent of 1.
      (c)   the numerator with a coefficient of 2.
      (d)   the numerator with an exponent of 2.

6.   The value of K_{eq} for the equilibrium of the previous question is about 1×10^{17} at 1000 °C. At a lower temperature,
      (a)   the reactants will be even more favored.
      (b)   the product will be even more favored.
      (c)   the equilibrium will shift to the left.
      (d)   there will be no change in K_{eq}.

7.   The ion-product constant for water is given by the equation

      (a) $K_w = \dfrac{\left[H^+\right]\left[OH^-\right]}{H_2O}$ (b) $K_w = \dfrac{\left[H_3O^+\right]\left[OH^-\right]}{\left[H_2O\right]^2}$

      (c) $K_w = \left[H^+\right]\left[OH^-\right]$ (d) $K_w = \left[Log\, pH\right]\left[\log pOH\right]$

8.   A solution was buffered for a pH of 4.5. An acid that might most likely be the acidic component of this buffer could have its
      (a) $pK_a = 4.6$ (c)   6.6
      (b) $K_a = 5 \times 10^{-4}$ (d)   2.5

9.   Which of the following make an acidic solution when added to pure water:
      (a) H_2SO_4 (c)   NaCl   (e) $AlCl_3$
      (b) NH_3 (d) Na_2CO_3 (f) Na_2HPO_4

10.   Which of the choices in question 9 make a basic solution when added to pure water?

11.   Dissolving NaOH in water produces a solution that
   (a)   turns blue litmus red
   (b)   turns phenolphthalein red
   (c)   has a tart taste
   (d)   turns red litmus blue

12.   The pH of a solution is 6.00. Hence,
   (a)   it is more acidic than a solution whose pH is 4.00
   (b)   its concentration of hydrogen ions is 1.00×10^{-8} moles per liter
   (c)   its concentration of hydrogen ions is 1.00×10^{-6} moles per liter
   (d)   its concentration of hydrogen ions is 1.00×10^{6} moles per liter

13.   If the pH of an aqueous solution cannot be changed by adding small amounts of a strong acid or a strong base, the solution contains
   (a)   an indicator
   (b)   a buffer
   (c)   a protective colloid
   (d)   a strong acid and a strong base already

14.   A solution of $KC_2H_3O_2$ in water has a pH value
   (a)   of 7.00   (c)   greater than 7.00
   (b)   less than 7.00   (d)   less than 1.00

15.   The pH of a solution with a concentration of 0.001 M nitric acid is closest to
   (a) 10^{-3} (b) 10^{-11} (c)   3   (d)   11

16.   If a 0.10 M solution of the monoprotic acid, HX, is known to have a pH of 4.50, we know that the acid HX is
   (a)   strong   (b)   weak   (c)   neutral   (d)   slightly soluble

17.   A weak acid with $K_a = 1.2 \times 10^{-6}$ has
   (a)   a pH of 5.92
   (b)   a conjugate base with $K_b = 1.2 \times 10^{-8}$
   (c)   a pK_a of 5.92
   (d)   a molarity of 1.2×10^{-6}

18.   A base with a pK_b of 3.45
   (a)   has a K_b of 3.55×10^{-4}
   (b)   has a conjugate acid with a pK_a of 10.55
   (c)   has a conjugate acid with a K_a of 2.82×10^{-11}
   (d)   is a stronger base than a base with a pK_b of 6.45

19.   The pK_a of acetic acid is 4.74. A solution that is 0.112 M in acetic acid and 0.112 M in sodium acetate
   (a)   is buffered for a pH of 4.74
   (b)   has a pH of 4.74
   (c)   is acidic
   (d)   is neutral

20.   The chief form in which waste carbon dioxide is carried by the blood to the lungs is
   (a) $CO_2(aq)$ (b) $CO_2(g)$ (c) $H_2CO_3(aq)$ (d) $HCO_3^-(aq)$

21. The normal value of $[CO_2]$ in arterial blood is
    (a) 24 mmol/L   (b) 1.2 mmol/L   (c) 1.2 M (d) 24 M

22. To combat acidosis, the body
    (a) uses the CO_2 in the blood buffer to neutralize base
    (b) uses the HCO_3^- in the blood buffer to neutralize acid
    (c) increases the rate of removal of CO_2 at the lungs
    (d) manufactures more HCO_3^- in the kidneys

23. To neutralize the base present in 21.3 mL of aqueous NaOH required 10.2 mL of 0.105 M H_2SO_4. The molarity of the NaOH solution was
    (a) 0.101 M NaOH   (c) 0.439 M NaOH
    (b) 0.0503 M NaOH   (d) 0.219 M NaOH

24. The end point in a titration of any acid by any base is reached when (pick the one best choice)
    (a) the pH of the solution is 7.00 (at room temperature)
    (b) the equivalence point is reached
    (c) the indicator is halfway through its characteristic change in color
    (d) an equal volume of acid has been mixed with an equal volume of base

25. To prepare 250 mL of 0.125 M H_2SO_4, you would need how many grams of H_2SO_4?
    (a) 6.14 g   (b) 3.07 g   (c) 61.4 g   (d) 0.614 g

ANSWERS

ANSWERS TO SELF–TESTING QUESTIONS

Completion

1. chemical nature of reactants; physical states of reactants, concentrations, temperature, catalysis
2. concentration
3. catalysis
4. (a) homogeneous
   (b) heterogeneous
   (c) heterogeneous
   (d) homogeneous
   (e) heterogeneous
5. energy of activation
6. slowly
7. collisions
8. energies (or average kinetic energies)
9. energy of activation
10. enzymes
11. exothermic

12. endothermic
13. (a) to the right
    (b) to the left
    (c) nothing

14. $K_{eq} = \dfrac{[N_2O_4]}{[NO]^2}$

15. products
16. (a) left   (b) yes   (c) no
17. ion-product constant of water, K_w
18. 2.5×10^{-7} mol/L
19. 1.40
20. 5.00
21. acidic
22. 1.00×10^{-7} mol/L
23. 10^{-8}
24. acidic
25. 1.6×10^{-4} mol/L
26. pH = 11.65. $[H^+] = 2.2 \times 10^{-12}$ mol/L

27. $K_a = \dfrac{[H^+][CN^-]}{[HCN]}$

28. weak
29. $NH_4^+(aq) + H_2O \rightleftharpoons NH_3(aq) + H_3O^+(aq)$
30. less than 7. Cu^{2+} is a transition metal cation and these hydrolyze to give acidic solutions.
31. $NH_3(aq) + H_2O \rightarrow NH_4^+(aq) + OH^-(aq)$

32. $K_b = \dfrac{[NH_4^+][OH^-]}{[NH_3]}$

33. HCO_3^-
34. (a) K^+, CO_3^{2-}
    (b) Yes; CO_3^{2-}
    (c) No
    (d) Raise it. (If CO_3^{2-} ties up some of the H^+ ions from the water, then there will be a slight excess of OH^- ions; the solution will have become slightly basic and, therefore, the pH will have gone up.)
35. basic
36. 3.17
37. HCO_3^-
38. $pK_b = 4.79$. $K_b = 1.6 \times 10^{-5}$
39. acidosis (The pH, while greater than 7, is *less* than normal.)

40. (a) greater than 7

(b) Yes

(c) The most likely event for neutralizing H^+ is
$$H^+ + PO_4^{3-} \rightarrow HPO_4^{2-}$$

(d) The most likely event for neutralizing OH^- is
$$OH^- + H_2PO_4^- \rightarrow HPO_4^{2-} + H_2O$$

41. (a) $CO_2 + OH^- \rightarrow HCO_3^-$

(b) $HCO_3^- + H^+ \rightarrow CO_2 + H_2O$

42. carbonic anhydrase

43. hypoventilation

44. acidosis

45. hyperventilation

46. It uses HCO_3^- to neutralize acid, and it expels "acid" (CO_2) via the lungs.

47. $$pH = pK_a + \log\frac{[anion]}{acid}$$

48. 3.84

49. HX. Its pK_a (5.0) is closer to the desired pH.

50. $$pH = pK' + \log\frac{[HCO_3^- (aq)]}{[CO_2 (aq)]}$$

51. 6.1

52. $[HCO_3^-] = 24$ mmol/L, $[CO_2] = 1.2$ mmol/L, pH = 7.4

53. $[HCO_3^-] = 19$ mmol/L, $[CO_2] = 6.2$ mmol/L, pH = 6.6, pH = 7.3

54. HCO_3^-

55. sodium acetate

56. greater than 7 (The acetate ion hydrolyzes in water.)

57. 0.103 M HCl

58. 0.103 M KOH

Multiple–Choice

1. b	2. d	3. b and possibly d
4. a	5. d	6. c
7. c	8. a	9. a and e
10. b, d, and f	11. b and d	12. c
13. b	14. c	15. c
16. b	17. c	18. a, b, c, and d
19. a, b, and c	20. d	21. b
22. b, c, d	23. a	24. c
25. b		

10

OXIDATION-REDUCTION EQUILIBRIA

You had a brief introduction to redox reactions and the terms used with them in Chapter 5. This chapter carries that study further. You learn how to tell if a reaction is actually a redox reaction or some other kind by seeing if any oxidation numbers change. You learn how to balance such reactions. Of probably the greatest importance, you learn how to use the reduction potentials of half-reactions to tell how powerfully a redox equilibrium favors one side or the other.

The most important skills to be learned in this chapter are

1. Determining oxidation numbers and using them to tell if a reaction is an oxidation or a reduction or neither.

2. Balancing a redox reaction.

3. Using standard reduction potentials to predict reactions.

4. Calculate a cell potential and an equilibrium constant for a redox system.

OBJECTIVES

When you have studied this chapter and worked its Practice Exercises and Review Exercises, you should be able to do the following.

1. Assign the oxidation number of any atom in a molecule or ion.
2. Tell if a reaction is a redox reaction by noting if oxidation numbers change.
3. Separate a redox reaction into its two half-reactions, one an oxidation and the other a reduction.
4. Balance a redox reaction.

5. Use a table of standard reduction potentials to tell the relative ability of a half-reaction to run as a reduction.

6. Use a table of standard reduction potentials to predict if a given redox equation represents a reaction that will proceed spontaneously.

7. Calculate the standard cell potential for a redox reaction.

8. Use a standard cell potential for a redox equilibrium to calculate the equilibrium constant for the system.

9. Use a statement of the Nernst equation to explain how a cell potential depends on the concentrations of the species involved in a redox equilibrium.

GLOSSARY

Cell Potential, Standard $\left(E^{\circ}_{cell}\right)$. The difference between the standard reduction potentials of the two half-cell reactions of a redox reaction.

Half-Reaction. An equation either for the reduction or for the oxidation part of a redox reaction and whose electrical balance is achieved by using electrons as reactants or as products.

Oxidation Number. For simple monatomic ions, the quantity and sign of the electrical charge on the ion.

Redox Reaction. Abbreviation of *reduction-oxidation*; a reaction in which oxidation numbers change.

Reduction Potential. The quantitative measure of a given half-reaction to proceed as a reduction relative to the standard hydrogen half-reaction.

Reduction Potential, Standard (E°). The reduction potential under standard conditions, 25 °C, 1 atm, and concentrations of 1 M.

Volt (V). The SI unit of electrical potential, the force that drives a flow of electrons when a current of electricity flows.

SELF-TESTING QUESTIONS

COMPLETION

1. A redox reaction is one in which what changes? _____

2. When an oxidation number becomes more positive (or less negative), we say that what kind of event has occurred, oxidation or reduction? _____

3. Assign the oxidation numbers to the specified elements in the following particles.

   (a) N in N_2 _____   (d) Cr in $Cr_2O_7{}^{2-}$ _____

   (b) O in H_2O _____   (e) Na in NaCl   _____

   (c) Mn in MnO_2 _____   (f) F in HF   _____

4. Does the following balanced, net ionic equation represent a redox reaction, or some other kind of reaction?

$$2NaOH + H_2SO_4 \rightarrow Na_2SO_4 + 2H_2O$$

Answer (yes or no): _____. If you answered yes, that it is a redox reaction, identify two atoms whose oxidation numbers change and state the new values of their oxidation numbers in the products.

_____

Which species, if any, is oxidized?   _____
Which is reduced?   _____

5. Does the following balanced, net ionic equation represent a redox reaction, or some other kind of reaction?

$$2MnO_4^- + 5H_2SO_3 \rightarrow 2Mn^{2+} + 3H_2O + 5SO_4^{2-} + 4H^+$$

Answer (yes or no): _____. If you answered yes, that it is a redox reaction, identify two atoms whose oxidation numbers change and state the new values of their oxidation numbers in the products.

_____

Which species, if any, is oxidized?   _____
Which is reduced?   _____

6. Balance the following redox reaction, which occurs in aqueous acid.

$$Cu + NO_3^- \rightarrow Cu^{2+} + NO$$

First show the half-reactions
For oxidation: _____
For reduction: _____
The balanced equation is _____

7. Balance the following redox reaction, which occurs in aqueous base.

$$MnO_4^- + C_2O_4^{2-} \rightarrow MnO_2 + CO_3^{2-}$$

First show the half-reactions as they occurred in acid.
For oxidation: _____
For reduction: _____
Assuming that the reaction is in acid, the balanced equation is,

_____

Now complete the steps needed to convert this equation into the equation for the reaction in aqueous base.

_____

8. Write the half-reaction used as the reference against which the reduction potentials of all other half-reactions are compared.

_____

Under what experimental conditions is the reduction potential for this half-reaction defined as 0.00 volt?

_____

9. When the standard reduction potential of a half-reaction is positive, what is the tendency (compared with the reference half-reaction), to run as a reduction or as an oxidation?

10. Consider the following half-reactions.

    I $Pb^{2+}(aq) + 2e^- \rightleftharpoons Pb(s)$ $E° = -0.13$ V

    II $I_2(s) + 2e^- \rightleftharpoons 2I^-(aq)$ $E° = +0.54$ V

(a) Which half-reaction, I or II, has the greater tendency to run in reverse, as an oxidation?

_____

(b) Write the equation for the *spontaneous* reaction that could be expected from the species in I and II.

_____

(c) The value of $E_{cell}^{°}$ for this redox reaction is _____

(d) If this reaction were treated as an equilibrium, what is the equilibrium constant (as calculated by equation 10.3 in the text)._____

(e) What does the answer in part (d) tell about the position of equilibrium? _____

11.   When a redox system reaches equilibrium, what is the cell potential, $E_{cell}^{°}$?_____

MULTIPLE–CHOICE

1.   What does the following equation represent?
$$NO_3^-(aq) + 4H^+(aq) + 3e^- \rightarrow NO(g) + 2H_2O$$
   (a)   acid-base neutralization
   (b)   a redox reaction
   (c)   oxidation
   (d)   reduction

2.   The oxidation number of S in H_2SO_4 is
   (a)   0   (b) +2   (c) +4   (d) +6

3.   The oxidation number of S in SO_3^{2-} is
   (a)   +4   (b) +2   (c) 0   (d) –2

4.   What is the coefficient of Cl^- in the following equation, after it has been correctly balanced?
$$PbO_2 + Cl^- + H^+ \rightarrow Pb^{2+} + H_2O + Cl_2$$
   (a)   1   (b) 2   (c) 3   (d) 4

5.   What is the coefficient of HNO_2 in the following equation, after it has been correctly balanced?
$$HNO_2 + MnO_4^- + H^+ \rightarrow NO_3^- + Mn^{2+} + H_2O$$
   (a)   4   (b) 5   (c) 6   (d) 7

6.   Given the following half-reactions with their standard reduction potentials, what redox reaction would be spontaneous?
$$Mg^{2+} + 2e^- \rightleftharpoons Mg(s) \qquad E^° = -2.37 \text{ V}$$
$$Pb^{2+}(aq) + 2e^- \rightleftharpoons Pb(s) \qquad E^° = -0.13 \text{ V}$$
   (a) $Mg^{2+}(aq) + Pb(s) \rightarrow Mg(s) + Pb^{2+}(aq)$
   (b) $Mg^{2+}(aq) + Pb^{2+}(aq) \rightarrow Mg(s) + Pb(s)$
   (c) $Mg(s) + Pb^{2+}(aq) \rightarrow Mg^{2+}(aq) + Pb(s)$
   (d) $Mg(s) + Pb(s) \rightarrow Mg^{2+}(aq) + Pb^{2+}(aq)$

7.   When a standard reduction potential is very negative, it means that (pick one)
   (a)   the half-reaction tends to take place as a reduction.
   (b)   the cell potential will also be very negative.
   (c)   the half-reaction tends to occur as an oxidation.
   (d)   one of the chemical reactants to the right of the arrow in the half-reaction is a powerful oxidizing agent.

8. The standard cell potential for the following reaction is 0.82 V.

$$Cl_2(g) + 2I^-(aq) \rightleftharpoons 2Cl^-(aq) + I_2(s)$$

The equilibrium constant for this reaction is

(a) 0.82 (b) 5×10^{27} (c) 5×10^{-27} (d) $1 \times 10^{0.82}$

ANSWERS

ANSWERS TO SELF–TESTING QUESTIONS

Completion

1. oxidation numbers
2. oxidation
3. (a) 0 (b) –2 (c) +4 (d) +6 (e) +1 (f) –1
4. No
5. Yes. The oxidation number of Mn changes from +7 (MnO_4^-) to +2 (in Mn^{2+}). The oxidation number of S changes from +4 (H_2SO_3) to +6 (SO_4^{2-}). S is oxidized and Mn is reduced.
6. Oxidation: $Cu \rightarrow Cu^{2+} + 2e^-$
    Reduction: $NO_3^- + 4H^+ + 3e^- \rightarrow NO + 2H_2O$
    Equation: $3Cu + 2NO_3^- + 8H^+ \rightarrow 3Cu^{2+} + 2NO + 4H_2O$
7. Oxidation: $C_2O_4^{2-} + 2H_2O \rightarrow 2CO_3^{2-} + 4H^+ + 2e^-$
    Reduction: $MnO_4^- + 4H^+ + 3e^- \rightarrow MnO_2 + 2H_2O$
    Equation in acid: $3C_2O_4^{2-} + 2MnO_4^- + 2H_2O \rightarrow 6CO_3^{2-} + 2MnO_2 + 4H^+$
    Equation in base: $3C_2O_4^{2-} + 2MnO_4^- + 4OH^- \rightarrow 6CO_3^{2-} + 2MnO_2 + 2H_2O$
8. $2H^+(aq) + 2e^- \rightleftharpoons H_2(g)$
    [H^+] = 1.00 M, H_2 pressure = 1 atm, temperature = 25 °C
9. As a reduction
10. (a) I
    (b) $I_2(s) + Pb(s) \rightarrow Pb^{2+}(aq) + 2I^-(aq)$
    (c) +0.67 V
    (d) 4.3×10^{22}
    (e) The products are very strongly favored at equilibrium.
11. Zero volt

Multiple–Choice

1. d 5. b
2. d 6. c
3. a 7. d
4. b 8. b

11

RADIOACTIVITY AND NUCLEAR CHEMISTRY

OBJECTIVES

After you have studied this chapter and worked the Practice Exercises and Review Exercises, you should be able to do the following. The first nine objectives are basic to the study of radioactivity and nuclear chemistry. Objectives 11 through 13 are most important for those who may one day work with radioisotopes. Finally, objectives 14 through 16 will help you in reading and studying current issues involving nuclear power and radioactive pollution.

1. Name three kinds of atomic radiation from natural sources.
2. Contrast a chemical change with a nuclear change.
3. Balance a nuclear equation when given all but one of the particles involved.
4. Contrast alpha, beta, and gamma rays according to their composition and their relative penetrating power.
5. Explain the term "half-life."
6. Do inverse square law calculations.
7. Describe the steps you can take to protect yourself from radiation.
8. Name three ways to detect radiation.
9. Describe the use of radiation in food preservation and what the safety issues are.
10. Describe in general terms how radiation damages cells.
11. Discuss five desirable properties of a radionuclide that is to be used in medical diagnosis.
12. Explain how technetium-99 is used in the diagnosis of disease.
13. Explain how I-131 or I-123 can be used in the diagnosis of disease.
14. Not all of the many units of radiation measurement (Section 11.3) may be assigned in your course.

For those that are, name the unit used to describe each of the following (as assigned) and give its symbol (if it has one).

(a) how radioactive is a sample;

(b) how intense is an exposure to X rays (or gamma rays);

(c) how much energy does a particular kind of radiation release in a given mass of tissue (irrespective of the kind of tissue);

(d) how much energy is associated with a specific radiation;

(e) how relatively stable is a particular radioactive isotope.

15. Describe the kinds of atomic events that occur in the burner reactor of a nuclear power plant.

16. Name three radioactive isotopes that can be released into the environment from a nuclear power plant.

17. Define each of the terms given in the Glossary.

GLOSSARY

Alpha (α) Particle. The nucleus of a helium atom; ^4_2He

Alpha (α) Radiation. A stream of high-energy alpha particles.

Background Radiation. Cosmic rays plus the natural atomic radiation emitted by the traces of radioactive isotopes in soils and rocks.

Becquerel (Bq). The SI unit of radioactive source activity; one nuclear disintegration (or other transformation) per second.

$$1 \text{ curie} = 3.7 \times 10^{10} \text{ Bq}$$

Beta (β) Particle. The electron; $^0_{-1}e$

Cosmic Radiation. A stream of ionizing radiation, from the sun and outer space, that consists mostly of protons but also includes alpha particles, electrons, and the nuclei of atoms up to atomic number 28.

Curie (Ci). A unit of activity of a radioactive source.

$$1 \text{ Ci} = 3.70 \times 10^{10} \text{ disintegrations/s}$$

Electron Volt (eV). A very small unit of energy used to describe the energy of radiation.

$$1 \text{ eV} = 1.6 \times 10^{-19} \text{ joule}$$

$$1 \text{ eV} = 3.8 \times 10^{-20} \text{ calorie}$$

$$1000 \text{ eV} = 1 \text{ KeV (1 kiloelectron volt)}$$

$$1000 \text{ KeV} = 1 \text{ MeV (1 megaelectron volt)}$$

Fission. The splitting of the nucleus of a heavy atom approximately in half and that is accompanied by the release of one or a few neutrons and energy.

Gamma Radiation. A natural radiation similar to but more powerful than X rays.

Gray (Gy). The SI unit of absorbed dose of radiation equal to one joule of energy absorbed per kilogram of tissue.

Half-Life. The time needed for half of the atoms in a sample of a radioactive isotope to undergo radioactive decay.

Inverse Square Law. The intensity of radiation varies inversely with the square of the distance from its source.

Ionizing Radiation. Any radiation that can create ions from molecules within the medium that it enters, such as alpha, beta, gamma, X, and cosmic radiation.

Nuclear Chain Reaction. The mechanism of nuclear fission by which one fission event makes enough fission initiators (neutrons) to cause more than one additional fission event.

Nuclear Equation. A representation of a nuclear transformation in which the chemical symbols of the reactants and products include mass numbers and atomic numbers.

Rad. One rad equals 100 ergs (1×10^{-5} J) of energy absorbed per gram of tissue as a result of ionizing radiation.

Radiation. A process whereby light or heat is emitted; also the emitted light or heat. In atomic physics, the emission of some ray such as an alpha, beta, or gamma ray.

Radiation Sickness. The set of symptoms that develops following exposure to heavy doses of ionizing radiation.

Radical. A particle with one or more unpaired electrons.

Radioactive. The property of unstable atomic nuclei whereby they emit alpha, beta, or gamma rays.

Radioactive Decay. The change of a radioactive isotope into another isotope by the emission of alpha rays or beta rays.

Radioactive Disintegration Series. A series of isotopes selected and arranged such that each isotope but the first is produced by the radioactive decay of the preceding isotope and the last isotope is nonradioactive.

Radionuclide. A radioactive isotope.

Rem. One rem is the quantity of a radiation that causes the same effect in humans as one roentgen of X rays or gamma rays.

Roentgen. The quantity of X rays or gamma radiation that generates ions with a total of 2.1×10^{9} units of charge in 1 mL of dry air at normal pressure and temperature.

Sievert, Sv. The SI unit of dose equivalent.

Threshold Exposure. The level of exposure to some toxic agent below which no harm is done.

Transmutation. The change of an isotope of one element into an isotope of a different element.

SELF-TESTING QUESTIONS

COMPLETION

Questions About General Aspects of Radioactivity

1. A substance that will ruin photographic film even when it is stored at room temperature in an air tight black wrapping is probably _____.

2. The nuclei of helium atoms are often called _____ particles.

3. If a substance emits beta radiation, its atoms have lost _____ from their _____, and their atomic number has changed by (how many) _____ unit(s) to a _____ value.

(higher or lower)

4. If a substance emits gamma radiation, its nuclei have lost _____ and they have experienced a change in _____ unit(s) of atomic number and _____ unit(s) of atomic mass.

5. Traces of radionuclides in soils and rocks contribute to our _____.

6. If a radioactive source initially weighing 8 grams had only 4 grams of that isotope left after 20 days, then the _____ of that source is 20 days.

7. If a radioactive source initially weighing 12 grams had only 3 grams of that isotope left after 8 days, its half-life is _____.

8. If a radionuclide emits an alpha particle, its atomic number changes by _____ unit(s) _____ (up or down) and its atomic mass changes by _____ unit(s) _____ (up or down).

9. Radiation that closely resembles gamma radiation is called _____.

10. Because alpha radiation emitted from radioactive sources has enough energy to knock electrons from neutral molecules of air, we say that this radiation is an _____.

11. Complete and balance these nuclear equations.

    (a) $^{210}_{84}\text{Po} \rightarrow {}^{4}_{2}\text{He} +$ _____

    (b) $^{212}_{86}\text{Rn} \rightarrow {}^{208}_{84}\text{Po} +$ _____

    (c) $^{212}_{82}\text{Pb} \rightarrow {}^{0}_{-1}e +$ _____

Questions About Radiation in the Food Industry

12. The energies of radiation used in food irradiation technology are classified as low-, medium-, and high-dosage. What energies are associated with these (in krad) and what are the effects?

	Energies (range)	Expected Effects
Low-dosage	_____	_____
Medium-dosage	_____	_____
High-dosage	_____	_____

13. High-dosage irradiation of food does not necessarily destroy all traces of which bacterial species associated with food poisoning? _____

Questions About Medical and Health Aspects of Radiation

14. Potentially, the most serious damage that a radiation can do to a cell is to hit its _____.

15. When a high-energy particle hits a water molecule, the molecule can lose first an electron and then a proton leaving an unstable particle with the formula _____.

16. Exposure to high intensity radiation can cause a set of symptoms that collectively are called

    _____.

17. Four kinds of serious, long-term consequences of exposure even to low levels of ionizing radiation are _____, _____, _____, and _____.

18. The most penetrating radiations are _____ and _____.

19. Two strategies for protecting oneself from exposure to the radiation of some radioactive source are _____ and _____.

20. The inverse square law states that _____

    _____

21. If the intensity of radiation, in arbitrary units, is 25.0 units at a point 5.00 m from a source, then at a point 10.0 m from the source the intensity will be _____ units.

22. If the intensity of radiation, in arbitrary units, is 100 units at a point 1.0 m from a source, then how many meters from the source would you have to move to reduce the exposure to 1.00 unit? _____

23. Because there are some naturally occurring radionuclides in such common substances as rocks and soil, we can never escape exposure to _____ radiation.

24. Three radionuclides produced as wastes in the operation of atomic reactors and the tissues they "seek" in the body are

Radionuclide	Tissue It Seeks
_____	_____
_____	_____
_____	_____

25. Which is more likely to be used in diagnosis and which in cancer therapy?

    X rays of 100 keV energy   _____

    X rays of 1.3 MeV energy   _____

26. When a film badge dosimeter is used, the amount of exposure to radiation is correlated with the degree of _____ on the film.

27. If a nucleus of a molybdenum-98 atom successfully captures a neutron, the product will be which radionuclide? _____

28. When selecting a radionuclide for use in diagnosis, the radiologist must find one with chemical properties that are compatible with the body, and besides this are five other properties:

    (1) _____

    (2) _____

    (3) _____

    (4) _____

    (5) _____

29. Complete the following table in the manner in which it is now partly filled. The first column contains the names of radioactive isotopes used in medicine and therapy. The second column gives the chemical form in which the isotope is administered. The third column is for a very brief statement describing the purpose(s) of the use of the isotope.

Isotope	Form	Purpose(s)
(a) technetium-99^{m}	TcO_4^-	_____
(b) iodine-131	_____	_____
(c) iodine-123	_____	_____
(d) cobalt-60	_____	_____
(e) phosphorus-32	_____	_____

Questions About Units of Radiation Measurements

30. Complete the following table relating the unit of measurement used to the kind of measurement taken.

Kind of Measurement	Common Unit Used	SI Unit
(a) The energy of the particles in a stream of alpha or beta rays or the energy of gamma rays	_____	_____

    (b) Exposure to X rays or
        gamma rays   _____ _____

    (c) Absorbed dose   _____ _____

    (d) Activity of a radioactive
        source   _____ _____

    (e) Dose equivalent   _____ _____

31. The energy released in tissue when it is exposed to ionizing radiation is called the _____, which is commonly described in units of _____.

32. A radioactive source with as many disintegrations per second as a 0.5 gram sample of radium has an activity, in common units, of _____.

33. To allow variations in the responses of different types of radiation to different types of tissues, the absorbed dose may be multiplied by various fractions (modifying factors or quality factors) to give a number called the _____ which is expressed in SI units of _____.

34. If a 0.10-gram sample of some radioactive source is rated as 5.0 microcurie in activity, a 0.20-gram sample would have an activity of _____.

35. If some radioactive source has a half-life of 15 years, then a 0.2-gram sample of this substance would have a half-life that is _____ (half, the same, or double) as a 0.1-gram sample.

Questions About Atomic Energy and Radionuclides

36. The disintegration of a nucleus of uranium-235 following neutron-capture is called _____. This event produces what subatomic particles? _____ that are able to initiate additional disintegrations of unchanged U-235 nuclei. The process is called a nuclear _____.

37. Which isotopes are serious potential pollutants from an accident in the operation of a reactor?
    A bone-seeking isotope   _____
    An isotope that mimics sodium ion   _____
    An isotope taken up by the thyroid gland   _____
    An isotope that enters the food chain by means of cows' milk   _____

38. The explosions at Chernobyl were caused by what event, an atomic bomb type explosion or a steam explosion? _____

39. What salt is given orally to those who have been exposed to diets that contain iodide-131 ion? _____

MULTIPLE–CHOICE

Questions About General Aspects of Radioactivity

1. If a radiation from a radioactive element consists of high-energy helium nuclei, the radiation is called
    (a) an alpha ray   (c) a gamma ray
    (b) a beta ray   (d) cosmic rays

2. In the nuclear reaction $^{210}_{83}\text{Bi} \rightarrow\, ^{210}_{84}\text{Po} +$ _____ the other product is
    (a) an alpha particle   (c) a neutron
    (b) a beta particle   (d) a proton

3.   In the nuclear reaction $^{230}_{90}\text{Th} \rightarrow \,^{-}_{88}\text{Ra}$ + alpha particle
      the blank line (the atomic mass of Ra-88) would contain
      (a) 230   (b) 226   (c) 234   (d) 229

Questions About Medical and Health Aspects of Radiation

4.   The best material for shielding yourself from ionizing radiation is
      (a) concrete   (b) Plexiglas   (c) glass   (d) lead
5.   If you can move away from a radioactive source so that you have doubled your distance from
      it, your exposure to its radiation will be reduced by a factor of
      (a) two   (b) three   (c) four   (d) sixteen
6.   If you were forced to live where you were exposed to a radioactive source, you would be wisest
      in selecting one with
      (a) a very short half-life   (c) gamma-ray emissions
      (b) a very long half-life   (d) beta-ray emissions
7.   The principal reason for the danger associated with radioactivity is that the radiation
      (a) liberates a great amount of energy in tissue
      (b) cannot be shielded
      (c) generates ions and radicals in tissue
      (d) provokes a rapid rise in the white-cell count

Questions About Units of Radiation Measurements

8.   The common unit of the dose equivalent is called the
      (a) curie   (b) roentgen   (c) rad   (d) rem
9.   A radiologist selecting an isotope for use in diagnosis would try to find one that
      (a) is quickly eliminated by the body
      (b) has a short half-life
      (c) can do the job in the least concentration
      (d) is a gamma emitter only
10.   A unit of the activity of a radioactive source is the
      (a) curie   (b) roentgen   (c) rad   (d) half-life
11.   If exposure to radiation results in the absorption of 10 joule of energy per kilogram of tissue,
      then the tissue has absorbed
      (a) 1 rad   (b) 10 Gy   (c) 1 rem   (d) 100 rem
12.   A radioactive source rated at 1 millicurie would be equivalent to
      (a) 100 curie   (c) 1,000 g of radium
      (b) 1 milligram of radium   (d) a half-life of 1 millisecond

Questions About Radiation Technology in the Food Industry

13.   In food exposed to low-dosage radiation,
      (a) the botulinum bacillus is killed
      (b) the ability of salmonella to reproduce is reduced
      (c) insects are made unable to reproduce
      (d) all of the above

14.   One of the safety issues concerning radiation technology used by the food industry is about
   (a)   the production of radiological products not normally present in food either naturally or following any cooking operation
   (b)   the dangers of the radiation itself coming from the food
   (c)   the survival of botulinum bacilli
   (d)   the survival of insects

Questions About Atomic Energy

15.   The initiation of the fission of a nucleus of uranium-235 is brought about by the capture of
   (a)   a neutron   (c)   an alpha particle
   (b)   a beta particle   (d)   a proton

16.   Besides gamma radiation, heat, and the nuclei of isotopes of atomic numbers roughly half of the atomic number of uranium-235, fission also produces
   (a)   intense beta radiation   (c)   cosmic radiation
   (b)   neutrons   (d)   all of the above

17.   What makes it impossible for a civilian nuclear reactor to experience an atom-bomb-like explosion is
   (a)   the cooling water
   (b)   the cladding tubes
   (c)   the low concentration of U-235 in the fuel
   (d)   the build-up of the ratio of new neutrons to captured neutrons

18.   Atomic wastes from nuclear reactors should be kept apart from human contact for at least
   (a)   1000 years   (c)   1000 centuries
   (b)   1000 half-lives   (d)   1000 cycles of radiation

ANSWERS

ANSWERS TO SELF–TESTING QUESTIONS

Completion

1.   radioactive
2.   alpha
3.   electrons, nuclei, one, higher
4.   energy (no particle is lost), no, no
5.   background radiation
6.   half-life
7.   four days
8.   two, down, four, down
9.   X rays
10.   ionizing radiation
11.   The missing formulas are (a) $^{206}_{82}\text{Pb}$ (b) $^{4}_{2}\text{He}$ (c) $^{212}_{83}\text{Bi}$

12. Low-dosage   up to 100 krad   makes insects unable to produce
                                                       inhibits sprouting
    Medium-dosage   100-1000 krad   reduces populations of salmonella
    High-dosage   1000-10,000 krad   sterilizes poultry, fish, and meats (but some
                                                       botulinum bacilli may survive)

13. Botulinum bacilli

14. nucleus

15. HO· (the hydroxyl radical)

16. radiation sickness

17. cancer, tumor, mutation, birth defect

18. X rays and gamma radiation

19. Use a dense shielding material like lead and get as far from the source as practical.

20. The intensity of radiation is inversely proportional to the square of the distance from the source.

21. 6.25

22. 10.0 m

23. background

24. strontium-90, bone seeker
    iodine-131, thyroid seeker
    cesium-137, general circulation

25. 100 keV— diagnosis
    1.3 MeV— therapy

26. fogging

27. molybdenum-99

28. (1) short $t_{1/2}$
    (2) decays to a nonradioactive product (or one with a long $t_{1/2}$)
    (3) a value of $t_{1/2}$ long enough for preparation and use
    (4) gamma-emitter only
    (5) give a hot spot or a cold spot

29.

Isotope	Form	Purpose(s)
(a) technetium-99^{m}	TcO_4^-	brain scanning
(b) iodine-131	I^-	testing of thyroid function; treatment of thyroid cancer
(c) iodine-123	I^-	same as for I-131
(d) cobalt-60	Co	gamma ray source for cancer treatment
(e) phosphorus-32	PO_4^{3-}	chronic leukemia treatment

30.

Common Unit Used	SI Unit
(a) electron volt	none
(b) roentgen	none
(c) rad	gray
(d) curie	becquerel
(e) rem	sievert

31. absorbed dose (or radiation absorbed dose), rad

32. 0.5 curie
33. dose equivalent, sieverts
34. 10 microcuries
35. the same
36. fission, neutrons, chain reaction
37. strontium-90
    cesium-137
    iodine-131
    iodine-131
38. steam explosion
39. NaI

Multiple–Choice

1. a	7. c	13. c
2. b	8. d	14. c
3. b	9. a, b, c, d	15. a
4. d	10. a	16. b
5. c	11. b	17. c
6. b	12. b	18. a

12

ORGANIC CHEMISTRY. SATURATED HYDROCARBONS

The most important *concepts* in this chapter are functional groups, isomerism, the idea of a structural "map sign," and the basic principles of naming organic compounds.

The *skills* that must be mastered involve the writing and interpreting of structural formulas, naming alkanes and alkyl groups, and using the two following structural "map signs:"

1. All substances whose molecules are wholly or mostly hydrocarbons are insoluble in water, and
2. Alkanes or alkane-like regions of molecules of other compounds do not react with strong alkalis, strong acids, water, reducing agents, or most oxidizing agents.

OBJECTIVES

After you have studied this chapter and worked the Practice Exercises and Review Exercises in it, you should be able to do the following. Objectives 6 through 9 are particularly important because they concern the symbols that we'll use in later work with organic compounds.

1. State what the vital force theory was and how it affected research in its day.
2. Describe Wöhler's experiment and explain how it helped to overthrow the vital force theory.
3. List the main differences between organic and inorganic compounds.
4. Give the ways in which carbon is a unique element.
5. State how a molecular formula and a structural formula are alike and how they are different.
6. Explain why each possible conformation of a carbon chain does not represent a different compound.
7. Give an example (both names and structures) of two compounds that are related as isomers.
8. Write condensed structures from full structures (both open-chain and ring compounds).

9. Examine a pair of structures and tell if they are identical, are related as isomers, or are different.
10. Recognize if a substance is a saturated hydrocarbon from its structure.
11. Write the IUPAC names of all of the straight-chain alkanes (through decane) and give their carbon content (the number of carbon atoms per molecule).
12. Write the name and structure of the simple cycloalkanes through rings of six carbons.
13. Write the names and structures of all alkyl groups through the C_4 set.
14. Write the common names of all alkanes through the C_4 set.
15. Write the IUPAC names of alkanes and cycloalkanes from their structures.
16. Write the structures of alkanes and cycloalkanes from their IUPAC names.
17. Recognize the primary, secondary, and tertiary carbons in a structure.
18. Write an equation for the complete combustion of any hydrocarbon.
19. Write an equation for the chlorination of any given alkane showing the structures of all the possible isomeric monochloro products.
20. Define and, where applicable, give an example of each of the terms in the Glossary.

GLOSSARY

Aliphatic Compound. An organic compound without benzene rings.

Alkane. Any saturated hydrocarbon, one that has only single bonds. A *normal* alkane is any whose molecules have straight chains.

Alkenes. Hydrocarbons with carbon-carbon double bonds.

Alkyl Group. A substituent group that is an alkane minus one H atom.

Alkynes. Hydrocarbons with carbon-carbon triple bonds.

Aromatic Compound. An organic compound with a benzene ring.

Branched Chain. A sequence of carbons atoms to which additional carbon atoms are attached at points other than the ends.

Condensed Structure. (See *Structure.*)

Conformation. One of the infinite number of contortions of a molecule that are permitted by free rotations around single bonds.

Constitutional Isomers. Compounds with identical molecular formulas but different atom-to-atom sequences; structural isomers.

Free Rotation. The absence of a barrier to the rotation of two groups with respect to each other when they are joined by a single, covalent bond.

Functional Group. An atom or a group of atoms in a molecule that is responsible for the particular set of reactions that all compounds with this group have.

Heterocyclic Compound. An organic compound with a ring in which at least one ring atom is not carbon.

Hydrocarbon. Any organic compound that consists entirely of carbon and hydrogen.

Inorganic Compound. Any compound that is not an organic compound.

International Union of Pure and Applied Chemistry System (IUPAC System). A set of systematic rules for naming compounds and designed to give each compound one unique name and for which only one structure can be drawn; the Geneva system of nomenclature.

Isomerism. The phenomenon of the existence of two or more compounds with identical molecular formulas but different structures.

Isomers. Compounds with identical molecular formulas but different structures.

IUPAC System. (See *International Union of Pure and Applied Chemistry System*.)

Like-Dissolves-Like Rule. Polar solvents dissolve polar or ionic solutes and nonpolar solvents dissolve nonpolar or weakly polar solutes.

Nomenclature. The system of names and the rules for devising such names, given structures, or for writing structures, given names.

Nonfunctional Group. A section of an organic molecule that remains unchanged during a chemical reaction at a functional group.

Organic Chemistry. The study of the structures, properties, and the syntheses of organic compounds.

Organic Compounds. Compounds of carbon with other nonmetal elements.

Primary Carbon. In a molecule, a carbon atom that is joined directly to just one other carbon, such as the end carbons in $CH_3CH_2CH_3$.

Ring Compound. A compound whose molecules contain three or more atoms joined in a ring.

Saturated Compound. A compound whose molecules have only single bonds.

Secondary Carbon. Any carbon atom in an organic molecule that has two and only two bonds to other carbon atoms, such as the middle carbon atom in $CH_3CH_2CH_3$.

Straight Chain. A continuous, open sequence of covalently bound carbon atoms from which no additional carbon atoms are attached at interior locations of the sequence.

Structural Isomer. (See *Constitutional Isomer*.)

Structure. A structural formula; an array of atomic symbols and lines (for covalent bonds) that shows how the parts of a molecule are organized.

Substitution Reaction. A reaction which one atom or group in a molecule is replaced by another atom or group.

Tertiary Carbon. Any carbon in an organic molecule that has three and only three bonds to adjacent carbon atoms.

Unsaturated Compound. Any compound whose molecules have a double or a triple bond.

Vital Force Theory. A discarded theory that organic compounds could be made in the laboratory only if the chemicals possessed a vital force contributed by some living thing.

DRILL EXERCISES

I. EXERCISES ON CONDENSED STRUCTURES

The rules for converting from a full structure to a condensed structure are:

1. $\begin{array}{c} \text{H} \\ | \\ \text{H} - \text{C} - \\ | \\ \text{H} \end{array}$ becomes CH_3 (sometimes H_3C)

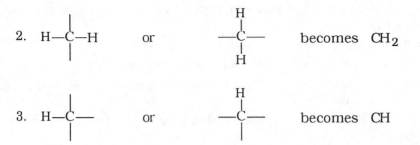

2. 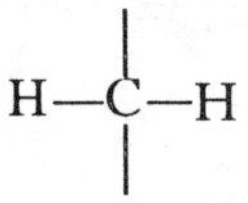 or 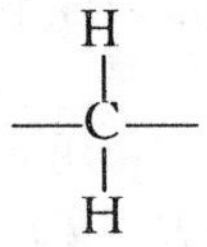 becomes CH_2

3. 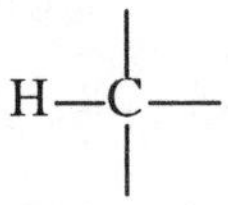 or 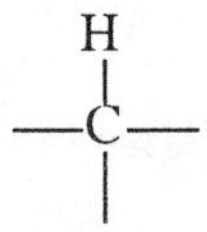 becomes CH

4. All bonds of hydrogen to carbon, oxygen, nitrogen, or sulfur may be "understood."
5. Any single bond between heavy atoms (C—C, C—O, C—N, C—S, for example) may be shown or it may be understood, provided that it would normally be drawn horizontally and, therefore, is part of the main chain.
6. Any single bond between heavy atoms that hold substituents onto the main chain must be shown. (In other words, we always show a substituent group attached to a main chain by writing the group either above the chain or below it, and by connecting the group to the main chain by a line representing the bond.)
7. All double and triple bonds must be shown. (A modification of this rule will appear in a later chapter when we study carbonyl compounds.)

Practice converting between full and condensed structures by doing these additional exercises.

SET A. Condense each of the following structures.

1. 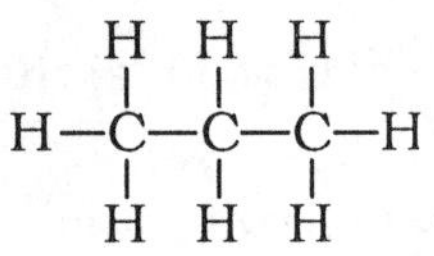 ____________________

2. 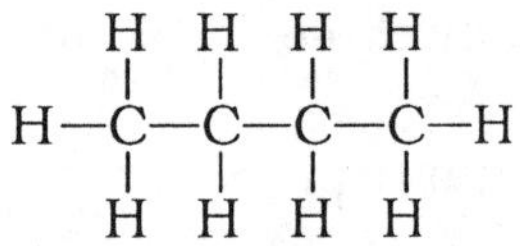 ____________________

3. 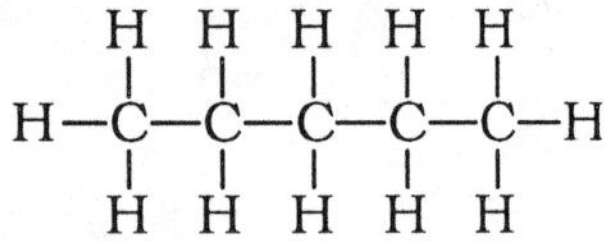 ____________________

4. 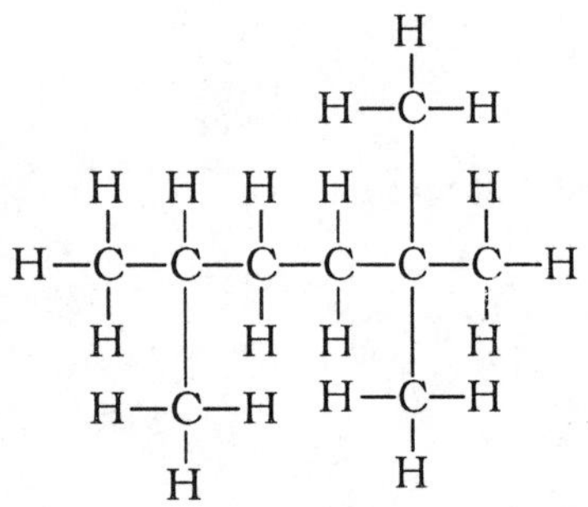 ____________________

5. 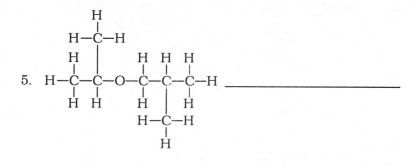 _____

6. 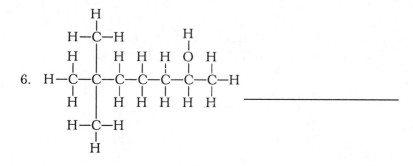 _____

7. 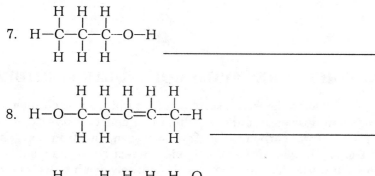 _____

8. 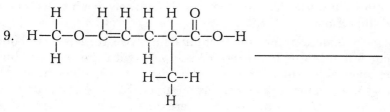 _____

9. 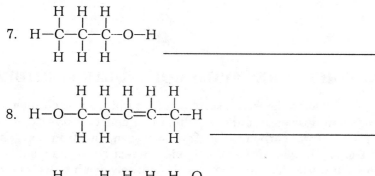 _____

10. 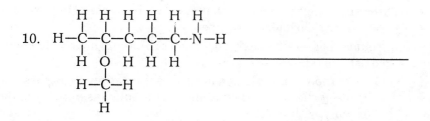 _____

SET B. Write the full structures that correspond to these condensed structures. Show all single bonds.

1. CH_3CH_3

2. $\underset{\displaystyle \overset{\displaystyle CH_3}{|}}{\underset{\displaystyle \underset{\displaystyle CH_3}{|}}{CH_3CCH_2CH_2CH_3}}$

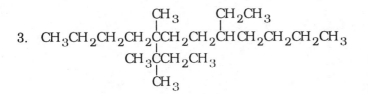

3.

4. $CH_3CH=CH-CH_3$

5. $HOCH_2CH_3$

6. $CH_3O\overset{\displaystyle \overset{O}{\|}}{C}CH_2CH_2NHCH_2CH_3$

7. $HC\equiv C-CH_2\overset{\displaystyle \overset{O}{\|}}{C}H$

8. $NH_2CH_2CH_2NH_2$

II.   EXERCISES ON DEVISING STRUCTURES FROM MOLECULAR FORMULAS

Review Exercise 12.12 in the text asks you to devise a structural formula from each molecular formula given. An answer cannot be correct unless each and every atom in a molecule has exactly the correct number of bonds going from it—four from carbon, three from nitrogen, two from oxygen (or sulfur), one from any halogen, and one from hydrogen. If the question in the text gives you trouble, see how the following semi-systematic approach works. The number of rules may seem a bit awesome, but you will quickly advance beyond needing them.

Rule 1.   Identify those atoms in the given molecular formula that must have two, three, or four bonds—all of the atoms other than a halogen or hydrogen. (We'll work with these to establish a "skeleton" for the structure upon which the hydrogen and halogen atoms will be hung. Think of each allowed bond of every atom (4 for carbon, etc.) as an unused arm. A correct structure will be one in which all the arms are in some way linked. (There can be "no unjoined arms" could be another way of stating it.)

Rule 2.   The number of unused bonds ("free arms") left over on the skeleton—**all being single bonds**—must equal the number of hydrogens or halogens to be appended.

Rule 3.   Don't put a halogen on anything but carbon—not on oxygen, not on sulfur, and not on nitrogen. (Although such possibilities do exist, we'll never encounter them.)

Rule 4.   In writing a structure, assemble the carbon atoms along a horizontal line as much as possible and pin the substituents to the resulting chain of carbon atoms. (This rule has nothing to do with rules about numbers of bonds, only with looks.)

When atoms have more than one bond, options exist as to how they may occur in structures. All of the bonds may be single, or some may be single and some double or even triple. Here are all the possible options for carbon, nitrogen, oxygen, the halogens, and hydrogen.

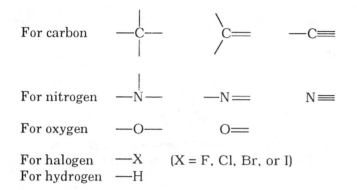

For carbon

For nitrogen

For oxygen

For halogen   —X   (X = F, Cl, Br, or I)
For hydrogen   —H

Now let's work a few sample exercises.

Sample Exercise 1: Write a structural formula for CH_4O.

Step 1.   The multivalent atoms are C and O. (Rule 1)
Step 2.   Assemble the options:

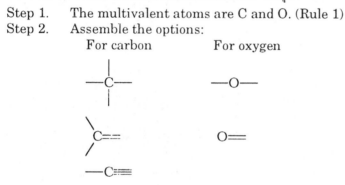

Step 3.   Try the possible combinations of those in the first column with those in the second.

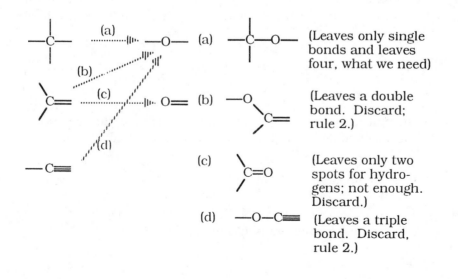

(a)   (Leaves only single bonds and leaves four, what we need)

(b)   (Leaves a double bond. Discard; rule 2.)

(c)   (Leaves only two spots for hydrogens; not enough. Discard.)

(d)   (Leaves a triple bond. Discard, rule 2.)

Step 4. Identify the skeleton, or skeletons, (rules 1 and 2) and append the hydrogens. In this sample exercise only one skeleton meets the rules, the one generated by combination (a)

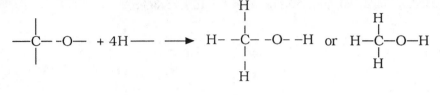

(the answer)

We may condense the answer to CH$_3$OH.

Step 5. Run a mental check; does the carbon have 4 bonds; the oxygen, 2; and the hydrogens 1 each? They do; therefore, the structure obeys the rules of covalence.

Sample Exercise 2: Convert C$_2$H$_4$ to a structural formula.

Step 1. The multivalent atoms are just the two Cs.
Step 2. Assemble the options:
First Carbon   Second Carbon

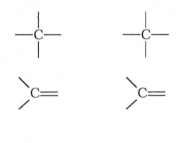

Step 3. Try combinations from each column. Remember that the remaining unused bonds must equal four in number, for the four hydrogens, and that these remaining bonds must all be single bonds. Mentally discarding all combinations that leave double or triple bonds "open," we have these possibilities:

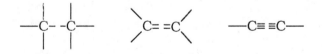

The first leaves room for six hydrogens, too many; the last for two hydrogens, too few. The middle will work; room is left for four hydrogens.

Step 4. Put the pieces together:

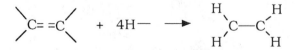

The condensed structure is: CH$_2$=CH$_2$.

Step 5. Check to see that each atom has the right number of bonds; that each carbon has four bonds, and each hydrogen has one.

_____

Sample Exercise 3: Convert C_2H_4O into a proper structural formula.

Step 1.   The multivalent atoms are two carbons and one oxygen.
Step 2.   Assemble the options:

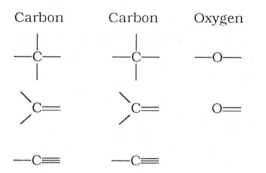

Step 3.   Try the possible combinations, remembering that the skeleton must have no double or triple bond left "hanging" and must have, via single bonds only, room for four hydrogens. Here are the possibilities that have only single bonds remaining. (Beneath each is a number equaling the spaces for hydrogens.)

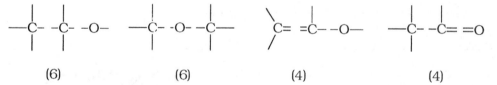

Any others you may have drawn, that avoid leaving open double or triple bonds, will be duplicates of one or more of these. (For instance,

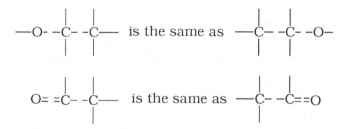

There are two combinations with four spaces for hydrogens. We must consider them both.

Step 4.   Put the pieces together:

Usually, you will see carbon-oxygen double bonds aligned vertically, and the last structure will usually be seen as

The second combination gives $CH_2=CHOH$.
(Remember that the single bonds in the main chain can be "understood.")
Step 5.   Check the answers: four bonds from the carbons; two from the oxygens. Either structure is correct; the two are isomers.

Write structural formulas for the following molecular formulas.

1. H_2O_2 _____

2. N_2H_4 _____

3. CH_4S _____

4. C_2H_5Br _____

5. C_2H_3Cl _____

III. EXERCISES ON STRUCTURAL FEATURES OF HYDROCARBONS

The following set of structures illustrates several features discussed in the text. Supply the information requested by writing the identifying number(s) of the structure(s).

A. $CH_3CH_2CH_2CH_2CH_2CH_3$

B. $CH_3CH-CHCH_3$ with CH_3 above and CH_3 below

C. $CH_3CH=CHCH_2CH_2CH_3$

D. $CH_3CH_2CH_2OH$

E.   F.

SET A.

1. Give the letters of
   (a) the saturated compounds   _____
   (b) the straight-chain compounds   _____
   (c) the branch-chain compounds   _____
   (d) any pairs of compounds related as isomers _____
   (e) any compound with a 3 ° carbon   _____

2. Write the IUPAC name   of A   _____

                              of B   _____

                              of E   _____

3. Write the structures of E and F using the geometric figure method illustrated in the discussion of "Ring Compounds" in Section 12.1 of the text.

   _____   _____

                  E   F

4. Write the structure and give the IUPAC name for the straight chain alkane with one less carbon than A.

   _____

5. Write the full structure of CH_3

   _____

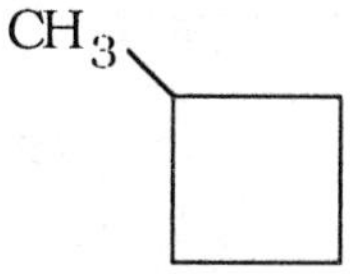

6. Write the full structure of   Cl

   _____

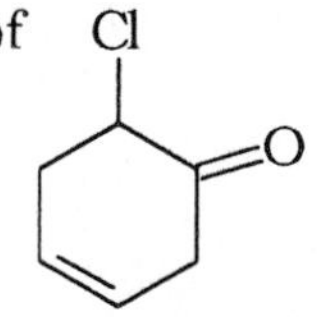

SET B

Examine the following compounds and supply the information requested.

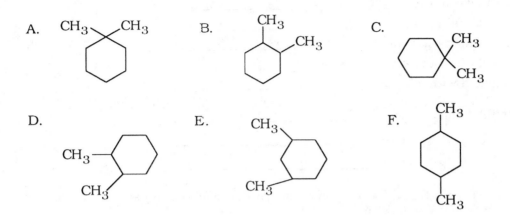

A.   B.   C.

D.   E.   F.

7. Group in sets the letters of structures representing identical compounds.

_____

8. Write IUPAC names   for A _____
                         for E _____

9. To develop skill in the rapid recognition of alkyl groups regardless of how they are oriented in space, place the name of each group on the line beneath its structure.

(a) CH_3
       $—CH_2$

(b) CH_3
       $—CH_2—CH—CH_3$

(c) CH_3
              $CH—$
       CH_3

_____   _____   _____

(d) $—CH_2\ CH_3$
       $CH_2—CH_2$

(e) CH_3
       $CH_3—CH—CH_2—$

(f) CH_3
       $CH_3—C—CH_3$

_____   _____   _____

(g) CH_3
       $CH_3—C—$
              CH_3

(h) CH_3
       $—CH—CH_3$

(i) $CH_2—$
       $CH_3—CH—CH_3$

_____   _____   _____

(j) $CH_3—CH—CH_3$

(k) $CH_3—CH_2—CH—CH_3$

(l) $CH_3—CH—CH_2—CH_3$

_____   _____   _____

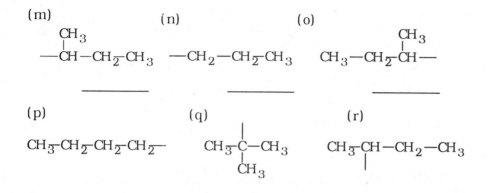

(m)   (n)   (o)

(p)   (q)   (r)

10. To develop the skill of looking at a structure and visualizing it with its longest continuous chain on one horizontal line, write the IUPAC names of each of the following.

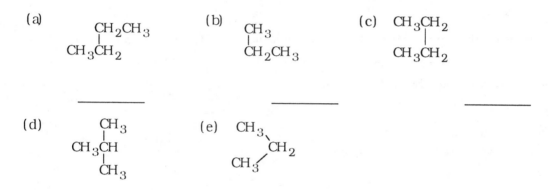

(a)   (b)   (c)

(d)   (e)

Before going on to the Self-Testing Questions, be sure to work all of the Practice Exercises and Review Exercises in the text first. As always, use the Self-Testing Questions as a "final exam" for the chapter.

SELF–TESTING QUESTIONS

COMPLETION

1. If compound X boils at 176 °C, it is almost certainly in the family of _____ (ionic or molecular) compounds. We would assign it to the organic class if, when analyzed, it was found to contain _____.

2. The structure

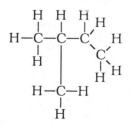

could be most neatly condensed to _____

3. The structure

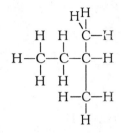

   could be most neatly condensed to _____

4. Are the compounds whose formulas are given in questions 2 and 3 isomers or are they identical?

   _____

5. Write full structural formulas for each of the following:

   _____   _____   _____   _____

   (a) CH_5N (b) CH_2Br_2 (c) C_3H_8 (d) C_3H_4

6. Write the condensed structure of at least one isomer of $CH_3CH_2CH_2OH$ (C_3H_8O).

   _____

7. The IUPAC name of $CH_3CH_2CH_2CH_3$ is _____.

8. The structure of 1-chloro-2,3-dimethylbutane is _____

9. The structure of isobutane is _____

10. Write the structure of each compound on the line above the name.

    (a) _____   (b) _____   (c) _____
        isopropyl chloride   t-butyl bromide   isobutyl chloride

    (d) _____   (e) _____   (f) _____
        sec-butyl bromide   butyl iodide   propyl chloride

11. Give the common names of the following compounds
    (a) the isomer of butane with a 3 ° carbon _____
    (b) the isomer of butane with two 2 ° carbons _____
    (c) the isomer of butane with three 1 ° carbons _____

12. When hexane burns completely in air the balanced equation is _____

13. The IUPAC names and structures of all the monobromo derivatives of pentane are:

    _____   _____   _____

14. Pentane has an isomer that can form only one monochloro derivative. Write the structure of this isomer of pentane. _____

15. The structure of 1,3-dimethylcyclohexane is _____

MULTIPLE–CHOICE

1. The compounds in which of the following pairs are related as isomers?

   (a) $CH_2=CH-CH_2-OH$ and $\overset{\overset{\textstyle HO}{|}}{C}H_2-CH-CH_2$

   (b) H_2 and D_2

   (c) $CH_3-CH_2-NH-CH_3$ and $CH_3-CH_2-CH_2-NH_2$

   (d) $CH_3-C\equiv C-CH_2NH_2$ and $CH_3-CH_2-CH_2-C\equiv N$

2. According to all the rules about allowed numbers of bonds, which compound(s) should not be possible?
   (a) AlPO4

   (b) $CH_3CH=C=CH_2$ (c) $H-O-\overset{\overset{\textstyle O}{||}}{C}-O-H$ (d) $CH=NH$

3. A structural formula for C_5H_{12} would be

   (a) $CH_3(CH_2)_3CH_3$ (b) $CH_3CH_2CH_2CH_2CH_3$

   (c) $CH_3\underset{\underset{\textstyle CH_3}{|}}{C}HCH_2CH_3$ (d) $CH_3\overset{\overset{\textstyle CH_3}{|}}{\underset{\underset{\textstyle CH_3}{|}}{C}}CH_3$

4. Which (if any) of the choices in question 3 are identical compounds?
5. Which (if any) of the choices in question 3 are isomers?

6. A family of organic compounds containing only carbon and hydrogen and having only single bonds are the
   (a) alkenes   (c) alkynes
   (b) alkanes   (d) cycloalkanes

7. The combustion of butane produces
   (a) butylene and water   (c) an alcohol
   (b) CO_2 and H_2O (d) cyclohexane

8. The compound $CH_3-⬡$ is

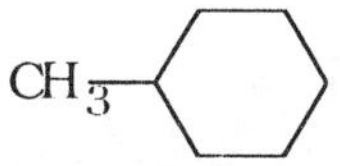

   (a) methylcyclopentane   (c) cycloheptane
   (b) a saturated compound   (d) cyclohexane

9.   What is the name of the following compound?

$$CH_2CH_2CH_3$$
$$CH_3CH_2CH_2CHCHCH_2CH_2CH_2CH_3$$
$$CH_3-CH-CH_3$$

   (a)   4-isobutyl-5-propylnonane
   (b)   2-methyl-3,4-dipropyloctane
   (c)   5-propyl-6-isopropylnonane
   (d)   4-isopropyl-5-propylnonane

10.   The chlorination of 2-methylpentane would produce how many isomeric monochloro compounds?

   (a)   6   (b)   5   (c)   4   (d)   3

11.   Because carbon and hydrogen have very similar electronegativities, hydrocarbons are generally

   (a)   electropositive   (c)   polar
   (b)   nonpolar   (d)   hydrogen-bonded

12.   The compound shown has how many hydrogens per molecule?

   (a)   8   (b)   7   (c)   12   (d)   10

13.   The common name of $CH_3-CH-CH_2-Cl$ is
   $$CH_3$$

   (a)   butyl chloride   (c) t-butyl chloride
   (b)   isobutyl chloride   (d) sec-butyl chloride

14.   The common name of

   (a)   cyclopropane   (c)   propane
   (b)   isopropane   (d)   dimethylmethane

15.   The compound $CH_3-C{\equiv}C-H$ is

   (a)   soluble in water   (c)   soluble in gasoline
   (b)   a hydrocarbon   (d)   unsaturated

ANSWERS

ANSWERS TO DRILL EXERCISES

I. Exercises on Condensed Structures

__Set A__

1. $CH_3CH_2CH_3$ or $CH_3-CH_2-CH_3$ (Single bonds along the main chain may be shown or they may be understood. You will see both practices often.)

2. $CH_3CH_2CH_2CH_3$ or $CH_3-CH_2-CH_2-CH_3$

3. $CH_3CH_2CH_2CH_2CH_3$ or $CH_3-CH_2-CH_2-CH_2-CH_3$

4.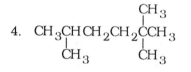

5.
$$CH_3\overset{\underset{|}{CH_3}}{CH}-O-CH_2\overset{\underset{|}{CH_3}}{CH}CH_3$$

6.
$$CH_3\overset{\underset{|}{CH_3}}{\underset{|}{\overset{|}{C}}}CH_2CH_2CH_2\overset{\overset{OH}{|}}{CH}CH_3$$

7. $CH_3CH_2CH_2OH$ (often seen as $CH_3CH_2CH_2-O-H$)

8. $HOCH_2CH_2CH=CHCH_3$ (Do not write this as
   $OHCH_2CH_2CH=CHCH_3$.
   It implies $O-H-CH_2-$ etc.,
   which is wrong.)

9.
$$CH_3-O-CH=CHCH_2\overset{\underset{|}{CH_3}}{CH}\overset{\overset{O}{||}}{C}OH$$

10.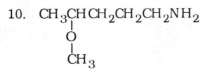

Set B

1.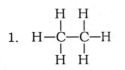

2.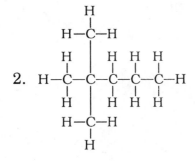

3.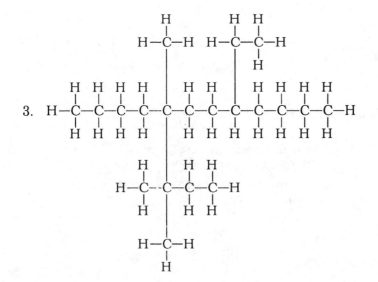

4.   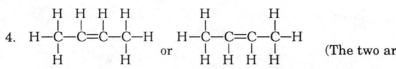   (The two are equivalent.)

5.
```
        H  H
        |  |
  H—O—C—C—H
        |  |
        H  H
```

6.
```
     H       O  H  H  H  H
     |       ||  |  |  |  |
  H—C—O—C—C—C—N—C—C—H
     |           |  |     |  |
     H           H  H     H  H
```

7.
```
           H  O
           |  ||
  H—C≡C—C—C—H
           |
           H
```

8.
```
     H  H  H  H
     |  |  |  |
  H—N—C—C—N—H
        |  |
        H  H
```

II. Exercises on Devising Structures from Molecular Formulas

1.   H—O—O—H

2.
```
     H—N—N—H
       |  |
       H  H
```

3.
```
     H
     |
  H—C—S—H
     |
     H
```

4.
```
     H  H
     |  |
  H—C—C—Br
     |  |
     H  H
```
(Satisfy yourself that the following,

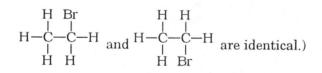

are identical.)

5.
```
     H  H
     |  |
  H—C=C—Cl
```

III. Exercises on Structural Features of Hydrocarbons

Set A

1. (a)   A, B, D, and E

   (b)   A, C, and D   (The term "straight-chain" cannot apply to rings. Among open-chain compounds, as long as the atoms C, O, N, or S are all in a continuous sequence with or without double or triple bonds, the chain is "straight." If the atoms O, N, or S are appended as part of substituents, the chain is still straight if all the carbons occur in a continuous sequence.)

   (c)   B (Ring compounds are not classified as branched, either.)

    (d)   A and B; C and E

    (e)   B (Only saturated carbons are designated as 1°, 2°, or 3°.)

2. A: hexane

    B: 2,3-dimethylbutane

    E: cyclohexane

3. E   F

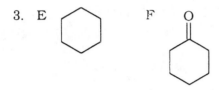

4. $CH_3CH_2CH_2CH_2CH_3$ pentane

5. 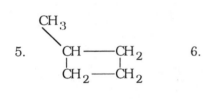   6. 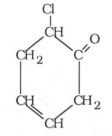

Set B

7. A and C; B and D

8. A 1,1-dimethylcyclohexane

    E 1,3-dimethylcyclohexane   (NOT 1,5-dimethylcyclohexane from counting around the ring in the wrong way. You count from position one, picked as the location of one CH_3 group, along the shortest path around the ring to the next group.)

9. (a)   ethyl   (Actually, ethyl group, but we may omit "group.")

    (b)   isobutyl   (Any four-carbon alkyl group must be one of the four butyl groups. The two derived from isobutane are either the isobutyl or the *t*-butyl group.)

    (c)   isopropyl (Any three-carbon alkyl group must be one of the two propyl groups— propyl or isopropyl.)

    (d)   butyl   (Straighten out the chain and you have a group based on butane, not isobutane. The two butyl groups based on butane are the butyl and the *sec*-butyl groups.)

    (e)   isobutyl   (Compare b and e)

    (f)   *t*-butyl   (It's the only butyl group where the unused bond is at a 3 ° carbon.)

    (g)   *t*-butyl   (This is simply f rotated through part of a circle.)

(h)   isopropyl   (A C_3-alkyl group; it must be either propyl or isopropyl.)

(i)   isobutyl   (Compare b, e, and i.)

(j)   isopropyl   (Compare c, h, and j.)

(k)   *sec*-butyl   (It's the only butyl group where the unused bond is at a 2 ° carbon.)

(l)   *sec*-butyl   (Compare with k.)

(m)   *sec*-butyl   (Carefully compare k, l, and m. After chain straightening, the chain is straight in all three and the free bond comes from a 2 ° carbon.)

(n)   propyl

(o)   *sec*-butyl   (Compare with m and the accompanying note.)

(p)   butyl

(q)   *t*-butyl   (Just f tipped upside down. They have to be the same. Do you become someone else if you stand on your head?)

(r)   *sec*-butyl

10.   (a)   butane   (d)   isobutane or 2-methylpropane

(b)   propane   (e)   propane

(c)   butane

ANSWERS TO SELF–TESTING QUESTIONS

Completion

1.   molecular; carbon

2. 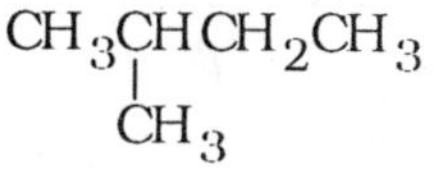 $CH_3CHCH_2CH_3$ 3. CH_3
      $\quad\ \ CH_3$ $CH_3CH_2CHCH_3$

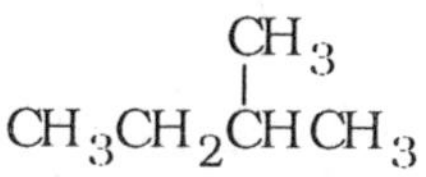

(Your answers to 2 and 3 may be correct but still not look exactly like those given here. All that matters is that they show the correct nucleus-to-nucleus sequence while obeying the accepted conventions for condensing. One of these conventions is that as much of the structure as possible is written out on one line. Should you have questions about your answers, consult your instructor or one of the assistants.)

4.   identical

5.   (a) 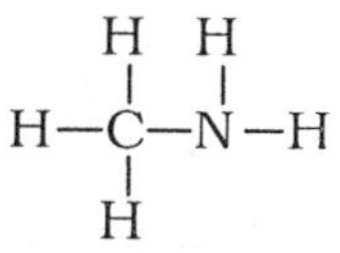   H—C—N—H   (c)   H—C—C—C—H
             (with H above and below C and N)   (with H above and below each C)

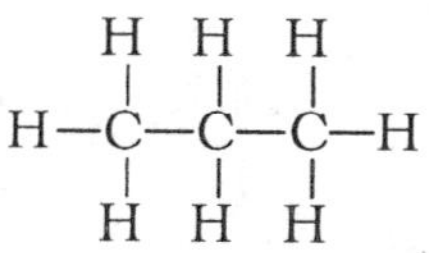

(b) 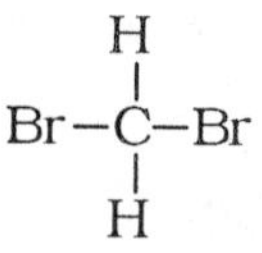   Br—C—Br   (d) 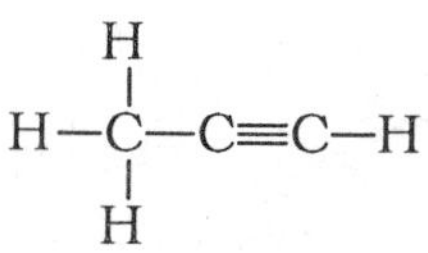   H—C—C≡C—H   or   H—C=C=C—H
             (with H above and below C)   (with H above and below first C)

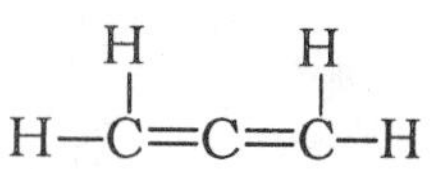

6. There are two isomers: $CH_3-O-CH_2CH_3$ and $CH_3\underset{\underset{OH}{|}}{C}HCH_3$.

7. butane

8. $Cl-CH_2\underset{\underset{CH_3}{|}}{\overset{\overset{CH_3}{|}}{C}}HCHCH_3$ 9. $CH_3\underset{\underset{CH_3}{|}}{C}HCH_3$

10. (a) $CH_3\underset{\underset{Cl}{|}}{C}HCH_3$ (b) $CH_3\underset{\underset{CH_3}{|}}{\overset{\overset{CH_3}{|}}{C}}-Br$ (c) $CH_3\overset{\overset{CH_3}{|}}{C}HCH_2-Cl$

(d) $CH_3\underset{\underset{Br}{|}}{C}HCH_2CH_3$ (e) $CH_3CH_2CH_2CH_2-I$ (f) $CH_3CH_2CH_2-Cl$

11. (a) isobutane   (b) butane   (c) isobutane
12. $2C_6H_{14} + 19O_2 \rightarrow 12CO_2 + 14H_2O$

13. $CH_3CH_2CH_2CH_2CH_2Br$ $CH_3CH_2CH_2\underset{\underset{Br}{|}}{C}HCH_3$ $CH_3CH_2\underset{\underset{Br}{|}}{C}HCH_2CH_3$

     1-bromopentane   2-bromopentane   3-bromopentane

14. $CH_3-\underset{\underset{CH_3}{|}}{\overset{\overset{CH_3}{|}}{C}}-CH_3$ 15.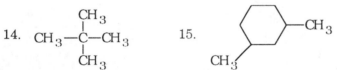

Multiple–Choice

1. c and d	6. b and d	11. b
2. d	7. b	12. d
3. a, b, c, and d	8. b	13. b
4. a and b	9. d	14. c
5. a (or b), c, and d are isomers	10. b	15. b, c, d

13

UNSATURATED HYDROCARBONS

The two topics in this chapter that are most important in our development of the molecular basis of life are:

1. The addition reactions of the carbon-carbon double bond, particularly those with hydrogen and water. (Double bonds occur in all fats and oils. They also occur in the intermediate stages of the chemical breakdown of sugars, fatty acids, and amino acids as well as in the enzymes for these reactions.)

2. The fact that benzene rings in aromatic hydrocarbons do not behave as alkenes, in spite of being highly unsaturated. These rings take part in substitution reactions rather than in addition reactions. (The benzene ring occurs in a few amino acids and in many drugs.)

OBJECTIVES

The specific objectives for this chapter are the following. Return to these to test yourself after you have completed studying all of the chapter, including the Practice Exercises and Review Exercises.

1. Predict whether a given alkene can exist as cis and trans isomers.
2. Write the structures of alkenes from their IUPAC names.
3. Write the IUPAC names of alkenes.
4. Name cycloalkenes.
5. Write equations for the reactions of a given alkene with:
   (a) hydrogen; (b) a halogen: (c) a hydrogen halide; (d) sulfuric acid; and (e) water (in the presence of acid).

6. Use Markovnikov's Rule to predict the correct products in the addition reactions of alkenes.
7. Explain why Markovnikov's Rule works.
8. Predict if a hydrocarbon will be oxidized by ozone, permanganate, and dichromate.
9. Correctly use terms associated with polymerizations, like polymer, monomer, polymerization, and promoter.
10. Describe the structure of benzene in molecular orbital terms.
11. Explain why benzene takes part in substitution reactions rather than in addition reactions.
12. Write equations for the reactions of benzene that result in halogenation, nitration, and sulfonation.
13. Write the common names of all of the monosubstituted benzenes given in this chapter.
14. Devise names for derivatives of benzene having two or more substituents.
15. Define each of the terms in the Glossary and give examples or illustrations where applicable.

GLOSSARY

Addition Reaction. Any reaction in which two parts of a reactant molecule add to a double or a triple bond.

Alkene. A hydrocarbon whose molecules have double bonds.

Alkene Group. The carbon-carbon double bond.

Aliphatic Compound. Any organic compound whose molecules lack a benzene ring or a similar structural feature.

Alkyne. A hydrocarbon whose molecules have triple bonds.

Aromatic Compound. Any organic compound whose molecules have a benzene ring (or a feature very similar to this).

Carbocation. Any cation in which a carbon atom has just six outer level electrons; a carbonium ion.

Geometric Isomerism. Isomerism caused by restricted rotations that give different geometries to the same structural organization; cis-trans isomerism.

Geometric Isomers. Isomers with identical atomic organizations but different geometries; cis-trans isomers.

Macromolecule. A molecule with a very large formula mass, upwards of several thousand.

Markovnikov's Rule. In the addition of an unsymmetrical reactant to an unsymmetrical double bond of a simple alkene, the positive part of the reactant (usually H^+) goes to the carbon with the greater number of hydrogen atoms and the negative part goes to the other carbon of the double bond.

Monomer. Any compound that can be used to make a polymer.

Polymer. Any substance with a very high formula mass whose molecules have a repeating structural unit.

Polymerization. A chemical reaction that makes a polymer from a monomer.

KEY MOLECULAR "MAP SIGNS"

Key Molecular "Map Signs" In Organic Molecules	The Associated Chemical and Physical Properties
If the molecule is largely (or, of course, entirely) hydrocarbon-like	Expect the substance to be relatively insoluble in water and relatively soluble in organic solvents. Expect the substance to be less dense than water.
Alkanelike portions of all molecules	In these portions, expect no chemical changes involving water, acids, alkalis, or chemical oxidizing agents or reducing agents.
An alkene double bond	Adds H—H; becomes saturated Adds X—X; forms di-halo compounds (X = Cl, Br) Markovnikov's Rule applies ⎡ Adds HX; forms alkyl halides (X = F, Cl, Br, I) Adds H_2O; forms alcohols Adds H_2SO_4; forms alkyl hydrogen sulfates ⎣ Adds its own kind; polymers form
Benzene ring	Not like an alkene—gives substitution, not addition reactions. Ring can nitrate, sulfonate, and halogenate [with iron(III) salts as catalysts].

DRILL EXERCISES

The chapter in the text has a number of drills on the reactions of alkenes and benzene. Do these Exercises first.

EXERCISE I

To review condensed structures, write out the following as full structures.

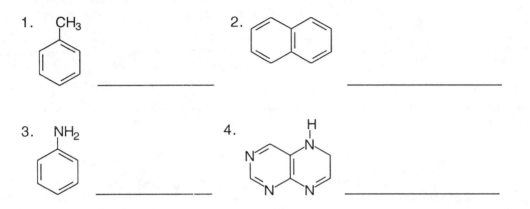

1.   CH₃

2.

_____

_____

3.   NH₂

4.

_____

_____

EXERCISE II

As drill in several things—names, cis-trans isomers, and the recognition of nonequivalent positions—write the structures and the IUPAC names of all of the monochloro derivatives of all of the alkenes through the C_4 alkenes. Be sure to show cis and trans forms with correct geometry; for example, the structure of *cis*-2-chloro-2-butene is:

There are a total of 16 compounds.

EXERCISE III

Memorize the names and structures of the monosubstituted benzenes given in the text. Then study how to use the designations o-, m- and p- for disubstituted benzenes. When you have done this study, test yourself with these. Beneath each structure write the correct name.

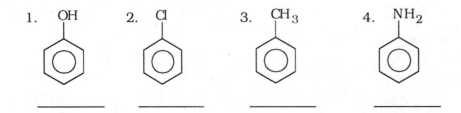

1.   OH   2.   Cl   3.   CH₃   4.   NH₂

_____   _____   _____   _____

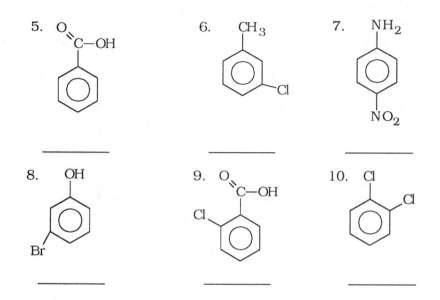

5.
6.
7.

8.
9.
10.

How to Work Problems in Organic Reactions

The *overall goal* of the chapters on organic chemistry in the text is to learn the chemical properties of functional groups. *You know you've reached this goal when you can write the products made by the reaction of a given set of starting materials.* In other words, it is not enough to be able to recognize the names and structural features of functional groups—although you can't do anything else without starting here.

It's also not enough to memorize a sentence that summarizes a chemical fact, such as "alkenes react with hydrogen in the presence of a metal catalyst, heat, and pressure to give alkanes"—although memorizing such sentences is also absolutely essential to the goal. Such sentences are fundamental facts about the world in which we live. What you have to be able to do is apply such knowledge to a specific set of reactants.

A typical problem, for example, is "What forms, if anything, in the following reaction:

$$CH_3-CH=CH_2 \ + \ H_2 \ \xrightarrow[\text{heat, pressure}]{\text{Ni}} \ ?"$$

Here's the strategy to follow in all of the reactions of organic compounds that we will study.

1. Figure out the family or families to which the organic starting materials belong(s). You might even want to write the names of these families beneath the specific structures. (In our example, the family is "alkene.")

2. Review your "memory list" of chemical facts about all alkenes. In your mental "storage," you should have the chemical-fact sentences that you will prepare in the next Exercise.

   FOR EVERY FUNCTIONAL GROUP THAT WE STUDY YOU MUST PREPARE A MEMORIZED LIST OF CHEMICAL–FACT SENTENCES THAT SUMMARIZE THE CHEMICAL PROPERTIES THAT WE STUDY.

3. If you go through the list and find no match to the stated problem, then assume that no reaction takes place and write "no reaction" as the answer.

4. When you find the match between the specific problem and one of the listed chemical properties, stop and construct the structure of the answer. The many worked examples in the text develop the patterns for doing this, and study them thoroughly first.

EXERCISE IV.   SUMMARIZING THE CHEMICAL PROPERTIES OF ALKENES

When you have completed this exercise, you will have a complete sentence summarizing each kind of chemical reaction of the carbon-carbon double bond that we have studied. These statements are the chemical properties of this double bond that must be memorized, but they have to be learned in such a way that you can apply them to specific situations. Hence, following this Exercise there are several drill problems to give you practice.

As you work each specific exercise among these drills, repeat to yourself the sentence statement that summarizes the property being illustrated. This kind of repeated reinforcement will soon give you a surprisingly good working knowledge of these organic reactions, and you will be able to apply what you have learned to much more complicated situations with ease.

1. The alkene double bond reacts with hydrogen (in the presence of a metal catalyst and heat) to give _____ .

2. The alkene double bond reacts with chlorine to give _____ .

3. The alkene double bond reacts with bromine to give _____ .

4. The alkene double bond reacts with hydrogen chloride to give _____ .

5. The alkene double bond reacts with hydrogen bromide to give _____ .

6. The alkene double bond reacts with concentrated sulfuric acid to give _____ .

7. The alkene double bond reacts with water (in the presence of an acid catalyst) to give

_____ .

8. The complete combustion of any alkene produces _____ and _____ .

Another way to organize chemical facts about a functional group such as the carbon-carbon double bond is by means of a 5 x 8" note card. An example is given below, but for the remaining functional groups it is vitally important that you prepare the cards yourself. Part of the learning process is in this preparation, and having someone else do it for you robs you of that benefit.

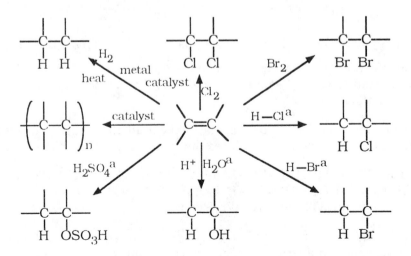

(a) Markovnikov's rule applies

Notice that the functional group is put in the center and its chemical properties are arranged about it. All of the arrows point outward. Later on, it will be useful to prepare cards summarizing key reactants, like H_2O or H_2 on which you'll list all of the reactions studied involving these substances.

EXERCISE V.   DRILL ON THE ADDITION OF HYDROGEN TO ALKENES

Write the structures of the products of the following reactions. If no reaction occurs, write "no reaction." (See Example 13.3 in the text.) In each, assume that the system is heated.

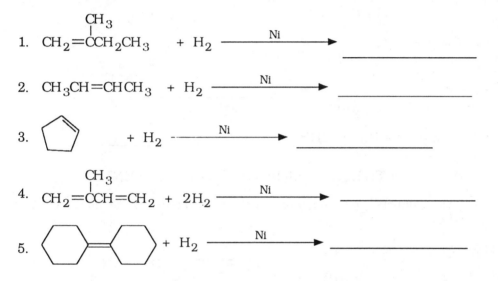

EXERCISE VI.   DRILL ON THE ADDITION OF CHLORINE OR BROMINE TO ALKENES

Write the structures of the products of the following reactions. If no reaction occurs, write "no reaction." (See Example 13.4 in the text.)

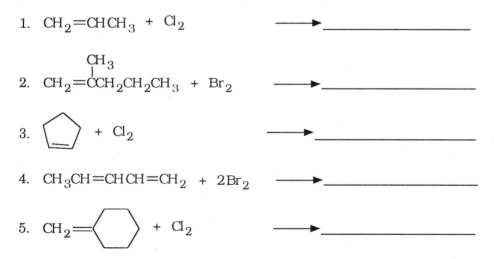

EXERCISE VII.   DRILL ON THE ADDITION OF H—Cl(g) OR H—Br(g) TO ALKENES

Write the structures of the products of each reaction. If no reaction occurs, write "no reaction."

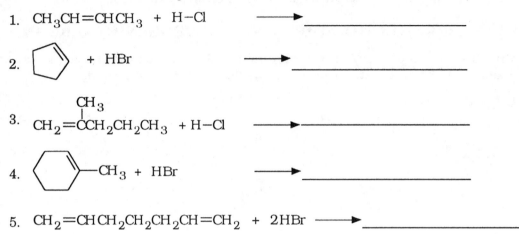

1. $CH_3CH=CHCH_3$ + H–Cl $\longrightarrow$ _____

2. + HBr $\longrightarrow$ _____

3. $CH_2=\overset{\overset{\displaystyle CH_3}{|}}{C}CH_2CH_2CH_3$ + H–Cl $\longrightarrow$ _____

4. —CH_3 + HBr $\longrightarrow$ _____

5. $CH_2=CHCH_2CH_2CH_2CH=CH_2$ + 2HBr $\longrightarrow$ _____

EXERCISE VIII.   DRILL ON THE ADDITION OF H₂O TO ALKENES

Write the structures of the products of each reaction. If no reaction occurs, write "no reaction." Note: H⁺ represents an acid catalyst.

1. $CH_2=CHCH_2CH_3$ + H_2O $\xrightarrow{H^+}$ _____

2. $CH_3CH=CHCH_3$ + H_2O $\xrightarrow{H^+}$ _____

3. $CH_2=\overset{\overset{\displaystyle CH_3}{|}}{C}CH_2CH_3$ + H_2O $\xrightarrow{H^+}$ _____

4. + H_2O $\xrightarrow{H^+}$ _____

5. CH_3CH_2— + H_2O $\xrightarrow{H^+}$ _____

SELF-TESTING QUESTIONS

Use the self-testing questions as a final examination for the chapter after you have worked the exercises in the text and those given above.

COMPLETION

1. In a molecule of ethylene, the number of atoms whose nuclei are all in the same plane equals _____.

2. The structures of the geometric isomers of 2-pentene are:

   _____   _____

3. In a cis isomer, two reference groups lie on _____ side(s) of the double bond.

4. Write the overall equation for the reaction of 1,4-dimethylbenzene with each of the following reagents, assuming that only monosubstitution occurs.

   (a) Br_2 ($FeBr_3$ or Fe catalyst)   _____

   (b) HNO_3 (in concd H_2SO_4)   _____

   (d) H_2SO_4, concd   _____

5. When hydrogen chloride adds to isobutylene, the intermediate organic cation is _____ and has the structure: (1°, 2°, or 3°)

6. The other organic cation that, at least on paper, could also form from isobutylene is _____ and has the structure:
   (1°, 2°, or 3°)

7. Arrange the following organic cations in the order of their increasing stability by **arranging the** letters that identify them in the correct order on this line:

   <   <

   _____
   least stable   most stable

   $$CH_3$$
   $$|$$
   A. $CH_3CH_2{}^+$ B. $CH_3CH_2\overset{+}{C}$ C. $CH_3CH_2\overset{+}{C}HCH_3$
   $$|$$
   $$CH_3$$

8. Complete these equations by writing the structure(s) of the product(s).

   (a)

   $$CH_3C=CHCH_3 + HCl(gas) \longrightarrow \text{_____}$$
   $$|$$
   $$CH_3$$

   (b)

   $$CH_3$$
   $$|$$
   $$CH_2=CCH_2CH_3 + H_2O \xrightarrow{H^+} \text{_____}$$

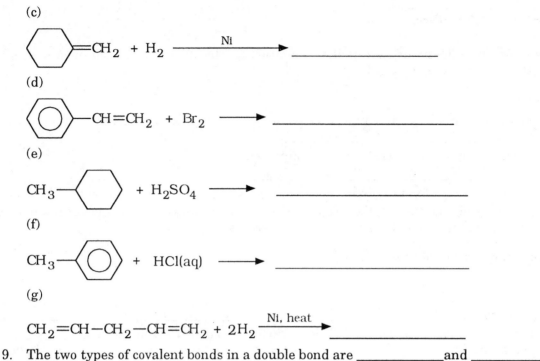

(c)

(d)

(e)

(f)

(g)

$$CH_2=CH-CH_2-CH=CH_2 + 2H_2 \xrightarrow{\text{Ni, heat}} \underline{\hspace{3cm}}$$

9.   The two types of covalent bonds in a double bond are _____and _____.

10. The pi bond results from the side-to-side overlap of two _____ orbitals on adjacent carbons.

MULTIPLE–CHOICE

1.   A family of organic compounds containing only carbon and hydrogen and having only single bonds are the
     (a) alkenes   (c) alkynes
     (b) alkanes   (d) cycloalkanes

2.   A family of organic compounds whose molecules will add water (under an acid catalysis) and change into alcohols are the
     (a) alkenes   (c) aromatic hydrocarbons
     (b) alkanes   (d) cycloalkenes

3.   A chemist, handed a sample of an organic compound, was told that it was either

$$CH_2=CHCH_2CH_3 \quad \text{or} \quad CH_3CH_2CH_2CH_3$$

Which one it was could be decided by determining if the sample would react with
     (a) sodium hydroxide
     (b) hydrogen (with nickel present and heated)
     (c) sodium chloride
     (d) water (in the presence of an acid catalyst)

4.   An aromatic hydrocarbon can be expected to undergo
     (a) substitution reactions   (c) addition reactions
     (b) reaction with water   (d) no reactions

5.   The combustion of 1-butene will produce
     (a) butylene and water   (c) an alcohol
     (b) carbon dioxide and water   (d) cyclobutane

6. An isomer of $\begin{matrix} CH_3 & CH_3 \\ \backslash & / \\ CH=CH \end{matrix}$ is

   (a) $\begin{matrix} CH_3 & CH_3 \\ | & / \\ CH_2-CH_2 \end{matrix}$

   (b) $\begin{matrix} & CH_3 \\ & / \\ CH_2-CH_2 \\ / \\ CH_3 \end{matrix}$

   (c) $\begin{matrix} & CH_3 \\ & / \\ CH=CH \\ | \\ CH_3 \end{matrix}$

   (d) $\begin{matrix} CH_3 \\ \backslash \\ CH=CH_2 \end{matrix}$

7. CH_3^+ is the
   (a) methyl radical
   (b) methyl group
   (c) methyl anion
   (d) methyl cation

8. The substance $\begin{matrix} & CH_3 \\ & | \\ CH_3-C-OH \\ & | \\ & CH_3 \end{matrix}$ could be made by addition of water to

   (a) $CH_3CH=CHCH_3$

   (b) $\begin{matrix} & & CH_3 \\ & & / \\ CH_2=C \\ & & \backslash \\ & & CH_3 \end{matrix}$

   (c) $CH_2=CHCH_2CH_3$

   (d) none of these

9. The substance $\begin{matrix} & CH_3 \\ & | \\ Cl-CH_2-CH-CH_3 \end{matrix}$ could be made by the addition of HCl to

   (a) $CH_3CH=CHCH_3$
   (b) $\begin{matrix} & & CH_3 \\ & & / \\ CH_2=C \\ & & \backslash \\ & & CH_3 \end{matrix}$
   (c) $CH_2=CHCH_2CH_3$

   (d) none of these

10. The substance $\hexagon$ is

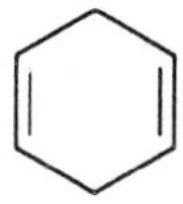

    (a) benzene
    (b) aromatic
    (c) a diene
    (d) none of these

11.   Action of aqueous alkali on CH$_3$—◯ could be
expected to produce

(a) CH$_3$—◯—OH   (b) CH$_3$—◯
                                          CH

(c) HO—CH$_2$—◯   (d) no reaction

12.   Action of aqueous hydrochloric acid on CH$_3$—◯
could be expected to produce

(a) CH$_3$—◯—Cl   (b) CH$_3$—◯ Cl
           Cl

(c) CH$_3$—◯ Cl   (d) no reaction

13.   Action of aqueous potassium permanganate on benzene could be expected to produce

(a) HO—◯   (b) HO—◯
           HO   OH

(c) HO—◯   (d) no reaction

14.   The trans isomer of 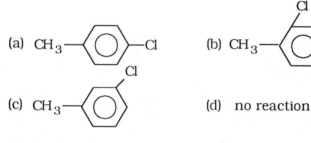 is

(a) 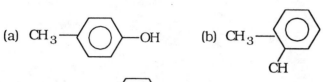   (b)

(c)   (d)

ANSWERS

ANSWERS TO DRILL EXERCISES

Exercise I

1.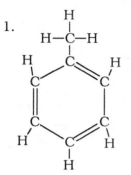

2.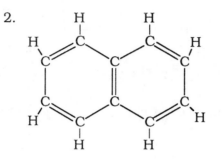

3.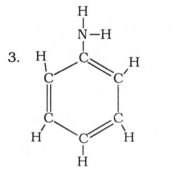

4.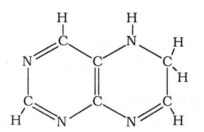

Exercise II

C_2 $CH_2=CH-Cl$ chloroethane

C_3 $Cl-CH_2-CH=CH_2$ 3-chloro-1-propene

$CH_3-\overset{\underset{\displaystyle Cl}{|}}{C}=CH_2$ 2-chloro-1-propene (in this case 2-chloropropene would be correct, too.)

$\overset{\displaystyle CH_3}{\underset{\displaystyle H}{}}\overset{\displaystyle Cl}{\underset{\displaystyle H}{}}$ C=C   cis-1-chloropropene

trans-1-chloropropene

C₄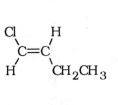

cis-1-chloro-1-butene

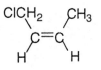

trans-1-chloro-1-butene

CH₂=CCH₂CH₃
     |
     Cl

2-chloro-1-butene

CH₂=CHCHCH₃
        |
        Cl

3-chloro-1-butene

CH₂=CHCH₂CH₂Cl

4-chloro-1-butene

cis-1-chloro-2-butene

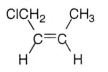

cis-2-chloro-2-butene (The CH₃ groups are cis.)

ClCH₂   CH₃
    C=C
   H   H

trans-1-chloro-2-butene

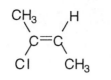

trans-2-chloro-2-butene

$$Cl-CH=C \begin{subarray}{l} CH_3 \\ \\ CH_3 \end{subarray}$$

1-chloro-2-methylpropene
(-1-propene is unnecessary.)

$$CH_2=C \begin{subarray}{l} CH_3 \\ \\ CH_2Cl \end{subarray}$$

3-chloro-2-methylpropene
(-1-propene is unnecessary.)

Exercise III

1. phenol
2. chlorobenzene
3. toluene
4. aniline
5. benzoic acid

6. *m*-chlorotoluene
7. *p*-nitroaniline
8. *m*-bromophenol
9. *o*-chlorobenzoic acid
10. *o*-dichlorobenzene

Exercise IV

1. an alkane (or more generally, a saturated site)
2. a 1,2-dichloro compound (where 1 and 2 refer to relative locations)
3. a 1,2-dibromo compound
4. an alkyl chloride
5. an alkyl bromide
6. an alkyl hydrogen sulfate
7. an alcohol
8. carbon dioxide and water

Exercise V

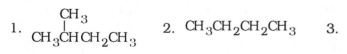

4.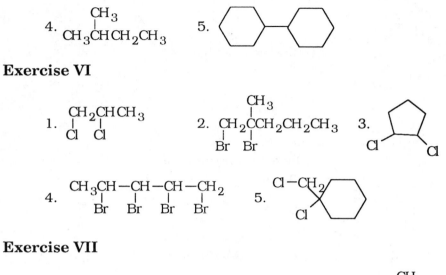
   $$\underset{\underset{CH_3}{|}}{CH_3CHCH_2CH_3}$$

5.

Exercise VI

1. $$\underset{\underset{Cl}{|}\ \underset{Cl}{|}}{CH_2CHCH_3}$$

2. $$\underset{\underset{Br}{|}\ \underset{Br}{|}}{CH_2\overset{\overset{CH_3}{|}}{C}CH_2CH_2CH_3}$$

3.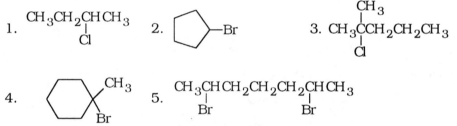

4. $$\underset{\underset{Br}{|}\ \underset{Br}{|}\ \underset{Br}{|}\ \underset{Br}{|}}{CH_3CH-CH-CH-CH_2}$$

5.

Exercise VII

1. $$\underset{\underset{Cl}{|}}{CH_3CH_2CHCH_3}$$

2. 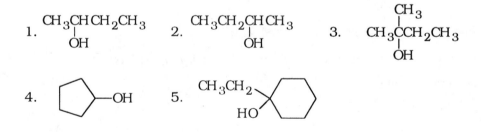—Br

3. $$\underset{\underset{Cl}{|}}{CH_3\overset{\overset{CH_3}{|}}{C}CH_2CH_2CH_3}$$

4.

5. $$\underset{\underset{Br}{|}\qquad\qquad\underset{Br}{|}}{CH_3CHCH_2CH_2CH_2CHCH_3}$$

Exercise VIII

1. $$\underset{\underset{OH}{|}}{CH_3CHCH_2CH_3}$$

2. $$\underset{\underset{OH}{|}}{CH_3CH_2CHCH_3}$$

3. $$\underset{\underset{OH}{|}}{CH_3\overset{\overset{CH_3}{|}}{C}CH_2CH_3}$$

4. 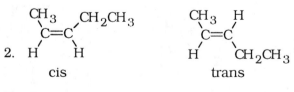—OH

5.

ANSWERS TO SELF–TESTING QUESTIONS

Completion

1. six

2.
$$\underset{\underset{cis}{}}{\overset{CH_3}{H}}C=C\overset{CH_2CH_3}{H}$$
$$\underset{\underset{trans}{}}{\overset{CH_3}{H}}C=C\overset{H}{CH_2CH_3}$$

3. the same

4. (a)

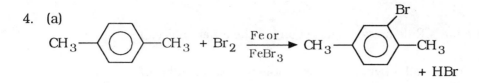

CH$_3$—〈ring〉—CH$_3$ + Br$_2$ $\xrightarrow[\text{FeBr}_3]{\text{Fe or}}$ CH$_3$—〈ring〉—CH$_3$ (with Br)

+ HBr

(b)

CH$_3$—〈ring〉—CH$_3$ + HNO$_3$ $\xrightarrow{\text{H}_2\text{SO}_4}$ CH$_3$—〈ring〉—CH$_3$ (with NO$_2$)

+ H$_2$O

(c)

CH$_3$—〈ring〉—CH$_3$ + H$_2$SO$_4$ $\xrightarrow{\text{heat}}$ CH$_3$—〈ring〉—CH$_3$ (with SO$_3$H)

+ H$_2$O

5. 3°, CH$_3$—C$^+$(CH$_3$)(CH$_3$)

6. 1°, $^+$CH$_2$—CH(CH$_3$)(CH$_3$)

7. A < C < B

8. (a) CH$_3$—CCl(CH$_3$)CH$_2$CH$_3$ (b) CH$_3$—COH(CH$_3$)CH$_2$CH$_3$ (c) 〈cyclohexane〉—CH$_3$

(d) 〈benzene ring〉—CH—CH$_2$ (with Br, Br)   (Br$_2$ needs Fe or FeBr$_3$ to attack the ring.)

(e)   no reaction (Sulfuric acid does not attack alkanes or cycloalkanes.)

(f)   no reaction (Aqueous acids do not attack the benzene ring or alkyl groups.)

(g)   CH$_3$CH$_2$CH$_2$CH$_2$CH$_3$

9. sigma, pi

10. p

Multiple–Choice

1. b and d
2. a and d
3. b and d
4. a
5. b
6. c

7. d

8. b

9. d (Markovnikov's Rule prevents use of any of the other choices.)

10. c

11. d (Benzene rings and alkyl groups are stable to aqueous alkali.)

12. d (Benzene rings and alkyl groups are stable to aqueous acids.)

13. d (Benzene is exceptionally stable toward oxidizing agents.)

14. b

14

ALCOHOLS, PHENOLS, ETHERS, AND THIOALCOHOLS

The three most important topics in this chapter relating to the molecular basis of life are:

1. Hydrogen bonds—which occur in nearly all of the biologically important molecules, such as carbohydrates, proteins, and nucleic acids.
2. Electron-transfer events (oxidations and reductions)—which occur at one or more of the stages in the breakdown of all substances used in the body's cells; and
3. Dehydrations of alcohols—which also occur several times in the reactions of metabolism.

We shall need the nomenclature of alcohols, ethers, and phenols if only to be able to talk and write about them.

OBJECTIVES

In greater detail, you should be able to do the following specific objectives after you have carefully studied this chapter and worked the Practice Exercises and Review Exercises in it.

1. Recognize the alcohol, phenol, ether, thioalcohol, and disulfide groups in structures.
2. Write the common names for alcohols (up through C_4).
3. Write the IUPAC names for alcohols.
4. Classify alcohols as 1°, 2°, or 3° and as mono-, di-, or polyhydric.
5. Write structures that illustrate how alcohol molecules form hydrogen bonds between each other or with water molecules in aqueous solutions.
6. Explain how alcohols have much higher boiling points and solubilities in water than do hydrocarbons of comparable formula mass.

7. Contrast phenols and alcohols in their acidities and in their abilities to neutralize strong bases (like OH⁻).

8. Give one reaction characteristic of phenols.

9. Given the structure of an alcohol, write the structure of the alkene or the ether that could be made from it by acid-catalyzed dehydration.

10. Given the structure of an alcohol, write the structure of the aldehyde and carboxylic acid that could be made from it (if it is a primary alcohol) or the ketone that could be made from it (if it is a secondary alcohol) by oxidation.

11. Write the structure of the disulfide that could be made by the oxidation of a thioalcohol.

12. Write the structure of the thioalcohol(s) that could be made by the reduction of a disulfide.

13. Write sentences that summarize each of the chemical reactions of alcohols, thioalcohols, disulfides, phenols, and ethers that are studied in this chapter.

14. Prepare 5 × 8" cards for each functional group studied on which are summarized the chemical properties they give.

15. Make lists of the functional groups we have so far studied that are chemically affected by (a) oxidizing agents, (b) reducing agents, (c) hot acid catalysts, (d) neutralizing agents (at room temperature) such as aqueous acids and aqueous hydroxides.

16. Define each term in the Glossary. Where appropriate, illustrate a definition with a structure or a reaction.

GLOSSARY

Alcohol. Any organic compound whose molecules have the OH group attached to a saturated carbon; R—OH.

Alcohol Group. The OH group when joined to a saturated carbon.

Dihydric Alcohol. An alcohol with two OH groups; a glycol.

Disulfide. A compound whose molecules have the sulfur-sulfur unit, S—S as in R—S—S—R.

Ether. An organic compound whose molecules have an oxygen attached by single bonds to separate carbon atoms neither of which is a carbonyl carbon atom; R—O—R'.

Glycol. A dihydric alcohol.

Mercaptan. A thioalcohol; R—S—H.

Monohydric Alcohol. An alcohol with one OH group per molecule.

Phenol. Any organic compound whose molecules have an OH group attached to a benzene ring.

Primary Alcohol. An alcohol in whose molecules an OH group is attached to a primary carbon, as in RCH_2OH.

Secondary Alcohol. An alcohol in whose molecules an OH group is attached to a secondary carbon atom; R_2CH—OH.

Tertiary Alcohol. An alcohol in whose molecules an OH group is held by a carbon from which three bonds extend to other carbon atoms; R_3C—OH.

Thioalcohol. A compound whose molecules have the SH group attached to a saturated carbon atom; a mercaptan.

Trihydric Alcohol. An alcohol with three OH groups per molecule.

KEY MOLECULAR "MAP SIGNS"

We have likened the functional groups to "map signs" that enable us to "read" the structural formulas of complicated systems. The principal map signs in this chapter are the following.

Key Molecular "Map Signs" In Organic Molecules	What to Expect When This Functional Group is Present
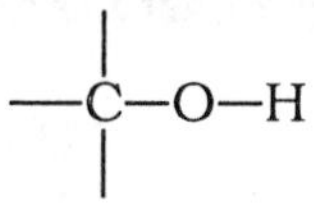 —C—O—H Alcohol group	*Influence on physical properties:* • The OH group is a good hydrogen-bond donor and hydrogen-bond acceptor. • Molecules with the OH group tend to be more polar (e.g., they have higher boiling points) and more soluble in water than are molecules with out any group that can participate in hydrogen bonding (formula masses being about the same). *Influence on chemical properties:* A molecule with the alcohol group is vulnerable to • dehydrating agents (acids + heat); either double bonds are introduced or ethers are made. • oxidizing agents (those that can pull out the pieces of the element hydrogen): 1° alcohols → aldehydes → acids 2° alcohols → ketones 3° alcohols → (no reaction) (The list for alcohols will be completed in later chapters.)
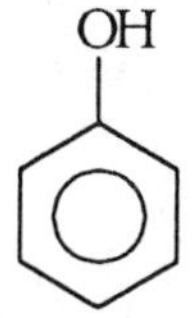 OH Phenol system	A phenolic OH group is a weak acid, but strong enough to neutralize the hydroxide ion.
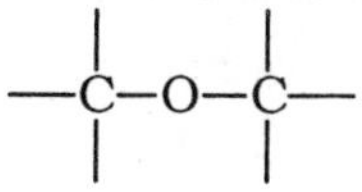 —C—O—C— Ether group (To be a simple ether, the carbons shown here must hold either Hs or Rs.)	*Influence on physical properties:* The oxygen of an ether molecule can accept hydrogen bonds; ethers therefore are slightly more soluble in water than alkanes; they are also slightly more polar. *Influence on chemical properties:* None. (As far as our study goes, the simple ether group is not attacked by water, dilute acids or bases, or oxidizing or reducing agents. We have to be able to recognize it, but then we can ignore it.)

—S—H	Easy oxidation to S—S; this property, which we need to understand in its relation to proteins, is the only property that concerns us.
Thioalcohol (sulfhydryl) group	

—S—S—	Easy reduction to 2 SH groups; this property, which we also need to understand in its relation to proteins, is the only property that concerns us.
Disulfide	

DRILL EXERCISES

I.   EXERCISES IN HYDROGEN BONDS

We define an H-bond donor as a molecule with a $\delta+$ on a hydrogen attached to oxygen or nitrogen (O—H or N—H).

An H-bond acceptor is a molecule with a $\delta-$ on an oxygen or a trisubstituted nitrogen in any functional group.

H-bond donors can establish H-bonds not only to their own kind but also to water molecules and to any other H-bond acceptors. H-bond donors are invariably H-bond acceptors.

Some molecules, such as ethers, ketones, aldehydes, and esters, can only be H-bond acceptors. They have oxygens (or nitrogens, as in examples not yet studied), but they do not have OH or NH (i.e., a hydrogen with a $\delta+$ and held by oxygen or nitrogen).

Examine these structures and answer the questions that follow.

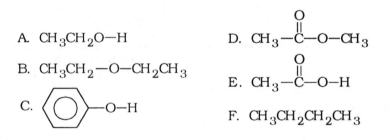

1.   Which are H-bond donors? _____
2.   Which are H-bond acceptors? _____
3.   Which are H-bond acceptors only? _____
4.   Which would be completely insoluble in water? _____
5.   Which would be more soluble in water, A or B? _____
6.   Which would be more soluble in water, C or E? _____

II.   DRILL IN WRITING THE PRODUCTS OF THE DEHYDRATION OF ALCOHOLS

After you have studied Example 14.2 in the text and have tried Practice Exercise 5 of Chapter 14, you might feel the need for further drill. Write the products of the dehydration of the following alcohols.

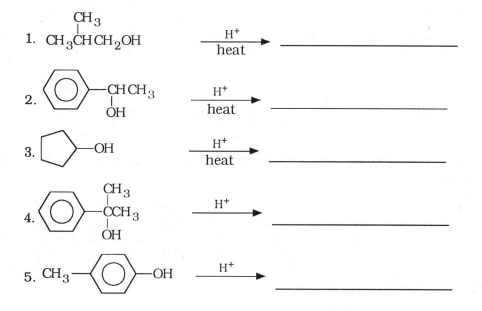

III. DRILL IN WRITING THE PRODUCTS OF THE OXIDATION OF ALCOHOLS

Examples 14.3 and 14.4 plus Practice Exercises 6, 7, and 8 of Chapter 14 are the places to begin this study. For more drill, write the products of the oxidation of the following alcohols. If oxidation in the sense being studied cannot occur, then write "no reaction." If the initial product can be oxidized further, then write the next product, too.

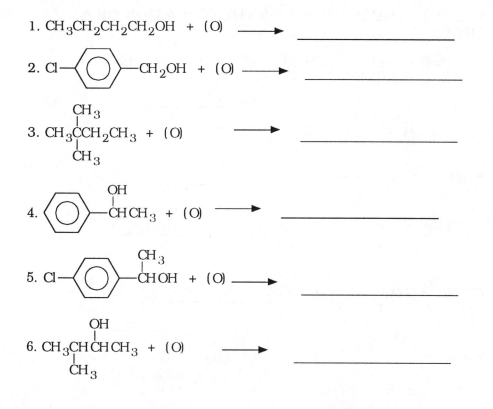

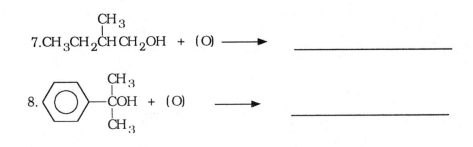

7. $CH_3CH_2\overset{\overset{\displaystyle CH_3}{|}}{C}HCH_2OH$ + (O) $\longrightarrow$ _____

8. 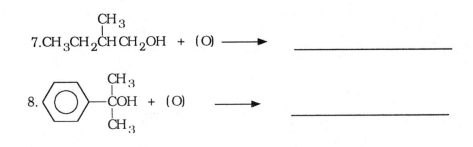 + (O) $\longrightarrow$ _____

IV. DRILL IN WRITING THE STRUCTURES OF ETHERS THAT CAN BE MADE FROM ALCOHOLS

Example 14.5 shows how this is done. In order to make this kind of exercise more helpful for applications in the next chapter, we will include in the drill examples in which you'll construct a structure of an unsymmetrical ether, like R—O—R', from two different given alcohols. We will also make this a review of the names of alcohols. If only one alcohol is named, then the question is what symmetrical ether can be made from this alcohol? If two alcohols are named, then the question is what unsymmetrical ether can be made from the two?

1. isobutyl alcohol _____

2. *t*-butyl alcohol _____

3. 4-methylcyclohexanol _____

4. isopropyl alcohol and methyl alcohol _____

5. cyclopentanol and *sec*-butyl alcohol _____

V. DRILL IN WRITING THE PRODUCT OF THE OXIDATION OF A THIOALCOHOL

Example 14.6 in the text shows how to do this kind of exercise. For practice, write the products of the oxidation of the following thioalcohols.

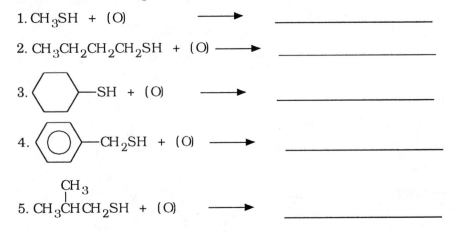

1. CH_3SH + (O) $\longrightarrow$ _____

2. $CH_3CH_2CH_2CH_2SH$ + (O) $\longrightarrow$ _____

3. ⬡—SH + (O) $\longrightarrow$ _____

4. ⬡—CH_2SH + (O) $\longrightarrow$ _____

5. $CH_3\overset{\overset{\displaystyle CH_3}{|}}{C}HCH_2SH$ + (O) $\longrightarrow$ _____

VI. DRILL IN WRITING THE PRODUCT OF THE REDUCTION OF A DISULFIDE

See page 438 in the text on how to do this. Remember that disulfides aren't always symmetrical, like R—S—S—R. Those that we'll encounter in biochemistry usually are not; they're like R—S—S—R'. The reduction of this kind gives two different thioalcohols, so both of them have to be written.

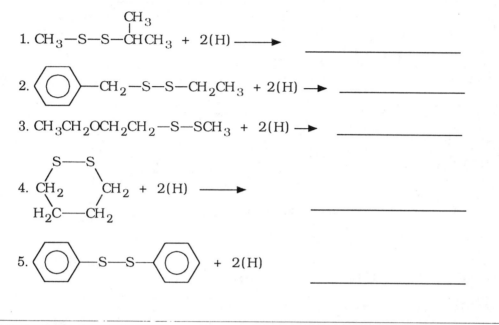

1. CH_3—S—S—$\overset{\overset{\displaystyle CH_3}{|}}{CH}CH_3$ + 2(H) ⟶ _____

2. ⬡—CH_2—S—S—CH_2CH_3 + 2(H) → _____

3. $CH_3CH_2OCH_2CH_2$—S—SCH_3 + 2(H) → _____

4. $CH_2 \overset{\displaystyle S\text{—}S}{\diagup\diagdown} CH_2$ + 2(H) ⟶ _____
   H_2C—CH_2

5. ⬡—S—S—⬡ + 2(H) _____

SELF-TESTING QUESTIONS

Treat the following questions as a final examination for the chapter. Work them only after you have done the drills with the in-chapter and end-of-chapter Review Exercises. As a review for these tests, go back to the chapter objectives, one by one, and see if you can do them.

COMPLETION

Test your knowledge of chemical properties by writing the structure(s) of the principal organic product(s) that would be expected to form in each of the following. If no reaction will occur, write "none." Reread Review Exercise 14.43 in the text, for stipulations concerning problems of this type. Notice particularly that whenever the dehydration of any given alcohol is intended to go to the corresponding ether, then the coefficient "2" will appear before the structure of that alcohol. If the "2" is absent, then the intended reaction is the internal dehydration of the alcohol to an alkene (if possible). (Normally, coefficients are not put in until after all structures of reactants and products have been written; "balancing comes last.") Where the oxidation of a 1° alcohol is indicated, show both the aldehyde and the carboxylic acid that are formed.

1. $CH_3CH_2CH_3$ $\xrightarrow[\text{heat}]{H_2SO_4}$ _____

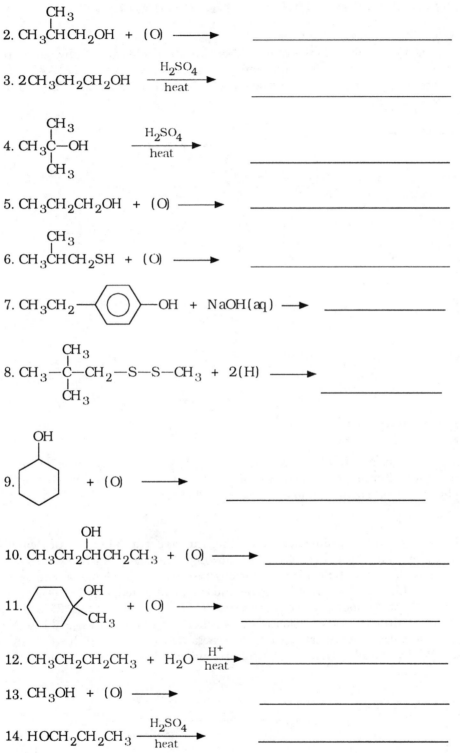

2. $\underset{\displaystyle CH_3}{CH_3CHCH_2OH}$ + (O) ⟶ _____

3. $2 CH_3CH_2CH_2OH \xrightarrow[\text{heat}]{H_2SO_4}$ _____

4. $\underset{\displaystyle CH_3}{\overset{\displaystyle CH_3}{CH_3C-OH}} \xrightarrow[\text{heat}]{H_2SO_4}$ _____

5. $CH_3CH_2CH_2OH$ + (O) ⟶ _____

6. $\underset{\displaystyle CH_3}{CH_3CHCH_2SH}$ + (O) ⟶ _____

7. CH_3CH_2-⟨◯⟩$-OH$ + NaOH(aq) ⟶ _____

8. $CH_3-\underset{\displaystyle CH_3}{\overset{\displaystyle CH_3}{C}}-CH_2-S-S-CH_3$ + 2(H) ⟶ _____

9. ⬡OH + (O) ⟶ _____

10. $\underset{\displaystyle OH}{CH_3CH_2CHCH_2CH_3}$ + (O) ⟶ _____

11. ⬡$\overset{\displaystyle OH}{\underset{\displaystyle CH_3}{}}$ + (O) ⟶ _____

12. $CH_3CH_2CH_2CH_3$ + $H_2O \xrightarrow[\text{heat}]{H^+}$ _____

13. CH_3OH + (O) ⟶ _____

14. $HOCH_2CH_2CH_3 \xrightarrow[\text{heat}]{H_2SO_4}$ _____

15. $CH_2=CHCH_2OH + H_2 \xrightarrow{\text{Ni, heat}}$ _____

16. $CH_3CH_2-O-CH_2-CH_2-\overset{\overset{\displaystyle OH}{|}}{C}HCH_3 + (O) \longrightarrow$ _____

MULTIPLE–CHOICE

1. The oxidation of $CH_3-\overset{\overset{\displaystyle OH}{|}}{C}H-CH_2-CH_3$ could be made to to produce

   (a) $CH_3-\overset{\overset{\displaystyle OH}{|}}{C}H-O-CH_2-CH_3$

   (b) $H-\overset{\overset{\displaystyle O}{||}}{C}-CH_2CH_2CH_3$

   (c) $CH_3-CH_2-\overset{\overset{\displaystyle O}{||}}{C}-CH_3$

   (d) $HO-\overset{\overset{\displaystyle O}{||}}{C}CH_2CH_2CH_3$

2. What is the best explanation for the solubility of glycerol in water?

   $HO-CH_2-\underset{\underset{\displaystyle OH}{|}}{C}H-CH_2-OH$

   Glycerol

   (a) Glycerol is a small molecule.
   (b) Glycerol molecules are polar.
   (c) Glycerol molecules can donate and accept hydrogen bonds to and from water molecules in the solution.
   (d) Glycerol's ions are well-solvated by water.

3. The substance whose structure is CH_3-OH is known as
   (a) wood alcohol
   (b) grain alcohol
   (c) methanol
   (d) potable alcohol

4. The substance whose structure is $CH_3CH_2OCH_2CH_3$ is
   (a) a common fuel
   (b) a common antifreeze
   (c) an anesthetic
   (d) an eye irritant in smog

5. The dehydration of 3-hexanol would produce
   (a) 2-hexene only
   (b) 3-hexene only
   (c) a mixture of 2-hexene and 3-hexene
   (d) cyclohexene

6. The oxidation of 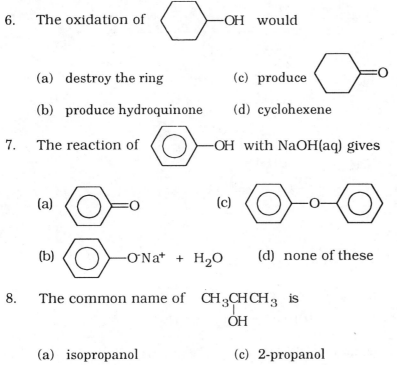 —OH would

    (a) destroy the ring

    (b) produce hydroquinone

    (c) produce

    (d) cyclohexene

7. The reaction of ⬡—OH with NaOH(aq) gives

    (a)

    (b) ⬡—O⁻Na⁺ + H_2O

    (c)

    (d) none of these

8. The common name of CH_3CHCH_3 is

                             |
                             OH

    (a) isopropanol

    (b) 2-propyl alcohol

    (c) 2-propanol

    (d) isopropyl alcohol

Multiple-choice questions 9 through 11 refer to this structure:

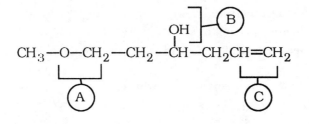

$$CH_3-O-CH_2-CH_2-CH-CH_2CH=CH_2$$

9. The group labeled (A) is

    (a) an easily hydrolyzed group

    (b) an easily oxidized group

    (c) an easily reduced group

    (d) a generally unreactive group

10. The group labeled (B) could be

    (a) oxidized to a ketone

    (b) oxidized to an aldehyde

    (c) involved in an acid-catalyzed dehydration

    (d) reduced to a ketone

11.   The group labeled ⓒ could be

(a)   made to react with dilute sodium hydroxide
(b)   made to add a water molecule (if an acid catalyst were available)
(c)   reduced to a carbon-carbon single bond by hydrogen (with a catalyst and heat)
(d)   involved in hydrogen bonding

12.   A substance that can neutralize aqueous sodium hydroxide is

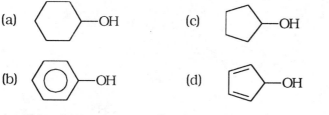

13.   A mild reducing agent will react with
(a) CH_3CH_2SH (c) CH_3—S—S—CH_3
(b) CH_3CH_2OH (d) CH_3CH_2—O—CH_2CH_3

ANSWERS

ANSWERS TO DRILL EXERCISES

I.   Exercises in Hydrogen Bonds

1.   A, C, and E

2.   A, B, C, D, and E

3.   B and D

4.   F   (an alkane)

5.   A   (It's of lower formula mass, and it can both donate and accept H—bonds to water, the solvent. B can only accept H—bonds from water.)

6.   E   (It's less hydrocarbon like, of lower-formula mass, and has two H— bond accepting sites—the two oxygens—whereas structure C has only one H—bond accepting site.)

II.   Drill in Writing the Products of the Dehydration of Alcohols

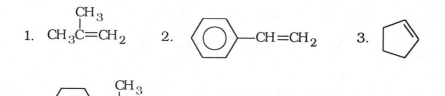

III.   Drill in Writing the Products of the Oxidation of Alcohols

1. $CH_3CH_2CH_2CHO \xrightarrow{\text{more (O)}} CH_3CH_2CH_2CO_2H$

2.

3.   no reaction

4.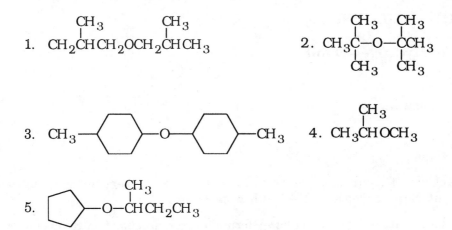

5.

6. $CH_3\underset{\underset{CH_3}{|}}{CH}\overset{\overset{O}{||}}{C}CH_3$ 7. $CH_3CH_2\underset{\underset{CH_3}{|}}{CH}CHO \xrightarrow{\text{more (O)}} CH_3CH_2\underset{\underset{CH_3}{|}}{CH}CO_2H$

8.   no reaction

IV.   Drill in Writing the Structures of Ethers That Can Be Made from Alcohols

1. $CH_2\underset{\underset{CH_3}{|}}{CH}CH_2OCH_2\underset{\underset{CH_3}{|}}{CH}CH_3$

2. $CH_3\underset{\underset{CH_3}{|}}{\overset{\overset{CH_3}{|}}{C}}-O-\underset{\underset{CH_3}{|}}{\overset{\overset{CH_3}{|}}{C}}CH_3$

3.

4. $CH_3\underset{\underset{CH_3}{|}}{CH}OCH_3$

5.

V.   Drill in Writing the Product of the Oxidation of a Thioalcohol

1. $CH_3-S-S-CH_3$

2. $CH_3CH_2CH_2CH_2-S-S-CH_2CH_2CH_2CH_3$

3.

4.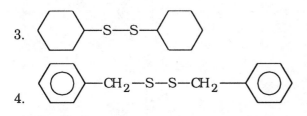

$$\text{5. } \underset{\underset{CH_3}{|}}{CH_3CHCH_2}-S-S-CH_2\underset{\underset{CH_3}{|}}{CHCH_3}$$

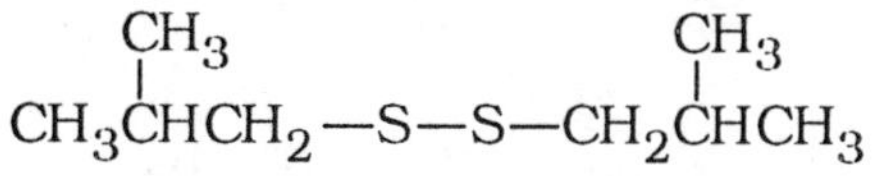

VI. Drill in Writing the Product of the Reduction of a Disulfide

1. 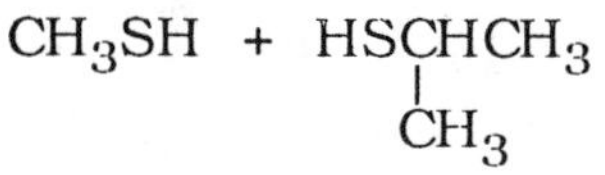 $CH_3SH + HS\underset{\underset{CH_3}{|}}{CHCH_3}$ 2. 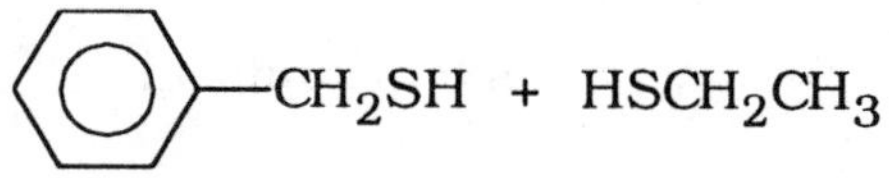   ⬡—$CH_2SH + HSCH_2CH_3$

3. $CH_3CH_2OCH_2CH_2SH + HSCH_3$ 4. $HSCH_2CH_2CH_2CH_2SH$

5. 2 ⬡—SH

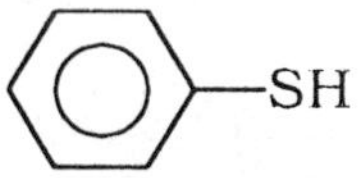

ANSWERS TO SELF-TESTING QUESTIONS

Completion

1. none   2. 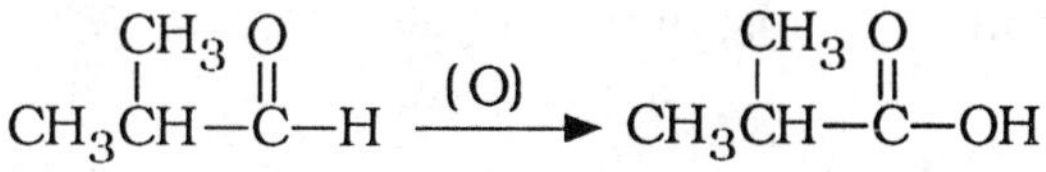 $\underset{\underset{CH_3}{|}}{CH_3CH}-\overset{\overset{O}{||}}{C}-H \xrightarrow{\text{(O)}} \underset{\underset{CH_3}{|}}{CH_3CH}-\overset{\overset{O}{||}}{C}-OH$

3. $CH_3CH_2CH_2-O-CH_2CH_2CH_3 + H_2O$ (Note the coefficient "2," our signal that the dehydration is intended to produce an ether, not an alkene.)

4. 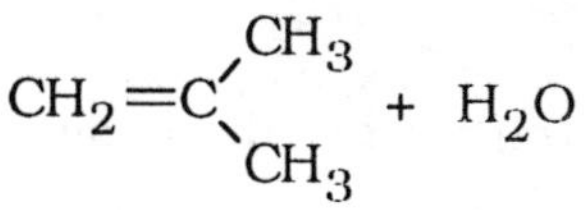 $CH_2=C\overset{\diagup CH_3}{\diagdown CH_3} + H_2O$

5. 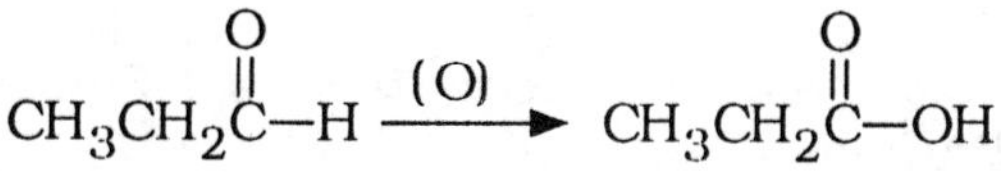 $CH_3CH_2\overset{\overset{O}{||}}{C}-H \xrightarrow{\text{(O)}} CH_3CH_2\overset{\overset{O}{||}}{C}-OH$

6. 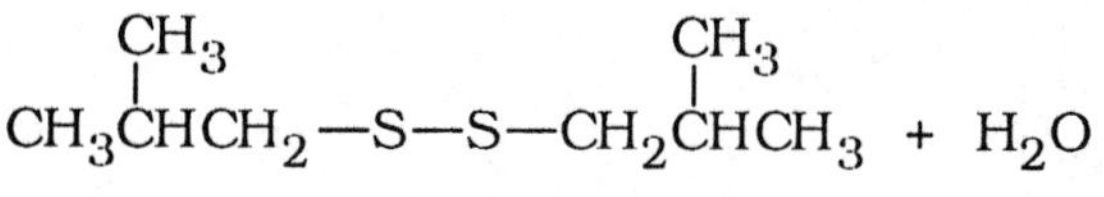 $\underset{\underset{CH_3}{|}}{CH_3CHCH_2}-S-S-CH_2\underset{\underset{CH_3}{|}}{CHCH_3} + H_2O$

7. 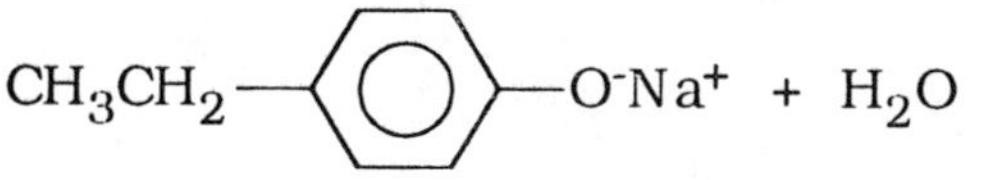 CH_3CH_2—⬡—$O^-Na^+ + H_2O$ (The electrical charges can be omitted.)

8. 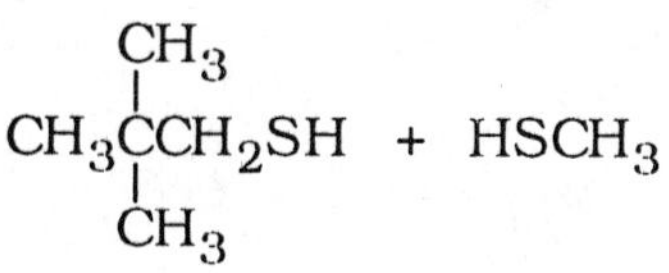 $CH_3\underset{\underset{CH_3}{|}}{\overset{\overset{CH_3}{|}}{C}}CH_2SH + HSCH_3$ 9. 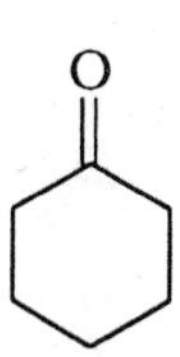 (cyclohexanone structure)   10. 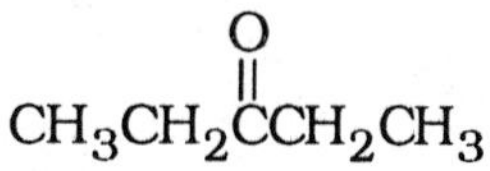 $CH_3CH_2\overset{\overset{O}{||}}{C}CH_2CH_3$

11. none (3° alcohols do not oxidize.)

12. none (Reactant is an alkane.)

13. $$H-\overset{\overset{\displaystyle O}{\|}}{C}-H \xrightarrow{\ (O)\ } H-\overset{\overset{\displaystyle O}{\|}}{C}-OH$$
(This will also continue to oxidize to

$$HO-\overset{\overset{\displaystyle O}{\|}}{C}-OH$$, which is carbonic acid.)

14. $CH_2{=}CHCH_3 \ + \ H_2O$

(Note the absence of the coefficient "2," a signal that internal dehydration to an alkene is intended.)

15. $CH_3CH_2CH_2OH$

(Only the double bond responds to hydrogenation. We studied no reaction of the alcohol group with hydrogen—and none, in fact, exists; therefore, we can assume that this group is unaffected by the hydrogen and all the conditions present for hydrogenation.)

16. $$CH_3CH_2-O-CH_2CH_2\overset{\overset{\displaystyle O}{\|}}{C}CH_3 \ + \ H_2O$$

(Only the 2° alcohol is affected by an oxidizing agent. We studied no reaction of an ether, the other functional group, with oxygen. Therefore, we can assume that it is untouched by the oxidizing agent, which is, in fact, true.)

Multiple–Choice

1. c
2. c
3. a and c
4. c
5. c (Water can split out from the carbon holding the OH group in two directions.)
6. c (The reactant is cyclohexanol, not phenol.)
7. b (The reactant is phenol.)
8. d (Choices a and b mix the common system and the IUPAC system—a definite no-no in organic chemistry. Choice c is the IUPAC name.)
9. d
10. a and c
11. b and c
12. b
13. c

15

ALDEHYDES AND KETONES

This chapter will prepare you for the study of carbohydrates as well as for those pathways of metabolism that involve aldehyde and ketone groups.

OBJECTIVES

After studying this chapter and working the exercises in it, you should be able to do the following. Pay particular attention to objectives 1, 5, and 8 through 13. They are very important to our future needs.

1. Recognize the following families in the structures of compounds: aldehydes, ketones, carboxylic acids, hemiacetals, hemiketals, acetals, and ketals.

2. Give the common and the IUPAC names and structures for aldehydes, ketones, and acids through C_4.

3. Compare the physical properties of aldehydes and ketones with those of alcohols or hydrocarbons of comparable formula masses.

4. Write specific examples of reactions for the synthesis of simple aldehydes and ketones from alcohols.

5. Write specific examples of reactions for the oxidation of aldehydes.

6. Describe what one does and sees in a positive Tollens' Test.

7. Describe what one does and sees in a positive Benedict's Test.

8. Illustrate specific reactions for the reduction of aldehydes and ketones.

9. Give specific equations for the addition of an alcohol to an aldehyde (or ketone) to form a hemiacetal (or a hemiketal).

10. Write the structures of the original alcohol and aldehyde (or ketone) from the structure of a hemiacetal (or hemiketal).

11.   Give specific examples of reactions forming acetals or ketals.
12.   Give specific examples of reactions showing the hydrolysis of acetals or ketals.
13.   Give definitions of the terms in the Glossary and provide illustrations where applicable.

Be sure to prepare and learn the one-sentence statements of chemical properties of aldehydes, ketones, hemiacetals, hemiketals, acetals, and ketals. Also, be sure to prepare the 5 × 8" reaction summary cards, and the cards that list the functional groups affected by various kinds of inorganic reactants.

GLOSSARY

Acetal. Any organic compound in which two ether linkages extend from one CH unit, as in:

$$RCH(OR')_2$$

Aldehyde. An organic compound that has a carbonyl group joined to H on one side and C on the other, R—CH=O

Aldehyde Group.   —CH=O

Benedict's Reagent. A solution of copper(II) sulfate, sodium citrate, and sodium carbonate that is used in the Benedict's test.

Benedict's Test. The use of Benedict's reagent to detect the presence of any compound whose molecules have easily oxidized functional groups—α-hydroxyaldehydes and α-hydroxyketones—such as those present in monosaccharides. In a positive test the intensely blue color of the reagent disappears and a reddish precipitate of copper(I) oxide separates.

Carbonyl Group.   C=O

Complex. (See *Complex Ion.*)

Complex Ion. A combination of a metal ion and one or more electron-rich molecules or anions.

Hemiacetal. Any compound whose molecules have both an OH group and an ether linkage coming to a —CH— unit:

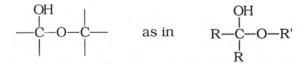

Hemiketal. Any compound whose molecules have both an OH group and an ether linkage coming to a carbon that otherwise bears no H atoms:

$$\begin{array}{c} OH \\ | \\ -C-O-C- \\ | \quad\quad | \end{array} \quad \text{as in} \quad \begin{array}{c} OH \\ | \\ R-C-O-R' \\ | \\ R \end{array}$$

Ketal. A substance whose molecules have two ether linkages joined to a carbon that also holds two hydrocarbon groups as in $R_2C(OR')_2$.

Keto Group. The carbonyl group when it is joined on each side to carbon atoms.

Ketone. Any compound with a carbonyl group attached to two carbon atoms, as in $R_2C{=}O$.

Tollens' Reagent. A slightly alkaline solution of the diammine complex of the silver ion, $Ag(NH_3)_2^+$, in water.

Tollens' Test. The use of Tollens' reagent to detect an easily oxidized group such as the aldehyde group.

KEY MOLECULAR "MAP SIGNS"

Key Molecular "Map Signs" In Organic Molecules	What to Expect When This Functional Group is Present
$\begin{array}{c} O \\ \parallel \\ -C-H \end{array}$ Aldehyde group	*Influence on physical properties:* The aldehyde group is moderately polar; it can accept H-bonds. *Influence on chemical properties:* • One of the most easily oxidized groups: Changes into a carboxyl group Gives Tollens' test • Can be reduced to a 1° alcohol group • Adds an alcohol molecule to form a hemiacetal • Can be converted into an acetal system
$\begin{array}{c} O \\ \parallel \\ R-C-R \end{array}$ Ketone	*Influence on physical properties:* Same as the aldehyde group *Influence on chemical properties:* • Strongly resists oxidation (unlike the aldehydes) • Can be reduced to a 2° alcohol group • Adds an alcohol to form a hemiketal (although not as readily as an aldehyde gives the hemiacetal) • Can be converted into a ketal system
$\begin{array}{c} OH \\ \mid \\ R-C-H \\ \mid \\ O-R' \end{array}$ Hemiacetal $\begin{array}{c} OH \\ \mid \\ R-C-R \\ \mid \\ O-R' \end{array}$ Hemiketal	*Two properties of importance:* • Both the hemiacetal and the hemiketal systems are unstable; they exist in equilibrium with the aldehyde or ketone and the alcohol (R'OH) that formed them. • Both systems can be changed to the acetal or ketal system by a reaction with another alcohol molecule.

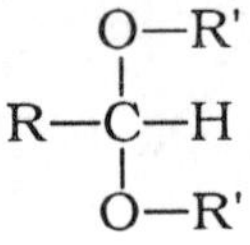

$$
\begin{array}{c}
\text{O—R'} \\
| \\
\text{R—C—H} \\
| \\
\text{O—R'}
\end{array}
$$

Acetal

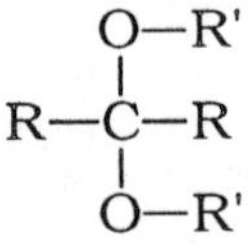

$$
\begin{array}{c}
\text{O—R'} \\
| \\
\text{R—C—R} \\
| \\
\text{O—R'}
\end{array}
$$

Ketal

One important property:
• Both the acetal and the ketal systems react with water when an acid catalyst is present, but they do not react in the presence of a basic catalyst; in so doing, they revert back to the original aldehyde

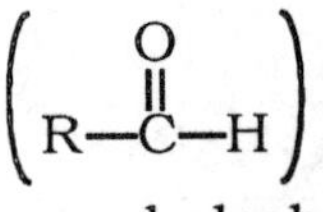

$$
\left(\begin{array}{c} \text{O} \\ \| \\ \text{R—C—H} \end{array} \right) \text{ or ketone } \left(\begin{array}{c} \text{O} \\ \| \\ \text{R—C—R} \end{array} \right)
$$

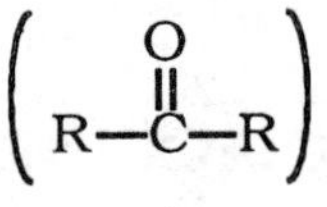

and alcohol (2R'OH)

SELF-TESTING QUESTIONS

COMPLETION

1. Write the full structure of each compound in the space above or to the side of its condensed structure.

   (a)

   $$CH_3CHO$$

   (b)

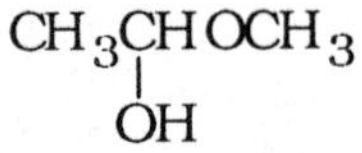

   $$\begin{array}{c} CH_3CHOCH_3 \\ | \\ OH \end{array}$$

   (c)

   $$CH_3CH_2OH$$

   (d)

   $$\begin{array}{c} CH_3CHOCH_3 \\ | \\ OCH_3 \end{array}$$

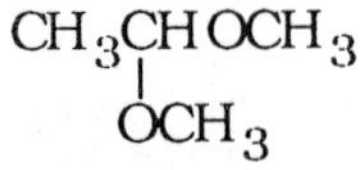

2. What functional groups have we studied that will be attacked by oxidizing agents? (Give the name of the product, too.)

   (a) In this chapter _____

   _____

   (b) In previous chapters _____

   _____

   _____

   _____

3. What functional groups have we studied that will be attacked by reducing agents? (Give the name of the product, too.)

   (a) In this chapter _____

   _____

   (b) In previous chapters _____

   _____

   _____

   _____

4. By means of short statements, summarize the chemical reactions of alcohols (from both this and earlier chapters).

Example: *Alcohols can be dehydrated to form alkenes.*

_____

_____

_____

_____

_____

_____

_____

_____

_____

5. Examine the structures shown in question 1, parts a through d. Answer the following questions by writing the condensed structures of both the reactants and the products.

(a) Which of the structures in question 1 will give a positive test with Tollens' Reagent?

_____

(b) Which can be hydrolyzed? _____

(c) Which can be oxidized under basic conditions? _____

(d) Which can be reduced? _____

6. Write the structure(s) of the principal organic product(s) that could be expected to form in each case. If no reaction occurs, write "none."

(a) $CH_3CH{=}O \xrightarrow{\text{(O)}}$ _____

(b) $CH_3CH{=}O + HOCH_3 \rightleftharpoons$ _____

(c) $CH_3\overset{\displaystyle OH}{\underset{\displaystyle OCH_3}{CH}} + HOCH_3 \xrightarrow{H^+}$ _____

(d) $CH_3\overset{\displaystyle O}{\overset{\displaystyle \|}{C}}CH_3 + H_2 \xrightarrow[\text{heat, pressure}]{\text{Ni}}$ _____

(e) $CH_3\overset{\displaystyle OCH_3}{\underset{\displaystyle |}{CH}}OCH_3 + H_2O \xrightarrow{H^+}$ _____ + _____

(f) $O=CHCH_2CH_3$ $\xrightarrow{(O)}$ _____

(g) $CH_3-S-S-CH_2CO_2H \xrightarrow[\text{agent}]{\text{mild reducing}}$ _____ + _____

(h) $HOCH_2CH_2\overset{\overset{\displaystyle O}{\|}}{C}CH_3 \xrightarrow[\text{heat}]{H_2SO_4}$ _____

7.   Write the common and the IUPAC name of each of the following.

	Common	IUPAC

(a) $CH_3CH_2\overset{\overset{\displaystyle O}{\|}}{C}H$ _____   _____

(b) $CH_3\overset{\overset{\displaystyle O}{\|}}{C}CH_3$ _____   _____

(c) $CH_3\overset{\overset{\displaystyle O}{\|}}{C}H$ _____   _____

(d) $CH_3CH_2\overset{\overset{\displaystyle O}{\|}}{C}CH_2CH_3$ _____   _____

MULTIPLE-CHOICE

1.   Which of these compounds could be hydrolyzed the most easily (assuming acid catalysis)?
(a) $CH_3CH_2OCH_2CH_3$
(b) $CH_3OCH_2OCH_3$
(c) $CH_3OCH_2CH_2OCH_3$
(d) $CH_3CH_2CH_2CH_2OH$

2.   Which of these compounds could be the most easily oxidized under mild conditions:

(a) $CH_3CH_2OCH_2CH_3$

(b) $CH_3CH_2CH_2CH_2\overset{\overset{\displaystyle O}{\|}}{C}H$

(c) $CH_3CH_2\overset{\overset{\displaystyle O}{\|}}{C}CH_2CH_3$

(d) $CH_3CH_2O\overset{\overset{\displaystyle CH_3}{|}}{C}HOCH_2CH_3$

3.   Which of these compounds would be most soluble in water:
(a) $CH_3CH_2CH_2CH_2OH$
(b) $CH_3CH_2CH_2CH_2\overset{\overset{\displaystyle O}{\|}}{C}H$
(c) $CH_3CH_2CH_2CH_2CH_3$
(d) $CH_3CH_2CH_2OCH_2CH_3$

4. The substance that precipitates in a positive Benedict's Test is
   (a) CuO   (b) Ag   (c) Cu_2O (d) Ag^+

5. The acetal that could be hydrolyzed to CH_3CH_2OH and CH_3CHO is

   (a) $CH_3CH_2\underset{\underset{\displaystyle O-CH_3}{|}}{\overset{\overset{\displaystyle OH}{|}}{C}H}$

   (c) $CH_3\underset{\underset{\displaystyle O-CH_2CH_3}{|}}{\overset{\overset{\displaystyle OH}{|}}{C}H}$

   (b) $CH_3CH_2\underset{\underset{\displaystyle OCH_2CH_3}{|}}{O}CHCH_3$

   (d) none of these

6. The alcohol that could be oxidized to $CH_3\underset{\underset{\displaystyle H}{|}}{\overset{\overset{\displaystyle CH_3}{|}}{C}}-\overset{\overset{\displaystyle O}{||}}{C}H$ is

   (a) $CH_3\underset{\underset{\displaystyle H}{|}}{\overset{\overset{\displaystyle CH_3}{|}}{C}}-\overset{\overset{\displaystyle O}{||}}{C}-OH$

   (c) $CH_3\underset{\underset{\displaystyle H}{|}}{\overset{\overset{\displaystyle CH_3}{|}}{C}}CH_2CH_2OH$

   (b) $CH_3\underset{\underset{\displaystyle H}{|}}{\overset{\overset{\displaystyle CH_3}{|}}{C}}-OH$

   (d) $CH_3\underset{\underset{\displaystyle CH_3}{|}}{\overset{\overset{\displaystyle H}{|}}{C}}-CH_2OH$

7. Isopropyl alcohol could be made by the catalytic reduction of
   (a) acetone   (c) methyl ethyl ketone
   (b) propionaldehyde   (d) acetaldehyde

8. The oxidation of $CH_3CH_2CH_2\overset{\overset{\displaystyle O}{||}}{C}H$ would give

   (a) isobutyraldehyde   (c) butyraldehyde
   (b) butyric acid   (d) 1-butanol

9. Which choice contains the best description of the functional group(s) present in this structure?

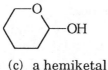

   (a) a hemiacetal   (c) a hemiketal
   (b) an acetal   (d) a ketal

10. If a hydride donor were used, which of the following systems would be able to accept it?
    (a) $CH_3CH_2CH_2CH_3$ (c) $CH_3OCH_2CH_3$

    (b) $CH_3CH_2CH_2OH$ (d) $CH_3CH_2CH_2\overset{\overset{\displaystyle O}{||}}{C}H$

ANSWERS

ANSWERS TO SELF-TESTING QUESTIONS

Completion

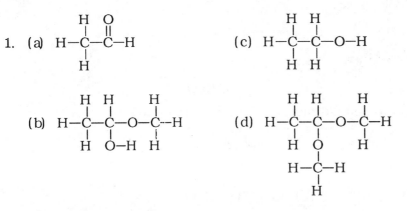

2. (a) Aldehydes are oxidized to carboxylic acids.
   (b) Alkenes are oxidized to various products (which we did not study in any detail).
   1° alcohols are oxidized to aldehydes or to carboxylic acids.
   2° alcohols are oxidized to ketones.
   Mercaptans are oxidized to disulfides.

3. (a) Aldehydes are hydrogenated to 1° alcohols.
   Ketones are hydrogenated to 2° alcohols.
   (b) Alkenes are hydrogenated to alkanes.
   Alkynes are hydrogenated to alkenes and thence to alkanes.
   Disulfides are reduced to mercaptans.

4. Alcohols can be dehydrated to form ethers.
   1° Alcohols can be oxidized to aldehydes, and then to carboxylic acids.
   2° Alcohols can be oxidized to ketones.
   Alcohols will add to aldehydes or ketones to form hemiacetals or hemiketals (both of which are generally too unstable to be isolated).
   Alcohols will react with hemiacetals or hemiketals to form acetals or ketals.

5. (a) $CH_3CHO \longrightarrow CH_3\overset{\displaystyle O}{\overset{\displaystyle \|}{C}}-OH$

   The hemiacetal, b, will also give a positive test because, in solution, it exists in equilibrium with acetaldehyde and methyl alcohol; acetaldehyde will react with Tollens' Reagent.

   (b) "To be hydrolyzed" means to undergo a chemical reaction with water. Only the acetal, d, reacts with water:

   $$CH_3\underset{\displaystyle \underset{\displaystyle OCH_3}{|}}{CH}OCH_3 \;+\; H_2O \;\xrightarrow{\;H^+\;}\; CH_3CHO \;+\; 2CH_3OH$$

(c) The aldehyde, a, the hemiacetal, b, and the alcohol, c, can be oxidized under basic conditions. The alcohol will give acetaldehyde or acetic acid, depending on other conditions. The oxidation of a and b was discussed in the answer to part a of this question. The acetal is stable in a base and will not hydrolyze; therefore, it cannot break down into oxidizable compounds.

(d) The aldehyde, a, can be reduced to CH_3CH_2OH. The hemiacetal, b, will also react because it is present in equilibrium with its parent aldehyde (CH_3CHO) and alcohol (CH_3OH). As with a, the aldehyde will be taken out by the reducing agent and changed to ethyl alcohol.

6. (a) CH_3CO_2H (b) $CH_3\overset{\underset{|}{OH}}{CH}OCH_3$ (c) $CH_3\overset{\overset{OCH_3}{\diagup}}{\underset{\underset{OCH_3}{\diagdown}}{CH}}$ (+ H_2O)

(d) $CH_3\overset{\underset{|}{OH}}{CH}CH_3$ (e) $CH_3CH{=}O + 2CH_3OH$ (f) $CH_3CH_2CO_2H$

(g) $CH_3SH + HSCH_2CO_2H$ (h) $CH_2{=}CH\overset{\overset{O}{||}}{C}CH_3$

7.   *Common*   *IUPAC*
  (a) propionaldehyde   propanal
  (b) acetone   propanone (2-propanone is all right, but the number 2 is unnecessary here.)
  (c) acetaldehyde   ethanal
  (d) diethyl ketone   3-pentanone

Multiple–Choice

1. b (an acetal)

   (a is an ether; c is a di-ether and not an acetal; and d is an alcohol)

2. b (an aldehyde)

   (a is an ether; c is a ketone; and d is an acetal. The oxidizing reagent is neutral or basic, as in Tollens' Test or Benedict's Test; therefore, the acetal will hold together. However, if the reagent is acidic, the acetal will hydrolyze to produce some acetaldehyde (and ethyl alcohol) and the aldehyde will be oxidized.)

3. a (an alcohol)

   (It is the only one that can both accept and donate hydrogen bonds.)

4. c
5. b
6. d
7. a
8. b
9. a
10. d

16
CARBOXYLIC ACIDS
AND ESTERS

The study of this chapter prepares you to study both lipids (e.g., fats and oils) and proteins as well as the metabolic pathways that involve the carboxyl group, its anionic form, and the ester group. Also introduced here are organophosphates, and their esters and anhydride system, which are systems of great importance at the molecular level of life.

OBJECTIVES

After you have studied this chapter and worked the Practice Exercises and Review Exercises in it, you should be able to do the following. Objectives 1 through 5 are very important for understanding the applications of this chapter in biochemistry and in our study of the molecular basis of life.

1. Recognize as structural "map signs" the carboxylic acid group, the carboxylate ion group, the ester group and ester bond, the acid chloride group, and the anhydride group.
2. By examining a structure of a substance, determine the probable ability of the substance to neutralize either a base or an acid or to be hydrolyzed, saponified, or esterified.
3. Write equations that are specific examples of the formation of:
   (a) an acid from an alcohol or an aldehyde
   (b) a carboxylic acid salt from the acid
   (c) a carboxylic acid from its salt
   (d) an ester from an alcohol and
      (1) a carboxylic acid
      (2) a carboxylic acid chloride
      (3) a carboxylic acid anhydride

    (e) an alcohol and an acid from an ester

    (f) an alcohol and the salt of a carboxylic acid from an ester

4.   Give a general explanation for the relative acidity of an acid over that of an alcohol.

5.   Explain through equations and discussion how the carboxyl group may be used as a "solubility switch."

6.   Write the structural features common to phosphate, diphosphate, and triphosphate esters.

7.   Define the terms in the Glossary, and give illustrations where applicable.

   Reaction summary cards should be made for acids, their salts, acid chlorides, acid anhydrides, and esters. The partly completed card for alcohols can now be completed. A list of sentences that summarize chemical facts should be prepared and learned. The lists of reactions organized by key reagents (e.g., acids, bases, water and so forth) should be brought up to date.

GLOSSARY

Acid Anhydride. In organic chemistry, a compound formed by splitting water out between two OH groups of the acid function of an organic acid. The structural features are:

               Carboxylic acid   Phosphoric acid

               anhydride system   anhydride system

Acid Chloride. A derivative of an acid in which the OH group of the acid has been replaced by Cl.

$$\overset{\displaystyle O}{\overset{\|}{R-C-Cl}}$$

Acid Derivative. Any organic compound that can be made from an organic acid or that can be changed back to the acid by hydrolysis. (Examples are acid chlorides, acid anhydrides, esters, and amides.)

Acyl Group. $R-\overset{\displaystyle O}{\overset{\|}{C}}-$

Acyl Group Transfer Reaction. Any reaction in which an acyl group transfers from a donor to an acceptor.

Amide. Any organic compound whose molecules have a carbonyl-nitrogen unit,

$$-\overset{\displaystyle O}{\overset{\|}{C}}-\overset{\displaystyle |}{N}-$$

Carboxylic Acid. A compound whose molecules have the carboxyl group, CO_2H.

Ester. A derivative of an acid and an alcohol that can be hydrolyzed to these parent compounds. Esters of carboxylic acids and phosphoric acid occur in living systems.

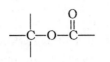

System in an ester of
a carboxylic acid   System in an ester of
phosphoric acid

Esterification. The formation of an ester.

Fatty Acid. Any carboxylic acid that can be obtained by the hydrolysis of animal fats or vegetable
oils.

Saponification. The reaction of an ester with sodium or potassium hydroxide to give an alcohol and
the salt of an acid.

KEY MOLECULAR "MAP SIGNS"

Key Molecular "Map Signs" In Organic Molecules	What to Expect When This Functional Group is Present
O ‖ —C—O—H Carboxyl group [Often written as CO_2H or COOH]	*Influence on physical properties:* The carboxyl group is a very polar group; it can both donate and accept H-bonds *Influence on chemical properties:* • Can neutralize OH^- (or HCO_3^- or CO_3^{2-}); in so doing, CO_2H becomes CO_2^- • Can be changed into an ester by reacting with an alcohol when an acid catalyst is present.
O ‖ —C—O⁻ Carboxylate ion	*Influence on physical properties:* • One of the most effective groups at bringing long hydrocarbon chains into solution. • All salts of the carboxylic acids are solids at room temperature. *Influence on chemical properties:* • Aqueous solutions will test slightly basic. • Can neutralize H^+
O ‖ —C—O—C— Ester	*Influence on physical properties:* The ester group is a moderately polar group; it can accept H-bonds but cannot donate them. *Influence on chemical properties:* • Can be hydrolyzed (to the carboxylic acid and alcohol). • Can be saponified (to the carboxylate ion and alcohol).

$$\overset{\overset{\displaystyle O}{\|}}{-C}-Cl$$

Acid chloride

$$-\overset{\overset{\displaystyle O}{\|}}{C}-O-\overset{\overset{\displaystyle O}{\|}}{C}-$$

Acid anhydride

Properties of importance:
Acid chlorides and acid anhydrides are
• easily hydrolyzed (to the carboxylic acid).
• easily react with alcohols to give esters.

$$R-O-\overset{\overset{\displaystyle O}{\|}}{\underset{\underset{\displaystyle OH}{|}}{P}}-O-\overset{\overset{\displaystyle O}{\|}}{\underset{\underset{\displaystyle \uparrow OH}{|}}{P}}-O-H$$

$$R-O-\overset{\overset{\displaystyle O}{\|}}{\underset{\underset{\displaystyle OH}{|}}{P}}-O-\overset{\overset{\displaystyle O}{\|}}{\underset{\underset{\displaystyle \uparrow OH}{|}}{P}}-O-\overset{\overset{\displaystyle O}{\|}}{\underset{\underset{\displaystyle \uparrow OH}{|}}{P}}-O-H$$

Di- and triphosphate esters

Influence on physical properties: Both esters exist at the pH of body fluids as negatively charged ions; therefore they are very soluble in water.

Influence on chemical properties:
• Can neutralize OH⁻ (to the extent they begin with OH groups on phosphorus and have not been neutralized).
• In absence of a catalyst, they only react very slowly with water at the pH of body fluids.
• In the presence of the appropriate enzymes, they react rapidly with the alcohol (and amino) groups of biochemicals and suffer breakage of the bonds indicated by the arrows (↑).

Additional Reactions of Functional Groups Introduced in Earlier Chapters

$$-\overset{\overset{\displaystyle |}{}}{\underset{\underset{\displaystyle |}{}}{C}}-O-H$$

Alcohol (or phenol)

• Forms esters with carboxylic acids, either by reacting with the carboxylic acid (when a mineral acid catalyst is present) or by reacting with an acid chloride or acid anhydride.

DRILL EXERCISES

I.   EXERCISES IN STRUCTURES AND NAMES

1. To make sure that you understand the condensed structures that are often used with carbonyl compounds, write out the following condensed structures as full structures.
   (a) CH_3CO_2H
   (b) $HO_2CCH_2CH_3$
   (c) CH_3CHO
   (d) CH_3CH_2OH
   (e) $CH_3CO_2CH_3$
   (f) CH_3CONH_2
   (g) $HOOCCH_3$

2. It is important to be able to recognize quickly the presence of functional groups in structures;

otherwise, the chemical and physical properties of such structures cannot be "read" (in the sense of "reading" a map with knowledge of "map signs"). Study each of the following structures and assign them to their correct families. Some will have more than one functional group; name them all.

Examples:

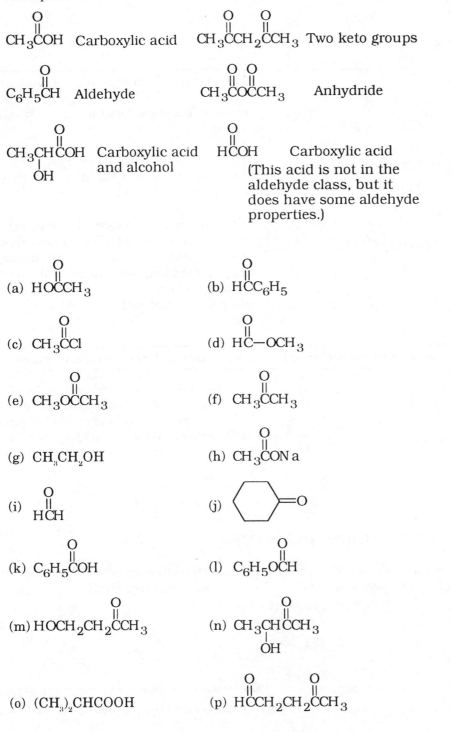

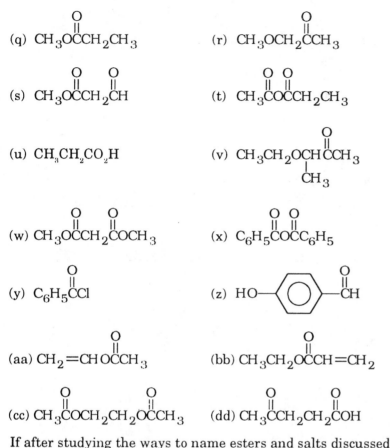

(q) $CH_3O\overset{O}{\overset{||}{C}}CH_2CH_3$

(r) $CH_3OCH_2\overset{O}{\overset{||}{C}}CH_3$

(s) $CH_3O\overset{O}{\overset{||}{C}}CH_2\overset{O}{\overset{||}{C}}H$

(t) $CH_3\overset{O}{\overset{||}{C}}O\overset{O}{\overset{||}{C}}CH_2CH_3$

(u) $CH_3CH_2CO_2H$

(v) $CH_3CH_2OCH\overset{O}{\overset{||}{C}}CH_3$ with CH_3 branch

(w) $CH_3O\overset{O}{\overset{||}{C}}CH_2\overset{O}{\overset{||}{C}}OCH_3$

(x) $C_6H_5\overset{O}{\overset{||}{C}}O\overset{O}{\overset{||}{C}}C_6H_5$

(y) $C_6H_5\overset{O}{\overset{||}{C}}Cl$

(z) $HO-\langle ring \rangle-\overset{O}{\overset{||}{C}}H$

(aa) $CH_2{=}CHO\overset{O}{\overset{||}{C}}CH_3$

(bb) $CH_3CH_2O\overset{O}{\overset{||}{C}}CH{=}CH_2$

(cc) $CH_3\overset{O}{\overset{||}{C}}OCH_2CH_2O\overset{O}{\overset{||}{C}}CH_3$

(dd) $CH_3\overset{O}{\overset{||}{C}}CH_2CH_2\overset{O}{\overset{||}{C}}OH$

3. If after studying the ways to name esters and salts discussed in the text, you continue to have trouble, try the following. Prefixes in the common names for esters and acid salts (and aldehydes) relate to the acid portion of the structure. You may need some drill simply in recognizing what the acid portion is. It is that part of the structure that contains the carbonyl group plus whatever else consists solely of carbon and hydrogen. In other words, the acid portion is the part of the structure of the acid derivative that came from the parent acid.

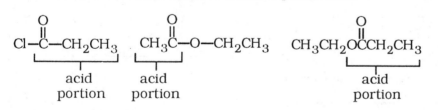

For the following structures, circle the acid portion in each structure and then write the prefix associated with its common name.

Examples:

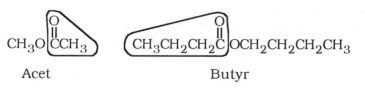

Acet   Butyr

Note that the oxygen that has only single bonds and the R-group attached to it are not included.

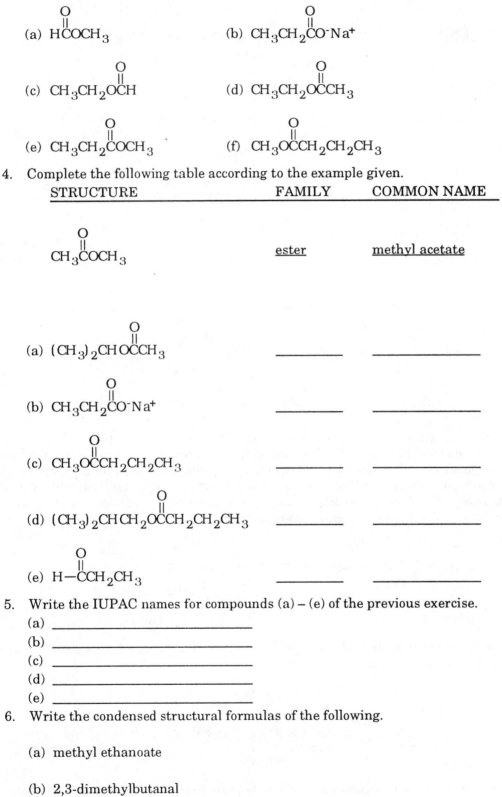

(a) $H\overset{O}{\overset{\|}{C}}OCH_3$

(b) $CH_3CH_2\overset{O}{\overset{\|}{C}}O^-Na^+$

(c) $CH_3CH_2O\overset{O}{\overset{\|}{C}}H$

(d) $CH_3CH_2O\overset{O}{\overset{\|}{C}}CH_3$

(e) $CH_3CH_2\overset{O}{\overset{\|}{C}}OCH_3$

(f) $CH_3O\overset{O}{\overset{\|}{C}}CH_2CH_2CH_3$

4. Complete the following table according to the example given.

STRUCTURE	FAMILY	COMMON NAME
$CH_3\overset{O}{\overset{\|}{C}}OCH_3$	ester	methyl acetate
(a) $(CH_3)_2CHO\overset{O}{\overset{\|}{C}}CH_3$	————	————————
(b) $CH_3CH_2\overset{O}{\overset{\|}{C}}O^-Na^+$	————	————————
(c) $CH_3O\overset{O}{\overset{\|}{C}}CH_2CH_2CH_3$	————	————————
(d) $(CH_3)_2CHCH_2O\overset{O}{\overset{\|}{C}}CH_2CH_2CH_3$	————	————————
(e) $H-\overset{O}{\overset{\|}{C}}CH_2CH_3$	————	————————

5. Write the IUPAC names for compounds (a) – (e) of the previous exercise.

    (a) ————————————————————
    (b) ————————————————————
    (c) ————————————————————
    (d) ————————————————————
    (e) ————————————————————

6. Write the condensed structural formulas of the following.

    (a) methyl ethanoate

    (b) 2,3-dimethylbutanal

(c) propanoic anhydride

(d) *sec*-butyl ethanoate

(e) 2-methylbutanoyl chloride

(f) sodium 3-chloropropanoate

II. DRILL ON THE REACTIONS OF CARBOXYLIC ACIDS WITH STRONG BASES

Write the structures of the salts that form in the following situations. Assume in every case that the aqueous base is being used at room temperature. You may write the structures showing the electrical charges (e.g., $CH_3CO_2^- Na^+$) or not (e.g., CH_3CO_2Na), but you should never draw a line between the two parts of the salts (e.g., CH_3CO_2—Na) because a line means a *covalent* bond, which is not present here.

1. $CH_3CH_2CH_2CO_2H + KOH(aq) \rightarrow$ _____

2. $CH_3(CH_2)_6CO_2H + NaOH(aq) \rightarrow$ _____

3. CH_3—O—$CH_2CO_2H + NaOH(aq) \rightarrow$ _____

4. $HOCH_2CH_2CO_2H + KOH(aq) \rightarrow$ _____

5. $HO_2CCH_2CH_2CO_2H + 2NaOH(aq) \rightarrow$ _____

III. DRILL ON THE REACTIONS OF CARBOXYLIC ACID SALTS WITH STRONG ACIDS

Write the structures of the acids that form in the following situations. Assume in every case that the aqueous acid is being used at room temperature.

1. $HCO_2^- Na^+ + HCl(aq) \rightarrow$ _____

2. $K^+ O_2CCH_2CH_2CH_3 + HCl(aq) \rightarrow$ _____

3. $CH_3(CH_2)_nCO_2^- Na^+ + HCl(aq) \rightarrow$ _____

4. 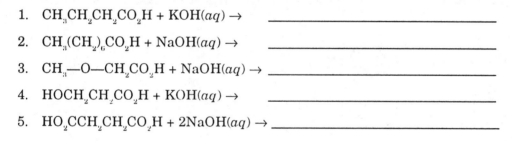 CH_3———$CO_2^- K^+$ + $HCl(aq) \rightarrow$ _____

5. $CH_3CH_2OCH_2CH_2CO_2^- Na^+ + HCl(aq) \rightarrow$ _____

IV. DRILL ON WRITING THE STRUCTURES OF ESTERS THAT CAN FORM FROM GIVEN ACIDS AND ALCOHOLS

Example 16.2 in the text provides the pattern. If after doing Review Exercises 6 and 7 you feel the need for more practice, try the following. Write the structures of the esters that can form between the following pairs of compounds. This will also serve as a review of the names of acids and alcohols. On the lines above the names write the structures of the reactants, and then form the structures of the products.

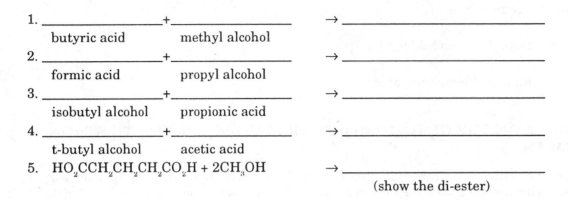

1. _____+_____ → _____
   butyric acid   methyl alcohol

2. _____+_____ → _____
   formic acid   propyl alcohol

3. _____+_____ → _____
   isobutyl alcohol   propionic acid

4. _____+_____ → _____
   t-butyl alcohol   acetic acid

5. $HO_2CCH_2CH_2CH_2CO_2H + 2CH_3OH$ → _____

(show the di-ester)

V. DRILL ON WRITING THE PRODUCTS OF THE HYDROLYSIS OF ESTERS

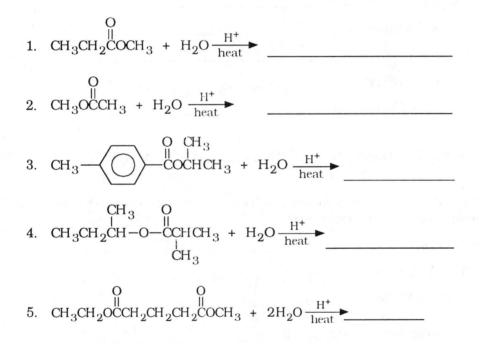

1. $CH_3CH_2\overset{\overset{\displaystyle O}{||}}{C}OCH_3$ + H_2O $\xrightarrow[\text{heat}]{H^+}$ _____

2. $CH_3O\overset{\overset{\displaystyle O}{||}}{C}CH_3$ + H_2O $\xrightarrow[\text{heat}]{H^+}$ _____

3. $CH_3-\!\!\langle\!\bigcirc\!\rangle\!\!-\overset{\overset{\displaystyle O}{||}}{C}O\overset{\overset{\displaystyle CH_3}{|}}{C}HCH_3$ + H_2O $\xrightarrow[\text{heat}]{H^+}$ _____

4. $CH_3CH_2\overset{\overset{\displaystyle CH_3}{|}}{C}H-O-\overset{\overset{\displaystyle O}{||}}{C}\underset{\underset{\displaystyle CH_3}{|}}{C}HCH_3$ + H_2O $\xrightarrow[\text{heat}]{H^+}$ _____

5. $CH_3CH_2O\overset{\overset{\displaystyle O}{||}}{C}CH_2CH_2CH_2\overset{\overset{\displaystyle O}{||}}{C}OCH_3$ + $2H_2O$ $\xrightarrow[\text{heat}]{H^+}$ _____

VI. DRILL IN WRITING THE PRODUCTS OF THE SAPONIFICATION OF ESTERS

Example 16.5 in the text describes how to do this kind of exercise. For additional drill, write the structures of the products of the complete saponification of the esters of the preceding drill exercise. Use NaOH(aq) as the saponifying agent.

1. _____

2. _____

3. _____

4. _____

5. _____

SELF-TESTING QUESTIONS

Use the following questions as your own final examination for the chapter. As a review, go back to the chapter objectives and find out if you can do them.

COMPLETION

1. Write the structure(s) of the organic product(s) that would form in each reaction. If no reaction occurs, write "none." Some of the reactions will involve a review of earlier chapters.

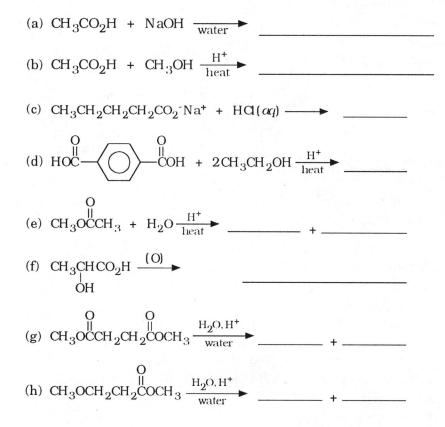

(a) CH_3CO_2H + $NaOH$ $\xrightarrow{\text{water}}$ _____

(b) CH_3CO_2H + CH_3OH $\xrightarrow[\text{heat}]{\text{H}^+}$ _____

(c) $CH_3CH_2CH_2CH_2CO_2^-Na^+$ + $HCl(aq)$ $\longrightarrow$ _____

(d) $HOC\!\!\overset{\displaystyle O}{\|}\!\!-\!\!\bigcirc\!\!-\!\!\overset{\displaystyle O}{\|}\!\!COH$ + $2CH_3CH_2OH$ $\xrightarrow[\text{heat}]{\text{H}^+}$ _____

(e) $CH_3O\overset{\displaystyle O}{\underset{\|}{C}}CH_3$ + H_2O $\xrightarrow[\text{heat}]{\text{H}^+}$ _____ + _____

(f) $CH_3\underset{\underset{\displaystyle OH}{|}}{CH}CO_2H$ $\xrightarrow{(O)}$ _____

(g) $CH_3O\overset{\displaystyle O}{\underset{\|}{C}}CH_2CH_2\overset{\displaystyle O}{\underset{\|}{C}}OCH_3$ $\xrightarrow[\text{water}]{H_2O,\,H^+}$ _____ + _____

(h) $CH_3OCH_2CH_2\overset{\displaystyle O}{\underset{\|}{C}}OCH_3$ $\xrightarrow[\text{water}]{H_2O,\,H^+}$ _____ + _____

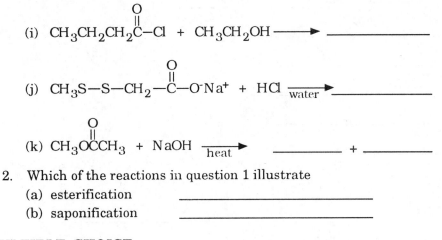

(i) $CH_3CH_2CH_2\overset{\overset{\displaystyle O}{\|}}{C}-Cl$ + CH_3CH_2OH ⟶ _____

(j) $CH_3S-S-CH_2-\overset{\overset{\displaystyle O}{\|}}{C}-O^-Na^+$ + HCl $\xrightarrow[\text{water}]{}$ _____

(k) $CH_3\overset{\overset{\displaystyle O}{\|}}{O}CCH_3$ + $NaOH$ $\xrightarrow[\text{heat}]{}$ _____ + _____

2. Which of the reactions in question 1 illustrate
    (a) esterification   _____
    (b) saponification   _____

MULTIPLE–CHOICE

1. The compound whose structure is

    $CH_3-O-CH_2-\overset{\overset{\displaystyle O}{\|}}{C}-O-CH_3$ has which functional group(s)?

    (a) two ether groups
    (b) an ether and an ester group
    (c) two ester groups
    (d) two ether and one ketone group

2. The structure of sodium butyrate is

    (a) $Na^+{}^-O\overset{\overset{\displaystyle O}{\|}}{C}OCH_2CH_2CH_3$ (c) $CH_3CH_2CH_2-\overset{\overset{\displaystyle O}{\|}}{C}-O-Na$

    (b) $Na^+{}^-\overset{\overset{\displaystyle O}{\|}}{C}-O-CH_2CH_2CH_2CH_3$ (d) $CH_3CH_2CH_2\overset{\overset{\displaystyle O}{\|}}{C}O_2^-Na^+$

3. The name of $CH_3\overset{\overset{\displaystyle CH_3}{|}}{C}HCO_2CH_2\overset{\overset{\displaystyle CH_3}{|}}{C}HCH_3$ is

    (a) isopropyl isobutyrate
    (b) isobutyl 2-methylpropanoate
    (c) isobutyl butyrate
    (d) isopropyl 3-methylbutanoate

4. The acid derivative that is most reactive toward water is
    (a) the ester   (c) the acid chloride
    (b) the acid salt   (d) both (b) and (c)

5. The action of aqueous hydrochloric acid on $CH_3CH_2CH_2CH_2CO_2^-K^+$ gives
    (a) $HO_2CCH_2CH_2CH_2CH_3$ + KCl
    (b) $CH_3CH_2CH_2CH_3$ + CO_2 + KCl

(c) $CH_3CH_2CH_2CH_2COCl + KOH$

(d) none of these

6. The action of aqueous potassium hydroxide at room temperature on CH_3CH_2—O—$CH_2CH_2CO_2H$ gives

(a) $CH_3CH_2H + HOCH_2CH_2CO_2^-K^+$

(b) $CH_3CH_2OCH_2CH_2CO_2^-K^+$

(c) $K^+OCH_2CH_2OCH_2CH_2CO_2H + H_2O$

(d) no reaction

7. In the following structure, the numbered arrows point toward functional groups. What are the numbers of the arrows pointing toward groups readily attacked by relatively mild oxidizing agents?

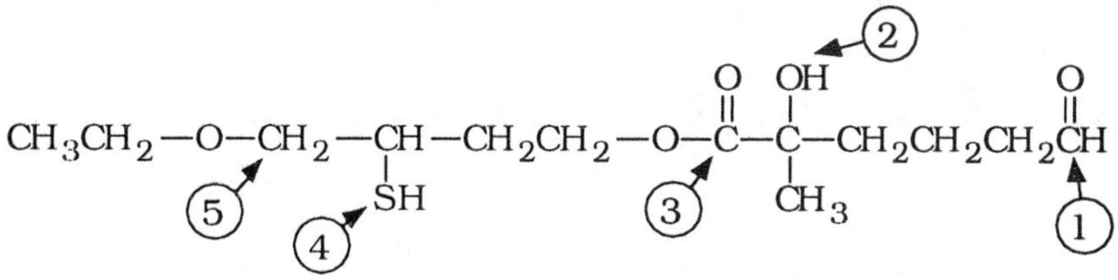

(a) 1   (b) 2   (c) 3   (d) 4   (e) 5

8. In the structure of question 7, which groups, if any, are subject to acid-catalyzed hydrolysis?

(a) 1   (b) 2   (c) 3   (d) 4   (e) 5   (f) none

9. In the structure of question 7, which groups, if any, will neutralize aqueous sodium hydroxide at room temperature?

(a) 1   (b) 2   (c) 3   (d) 5   (e) none of these

10. The action of one mole of water (containing a trace of acid catalyst) on one mole of compound Y produces one mole of CH_3CO_2H and one mole of CH_3CH_2OH. The structure of Y is

(a) $CH_3CH_2OCH_2CH_3$

(c) CH_3CH—O—CH_2CH_3
              |
             OH

(b) $CH_3CH_2O\overset{\overset{\displaystyle O}{\|}}{C}CH_3$

(d) $CH_3\overset{\overset{\displaystyle O}{\|}}{C}$—O—$\overset{\overset{\displaystyle O}{\|}}{C}CH_2CH_3$

11. The esterification of propionic acid by ethyl alcohol gives

(a) $CH_3CH_2CH_2O\overset{\overset{\displaystyle O}{\|}}{C}CH_3$

(c) $CH_3CH_2\overset{\overset{\displaystyle O}{\|}}{C}CH_2CH_3$

(b) $CH_3CH_2\overset{\overset{\displaystyle O}{\|}}{C}OCH_2CH_3$

(d) $CH_3CH_2\overset{\overset{\displaystyle OH}{|}}{C}OCH_2CH_3$
                          |
                          H

12. The saponification of $CH_3CH_2CH_2O$—$CH_2CH_2\overset{\overset{\displaystyle O}{\|}}{C}$—O—$CH_3$ by sodium hydroxide would produce

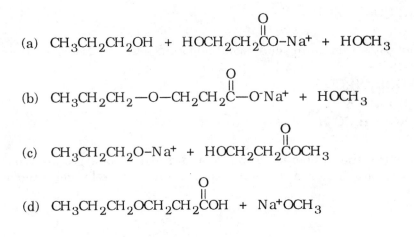

(a) $CH_3CH_2CH_2OH$ + $HOCH_2CH_2\overset{\overset{\displaystyle O}{\|}}{C}O\text{-}Na^+$ + $HOCH_3$

(b) $CH_3CH_2CH_2\text{—}O\text{—}CH_2CH_2\overset{\overset{\displaystyle O}{\|}}{C}\text{—}O^-Na^+$ + $HOCH_3$

(c) $CH_3CH_2CH_2O\text{-}Na^+$ + $HOCH_2CH_2\overset{\overset{\displaystyle O}{\|}}{C}OCH_3$

(d) $CH_3CH_2CH_2OCH_2CH_2\overset{\overset{\displaystyle O}{\|}}{C}OH$ + Na^+OCH_3

ANSWERS

ANSWERS TO DRILL EXERCISES

I. Exercises in Structures and Names

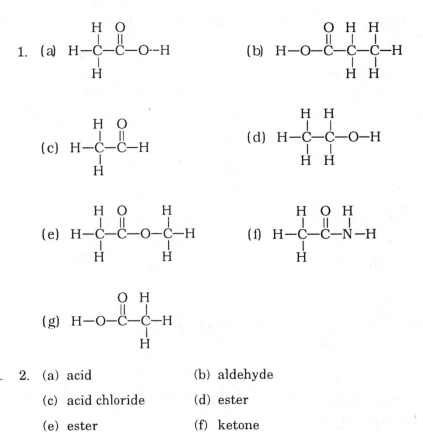

1. (a)

(b)

(c)

(d)

(e)

(f)

(g)

2. (a) acid   (b) aldehyde

   (c) acid chloride   (d) ester

   (e) ester   (f) ketone

(g) alcohol

(h) acid salt

(i) aldehyde

(j) ketone

(k) acid

(l) ester

(m) alcohol, ketone

(n) alcohol, ketone

(o) acid

(p) aldehyde, ketone

(q) ester

(r) ether, ketone

(s) ester, aldehyde

(t) anhydride

(u) acid

(v) ether, ketone

(w) diester

(x) anhydride

(y) acid chloride

(z) phenol, aldehyde

(aa) alkene, ester

(bb) ester, alkene

(cc) diester

(dd) ketone, acid

3. (a)  $\boxed{HC\overset{\overset{\displaystyle O}{\|}}{}OCH_3}$

Form

(b) 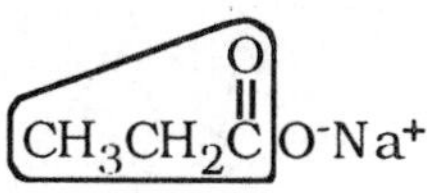 $\boxed{CH_3CH_2\overset{\overset{\displaystyle O}{\|}}{C}O^-Na^+}$

Propion

(c) 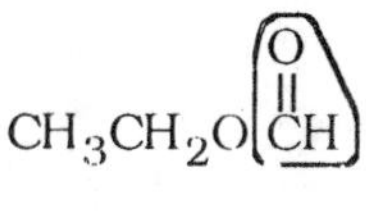 $CH_3CH_2O\boxed{\overset{\overset{\displaystyle O}{\|}}{CH}}$

Form

(d) 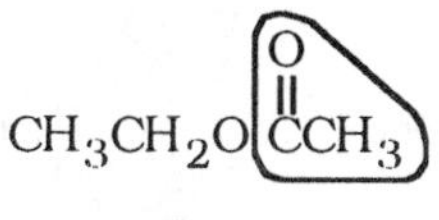 $CH_3CH_2O\boxed{\overset{\overset{\displaystyle O}{\|}}{C}CH_3}$

Acet

(e) 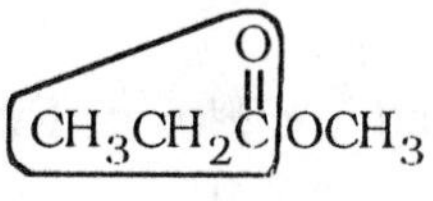 $\boxed{CH_3CH_2\overset{\overset{\displaystyle O}{\|}}{C}OCH_3}$

Propion

(f)  $CH_3O\boxed{\overset{\overset{\displaystyle O}{\|}}{C}CH_2CH_2CH_3}$

Butyr

4. (a) ester   isopropyl acetate

(b) salt   sodium propionate

(c) ester   methyl butyrate

(d) ester   isobutyl butyrate

(e) aldehyde   propionaldehyde

5. (a) isopropyl ethanoate (d) isobutyl butanoate

(b) sodium propanoate (e) propanal

(c) methyl butanoate

6. (a) $CH_3CO_2CH_3$

(b) $CH_3\overset{\overset{\displaystyle CH_3}{|}}{CH}\overset{\overset{\displaystyle }{}}{\underset{\underset{\displaystyle CH_3}{|}}{CH}}CHO$

(c) $CH_3CH_2\overset{\overset{\displaystyle O}{||}}{C}\overset{\overset{\displaystyle O}{||}}{C}CH_2CH_3$

(d) $CH_3CO_2\overset{\overset{\displaystyle CH_3}{|}}{CH}CH_2CH_3$

(e) $CH_3CH_2\overset{\overset{\displaystyle CH_3}{|}}{CH}COCl$

(f) $ClCH_2CH_2CO_2^-Na^+$

II.   Drill on the Reactions of Carboxylic Acids with Strong Base

1. $CH_3CH_2CH_2CO_2^-K^+$ 2. $CH_3(CH_2)_6CO_2^-Na^+$

3. $CH_3-O-CH_2CO_2^-Na^+$ 4. $HOCH_2CH_2CO_2^-K^+$

5. $Na^+O_2CCH_2CH_2CO_2^-Na^+$

III.   Drill on the Reactions of Carboxylic Acid Salts with Strong Acids

1. HCO_2H 2. $HO_2CCH_2CH_2CH_3$

3. $CH_3(CH_2)_8CO_2H$ 4. 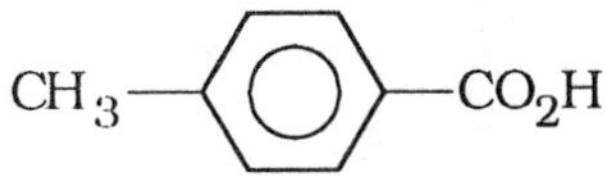 $CH_3-\langle\bigcirc\rangle-CO_2H$

5. $CH_3CH_2OCH_2CH_2CO_2H$

IV.   Drill on Writing the Structures of Esters That Can Form From Given Acids and Alcohols

1. $CH_3CH_2CH_2CO_2CH_3$ 2. $HCO_2CH_2CH_2CH_3$

3. $CH_3CH_2CO_2CH_2\overset{\overset{\displaystyle CH_3}{|}}{CH}CH_3$ 4. $CH_3CO_2\overset{\overset{\displaystyle CH_3}{|}}{\underset{\underset{\displaystyle CH_3}{|}}{C}}CH_3$

5. $CH_3O_2CCH_2CH_2CH_2CO_2CH_3$

V.   Drill on Writing the Products of the Hydrolysis of Esters

1. $CH_3CH_2CO_2H + HOCH_3$ 2. $CH_3OH + HO_2CCH_3$

3. 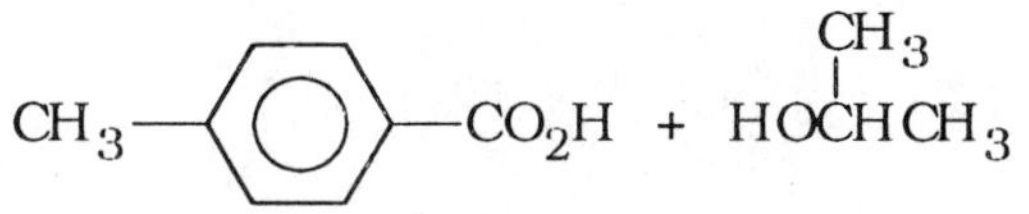 CH_3—⟨O⟩—CO_2H + $HOCHCH_3$ with CH_3 on the carbon

4. 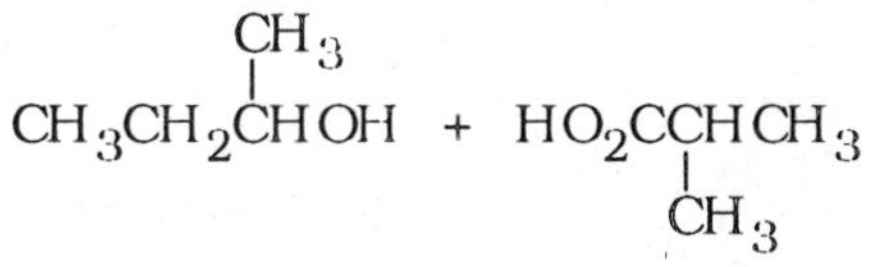 CH_3CH_2CHOH (with CH_3) + HO_2CCHCH_3 (with CH_3)

5. $CH_3CH_2OH + HO_2CCH_2CH_2CH_2CO_2H + HOCH_3$

VI.   Drill in Writing the Products of the Saponification of Esters

1. $CH_3CH_2CO_2Na + HOCH_3$

2. $CH_3OH + CH_3CO_2Na$

3.  CH_3—⟨O⟩—CO_2Na + $HOCH(CH_3)_2$

4. 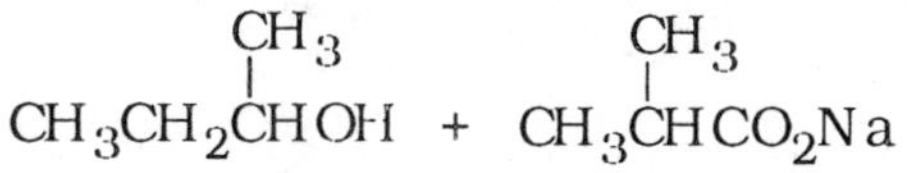 CH_3CH_2CHOH (with CH_3) + CH_3CHCO_2Na (with CH_3)

5. $CH_3CH_2OH + NaO_2CCH_2CH_2CH_2CO_2Na + HOCH_3$

ANSWERS TO SELF–TESTING QUESTIONS

Completion

1. (a) $CH_3CO_2^-Na^+ (+ H_2O)$
   (b) $CH_3CO_2CH_3 (+ H_2O)$
   (c) $CH_3CH_2CH_2CH_2CO_2H (+ NaCl)$

   (d) 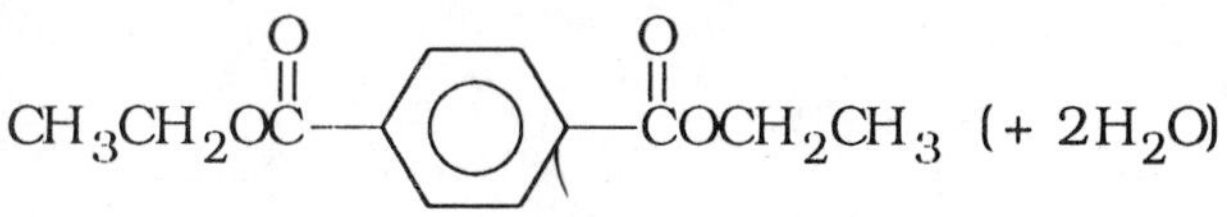 $CH_3CH_2O\overset{O}{\overset{\|}{C}}$—⟨O⟩—$\overset{O}{\overset{\|}{C}}OCH_2CH_3$ $(+ 2H_2O)$

   (e) $CH_3OH + CH_3CO_2H$

   (f) 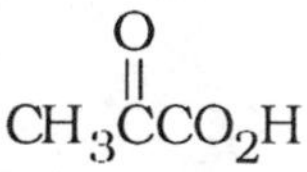 $CH_3\overset{O}{\overset{\|}{C}}CO_2H$

   (g) $2CH_3OH + HO_2CCH_2CH_2CO_2H$

   (h) $CH_3OCH_2CH_2CO_2H + HOCH_3$

(i) $CH_3CH_2CH_2\overset{\overset{\displaystyle O}{\displaystyle \|}}{C}-O-CH_2CH_3$ (+ HCl)

(j) $CH_3S-SCH_2CO_2H$ (+ NaCl)

(k) $CH_3OH + CH_3CO_2^- Na^+$

2.   (a) b, d, and i   (b) k

Multiple–Choice

1. b	2. d	3. b
4. c	5. a	6. b
7. a and d	8. c	9. e
10. b	11. b	12. b

17

AMINES AND AMIDES

The chemistry of the amino group and the amide function is essential to our study of proteins and nucleic acids as well as those pathways of metabolism that involve the amine and amide functional groups.

OBJECTIVES

After you have studied Chapter 17 in the text and worked its Practice Exercises and Review Exercises, you should be able to do the following.

1. Identify the amine and amide functions in given structures, whether open-chain or heterocyclic.
2. Write the names of simple amines and amides.
3. Write the structures of simple amines and amides from their names.
4. Describe hydrogen bonding as it occurs among amines and amides and discuss its effects on physical properties.
5. Write equations for the reactions of amines with strong, aqueous acids.
6. Write equations for the reactions of protonated amines with strong, aqueous bases.
7. Write the structures of amides that can be formed (directly or indirectly) from given carboxylic acids and NH_3, RNH_2, or R_2NH.
8. Given the structure of an amide, write the products that form when it is hydrolyzed.
9. Define the terms in the Glossary.

GLOSSARY

Alkaloid. A physiologically active, heterocyclic amine isolated from plants.

Amide. Any organic compound whose molecules have a carbonyl-nitrogen unit, $-\overset{\overset{\displaystyle O}{\|}}{C}-\overset{|}{N}-$.

Amide Bond. The single bond that holds the carbonyl group to the nitrogen atom in an amide.

Amine. Any organic compound whose molecules have a trivalent nitrogen atom, as in $R-NH_2$, $R-NH-R$, or R_3N.

Amine Salt. Any organic compound whose molecules have a positively charged, tetravalent, protonated nitrogen atom, as in RNH_3^+, $R_2NH_2^+$, or R_3NH^+.

Base Ionization Constant (K_b). For the equilibrium (where B is a base), $B + H_2O \rightleftharpoons BH^+ + OH^-$,

$$K_b = \frac{\left[BH^+ \right]\left[OH^- \right]}{B}$$

You should prepare the $5 \times 8''$ "reactions" cards for the amino group, the protonated amino group, and the amide group. Now is the time to bring up to date the lists of functional groups that react with aqueous acids, aqueous bases, and water.

KEY MOLECULAR "MAP SIGNS"

Key Molecular "Map Signs" In Organic Molecules	What to Expect When This Functional Group is Present
$-\overset{|}{\underset{|}{N}}:$ Amino group	*Influence on physical properties*: • If present as $R-NH_2$ or R_2NH, the amino group can both donate and accept hydrogen bonds to and from water, amines, or alcohols. • If present as R_3N, the amino group can only accept hydrogen bonds; it is as soluble in water as alcohols are. *Influence on chemical properties*: • The presence of an amino group makes the molecule a proton acceptor, a Brønsted base. • The easy room-temperature changes:

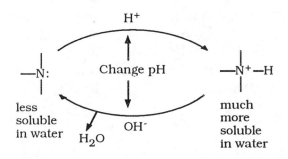

	Makes the amino group one of the major solubility switches in nature's biochemical molecules.
Amines (with at least one H on N)	• Form amides with acids; best done by a reaction of the amine with the acid chloride or anhydride.

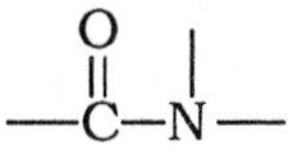

$$\underset{\text{Amide}}{-\overset{\overset{\displaystyle O}{\|}}{C}-\overset{\displaystyle |}{N}-}$$

Influence on physical properties:
Amides have a very polar group (particularly if at least one hydrogen is attached to the nitrogen); virtually all amides are solids at room temperature.

Influence on chemical properties:
• Amides are not basic; they are not proton acceptors in the way that makes amines basic.
• Can be hydrolyzed by aqueous acids or bases, if heated, to give the carboxylic acid and the amine (or ammonia).

DRILL EXERCISES

I.   DRILL IN WRITING PRODUCTS OF THE REACTIONS OF AMINES WITH STRONG ACIDS

Example 17.1 in the text describes how these products can be written. For additional practice, write the structures of the organic cations that form when each of the following amines reacts with something like hydrochloric acid (which is really a reaction with H_3O^+).

1. $CH_3CH_2CH_2NH_2$ _____

2. 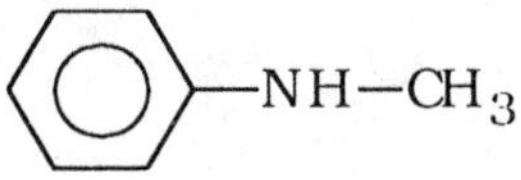   ⬡—NH—CH_3 _____

3. $CH_3CH_2\underset{\underset{\displaystyle CH_3}{|}}{N}CH_2CH_3$ _____

4.    ⬠NH _____

5. $CH_3NHCH_2CH_2NHCH_3$ (and 2HCl) _____

II. DRILL IN WRITING THE PRODUCTS OF THE REACTIONS OF PROTONATED AMINES WITH STRONG, AQUEOUS BASE

Example 17.2 in the text explains how to work this kind of problem. For further drill, write the products of the deprotona- tion of the following cations.

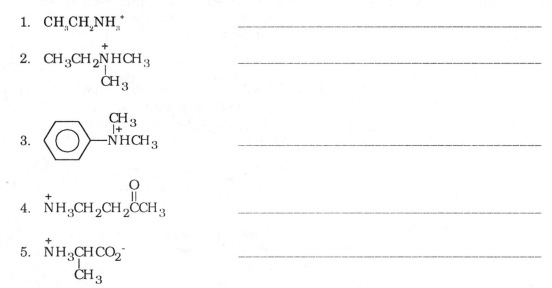

1. $CH_3CH_2NH_3^+$ _____

2. $CH_3CH_2\overset{+}{N}HCH_3$ _____
    $\mid$
    CH_3

3. ⟨O⟩—$\overset{CH_3}{\underset{}{\overset{\mid+}{N}HCH_3}}$ _____

4. $\overset{+}{N}H_3CH_2CH_2\overset{O}{\overset{\|}{C}}CH_3$ _____

5. $\overset{+}{N}H_3CHCO_2^-$ _____
    $\mid$
    CH_3

III. DRILL IN WRITING THE STRUCTURES OF THE AMIDES THAT CAN BE MADE (DIRECTLY OR INDIRECTLY) FROM GIVEN CARBOXYLIC ACIDS AND AMINES

See Example 17.3 for a discussion of how to work this kind of problem. The following will give extra opportunities to drill yourself. Write the structure of the amides that can be made from the given acids and amines (or ammonia).

1. ⟨O⟩—CO_2H + NH_3 _____

2. $CH_3CH_2CO_2H$ + NH_3 _____

3. $CH_3\overset{CH_3}{\overset{\mid}{C}H}CH_2CO_2H$ + NH_3 _____

4. ⟨O⟩—CO_2H + CH_3NH_2 _____

5. CH_3CO_2H + $CH_3CH_2NH_2$ _____

IV. DRILL IN WRITING THE PRODUCTS OF THE HYDROLYSIS OF AMIDES

Example 17.4 in the text discusses how this kind of problem can be worked. For more practice, do the following. Write the structures of the products that can form by the hydrolysis of the following amides. Show the acids as acids, not as their salts. Similarly, show the amines as amines, not in protonated forms.

1. $CH_3CH_2\overset{\overset{\displaystyle O}{\|}}{C}NH_2$ _____

2. $CH_3CH_2CH_2\overset{\overset{\displaystyle O}{\|}}{C}NHCH_3$ _____

3. $CH_3CH_2NH\overset{\overset{\displaystyle O}{\|}}{C}CH_2CH_3$ _____

4. $CH_3\underset{\underset{\displaystyle CH_3}{|}}{C}HNH\overset{\overset{\displaystyle O}{\|}}{C}CH_2\underset{\underset{\displaystyle }{}}{C}\overset{\overset{\displaystyle CH_3}{|}}{H}CH_3$ _____

5. 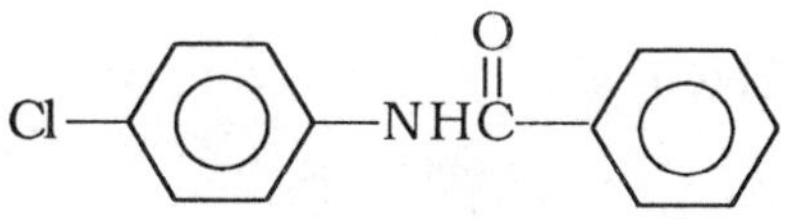 $Cl-\text{⟨O⟩}-NH\overset{\overset{\displaystyle O}{\|}}{C}-\text{⟨O⟩}$ _____

V. EXERCISES IN HYDROGEN BONDS

Amines can accept and donate H-bonds like alcohols, but the H-bonds in amines are weaker. (Amines with three groups on nitrogen and no N—H bond left can only accept hydrogen bonds.) The questions in this exercise refer to the following structures.

A. $CH_3CH_2CH_2-\overset{\displaystyle ..}{\underset{\displaystyle ..}{O}}-H$ B. $CH_3CH_2CH_2-\overset{\overset{\displaystyle H}{|}}{\underset{\displaystyle ..}{N}}-H$

C. $CH_3-\overset{\overset{\displaystyle H}{|}}{\underset{\displaystyle ..}{N}}-H$ D. $CH_3-\overset{\overset{\displaystyle CH_3}{|}}{\underset{\underset{\displaystyle CH_3}{|}}{N}}:$

E. $CH_3CH_2CH_2CH_2-Br$ F. 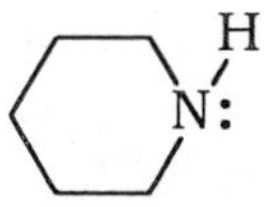 $\text{⟨} \rangle\overset{\displaystyle H}{\underset{\displaystyle }{N}}:$

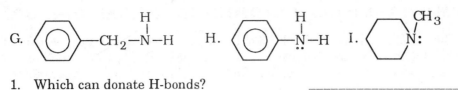

1. Which can donate H-bonds? _____
2. Which can accept H-bonds? _____
3. Which can only accept H bonds? _____
4. Which is totally insoluble in water? _____
5. Which has a higher boiling point, A or B? _____
6. Which is (are) the aromatic amine(s)? _____

A BRIEF SURVEY OF THE PRINCIPAL FUNCTIONAL GROUPS ATTACKED BY WATER, OXIDIZING AGENTS, REDUCING AGENTS OR NEUTRALIZING AGENTS

[**Note**: We summarize here only those reactions we have studied. In terms of the whole field of organic chemistry, the list is of course very incomplete. Omitted are the reactions of acid chlorides and anhydrides, including the phosphoric anhydrides.]

1. Groups that are split apart by water (hydrolysis) in the presence of acids or appropriate enzymes.
   Acetals and **ketals** are hydrolyzed to aldehydes and alcohols. For example, using the acetal,

$$RCH\overset{OR'}{\underset{OR'}{\diagup}} + H_2O \xrightarrow{H^+} RCHO + 2HOR'$$

Esters are hydrolyzed to acids and alcohols.

$$R\overset{O}{\overset{\|}{C}}{-}OR' + H_2O \xrightarrow{H^+} RCO_2H + HOR'$$

Amides are hydrolyzed to acids and amines (or ammonia).

$$R\overset{O}{\overset{\|}{C}}{-}N{-} + H_2O \xrightarrow{H^+} RCO_2H + H{-}N{-}$$

2. Groups that are affected by oxidizing agents.
   Alkenes are attacked by ozone and permanganate.
   Alcohol groups are converted to carbonyl groups.

$$-\overset{|}{\underset{H}{C}}-\overset{}{\underset{H}{O}} + (O) \longrightarrow \overset{\diagdown}{\underset{\diagup}{C}}{=}O + H_2O$$

Mercaptans are changed to disulfides.

$$2R{-}S{-}H + (O) \longrightarrow R{-}S{-}S{-}R + H_2O$$

Aldehydes are converted to carboxyl groups.

$$RCHO + (O) \longrightarrow RCO_2H$$

3. Groups that are affected by reducing agents (e.g., H_2 or donors of $H:^-$).
   Carbon-carbon double bonds become saturated.

$$\text{C=C} + H_2 \xrightarrow[\text{heat}]{\text{Ni}} \text{H-C-C-H}$$

Disulfides are changed to mercaptans.

$$R-S-S-R + 2(H) \longrightarrow 2RSH$$

Aldehydes and **ketones** are changed to 1° and 2° alcohols.

$$\text{C=O} + H_2 \xrightarrow[\text{P, heat}]{\text{Ni}} \text{CHOH}$$

4. Groups that can neutralize strong acids at room temperature.

   Amines: $RNH_2 + H_3O^+ \longrightarrow \overset{+}{R}NH_3 + H_2O$

   Acid Salts: $R\overset{O}{\overset{\|}{C}}O^- + H_3O^+ \longrightarrow R\overset{O}{\overset{\|}{C}}OH + H_2O$

5. Groups that can neutralize strong bases at room temperature.

   Amine Salts: $\overset{+}{R}NH_3 + {}^-OH \longrightarrow RNH_2 + H_2O$

   Acids: $RCO_2H + {}^-OH \longrightarrow RCO_2^- + H_2O$

   Phenols:

$$\text{C}_6\text{H}_5\text{-OH} + {}^-OH \longrightarrow \text{C}_6\text{H}_5\text{-O}^- + H_2O$$

6. Other reactions involving water.
   Water is a *reactant* when carbon-carbon double bonds add water to form alcohols.
   Water is a *product* when carbon-carbon double bonds are introduced by the dehydration of an alcohol; acetals are formed from hemiacetals and alcohols; esters are formed from acids and alcohols; amides are formed from acids and amines.

SELF-TESTING QUESTIONS

COMPLETION

Complete the following equations by writing the structures of the principal organic products. If no reaction occurs, write "none." Several of the following involve a review of reactions studied in earlier chapters.

1. $NH_2\overset{O}{\overset{\|}{C}}CH_3 + H_2O \xrightarrow{\text{heat}}$ _____

2. $CH_3-S-H + HCl(aq) \longrightarrow$ _____

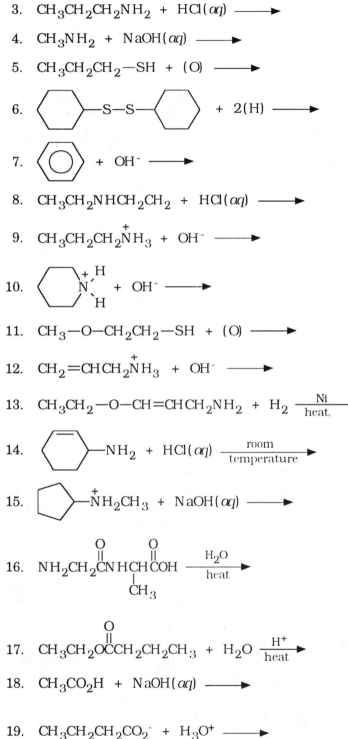

3. $CH_3CH_2CH_2NH_2$ + HCl(aq) $\longrightarrow$ _____

4. CH_3NH_2 + NaOH(aq) $\longrightarrow$ _____

5. $CH_3CH_2CH_2-SH$ + (O) $\longrightarrow$ _____

6. [cyclohexyl]—S—S—[cyclohexyl] + 2(H) $\longrightarrow$ _____

7. [benzene] + OH⁻ $\longrightarrow$ _____

8. $CH_3CH_2NHCH_2CH_2$ + HCl(aq) $\longrightarrow$ _____

9. $CH_3CH_2CH_2\overset{+}{N}H_3$ + OH⁻ $\longrightarrow$ _____

10. [piperidinium $\overset{+}{N}$ with H, H] + OH⁻ $\longrightarrow$ _____

11. $CH_3-O-CH_2CH_2-SH$ + (O) $\longrightarrow$ _____

12. $CH_2=CHCH_2\overset{+}{N}H_3$ + OH⁻ $\longrightarrow$ _____

13. $CH_3CH_2-O-CH=CHCH_2NH_2$ + H_2 $\xrightarrow[\text{heat,}]{\text{Ni}}$ _____

14. [cyclohexenyl]—NH_2 + HCl(aq) $\xrightarrow[\text{temperature}]{\text{room}}$ _____

15. [cyclopentyl]—$\overset{+}{N}H_2CH_3$ + NaOH(aq) $\longrightarrow$ _____

16. $NH_2CH_2\overset{O}{\overset{\|}{C}}NHCH\overset{O}{\overset{\|}{C}}OH$ $\xrightarrow[\text{heat}]{H_2O}$ _____ + _____
    $\quad\quad\quad\quad\quad\underset{CH_3}{|}$

17. $CH_3CH_2O\overset{O}{\overset{\|}{C}}CH_2CH_2CH_3$ + H_2O $\xrightarrow[\text{heat}]{H^+}$ _____

18. CH_3CO_2H + NaOH(aq) $\longrightarrow$ _____

19. $CH_3CH_2CH_2CO_2^-$ + H_3O^+ $\longrightarrow$ _____

20. $CH_3CHOCH_3 + H_2O \xrightarrow[\text{heat}]{H^+}$ _____
     $\overset{|}{O}CH_3$

MULTIPLE-CHOICE

1. Organic functional groups that are hydrolyzed by water (usually in the presence of an acid catalyst and heat) are
    (a) ethers   (d) disulfides
    (b) acetals   (e) esters
    (c) amides   (f) carboxylic acids

2. Organic functional groups that are rather easily oxidized are
    (a) alkanes   (d) ketones
    (b) aromatic hydrocarbons (e) aldehydes
    (c) mercaptans   (f) amides

3. Organic functional groups that are good proton acceptors are
    (a) amino groups   (d) carboxylate ions
    (b) amides   (e) aromatic hydrocarbons
    (c) alkanes   (f) mercaptans

4. Organic functional groups that are good proton donors are
    (a) amino groups   (d) substituted ammonium ions
    (b) amides   (e) carboxylic acids
    (c) alkanes   (f) alcohols

5. Which compound is the most acidic?
    (a) CH_3CH_2OH

    (c) $CH_3\overset{\overset{\displaystyle O}{\|}}{C}-NH_2$

    (b) $CH_3CH=O$

    (d) CH_3CO_2H

6. Which compound is the most basic?
    (a) CH_3CH_2OH (c) $CH_3CH_2NH_3{}^+Cl^-$

    (b) $CH_3CH_2NH_2$ (d) $CH_3\overset{\overset{\displaystyle O}{\|}}{C}-NH_2$

7. The compound $CH_3O-CH_2\overset{\overset{\displaystyle O}{\|}}{C}-NH_2$ could be made from

    (a) CH_3OH and $HOCH_2\overset{\overset{\displaystyle O}{\|}}{C}NH_2$ (c) $CH_3OCH_2\overset{\overset{\displaystyle O}{\|}}{C}H$ and NH_3

(b) CH_3OCH_2OH and $H-\overset{\overset{O}{\|}}{C}-NH_2$ (d) $CH_3OCH_2\overset{\overset{O}{\|}}{C}OH$ and NH_3

8. If the following compounds were arranged in the order of their increasing boiling points, that order would be

   A. CH_3CH_3 B. CH_3OH C. CH_3NH_2

   (a) A < B < C   (c) C < A < B
   (b) A < C < B   (d) B < A < C

9. If the following compounds were arranged in the order of their increasing solubility in water, that order would be

   A. $CH_3CH_2CH_2CH_2CH_2OH$ B. $CH_3CH_2CH_2CH_2CH_2CH_3$ C. $CH_3CH_2CH_2CH_2CH_2NH_2$

   (a) A < B < C   (c) B < A < C
   (b) C < B < A   (d) B < C < A

10. Which compound could neutralize aqueous sodium hydroxide?

   (a) CH_3OH (c) $CH_3S-S-CH_3$
   (b) CH_3NH_2 (d) $CH_3NH_3{}^+Cl^-$

11. The compound whose structure is $CH_3CH_2CH_2NH_2$ is called

   (a) methylethylamine   (c) 1-aminopropane
   (b) propylamine   (d) butylamine

12. The reaction of $CH_3-\underset{\underset{CH_3}{|}}{N}H_2{}^+$ with aqueous sodium hydroxide at room temperature will give

   (a) CH_3NHCH_3

   (b) $CH_3\underset{\underset{CH_3}{|}}{N}-OH$

   (c) $CH_3-\underset{\underset{CH_3}{|}}{N}{}^-$

   (d) $CH_3-\underset{\underset{CH_3}{|}}{N}-CH_3$

13. The presence of NH_2 group in an organic compound makes the compound

   (a) a good proton donor   (c) more soluble in water
   (b) less soluble in water   (d) a good proton acceptor

14. What is the best representation for hydrogen bonding in methylamine?

   (a) $CH_3-\underset{\underset{H}{|}}{N}-H\cdots\cdots CH_3-\underset{\underset{H}{|}}{N}-H$

   (c) $CH_3-\overset{\overset{H\ H}{}}{N}\cdots\cdots\overset{\overset{H}{}}{N}-CH_3$

   (b) $CH_3-\underset{\underset{H}{|}}{N}-H\cdots\cdots H-\underset{\underset{H}{|}}{N}-CH_3$

   (d) $CH_3-\underset{\underset{H}{|}}{N}-H\cdots\cdots\underset{\underset{H}{|}}{N}-CH_3$

Questions fifteen through eighteen refer to this compound:

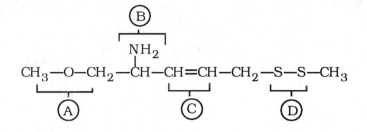

15. The group at (A) would

   (a) react with NaOH(aq)

   (b) react with HCl(aq)

   (c) be reduced by catalytic hydrogenation

   (d) be oxidizable by mild reagents

   (e) none of these

16. The group at (B) would

   (a) neutralize aqueous HCl   (c) react with H_2

   (b) accept H-bonds from water (d) none of these

17. The group at (C) would

   (a) add hydrogen chloride

   (b) donate hydrogen bonds

   (c) be attacked by OH^-

   (d) none of these

18. The group at (D) would

   (a) be easily reduced   (c) neutralize NaOH(aq)

   (b) react with HCl(aq)   (d) react with water

ANSWERS

ANSWERS TO DRILL EXERCISES

I. Drill in Writing Products of the Reactions of Amines with Strong Acids

1. $CH_3CH_2CH_2NH_3^+$ 2. ⟨O⟩—$\overset{+}{N}H_2CH_3$ 3. $CH_3CH_2\overset{+}{N}HCH_2CH_3$

                                                          $\underset{CH_3}{|}$

4. ▱$\overset{+}{N}H_2$ 5. $CH_3\overset{+}{N}H_2CH_2CH_2\overset{+}{N}H_2CH_3$

II.   Drill in Writing the Products of the Reactions of Protonated Amines with Strong, Aqueous Base

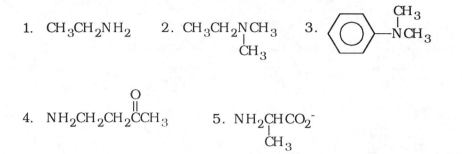

1. $CH_3CH_2NH_2$

2. $CH_3CH_2NCH_3$
       $\overset{|}{C}H_3$

3. phenyl—$N\overset{CH_3}{\underset{CH_3}{|}}$

4. $NH_2CH_2CH_2\overset{\overset{O}{||}}{C}CH_3$

5. $NH_2CHCO_2^-$
       $\overset{|}{C}H_3$

III.   Drill in Writing the Structures of the Amides That Can Be Made (Directly or Indirectly) from Given Carboxylic Acids and Amines

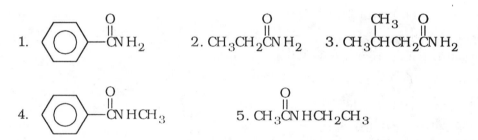

1. phenyl—$\overset{\overset{O}{||}}{C}NH_2$

2. $CH_3CH_2\overset{\overset{O}{||}}{C}NH_2$

3. $CH_3\overset{CH_3}{\underset{|}{C}}HCH_2\overset{\overset{O}{||}}{C}NH_2$

4. phenyl—$\overset{\overset{O}{||}}{C}NHCH_3$

5. $CH_3\overset{\overset{O}{||}}{C}NHCH_2CH_3$

IV.   Drill in Writing the Products of the Hydrolysis of Amides

1. $CH_3CH_2CO_2H + NH_3$

2. $CH_3CH_2CH_2CO_2H + NH_2CH_3$

3. $CH_3CH_2NH_2 + HO_2CCH_2CH_3$

4. $CH_3CHNH_2 + HO_2CCH_2\overset{CH_3}{\underset{|}{C}}HCH_3$
       $\overset{|}{C}H_3$

5. Cl—phenyl—$NH_2 + HO_2C$—phenyl

V.   Exercises in Hydrogen Bonds

1. A, B, C, F, G, and H

2. A, B, C, D, F, G, H, and I

3.   D and I

4.   E

5.   A   (The amine, B, boils at a lower temperature because it forms weaker H-bonds than does the alcohol. The formula masses of both are essentially equal.)

6.   H   (To be an aromatic amine, the amino group must be joined directly to the aromatic ring. While G is an aromatic compound, it is not an aromatic amine; instead, it is an aliphatic amine.)

ANSWERS TO SELF–TESTING QUESTIONS

Completion

1. $NH_3 + HO_2CCH_3$ (The hydrolysis of an amide.)

2.   none   (The only reaction of mercaptans, as far as we are concerned, is their oxidation to disulfides.)

3. $CH_3CH_2CH_3NH_3Cl$

4.   none (Amines do not react with aqueous bases.)

5. $CH_3CH_2CH_2—S—S—CH_2CH_2CH_3 + H_2O$

6.   2 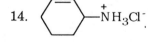—SH

7.   none (Benzene has no reaction with bases.)

8. $CH_3CH_2—\overset{\overset{\displaystyle H}{|+}}{\underset{\underset{\displaystyle H}{|}}{N}}—CH_2CH_3Cl^-$

9. $CH_3CH_2CH_2NH_2 + H_2O$

10.   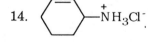 $+ H_2O$

11. $CH_3—O—CH_2CH_2—S—S—CH_2CH_2—O—CH_3 + H_2O$ (The ether group is unaffected; it remains intact during the reaction.)

12. $CH_2=CHCH_2NH_2 + H_2O$ (The double bond is not affected by an aqueous hydroxide ion.)

13. $CH_3CH_2—O—CH_2CH_2CH_2NH_2$ (Only the double bond is hydrogenated; neither the ether group nor the amino group is changed by hydrogenation.)

14. $—\overset{+}{N}H_3Cl^-$.   (Aqueous hydrochloric acid does not affect the double bond at room temperature.)

15. $—NH—CH_3$ $(+H_2O)$

16. $NH_2CH_2CO_2H$ + NH_2CHCO_2H (Only the amide group
                            | is affected.)
                         CH_3

17. CH_3CH_2OH + $HO_2CCH_2CH_2CH_3$ (The hydrolysis of an ester.)

18. $CH_3CO_2^-Na^+$ (+H_2O)   19. $CH_3CH_2CH_2CO_2H$ (+H_2O)

20. CH_3CHO + 2$HOCH_3$ (The hydrolysis of an acetal.)

Multiple–Choice

1.	b, c, e	2.	c, e	3.	a, d
4.	d, e	5.	d	6.	b
7.	d	8.	b	9.	d
10.	d	11.	b, c	12.	a
13.	c, d	14.	d	15.	e
16.	a, b	17.	a	18.	a

18

OPTICAL ISOMERISM

Life is as dependent on molecular geometry as it is on other features of molecules. Nearly all biochemical substances consist of molecules that exhibit some type of *chirality*, or handedness. This is particularly true of all enzymes. Here we learn that the chemical properties of a substance whose molecules are chiral can depend, often dramatically, upon its *kind* of chirality. The chapter develops this point and gives some illustrations. You, in turn, should learn the definitions of the terms of optical isomerism given in the Glossary in such a way that you are able to illustrate them by examples.

OBJECTIVES

After studying this chapter and working the Practice and Review Exercises in it, you should be able to do all of the following.

1. Examine the structures of a set of isomers and pick out which are related as constitutional isomers and which are related as stereoisomers.
2. Examine a molecular structure and pick out any tetrahedral stereocenters.
3. Examine the tetrahedral stereocenters in a structure and pick out which are identical and which are different.
4. If all of the tetrahedral stereocenters in a structure are different, calculate the number of optical isomers possible.
5. Examine a structure and predict whether it can exist in two forms related as enantiomers.
6. Examine the structures of a set of stereoisomers and pick out which are related as enantiomers, which are related as diastereomers, and which are meso compounds. (From Special Topic 18.1.)
7. Write structures that illustrate the composition of a racemic mixture. (See Special Topic 18.1.)
8. Calculate the specific rotation of a substance from its observed rotation, its concentration, and the path length of light passing through it.

9. Calculate the concentration of an optically active substance from data on its observed optical rotation, its specific rotation, and the path length of light passing through it.
10. Define all of the terms in the Glossary and give illustrations where applicable.

GLOSSARY

Achiral. Not possessing chirality; that quality of a molecule (or other object) that allows it to be superimposed on its mirror image.

Chiral. Having handedness in a molecular structure. (See also *Chirality.*)

Chiral Carbon. (See *Tetrahedral Stereocenter.*)

Chirality. The quality of handedness that a molecular structure has that prevents this structure from being superimposable on its mirror image.

Constitutional Isomer. One of a set of isomers whose molecules differ in their atom-to-atom sequence.

Dextrorotatory. That property of an optically active substance by which it can cause the plane of plane-polarized light to rotate clockwise.

Enantiomer. One of a pair of stereoisomers that are related as an object is related to its mirror image but that cannot be superimposed one on the other.

Levorotatory. The property of an optically active substance that causes a counterclockwise rotation of the plane of plane-polarized light.

Optical Activity. The ability of a substance to rotate the plane of polarization of plane-polarized light.

Optical Isomer. One of a set of compounds whose molecules differ only in their chiralities.

Optical Rotation. The degrees of rotation of the plane of plane-polarized light caused by an optically active solution; the observed rotation of such a solution.

Plane-Polarized Light. Light whose electrical field vibrations are all in the same plane.

Polarimeter. An instrument for detecting and measuring optical activity.

Racemic Mixture. A 1:1 mixture of enantiomers which is therefore optically inactive.

Specific Rotation [α]. The optical rotation of a solution per unit of concentration per unit of path length.

$$[\alpha] = \frac{\alpha}{cl}$$

where α = observed rotation; c = concentration in g/mL;

and l = path length in decimeters.

Stereoisomer. One of a set of isomers whose molecules have the same atom-to-atom sequences but different geometric arrangements; a geometric (cis-trans) or optical isomer.

Substrate. The substance on which an enzyme performs its catalytic work.

Superimposition. An operation to see if one molecular model can be made to blend simultaneously at exactly every point with another model.

Tetrahedral Stereocenter. An atom in a molecule to which are attached four different atoms or groups.

SELF-TESTING QUESTIONS

COMPLETION

1. These two structures:

    represent what kind of isomerism:_____

2. These two structures:

    represent _____

3. These two structures:
    $$CH_3—O—CH_2—CO_2H \text{ and } HO—CH_2CO_2CH_3$$
    represent what kind of isomerism? _____

4. Complete the two perspective structures to represent the two enantiomers of 1-bromo-1-chloroethane:

    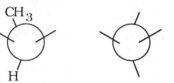

5. Add two Cls and two Hs to each of these structures to show two diastereomers. (Cf. Special Topic 18.1)

    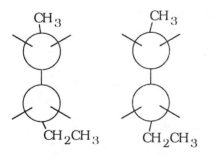

6. Let the surface depicted below represent the surface of an enzyme with the structural features A, B, and C that are involved in the enzyme's work as a catalyst. Examine structures 1, 2, and 3. If the reaction of this enzyme requires that A meet A, B meet B, and C meet C simultaneously as the molecule nestles to the surface of the enzyme, then which molecule(s) can interact with the enzyme? _____

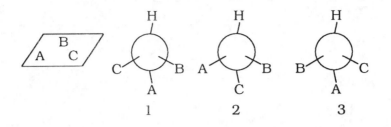

MULTIPLE–CHOICE

1. A substance that is optically active can
   (a) rotate polarized light
   (b) rotate the plane of light
   (c) polarize light
   (d) rotate the plane of plane-polarized light

2. If a substance has a specific rotation described as

   $[\alpha]_D^{20} = -15.6°$, the substance is

   (a) levorotatory   (c) optically active
   (b) dextrorotatory   (d) superimposable

3. A bottle labeled "(+)-glucose" contains a substance that is
   (a) achiral   (c) dextrorotatory
   (b) optically active   (d) positively charged

4. If a solution of 0.06 g/mL of compound X in a polarimeter tube 20 centimeters long has an optical rotation of 1.2°, then its specific rotation is
   (a) 23°   (b) 10°   (c) 100°   (d) 1°

5. If the solution of question 4 were put in a tube 1 dm long, the observed rotation would be
   (a) 5°   (b) 10°   (c) 50°   (d) 0.6°

6. How many tetrahedral stereocenters are present in the following structure?

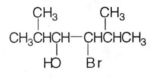

   (a) 1   (b) 2   (c) 3   (d) 4

7. The molecule in question 6 could exist as
   (a) one enantiomer   (c) two pairs of enantiomers
   (b) two enantiomers   (d) one pair of enantiomers

ANSWERS

ANSWERS TO SELF–TESTING QUESTIONS

Completion

1. stereoisomerism (or cis-trans isomerism or geometrical isomerism)
2. constitutional isomerism
3. constitutional isomerism

4.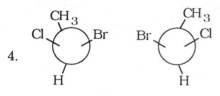

5.

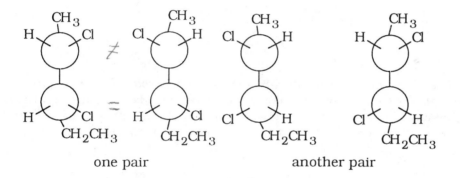

one pair   another pair

6. Structure 1 (Imagine that you rotate it counterclockwise 120° about the bond from the central atom to the H. The other two structures are enantiomers of structure 1.)

Multiple–Choice

1. d
2. a, c
3. b, c
4. b (20 cm = 2 dm)
5. d
6. b
7. c

19

CARBOHYDRATES

In a course of study such as this, *we cannot claim to know what carbohydrates are unless we know their molecular structures.* The emphasis in this chapter, therefore, is structure, particularly the structure of glucose (the most important monosaccharide), of maltose (a representative disaccharide), and of amylose (a representative polysaccharide and one of the two constituents of starch).

OBJECTIVES

After studying this chapter and working the Exercises in it, you should be able to do the following.

1. Describe carbohydrates by their structural features.
2. Name the three classes of carbohydrates we have studied.
3. Interpret such terms as "aldose," "hexose," and "aldohexose."
4. Name the three nutritionally important monosaccharides and give at least one source of each.
5. Name the three nutritionally important disaccharides, give a source of each, and name the products each gives when hydrolyzed.
6. Name three polysaccharides made entirely from glucose units and state where each is found in nature.
7. Write the structures for the α–, β–, and the open forms of glucose. (This would be a minimum goal as far as monosaccharide structures are concerned.)
8. Look at the cyclic structure of a given monosaccharide and point out its hemiacetal system.
9. Look at the cyclic structure of a given disaccharide and point out its acetal-oxygen bridge; tell if the disaccharide will give a positive result in Benedict's or Tollens' Test.
10. Explain what is meant by "deoxy–."

11. Write the structure of α– and β– maltose. (This is a minimum goal as far as disaccharide structures are concerned.)

12. Write the structure of the repeating unit in amylose (as a minimum goal for illustrating what polysaccharides are).

13. Describe an instance in which two polysaccharides differ only in the orientation (i.e., geometry) of their oxygen bridges.

14. Describe what one does and sees in the starch-iodine test.

15. Name the principal components of starch.

16. Describe the structural relations between amylopectin and amylose. (Do this in words if not by writing the structures.)

17. Write the plane projection structure of D-glucose and explain why it is in the D-family.

18. Tell from the plane projection structure of any aldose or ketose whether it is in the D- or L-family.

19. Define all of the terms in the Glossary.

GLOSSARY

Absolute Configuration. The arrangement in space about each tetrahedral stereocenter in a molecule.

Aldohexose. A monosaccharide whose molecules have six carbon atoms and an aldehyde group.

Aldose. A monosaccharide whose molecules have an aldehyde group.

Biochemistry. The study of the structures and properties of substances found in living systems.

Blood Sugar. The carbohydrates – mostly glucose – that are present in blood.

Carbohydrate. Any naturally occurring substance whose molecules are polyhydroxyaldehydes or polyhydroxyketones or can be hydrolyzed to such compounds.

D-Family; L-Family. The names of the two optically active families to which substances can belong when they are considered solely according to one kind of molecular chirality (molecular handedness) or the other.

Disaccharide. A carbohydrate that can be hydrolyzed into two monosaccharides.

Glycosides. Acetals of carbohydrates.

Glycosidic Link. The acetal oxygen bridge between monosaccharide units in di- and polysaccharides.

Iodine Test. The test for starch by which a drop of iodine reagent produces an intensely purple color if starch is present.

Ketohexose. A monosaccharide whose molecules contain six carbon atoms and have a keto group.

Ketose. A monosaccharide whose molecules have a ketone group.

Monosaccharide. A carbohydrate that cannot be hydrolyzed.

Mutarotation. The gradual change in the specific rotation of a substance in solution but without a permanent, irreversible chemical change occurring.

Photosynthesis. A series of reactions in plants, powered by solar energy absorbed by chlorophyll, by which CO_2, H_2O, and minerals are used to make complex molecules like glucose.

Polysaccharide. A carbohydrate whose molecules are polymers of monosaccharides.

Reducing Carbohydrate. A carbohydrate that gives a positive Benedict's Test.

Simple Sugar. Any monosaccharide.

DRILL EXERCISES

EXERCISES IN CARBOHYDRATE STRUCTURES AND SYMBOLS

In the simplified structures of the cyclic forms of carbohydrates, the bonds or lines that are parts of the rings (hexagons or pentagons) form a flat surface. You should imagine that this surface comes out of the page, perpendicular to it. Bonds or lines that point downward from corners of these rings actually point below the plane of the ring. Those pointing up from a corner project above the plane. These relations hold even if we rotate the ring around an imaginary axis going through the center of the ring and perpendicular to the plane of the ring.

1. Just to make sure that the condensed structural symbols for the monosaccharides are understood, convert this symbol into its full structural formula with the atomic symbols given for all carbon, hydrogen, and oxygen atoms and with all bonds represented by lines.

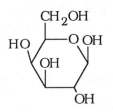

2. Study the following Fischer projection structures and answer the questions. (Not all of these plane projections are in strict accord with all of the rules for making them, but the rearward projections of vertical lines and the forward projections of horizontal lines are intended to be as specified by these rules.) Remember that in imaginary operations with Fisher projections, they may be slid around on the plane, but they may not be taken out of the plane and tipped in any way.

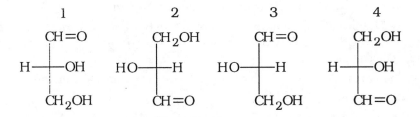

   (a) Which, if any, are D-glyceraldehyde? _____
   (b) Which, if any, are L-glyceraldehyde? _____

3. Given the following Fischer projection structure for D-galactose, write the Fischer projection structures for L-galactose.

   D-galactose   L-galactose _____

4. Modify the structure of D-galactose given above to show the structure of D-2-deoxygalactose.

_____

SELF-TESTING QUESTIONS

COMPLETION

1. A carbohydrate whose molecules will react with water to produce two sugar units is a

   _____.

2. The structural feature involved in the link between two glucose units in maltose is the

   _____.

3. The hydrolysis of sucrose produces _____ and _____.

4. The partial hydrolysis of starch gives a mixture called _____.

5. The iodine test is used to detect the presence of _____.

6. Carbohydrates all have high melting points, which means that their molecules are strongly attracted to each other in the crystals. The force of attraction responsible for this property is the

   _____.

7. The names of the two very broad families of optically active compounds, which are organized solely on the bases of "handedness," are the _____ family and the _____ family.

8. The hydrolysis of lactose produces _____ and _____.

9. The linear polymer of α-glucose is _____.

10. Starch is a mixture of _____ and _____.

11. The technical name for a potential aldehyde group is the _____.

12. The hydrolysis of maltose produces _____.

13. Because maltose and lactose have the _____ group, they are reducing disaccharides.

14. The storage form of glucose molecules in animals is _____, which structurally is similar to _____, one of the storage forms of glucose units in plants.

15. If a polysaccharide can be hydrolyzed into nothing but glucose, it might be any one of the following (make a complete list):_____

   _____

MULTIPLE-CHOICE

1. Which is (are) the structure(s) of α-glucose?

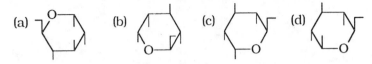

(a)   (b)   (c)   (d)

2. If the symbol Gl is used to represent a glucose unit, then the symbol:

   etc. —O—Gl—O—Gl—O—Gl—O—Gl—O—Gl—etc.

   could be a way of showing the basic structural feature of
   (a) amylopectin   (b) amylose
   (c) glycogen   (d) galactose

3. An example of a reducing carbohydrate is
   (a) sucrose   (b) maltose   (c) cellulose   (d) galactose

4. An aldohexose would have
   (a) a potential aldehyde group
   (b) five hydroxyl groups in its open form
   (c) six carbons
   (d) one CH_2OH group

5. The 50:50 mixture of glucose and fructose
   (a) is called dextromaltose
   (b) is obtainable by the hydrolysis of sucrose
   (c) is called invert sugar
   (d) is a disaccharide

6. If the molecules of a substance have the structure

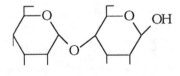

   (a) it is a disaccharide
   (b) it is in the D-family
   (c) it can mutarotate
   (d) it has a β-acetal oxygen bridge

7. If the molecules of a substance have the structure:

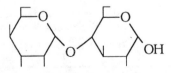

   (a) it can be hydrolyzed into two glucose units
   (b) it can be hydrolyzed into one glucose unit plus another monosaccharide
   (c) it will not give a Benedict's Test
   (d) it will not mutarotate

8.   If the molecules of a substance have the structure:

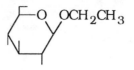

   (a)   it is an α-glucoside
   (b)   it is a β-glucoside
   (c)   it will mutarotate
   (d)   it will give a positive Benedict's Test

9.   If the molecules of a substance have the structure:

   (a)   it is an α-glucoside
   (b)   it is a β-glucoside
   (c)   it will give a positive Benedict's Test
   (d)   it is a disaccharide

10.   If the molecules of a substance have the structure:

   (a)   it is a disaccharide
   (b)   it will give a positive Benedict's Test
   (c)   it will mutarotate
   (d)   it will hydrolyze into two D-galactose units

ANSWERS

ANSWERS TO DRILL EXERCISES

Exercises in Carbohydrate Structures and Symbols

1.

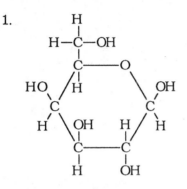

2. (a)   1 and 2 (Note that 2 results from spinning 1 by 180° in the plane of the paper.)

    (b)   3 and 4 (3 is the mirror image of 1; 4 results from turning 3 by 180° in the plane of the paper.)

3.   4.

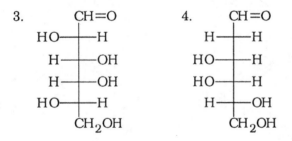

ANSWERS TO SELF–TESTING QUESTIONS

Completion
1.   disaccharide
2.   α-acetal bridge or an α(1→4) glycosidic link)
3.   fructose, glucose
4.   dextrin
5.   starch
6.   hydrogen bond
7.   D- and L- (families)

8.   glucose, galactose

9.   amylose

10   amylose, amylopectin

11.   hemiacetal group

12.   glucose

13.   hemiacetal (or potential aldehyde)

14.   glycogen, ~~amylopectin~~ -should be cellulose?

15.   starch, amylose, amylopectin, glycogen, cellulose, dextrin

Multiple–Choice

1.   a, b, and d

2.   b

3.   b and d

4.   a, b, c, and d

5.   b and c

6.   a, b, and c

7.   b

8.   b (Only when the hemiacetal group—or the hemiketal group — is present will the substance mutarotate and give a positive Benedict's Test.)

9.   c (To be a glucoside, the CH_3 group would have to be part of an acetal system at carbon number one.)

10.   a (It has no hemiacetal system and therefore cannot mutarotate or give a positive Benedict's Test.)

20

LIPIDS

Just as with carbohydrates, so with lipids; we don't know these substances until we know their structures. With lipids, however, we learn the features of the structures held in common by all lipids in a given family, not the structures of specific lipids.

OBJECTIVES

Although all of these objectives are important, one through five constitute minimum goals in our preparation for later chapters. Objectives 11 and 12 are necessary for an understanding of how the membranes of animal cells are organized and how they can hold a cell together while letting substances in and out.

After you have studied this chapter and worked the exercises in it, you should be able to do the following.

1. Write the structure of a molecule that includes at least one carbon-carbon double bond and is typically found in a triacylglycerol.
2. Using that structure, write the products of its reaction with
    (a) water—catalyzed by an enzyme (as in digestion);
    (b) aqueous sodium hydroxide—saponification; and
    (c) hydrogen—hydrogenation with a catalyst and heat.
3. Write the names and structures for at least three saturated and three unsaturated fatty acids.
4. Describe the principal structural differences between animal fats and vegetable oils.
5. Explain what polyunsaturated means when used to describe vegetable oils.
6. Look at the structures of two triacylglycerols that have essentially identical formula masses and tell which has the higher degree of unsaturation.

7. Name two kinds of glycerophospholipids and tell where they may be found in the body.
8. Do the same for two kinds of sphingosine-based lipids.
9. Name several steroids and briefly describe their purposes.
10. Briefly explain why steroids are classified as lipids.
11. Describe the composition and the structure of a biological membrane.
12. Define each of the terms in the Glossary.

GLOSSARY

Amphipathic Molecule. A molecule with both hydrophilic and hydrophobic groups.

Fatty Acid. Any carboxylic acid that can be obtained by the hydrolysis of animal fats or vegetable oils.

Glycerophospholipid. A hydrolyzable lipid—a phosphatide or a plasmalogen—with an ester linkage between glycerol and one phosphoric acid unit that, in turn, is joined by a phosphate ester linkage to a small molecule

Glycolipid. A lipid whose molecules include a glucose unit, a galactose unit or some other carbohydrate unit.

Hydrolyzable Lipid. Any lipid with ester groups.

Hydrophilic Group. Any part of a molecular structure that attracts water molecules; a polar or ionic group such as OH, CO_2^-, NH_3^+, or NH_2.

Hydrophobic Group. Any part of a molecular structure that has no attraction for water molecules; a nonpolar group such as any alkyl group.

Lipid. A plant or animal product that tends to dissolve in such nonpolar solvents as ether, carbon tetrachloride, and benzene.

Lipid Bilayer. The sheetlike array of two layers of lipid molecules, interspersed with molecules of cholesterol and proteins, that make up the membranes of cells in animals.

Micelle. A globular arrangement of the molecules of an amphipathic compound in water in which hydrophobic parts intermingle inside the globule and hydrophilic parts are exposed to water.

Nonhydrolyzable Lipid. Any lipid, such as the steroids, that cannot be hydrolyzed or similarly broken down by aqueous alkali.

Phosphatide. A glycerophospholipid whose molecules are esters between glycerol, two fatty acids, phosphoric acid and a small alcohol.

Phosphoglyceride. (See *Glycerophospholipid.*)

Phospholipid. Lipids such as the glycerophospholipids and the sphingomyelins whose molecules include phosphate ester units.

Plasmalogens. Glycerophospholipids whose molecules also include an unsaturated fatty alcohol unit.

Saponifiable Lipid. (See *Hydrolyzable Lipid.*)

Sphingolipid. A lipid that, when hydrolyzed, gives sphingosine instead of glycerol, plus fatty acids, phosphoric acid, and a small alcohol or a monosaccharide; sphingomyelins and cerebrosides.

Steroids. Nonsaponifiable lipids such as cholesterol and several sex hormones whose molecules have the four fused rings of the steroid nucleus.

Triacylglycerol. A lipid that can be hydrolyzed to glycerol and fatty acids; a triglyceride; sometimes, simply called a glyceride.

Triglyceride. (See *Triacylglycerol.*)

Wax. A lipid whose molecules are esters of long-chain monohydric alcohols and long-chain fatty acids.

SELF-TESTING QUESTIONS

COMPLETION

1. Write the structures of all of the products that would form from the complete hydrolysis of the following lipid.

$$CH_2-O-\overset{\overset{\textstyle O}{\|}}{C}(CH_2)_7CH=CHCH_2CH=CH(CH_2)_4CH_3$$

$$CH-O-\overset{\overset{\textstyle O}{\|}}{C}(CH_2)_8CH_3$$

$$CH_2-O-\overset{\overset{\textstyle O}{\|}}{C}(CH_2)_7CH=CH(CH_2)_7CH_3$$

2. If the lipid of question 1 had been saponified by sodium hydroxide instead of hydrolyzed, the fatty acids would have been produced in the form of their _____.

3. Write the structure of the product of the hydrogenation of all the alkene groups in the lipid in question 1.

4. A molecule of vegetable oil will normally have more _____ than a molecule of animal fat.

5. The two functional groups in a simple lipid are _____ and _____.

6. An example of a nonsaponifiable lipid is any member of the family of _____.

7. Lipids with the general structure $R-O-\overset{\overset{\textstyle O}{\|}}{C}-R'$ (where R and R' are both long-chain) are in the family of _____.

8. The acid, other than fatty acids, liberated when complex lipids are hydrolyzed is _____.

9. A vegetable oil is said to be more _____ than an animal fat (referring to double bonds).

10. The complete hydrolysis (digestion) of this phosphatidyl-choline would give what products? (Write their structures and names.)

$$CH_2-O-\overset{\overset{\displaystyle O}{\|}}{C}(CH_2)_7CH=CH(CH_2)_7CH_3$$

$$CH-O-\overset{\overset{\displaystyle O}{\|}}{C}(CH_2)_7CH=CHCH_2CH=CH(CH_2)_4CH_3$$

$$CH_2-O-\overset{\overset{\displaystyle O}{\|}}{\underset{\underset{\displaystyle O^-}{|}}{P}}-O-CH_2CH_2\overset{+}{N}(CH_3)_3$$

11. Another name for the structure in question 10 is _____.

12. Because the hydrocarbon chains in the structure in question 10 are water-avoiding, they are said to be _____. In the region of the phosphate group, however, the molecule is _____. The molecule in question 10, taken as a whole, is described as _____.

13. Because the hydrocarbon chains of the structure in question 10 have double bonds, the lipid would be described as poly-_____.

MULTIPLE-CHOICE

1. To reduce the degree of polyunsaturation of a triacylglycerol, a manufacturer might
   (a) hydrate it   (c) hydrolyze it
   (b) hydrogenate it   (d) dehydrogenate it

2. If a manufacturer hydrogenated a vegetable oil, the substance might
   (a) turn rancid
   (b) become a detergent
   (c) become a solid at room temperature
   (d) become a diglyceride

3. In glycerides, aqueous sodium hydroxide will attack
   (a) ester linkages   (c) alkene groups
   (b) ether linkages   (d) alkenelike portions

4. Fatty acids obtained from natural lipids are generally
   (a) of even carbon number   (c) insoluble in water
   (b) monocarboxylic   (d) long chain

5. The hydrolysis of a naturally occurring triacylglycerol will give
   (a) glycerol + RCO_2H + $R'CO_2H$ + $R''CO_2H$
   (b) glycerol + RCO_2^- + $R'CO_2^-$ + $R''CO_2^-$
   (c) glycerol + $3RCO_2H$
   (d) glycerol + $3RCO_2H$

6. The name of a C_{18} acid with three alkene groups is
   (a) stearic acid   (c) linoleic acid
   (b) oleic acid   (d) linolenic acid

7. Phospholipids are esters of
   (a) sphingosine only
   (b) either glycerol or sphingosine
   (c) cholesterol only
   (d) glycerol only

8. Glycerophospholipids include
   (a) esters of phosphatidic acids
   (b) cerebrosides
   (c) esters of sphingosine
   (d) glycolipids

9. Cholesterol is classified as a lipid because
   (a) it is an ester
   (b) it dissolves in fat solvents
   (c) it is present in gallstones
   (d) it can be saponified

10. The cell membranes of animals are made of
    (a) lipids
    (b) amylose
    (c) proteins
    (d) cholesterol

11. Molecules of hydrolyzable lipids have
    (a) hydrophobic groups
    (b) ester groups
    (c) amide groups
    (d) alkene groups

12. The cell membranes of animals are organized
    (a) with hydrophobic groups projecting outward away from the membrane
    (b) as lipid bilayers with imbedded proteins
    (c) with hydrophilic groups projecting inward
    (d) with cellulose molecules lending structural support

ANSWERS

ANSWERS TO SELF-TESTING QUESTIONS

Completion

1.

$$HOCH_2CHCH_2OH + CH_3(CH_2)_4CH=CHCH_2CH=CH(CH_2)_7CO_2H$$
$$\underset{OH}{}$$
$$+ CH_3(CH_2)_8CO_2H$$
$$+ CH_3(CH_2)_7CH=CH(CH_2)_7CO_2H$$

2. sodium salts

3.

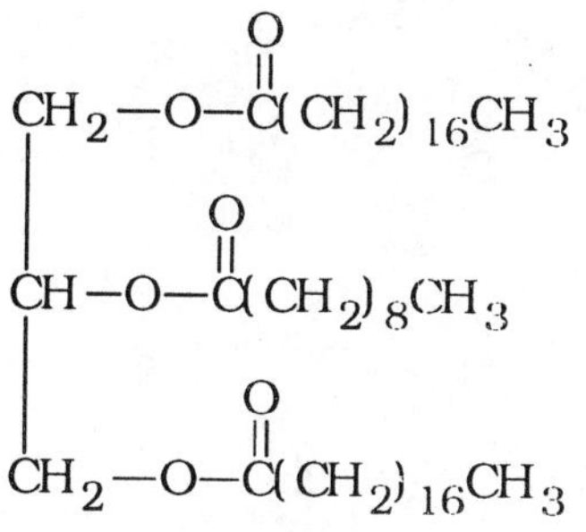

$$CH_2-O-\overset{\overset{O}{\|}}{C}(CH_2)_{16}CH_3$$

$$CH-O-\overset{\overset{O}{\|}}{C}(CH_2)_8CH_3$$

$$CH_2-O-\overset{\overset{O}{\|}}{C}(CH_2)_{16}CH_3$$

4. carbon-carbon double bonds (or alkene groups or **unsaturation**)
5. esters, alkenes
6. steroids
7. waxes
8. phosphoric acid
9. unsaturated

10.

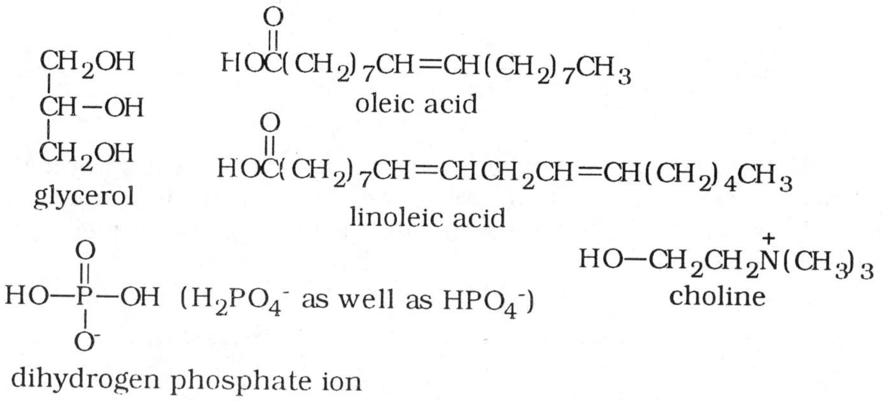

$$\begin{array}{l} CH_2OH \\ CH-OH \\ CH_2OH \end{array}$$

glycerol

$$HO\overset{\overset{O}{\|}}{C}(CH_2)_7CH=CH(CH_2)_7CH_3$$

oleic acid

$$HO\overset{\overset{O}{\|}}{C}(CH_2)_7CH=CHCH_2CH=CH(CH_2)_4CH_3$$

linoleic acid

$$HO-CH_2CH_2\overset{+}{N}(CH_3)_3$$

choline

$$HO-\overset{\overset{O}{\|}}{\underset{\underset{O^-}{|}}{P}}-OH \quad (H_2PO_4^- \text{ as well as } HPO_4^-)$$

dihydrogen phosphate ion

11. lecithin
12. hydrophobic; hydrophilic; amphipathic
13. unsaturated

Multiple–Choice

1. b	2. c	3. a
4. a, b, c, and d	5. a	6. d
7. b	8. a	9. b
10. a, c, and d	11. a, b, and d	12. b

21

PROTEINS

Proteins, like carbohydrates, are known only when their *structures* are known, so the main emphasis in this chapter is the structural features of proteins. Another emphasis is the importance of *molecular shape* and the factors that affect it. This carries over into the study of the protein (glycoprotein) components of animal cell membranes.

OBJECTIVES

These objectives are designed to promote general knowledge about proteins and are important for our understanding of later chapters. When you have completed your study of this chapter and have worked the Practice and Review Exercises in it, you should be able to do the following.

1. Write the names and structures of five representative amino acids, for example
   (a) glycine—because it is the simplest amino acid;
   (b) alanine—as representative of an amino acid with a hydrocarbon side chain (a hydrophobic group);
   (c) cysteine—because it has the important sulfhydryl group;
   (d) glutamic acid—to represent an amino acid with a side chain CO_2H (or CO_2^-) group;
   (e) lysine—to represent amino acids with a side chain NH_2 (or NH_3^+) group.
2. Based on the amino acids you have learned, write the structure of any di-, tri-, tetra-, or pentapeptide and identify the peptide bonds.
3. Translate a structure such as Gly-Ala-Glu into a condensed structural formula.
4. Examine the structure of a polypeptide and identify what parts are amino acid *residues* (peptide units) and what parts are *peptide groups*.

5. Write structures that illustrate how hydrogen bonds and salt bridges participate in the structure of proteins.

6. Name the four levels of structure in proteins and briefly describe each in terms of the kinds of forces that stabilize it and the kinds of geometric forms it takes.

7. Write the structures that show how disulfide bonds occur in proteins.

8. Describe and explain hydrophobic interactions and their origin.

9. Explain the relation between a polypeptide and a protein.

10. Explain how the solubility of a protein can be changed by changing the pH of its medium.

11. Given the structure of a small polypeptide, write the structures of the products of its digestion.

12. Describe what happens structurally when a protein is denatured.

13. Describe, in general terms, how denaturation affects the properties of a protein.

14. List at least four denaturing agents.

15. Explain in general terms how the proteins in a cell membrane participate in active transport to maintain concentration gradients.

16. Describe what gap junctions are and what purpose they serve.

17. In general terms, describe the services performed by the oligosaccharide components of membrane proteins.

18. In general terms, describe the composition and function of ground substance.

19. Name five fibrous proteins.

20. Name two globular proteins.

21. Define each of the terms in the Glossary.

GLOSSARY

Active Transport. The movement of a species across a cell membrane for which the needed energy is supplied by metabolism.

Albumin. One of a family of globular proteins that tend to dissolve in water, and that in blood contribute to the blood's colloidal osmotic pressure and aid in the transport of metal ions, fatty acids, cholesterol, triacylglycerols, and other water-insoluble substances.

Amino Acid. Any organic compound whose molecules have both an amino group and a carboxyl group.

Amino Acid Residue. A structural unit in a polypeptide,

$$NH-CH-CO-,$$
$$\underset{R}{|}$$

furnished by an amino acid, where R is a side chain group; a peptide unit.

Collagen. The fibrous protein of connective tissue that changes to gelatin in boiling water.

Denatured Protein. A protein whose molecules have suffered the loss of their native shape and form as well as their ability to function biologically.

Denaturation. The loss of the natural shape and form of a protein molecule together with its ability to function biologically, but not necessarily accompanied by the rupture of any of its peptide bonds.

Dipeptide. A compound whose molecules have two α-amino acid residues joined by a peptide (amide) bond.

Dipolar Ion. A molecule that carries one plus charge and one minus charge, such as an α-amino acid; a zwitterion.

Disulfide Link. The S—S unit in cystine.

Elastin. The fibrous protein of tendons and arteries.

Fibrin. The fibrous protein of a blood clot that forms from fibrinogen during clotting.

Fibrous Proteins. Water-insoluble proteins found in fibrous tissues.

Gap Junctions. Tubules made of membrane-bound proteins that interconnect one cell to neighboring cells and through which materials can pass directly.

Globular Proteins. Proteins that are soluble in water or in water that contains certain dissolved salts.

Globulins. Globular proteins in the blood that include γ-globulin, an agent in the body's defense against infectious diseases.

Glycolipids. A lipid whose molecules include a glucose unit, a galactose unit, or some other carbohydrate unit.

Glycoproteins. Proteins, often membrane-bound, whose molecules include a carbohydrate unit.

Gradient. The occurrence of a change in the value of some physical quantity with distance, as in a *concentration gradient* in which the concentration of a solute is different in different parts of the system.

Ground Substance. A gel-like material present in cartilage and other extracellular spaces that gives flexibility to collagen and other fibrous proteins.

α-Helix. One kind of secondary structure of a polypeptide in which its molecules are coiled.

Hemoglobin (HHb). The oxygen-carrying protein in red blood cells.

Hydrophobic Interaction. The water-avoidance by nonpolar groups or side chains that is partly responsible for the shape adopted by a polypeptide molecule in an aqueous environment.

Isoelectric Molecule. A molecule that has an equal number of positive and negative sites.

Isoelectric Point (pI). The pH of a solution in which a specified amino acid or a protein is in an isoelectric condition; the pH at which there is no net migration of the amino acid or protein in an electric field.

Keratin. The fibrous protein of hair, fur, fingernails, and hooves.

Myosins. Proteins in contractile muscle.

Native Protein. A protein whose molecules are in the configuration and shape they normally have within a living system.

Peptide Bond. The amide linkage in a protein; a carbonyl-to-nitrogen bond.

Peptide Unit. (See *Amino Acid Residue*.)

pI. (See *Isoelectric Point*.)

β-Pleated Sheet. A secondary structure for a polypeptide in which the molecules are aligned side by side in a sheetlike array with the sheet partially pleated.

Polypeptide. A polymer with repeating α-aminoacyl units joined by peptide (amide) bonds.

Primary Structure. The sequence of aminoacyl residues held together by bonds in a polypeptide.

Prosthetic Group. A nonprotein molecule joined to a polypeptide to make a biologically active protein.

Protein. A naturally occurring polymeric substance made up wholly or mostly of polypeptide molecules.

Quaternary Structure. An aggregation of two or more polypeptide strands each with its own primary, secondary, and tertiary structure.

Receptor Molecule. A molecule of a protein built into a cell membrane that can accept a molecule of a hormone or a neurotransmitter.

Salt Bridge. A force of attraction between (+) and (−) sites on polypeptide molecules.

Secondary Structure. A shape, such as the α-helix or a unit in a β-pleated sheet, that all or a large part of a polypeptide molecule adopts under the influence of hydrogen bonds or salt bridges after its peptide bonds have been made.

Side Chain. An organic group that can be appended to a main chain or to a ring.

Tertiary Structure. The shape of a polypeptide molecule that arises from further folding or coiling of secondary structures.

Triple Helix. The quaternary structure of tropocollagen in which three polypeptide chains are twisted together.

Zwitterion. (See *Dipolar Ion*)

SELF-TESTING QUESTIONS

COMPLETION

1. In their dipolar ionic forms, all amino acids have the same basic unit that (without side chains) has the structure:

    _____

2. Objective 1 asks you to know the structures of five representative amino acids. The best way to learn them is to learn their side chains, because these are always affixed to the basic unit you wrote in question 1. On the lines provided, write the structures of these side chains.

    _____   _____   _____
    glycine side chain   alanine side chain   cysteine side chain

    _____   _____
    glutamic acid side chain   lysine side chain

3. Write the structure of the dipeptide that could form from two glycine units.

    _____

4. In terms of the three-letter symbols for amino acids, the dipeptide in question 3 would be represented as _____.

5. Write the structure of a tripeptide that could be made from alanine, glutamic acid, and cysteine. Let alanine be the N-terminal residue and cysteine the C-terminal residue.

_____

6. In terms of the three-letter symbols, the tripeptide in question 5 has the formula _____ and it contains_____ peptide bonds.

7. Write the structure of the tetrapeptide: Ala-Gly-Lys-Cys

_____

8. Write the structure of cysteine in its dipolar ionic form.

_____

9. If the following polypeptide were subjected to mild reducing conditions, what would form? Write the structure(s) using the three-letter symbols.

Gly-Ala-Cys-Lys-Glu
         |
         S
         |
         S
         |
Gly-Ala-Cys-Lys-Glu   _____

10. In a discussion of how a polypeptide coils or otherwise assumes some geometric shape, we are talking about what structural level? _____

11. Three non-covalent forces that can determine the shape that will be adopted by a polypeptide are

_____ .

12. When we speak of an α-helix itself undergoing folding or twisting, we are talking about what level of protein structure? _____

13. Which level of protein structure is not necessarily attacked by denaturing agents?

_____

14. The side chains of which of the five amino acids in Objective 1 are the most susceptible to being altered by a change in the pH of the medium?(Name the amino acids.)

_____

15. When we speak of two or more polypeptides becoming associated in some way in a gigantic protein system, we are talking about which level of protein structure? _____

16. Because the concentration of dissolved calcium ion inside a cell is different from that outside the cell, we can say that a _____ for calcium ion exists across the cell membrane.

17. Tubules that connect cells to each other are called _____ and they are made of _____ molecules present in cell membranes.

18. The membrane-bound molecules of a _____ protein can uniquely recognize a particular hormone because something about the _____ of the protein molecule is complementary to that of the hormone.

19. Membrane-bound proteins are usually covalently linked to _____ molecules made from aminosugars.

20. Glycosaminoglycans are found in a gel-like material called _____, which helps to give flexibility to a kind of tissue known as _____. In this tissue, tensile strength is supplied by the fibrous protein called _____.

MULTIPLE–CHOICE

1. The partial hydrolysis of a protein produces a number of amino acids together with several dipeptides. Which of the following fragments would not be present?

(a) $NH_2CH_2CH_2CO_2H$

$$(c) \quad HO_2CCH_2NH\overset{\overset{\textstyle O}{\|}}{C}CH_3$$

$$(b) \quad NH_2\overset{}{\underset{CH_3}{C}}H\overset{\overset{\textstyle O}{\|}}{C}NHCH_2CO_2H$$

$$(d) \quad NH_2\overset{}{\underset{(CH_2)_4NH\overset{}{\underset{\overset{\|}{O}}{C}}CH_2NH_2}{C}}HCO_2H$$

2. If the dipolar ionic form of alanine neutralized H^+, it would be changed into

$$(a) \quad \overset{+}{N}H_3\overset{}{\underset{CH_3}{C}}HCO_2^-$$

$$(c) \quad NH_2\overset{}{\underset{CH_3}{C}}HCO_2^-$$

$$(b) \quad NH_2\overset{}{\underset{CH_3}{C}}HCO_2H$$

$$(d) \quad \overset{+}{N}H_3\overset{}{\underset{CH_3}{C}}HCO_2H$$

3. The peptide bonds in a protein can be broken by
   (a) hydrolysis   (c) denaturation
   (b) buffer action   (d) hydration

4. Two proteins might be joined together by the action of a mild oxidizing agent if among their amino acid units there is present
   (a) glutamic acid   (c) glycine
   (b) cysteine   (d) lysine

5. Ions of heavy metals (e.g., Hg^{2+} or Pb^{2+}) denature proteins by combining with
   (a) SH groups   (c) peptide bonds
   (b) CH_3 groups   (d) the protein backbones

6. In very strongly acidic solutions, the molecules of alanine would mostly be in what form?

(a) NH_2CHCO_2H
      |
      CH_3

(c) $NH_2CHCO_2^-$
      |
      CH_3

(b) $\overset{+}{N}H_3CHCO_2H$
      |
      CH_3

(d) $\overset{+}{N}H_3CHCO_2^-$
      |
      CH_3

7.   In their dipolar ionic forms, amino acids are
     (a) electrically neutral
     (b) weak acids
     (c) weak bases
     (d) solids at room temperature

8.   An amino acid with an isoelectric point of 6.8 would consist of molecules with side chains that have
     (a) an extra NH_2 group
     (b) an extra CO_2H group
     (c) a hydrophobic group
     (d) an extra SO_3H group

9.   All the common, naturally occurring amino acids (except glycine) are members of the
     (a) D-family
     (b) L-family
     (c) lipid family
     (d) peptide family

10. The level of protein structure that has amide bonds is the
     (a) primary
     (b) secondary
     (c) tertiary
     (d) quaternary

11. If two molecules of alanine were joined as a dipeptide
     (a) two isomeric dipeptides are possible
     (b) one dipeptide is possible
     (c) the structural symbol would be Ala-Ala
     (d) one peptide bond would be present

12. When proteins are digested

     (a) $-\overset{\overset{O}{\|}}{C}-NH-$ units become $-CO_2H + NH_2-$ units

     (b) $-SH$ groups become $-S-S-$ groups
     (c) $-S-S-$ groups become $-SH$ groups

     (d) CO_2H and NH_2 units join to become $-\overset{\overset{O}{\|}}{C}-NH-$ units

13. If somehow the protein $\underset{NH_3{}^+}{\overset{\wedge\wedge\wedge\wedge\wedge\wedge}{|}} \quad \underset{CO_2^-}{|}$ were changed to

     $\underset{NH_3{}^+}{\overset{\wedge\wedge\wedge\wedge\wedge\wedge}{|}} \quad \underset{CO_2H}{|}$ the protein would be

(a) less soluble in water

(b) more soluble in water

(c) at its isoelectric point

(d) digested

14. In the pentapeptide Gly-Ala-Lys-Cys-Glu, the N-terminal unit is

(a) glycine   (b) glutamic acid (c) lysine   (d) NH_2

15. If the conventions for writing the structures of proteins with the three-letter symbols of amino acids are properly obeyed, the symbol for this tripeptide would be

$$HOCCH_2NHCCHNHCCHNH_2$$

(a) Gly-Ala-Cys   (c) Ala-Gly-Cys

(b) Cys-Ala-Gly   (d) Ala-Cys-Gly

16. The principal non-covalent force in protein structure is the

(a) salt bridge   (c) helix

(b) disulfide link   (d) hydrogen bond

17. An important secondary structural feature in proteins is the

(a) salt bridge   (c) disulfide link

(b) hydrogen bond   (d) α-helix

18. Nonprotein molecules that often are associated with proteins are called

(a) prosthetic groups   (c) side chains

(b) zwitterions   (d) 3° structures

19. A hormone molecule attaches to a cell at

(a) a gap junction   (c) a glycosaminoglycan

(b) a receptor molecule   (d) an N-link

20. Oligosaccharides are present in

(a) glycoproteins   (c) gradients

(b) hydrophobic groups   (d) collagen fibrils

21. Gap junctions are

(a) spaces between nerve cells

(b) spongy materials in cartilage

(c) tubules between adjacent cells

(d) regions between overlapping collagen fibrils

22. The principal protein in the walls of blood vessels is

(a) keratin   (b) myosin   (c) elastin   (d) fibrin

23. An important protein in contractile muscle is

(a) keratin   (b) myosin   (c) elastin   (d) fibrin

24. A protein in hair is

(a) keratin   (b) myosin   (c) elastin   (d) fibrin

25. One important transport protein is

(a) hemoglobin   (b) λ-globulin   (c) casein   (d) nucleoprotein

ANSWERS

ANSWERS TO SELF-TESTING QUESTIONS

Completion

1.

2. glycine   alanine   cysteine   glutamic acid   lysine
       H CH_3 CH_2SH $CH_2CH_2CO_2H$ $CH_2CH_2CH_2CH_2NH_2$

3.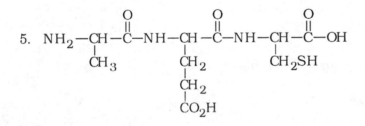

    (Better yet, the dipolar ionic form:

4. Gly-Gly

5.

6. Ala-Glu-Cys, two

7.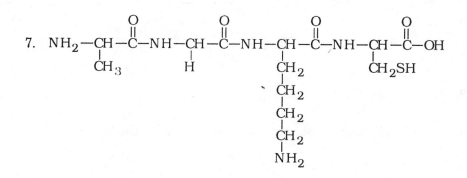

8. $\overset{+}{N}H_3-CH-\overset{\overset{\displaystyle O}{\|}}{C}-O^-$
   $\quad\quad\;|$
   $\quad\;\;CH_2SH$

9. Gly-Ala-Cys-Lys-Glu
   Gly-Ala-Cys-Lys-Glu (Two identical molecules would form.)

10. the secondary structure

11. salt bridges, hydrogen bonds, and the water-avoiding (or attracting) responses of hydrophobic (or hydrophilic) groups

12. the tertiary structure

13. the primary structure

14. lysine and glutamic acid

15. the quaternary structure

16. concentration gradient

17. gap junctions; protein

18. receptor; shape

19. oligosaccharide

20. ground substance; cartilage; elastin

Multiple–Choice

1. a, c, and d (Choice b is a dipeptide, Ala-Gly, and could be one of the several dipeptides formed. Choice a is not an α-amino acid. While choice c has an amide bond, the unit on the right is not an amino acid but rather an acetyl unit. Choice d involves lysine but not in a form found in proteins; the amide bond involves the side chain and not the α-amino group.)

2. d   3. a

4. b   5. a

6. b   7. a, b, c, and d

8. c   9. b

10. a   11. b, c, and d

12. a   13. b (It no longer is isoelectric.)

14. a

15. b (The N-terminal unit is Cys, and the conventions tell us to write the N-terminal unit on the left.)

16. d

17. d (All of the others stabilize secondary structures.)

18. a   19. b

20. a   21. c

22. c   23. b

24. a   25. a

22

ENZYMES, HORMONES, AND NEUROTRANSMITTERS

The heart of this chapter is the study of the ways in which the body controls which reactions go, which shut down, which accelerate, and which go slower. The different chemical and physiological functions of enzymes, hormones, and neurotransmitters are "must" topics of the chapter.

OBJECTIVES

Objectives 1 through 8 are mostly concerned with the basic vocabulary of enzymes; 9 and 10 are about how enzymes work in general. After you have studied this chapter and worked its Exercises, you should be able to do the following.

1. Describe the composition of enzymes and the kinds of cofactors in general terms.
2. Describe what enzymes do.
3. Explain how enzymes possess "specificity."
4. Explain why enzymes are sensitive to denaturing conditions and pH.
5. Describe in general terms how certain B vitamins are vital to some enzymes.
6. Recognize from the name of a substance whether it is an enzyme.
7. Tell what an enzyme's substrate (or type of reaction) is from its name.
8. Define and give an example of an isoenzyme and describe how an analysis of serum isoenzymes can be used in medical diagnosis.
9. Describe the "lock and key" mechanism of enzyme action and how "induced fit" is part of this mechanism.
10. Describe the relationship between the initial rate of an enzyme-catalyzed reaction, the initial enzyme concentration, and the substrate concentration, and explain why the rate levels off at sufficiently high substrate concentration.

11. Explain (using drawings to illustrate your explanation) how an allosteric activation of an enzyme with two active sites results in a sigmoid rate curve.
12. Explain how an effector influences enzyme activity.
13. Describe what happens in a zymogen-enzyme conversion and give an example.
14. Explain how feedback inhibition works and what homeostasis means.
15. Describe how allosteric inhibition works.
16. Explain how some poisons work, and name three kinds of poisons that act as irreversible enzyme inhibitors.
17. Explain in general terms what kind of substance is used to measure the concentration of an enzyme in some body fluid.
18. Name the enzymes whose serum levels are measured in (a) viral hepatitis and (b) myocardial infarction.
19. Name at least two blood-clot-dissolving enzymes and how they work.
20. Name the two kinds of primary chemical messengers.
21. Without necessarily reproducing molecular structures, describe what cyclic nucleotides are.
22. List the steps in the overall process that occurs when cyclic AMP is involved after a signal releases a hormone or a neurotransmitter.
23. Describe in general terms how the inositol phosphate system works.
24. Describe in general terms the four broad types of hormones.
25. Describe how a hormone finds its target cells and recognizes them.
26. In general terms, explain how neurotransmitters work and why they must eventually be deactivated.
27. Describe in general terms what the following do.
    (a) acetylcholine and cholinesterase
    (b) norepinephrine
    (c) monoamine oxidases
    (d) antidepressant drugs
    (e) dopamine
    (f) drugs for schizophrenia, like Thorazine and Haldol
    (g) GABA
    (h) mild tranquilizers, like Valium and Librium
    (i) enkaphalins and endorphins
    (j) substance P
28. Explain how calcium channel blockers work.

GLOSSARY

Agonist. A compound whose molecules can bind to a receptor on a cell membrane and cause a response by the cell.

Allosteric Activation. The activation of an enzyme's catalytic site by the binding of some molecule at a position elsewhere on the enzyme.

Allosteric Inhibition. The inhibition of the activity of an enzyme caused by the binding of an inhibitor molecule at some site other than the enzyme's catalytic site.

Antagonist. A compound that can bind to a membrane receptor but not cause any response by the cell.

Antibiotic. Antimetabolites made by bacteria and fungi.

Antimetabolite. A substance that inhibits the growth of bacteria.

Apoenzyme. The wholly polypeptide part of an enzyme.

Coenzyme. An organic compound needed to make a complete enzyme from an apoenzyme.

Cofactor. A nonprotein compound or ion that is an essential part of an enzyme.

Competitive Inhibition. The inhibition of an enzyme by the binding of a molecule that can compete with the substrate for the occupation of the catalytic site.

Effector. A chemical other than a substrate that can allosterically activate an enzyme.

Enzyme. A catalyst in a living system.

Enzyme-Substrate Complex. The temporary combination that an enzyme must form with its substrate before catalysis can occur.

Feedback Inhibition. The competitive inhibition of an enzyme by a product of its own action.

Homeostasis. The response of an organism to a stimulus such that the organism is restored to its pre-stimulated state.

Hormone. A primary chemical messenger made by an endocrine gland and carried by the bloodstream to a target organ where a particular chemical response is initiated.

Hydrolase. An enzyme that catalyzes a hydrolysis reaction.

Induced Fit Theory. Certain enzymes are induced by their substrate molecules to modify their shapes to accommodate the substrate.

Inhibitor. A substance that interacts with an enzyme to prevent its acting as a catalyst.

Isoenzymes. Enzymes that have identical catalytic functions but which are made of slightly different polypeptides.

Isomerase. An enzyme that catalyzes the conversion of a compound into an isomer.

Ligase. An enzyme that catalyzes the formation of covalent bonds at the expense of triphosphate energy.

Lock-and-Key Theory. The specificity of an enzyme for its substrate is caused by the need for the substrate molecule to fit to the enzyme's surface much as a key fits to and turns only one tumbler lock.

Lyase. An enzyme that catalyzes an elimination reaction to form a double bond.

Monoamine Oxidase. An enzyme that catalyzes the inactivation of neurotransmitters or other amino compounds of the nervous system.

Neurotransmitter. A substance released by one nerve cell to carry a signal to the next nerve cell.

Oxidoreductase. An enzyme that catalyzes the formation of an oxidation-reduction equilibrium.

Poison. A substance that reacts in some way in the body to cause changes in metabolism that threaten health or life.

Proenzyme. An inactive form of an enzyme; a zymogen.

Target Cell. A cell at which a hormone molecule finds a site where it can become attached and then cause some action that is associated with the hormone.

Target Tissue. The tissue where a particular hormone is taken up by target cells.

Transferase. An enzyme that catalyzes the transfer of some group.

Zymogen. A polypeptide that is changed into an enzyme by the loss of a few amino acid residues or by some other change in its structure; a proenzyme.

SELF-TESTING QUESTIONS

COMPLETION

1. An organic compound that is needed, in some cases, to complete an enzyme is called a _____.

2. The specific site on a large enzyme molecule where a substrate experiences the catalytic activity of the enzyme is called the _____.

3. An enzyme might lose its catalytic ability through the action of heat or a change in pH because an enzyme is made up mostly of a _____.

4. The temporary union of an enzyme with the compound on which it acts is called the _____.

5. The theory that accounts for the unusual specificity of an enzyme is the _____ theory.

6. Coenzymes can be made in the body, but in many cases it is essential that the body be supplied with _____ via the diet because they are a necessary part of many coenzyme molecules.

7. Some metabolic sequences are shut down when molecules of their final product combine with and inactivate an _____ for one of the early steps in the sequence.

8. An enzyme that catalyzes the hydrolysis of an ester link would be called an _____; and an enzyme that helps in transferring a phosphate group is called a_____.

9. The enzyme sucrase catalyzes the hydrolysis of _____.

10. Some enzymes will remove a pair of electrons from a substrate; because of this particular kind of action, they are called _____.

11. What are the names of the vitamins needed to make each of these coenzymes?

    NAD^+ _____

    FAD _____

    thiamine pyrophosphate _____

12. For a fixed concentration of enzyme in an enzyme-catalyzed reaction, the initial rate doubles when the initial concentration of substrate, $[S]$, is doubled only when the value of $[S]$ is relatively _____(low or high). The initial rate becomes essentially independent of the initial value of $[S]$ when the latter is relatively _____(low or high). This is because at the higher initial values of $[S]$, all of the molecules of the _____ are saturated with molecules of the _____.

13. The following statements describe ways in which enzymes might be activated or otherwise controlled. On the blank line write the name of the kind of control described.

    (a) An enzyme's catalytic site is activated by the binding of a nonsubstrate molecule elsewhere on the enzyme.

    _____

    (b) An enzyme with two (or more) catalytic sites has the second site activated by the binding of a substrate to the first site.

    _____

(c) The activity of an enzyme for its substrate is suppressed by the binding at its active site of a nonsubstrate molecule of similar shape to the substrate molecule.

_____

(d) The activity of an enzyme is suppressed by its binding at its active site a molecule of one of the products of the action of the enzyme.

_____

(e) The activity of an enzyme is suppressed by its binding another molecule at a place away from its active site

_____

(f) An enzyme forms when a small fragment is cut off from a polypeptide chain letting the active site emerge or unfold.

_____

14. Feedback inhibition is an example of a general kind of ability for self-regulation called _____.

15. Compounds that inhibit normal metabolism in disease-causing bacteria have the general name of _____.

16. By using the _____ for an enzyme as an analytical reagent, the concentration of the enzyme in some body fluid can be measured.

17. In diseases or injuries of the liver, one of the liver enzymes with the symbol _____ escapes into the _____ along with a lower level of another liver enzyme with the symbol _____. The ratio of these two enzymes is typically _____ (higher or lower) in victims of viral hepatitis than in healthy individuals.

18. In a myocardial infarction, three enzymes with the short symbols of _____, _____, and _____ leak from heart tissue into general circulation. One of these can be found in the form of three isoenzymes which have the symbols _____ if present in skeletal muscle, _____ when found in heart muscle, and _____ when present in brain tissue.

19. In an infarct, the enzyme lactate dehydrogenase, symbolized as _____, appears in the blood, but there are _____ isoenzymes for it. Normally, the first two of these isoenzymes appear in relative concentrations in which the level of the first is less than that of the second. This relative relationship is inverted in an infarct, and the phenomenon is called an_____.

20. Three enzymes that can be used to help dissolve a blood clot in a myocardial infarction are named _____, _____ and _____.

21. The protease that catalyzes the hydrolysis of _____, the protein of a blood clot, is named _____ In its inactive stage, as a zymogen, it is called _____.

22. The general names for the two kinds of primary chemical messengers are _____ and _____. Endocrine glands make the _____ and _____ make the other kind of messenger.

23. In the cyclic-AMP system for the delivery of chemical information, the hormone or neurotransmitter binds to its target cell by a _____ mechanism to form a complex. This complex alters a polypeptide called the_____. This then activates the enzyme _____, which catalyzes the conversion of _____ into _____. This product then activates an _____ inside the cell, and thus the message of the primary messenger is delivered. To bring this activation to its close, another cellular enzyme, _____, catalyzes the hydrolysis of _____ to _____.

24. Another receptor system that involves the alteration of the G-protein is called the _____.

25. Hormones exert their influence in a variety of ways. Adrenaline, for example, is an _____ activator. Insulin and human growth hormone affect the _____ of the membranes of their target cells. Some sex hormones function by activating _____ which then direct the synthesis of _____. "Local" hormones or _____ work right where they are synthesized.

26. Chemical communication from one neuron to another occurs across a very narrow, fluid-filled space called a _____ , and the general name for substances that move across this space carrying a "message" is _____ .

27. The neuron from which this messenger moves is called the _____ neuron, and the neuron to which the messenger migrates is called the _____ neuron.

28. A complex forms between a receptor in the postsynaptic neuron and the _____ that works to activate_____. This enzyme then catalyzes the formation of _____ in the membrane of the postsynaptic neuron.

29. To switch a nerve signal off, enzyme-catalyzed reactions have to degrade or otherwise deactivate molecules of a_____ .

30. Cholinesterase catalyzes the hydrolysis of the neurotransmitter called _____. Nerve gases work by _____and the botulinus bacillus works by _____. Local anesthetics like nupercaine and procaine block pain signals by _____.

31. Several antidepressants work by interfering with the use of a neurotransmitter named _____. The deactivation of excess or unused amounts of this substance is catalyzed by enzymes called the _____, symbolized as _____. If this enzyme is inhibited by one kind of antidepressant, then the signal carried by the neurotransmitter is _____. (kept up or blocked)

32. The neurotransmitter called _____ is believed to be involved with schizophrenia. Drugs that bind to receptors for this neurotransmitter inhibit its _____ to these receptors. Symptoms similar to those of schizophrenia can be induced by the abuse of drugs called _____ that work by triggering the _____ (release or decomposition) of this neurotransmitter.

33. The full name of GABA is _____. If the work of this neurotransmitter is enhanced, the result is that nerve signals are _____ (accelerated or inhibited).

34. Two families of neurotransmitters that include powerful painkillers are named the _____ and the _____ .

35. The chemical symbol of the metal ion that is a major secondary chemical messenger is _____. Its concentration in the cytosol as the free ion is extremely low because at higher concentrations it could precipitate as a salt with the _____ ion. The metal ion is let into the cell through _____ every time it is needed to activate some cellular work (like muscle contraction). To tone down such activation, medications called _____ can be used.

36. The molecular basis of memory might involve a kind of chemical messenger called a _____messenger because it can move back into the cell from which a signal has been sent. Two compounds having the formulas _____and _____ are believed to constitute such messengers. Their mechanism of action apparently does not require a _____protein; their molecules can enter cells simply by _____.

MULTIPLE–CHOICE

1. The site on an enzyme that is able to accept the corresponding substrate is called the
    (a) allosteric site   (c) catalytic site
    (b) binding site   (d) effector site

2. A substance with the name protease is
    (a) a prostaglandin   (c) an enzyme
    (b) a coenzyme   (d) a hormone

3. An enzyme for the reaction: $A + B \rightleftharpoons C + D$
    (a) increases the quantity of C that forms
    (b) increases the quantity of A that remains unreacted
    (c) shifts the equilibrium to favor the right side
    (d) accelerates the establishment of the equilibrium

4. The catalytic activity of an enzyme will generally
    (a) increase with increasing temperature
    (b) increase with decreasing temperature
    (c) be unaffected by temperature
    (d) be greatest in a particular temperature range

5. Several coenzymes
    (a) activate apoenzymes
    (b) are made from various B-vitamins
    (c) catalyze hydrolysis reactions
    (d) are esters of carboxylic acids

6. The symbol NAD^+ stands for
    (a) an enzyme   (c) a coenzyme
    (b) a vitamin   (d) an isoenzyme

7. When an enzyme that contains FMN interacts with one having NADH, then which can form?
    (a) $FMNH + NAD^+$ (c) $NADP^+ + FMNH_2$
    (b) $NAD^+ + FMNH_2$ (d) $NAD^+ + H^+ + FMN$

8. Isoenzymes usually differ in
    (a) the substrates they will accept
    (b) their coenzymes
    (c) their apoenzyme portions
    (d) their cofactors

9. The symbol CK stands for
    (a) creatine kinase   (c) cofactor kinase
    (b) carbon-potassium   (d) an isoenzyme

10. A theory that is used to explain enzyme specificity is called the
    (a) theory of allosteric activation
    (b) the sigmoid rate curve theory
    (c) induced fit theory
    (d) lock-and-key theory

11. The Michaelis-Menton equation for the rate of a simple enzyme-catalyzed reaction
   (a) shows that a plot of rate versus substrate concentration is linear.
   (b) describes how the rate becomes constant when $[S]$ is relatively high relative to $[E_0]$.
   (c) says that the rate is independent of initial enzyme concentration.
   (d) reduces to rate $\propto 1/2[S]$ at low values of $[S]$.

Questions 12 through 14 refer to this sequence of reactions:
$$A \overset{E_a}{\rightarrow} B \overset{E_b}{\rightarrow} C \overset{E_c}{\rightarrow} D \overset{E_d}{\rightarrow} E$$

12. If the enzyme, E_a, for the conversion of A to B is activated by molecules of A, and if the graph or plot of the rate of the conversion versus the concentration of E_a has a sigmoid shape, then we probably have the operation of
   (a) feedback inhibition
   (b) gene activation
   (c) activation by an effector
   (d) allosteric activation

13. If molecules of final product, E, deactivate the enzyme E_a for the first step by binding to the active site of that enzyme, we are probably seeing the operation of
   (a) competitive inhibition by nonproduct
   (b) feedback inhibition
   (c) allosteric inhibition
   (d) inhibition by effector

14. If molecules of a substance, A', that resemble the molecules of A but that cannot be changed to B, deactivate the enzyme E_a by binding to the active site of that enzyme, then we are probably observing
   (a) competitive inhibition by nonproduct
   (b) allosteric inhibition by nonproduct
   (c) feedback inhibition by nonproduct
   (d) allosteric action by nonproduct

15. A polypeptide that changes into an enzyme when a small fragment is broken off by some activating reaction is
   (a) a prostaglandin   (c) a coenzyme
   (b) an apoenzyme   (d) a proenzyme

16. The general principle that makes possible the measurement of just one enzyme out of several that are present in blood serum is that of
   (a) enzyme specificity   (c) enzyme inhibition
   (b) electrophoresis   (d) allosteric activation

17. Symptoms of a myocardial infarction include
   (a) LD_1–LD_2 flip
   (b) a rise in the serum level of the CK(MB) isoenzyme
   (c) a drop in the serum level of GOT
   (d) a change in the serum level of glucose oxidase

18. Primary chemical messengers are
   (a) enzymes and hormones
   (b) hormones and neurotransmitters

    (c) neurotransmitters and cyclic nucleotides

    (d) cyclic nucleotides and axons

19. The ability of a hormone to recognize its own target cells depends on a "lock-and-key" fit of the hormone molecule to

    (a) a receptor protein   (c) cyclic AMP

    (b) a neurotransmitter   (d) adenyl cyclase

20. An example of a hormone that activates an enzyme is

    (a) adrenalin   (c) testosterone

    (b) insulin   (d) human growth hormone

21. In a postsynaptic neuron, adenylate cyclase is activated by

    (a) a neurotransmitter

    (b) a receptor

    (c) a neurotransmitter-receptor complex

    (d) phosphodiesterase

22. A substance that serves as both a neurotransmitter and a hormone is

    (a) acetylcholine   (c) epinephrine

    (b) cholinesterase   (d) norepinephrine

23. Norepinephrine that is reabsorbed by a presynaptic neuron is degraded by

    (a) GABA   (b) MAO   (c) LD   (d) CK(MB)

24. A drug that binds to a postsynaptic neuron's receptor protein

    (a) inhibits the transmission of a nerve's signal

    (b) accelerates the activation of adenylate cyclase

    (c) prolongs the receipt of signals from the presynaptic neuron

    (d) inactivates MAO enzymes

25. Amphetamines stimulate presynaptic neurons to release

    (a) L-DOPA   (b) dopamine   (c) GABA   (d) MAO

26. A pain-killer produced in the brain itself is

    (a) substance P   (b) GABA   (c) enkephalin   (d) morphine

27. To make heart muscle contractions less vigorous, some medications block

    (a) adrenaline   (c) G-protein

    (b) plasminogen   (d) calcium channels

ANSWERS

ANSWERS TO SELF–TESTING QUESTIONS

Completion

1. coenzyme (Cofactor is not correct because it would include trace elements too. Vitamin as the answer is close, but coenzyme is better here because vitamins usually have to be changed into coenzymes first. Also, remember that just a few vitamins work this way.)

2. catalytic site

3. protein (It is more specific than apoenzyme.)
4. enzyme-substrate complex
5. lock-and-key
6. vitamins
7. enzyme
8. esterase; kinase
9. sucrose
10. oxidases
11. nicotinamide (or nicotinic acid, but it is the amide that is used); riboflavin; thiamine
12. low; high; enzyme; substrate
13. (a) activation by an effector
    (b) allosteric activation
    (c) competitive inhibition by a nonsubstrate
    (d) feedback inhibition
    (e) allosteric inhibition
    (f) zymogen activation
14. homeostasis
15. antimetabolite
16. substrate
17. GPT; bloodstream; GOT; higher
18. CK, LD, and GOT; CK(MM); CK(MB); CK(BB)
19. LD; 5; LD_1–LD_2 flip
20. streptokinase, tissue plasminogen activator (TPA), and APSAC (acylated plasminogen-streptokinase-activator complex)
21. fibrin; plasmin; plasminogen
22. hormones and neurotransmitters; hormones; neurons (nerve cells)
23. lock-and-key; G-protein; adenylate cyclase; ATP into cyclic-AMP; enzyme; phosphodiesterase;cyclic-AMP into AMP
24. inositol phosphate system
25. enzyme; permeabilities; genes; enzymes; prostaglandins
26. synapse; neurotransmitter
27. presynaptic; postsynaptic
28. neurotransmitter; adenylate cyclase; cyclic AMP
29. neurotransmitter
30. acetylcholine; inhibiting cholinesterase; blocking the synthesis of acetylcholine; blocking the receptor protein for acetylcholine
31. norepinephrine; monoamine oxidases; MAO; kept up
32. dopamine; binding; amphetamines; release
33. gamma-aminobutyric acid; inhibited
34. endorphins and enkephalins
35. Ca^{2+}; phosphate; calcium channels; calcium channel blockers
36. retrograde; NO and CO; receptor; diffusion

Multiple–Choice

1.	b	10.	c, d	19.	a
2.	c	11.	b	20.	a
3.	d	12.	d	21.	c
4.	d	13.	b	22.	d
5.	b	14.	a	23.	b
6.	c	15.	d	24.	a
7.	b	16.	a	25.	b
8.	c	17.	a, b	26.	c
9.	a	18.	b	27.	d

23

EXTRACELLULAR FLUIDS OF THE BODY

In the professional health areas, the chemistry of respiration and the chemistry of the blood are areas of vital importance because *respiratory problems arise in a number of emergency situations.* To deal swiftly and correctly with the emergency, primary health care personnel both physicians and nurses must obtain and quickly evaluate several measurements, including the blood pH, its bicarbonate level, and the partial pressures of the blood gases. Early in your career, you will most likely have to learn about the chemistry of respiration and the chemistry of blood in order to increase your professional capabilities. If you use this occasion for a thorough study, your value as a professional will improve that much more quickly.

OBJECTIVES

Objectives 1 through 4 are concerned with the chemistry of digestion and the digestive juices. The first objective should be considered a minimum goal for this area. Objectives 5 through 17 deal with the chemistry of respiration and the chemistry of blood (although a study of the latter is not complete without a study of the function of the kidneys, the subject of objectives 19 and 20).

After you have studied this chapter and worked the exercises in it, you should be able to do the following.

1. Name the end products of the digestion of carbohydrates, proteins, and lipids.
2. List the major digestive reactions of the mouth, the stomach, and the duodenum.
3. Name the digestive juices and their principal enzymes and zymogens.
4. Describe the functions of bile salts.
5. Describe the functions of the principal components of the blood.
6. Give the names and formulas and general uses of the two Group IA cations that occur in the body.

7. Describe the levels of the Group IA cations in plasma and intracellular fluids.
8. Describe in general terms the problems associated with hypo- and hypernatremia as well as hypo- and hyperkalemia.
9. Give the names, formulas, and general uses of the two Group IIA cations present in the body, and describe their levels in blood and intracellular fluids.
10. Describe in general terms the problems associated with hypo- and hypercalcemia as well as hypo- and hypermagnesemia.
11. Describe the chemical composition of bone giving the name and the formula of its chief mineral and the name of its principal nonmineral substance.
12. State the range of values for the chloride ion level in blood and inside cells, and describe (in general terms) its function.
13. Describe what problems are associated with hypo- and hyperchloremia.
14. Explain how fluids and nutrients exchange at capillary loops.
15. Name two situations in which proteins leave the blood and describe the consequences.
16. Give three ways edema may arise.
17. Describe the main features of the composition of hemoglobin.
18. Explain what 2,3-bisphosphoglycerate (BPG) does.
19. Referring to the allosteric effect and the hemoglobin-oxygen dissociation curve, explain how oxygen binds cooperatively to hemoglobin.
20. Discuss how oxygen affinity varies with blood pH.
21. Discuss how oxygen affinity varies with the pCO_2 of blood.
22. Describe how partial pressure gradients aid in gas exchange.
23. Describe how localized changes in pH aid in gas exchange.
24. Describe the functions of the isohydric shift and the chloride shift.
25. Explain how waste CO_2 is transported in blood.
26. Explain how myoglobin in certain tissue aids in gas exchange.
27. Outline how values of blood pH, pCO_2, and $[HCO_3^-]$ change from the normal in clinical situations involving metabolic or respiratory acidosis and alkalosis.
28. Describe the role of the kidneys in preventing acidosis.
29. Describe what vasopressin, aldosterone, and renin do.
30. Define the terms in the Glossary.

GLOSSARY

Acidosis. A condition in which the pH of the blood is below normal. *Metabolic acidosis* is brought on by a defect in some metabolic pathway. *Respiratory acidosis* is caused by a defect in the respiratory centers or in the mechanisms of breathing.

Albumin. One of a family of globular proteins that tend to dissolve in water, and that in blood contribute to the blood's colloidal osmotic pressure and aid in the transport of metal ions, fatty acids, cholesterol, triacylglycerols, and other water-insoluble substances.

Aldosterone. A steroid hormone, made in the adrenal cortex, secreted into the bloodstream when the sodium ion level is low, and that signals the kidneys to leave sodium ions in the bloodstream.

Alkalosis. A condition in which the pH of the blood is above normal. *Metabolic alkalosis* is caused by a defect in metabolism. *Respiratory alkalosis* is caused by a defect in the respiratory centers of the brain or in the apparatus of breathing.

Bile. A secretion of the gall bladder that empties into the upper intestine and furnishes bile salts; a route of excretion for cholesterol and bile pigments.

Carbaminohemoglobin. Hemoglobin that carries chemically bound carbon dioxide.

Cardiovascular Compartment. The entire network of blood vessels and the heart.

Chloride Shift. An interchange of chloride ions and bicarbonate ions between a red blood cell and the surrounding blood serum.

Digestive Juice. A secretion into the digestive tract that consists of a dilute aqueous solution of digestive enzymes (or their zymogens) and inorganic ions.

2,3-Bisphosphoglycerate (BPG). An organic ion that nestles within the hemoglobin molecule in deoxygenated blood but is expelled from the hemoglobin molecule during oxygenation.

Edema. The swelling of tissue caused by the retention of water.

Electrolytes, Blood. The ionic substances dissolved in the blood.

Erythrocyte. A red blood cell.

Extracellular Fluids. Body fluids that are outside of cells.

Fibrin. The fibrous protein of a blood clot that forms from fibrinogen during clotting.

Fibrinogen. A protein in blood that is changed to fibrin during clotting.

Gastric Juice. The digestive juice secreted into the stomach and that contains pepsinogen, hydrochloric acid, and gastric lipase.

Globulins. Globular proteins in the blood that include gamma-globulin, an agent in the body's defense against infectious diseases.

Hemoglobin (HHb). The oxygen-carrying protein in red blood cells.

Hypercapnia. An elevated value of pCO_2 in blood.

Hyperkalemia. An elevated level of potassium ion in blood—above 5.0 meq/L.

Hypernatremia. An elevated level of sodium ion in blood—above 145 meq/L.

Hypocapnia. A lower than normal value of pCO_2 in blood.

Hypokalemia. A low level of potassium ion in blood—below 3.5 meq/L.

Hyponatremia. A low level of sodium ion in blood—below 135 meq/L.

Internal Environment. Everything enclosed within an organism.

Interstitial Fluids. Fluids in tissues but not inside cells.

Intestinal Juice. The digestive juice that empties into the duodenum from the intestinal mucosa and whose enzymes also work within the intestinal mucosa as molecules migrate through.

Isohydric Shift. In actively metabolizing tissue, the use of a hydrogen ion released from newly formed carbonic acid to react with and liberate oxygen from oxyhemoglobin; in the lungs, the use of hydrogen ion released when hemoglobin oxygenates to combine with bicarbonate ion and liberate carbon dioxide for exhaling.

Mucin. A viscous glycoprotein released in the mouth and the stomach that coats and lubricates food particles and protects the stomach from the acid and pepsin of gastric juice.

Oxygen Affinity. The percentage to which all of the hemoglobin molecules in the blood are saturated with oxygen molecules.

Oxyhemoglobin. Hemoglobin holding its maximum load of oxygen.

Pancreatic Juice. The digestive juice that empties into the duodenum from the pancreas.

Respiratory Gases. Oxygen and carbon dioxide.

Saliva. The digestive juice secreted in the mouth whose enzyme, amylase, catalyzes the partial digestion of starch.

Shock, Traumatic. A medical emergency in which relatively large volumes of blood fluid leave the vascular compartment and enter the interstitial spaces.

Vascular Compartment. The entire network of blood vessels and their contents.

Vasopressin. A hypophysis hormone that acts at the kidneys to help regulate the concentrations of solutes in the blood by instructing the kidneys to retain water (if the blood is too concentrated) or to excrete water (if the blood is too dilute).

SELF-TESTING QUESTIONS

COMPLETION

Questions 1 through 13 are concerned with the chemistry of digestion.

1. The first digestive juice to have much effect on proteins in the diet is _____.

2. Some digestive enzymes occur in their respective digestive juices initially in inactive forms called _____.

3. The proteolytic enzyme active in the stomach is called _____ and its zymogen is _____.

4. One kind of gastric cell contains a "pump" called the _____ ion pump. It moves _____ ion into the stomach and pumps _____ ion out of the stomach. However, the latter reenters the stomach together with _____ ion, so the net effect of all this action is the delivery of _____ acid to the stomach. One treatment for ulcers uses _____ to close down the _____ pump.

5. The partially digested material in the stomach that moves into the upper intestinal tract is called _____.

6. Starch in the diet is acted upon first in the _____ by the enzyme _____ found in _____.

7. All of the reactions of digestion are classified as _____ reactions.

8. For the most effective digestion of fats and oils in the diet, we depend on the emulsifying action of _____, compounds that are best described as _____ and that are released into the _____ of the digestive tract from an organ called the _____.

9. A special enzyme in intestinal juice called _____ helps convert trypsinogen to trypsin.

10. Besides helping to digest proteins in the diet, trypsin also catalyzes the conversion of _____ to chymotrypsin and of _____ to carboxypeptidase.

11. The arrival of acidic chyme in the duodenum causes the release of enzyme-rich fluids called _____ and _____.

12. Another fluid stimulated by the arrival of chyme in the upper intestinal tract is called _____.

13. The principal fat-digesting enzyme released in pancreatic juice is called _____.

14. Complete the following table by writing the names of the end products of the complete digestion of each family of foods given in the first column.

Food	End-Products of Digestion
Proteins	_____
Starch	_____
A mixture of lactose, maltose, and sucrose	_____
Triacylglycerols	_____

15. The chief cation in the blood has the formula _____, and its normal concentration is from _____ to _____ (include the unit). When its level exceeds the higher of these two values, the condition is called _____, and when it falls below the lower value, the condition is _____.

16. The chief cation inside cells has the formula _____, and its concentration is generally _____ (include the unit).

17. When the K^+ ion level of the blood drops below _____ (include the unit), the condition is called _____, and when its level rises above _____ (include the unit), the condition is _____.

18. Three health conditions that can cause severe hyperkalemia are _____, _____, and _____.

19. (Supply the prefixes, either hypo or hyper.) A general and unusual decrease in body fluids can cause

    _____-natremia as well as _____-kalemia.
    (hypo or hyper)   (hypo or hyper)

20. The formulas of the two Group IIA cations in the body are _____ and _____.

21. The second most abundant cation inside cells has the formula _____.

22. The chief cation in bones has the formula _____.

23. Besides being necessary in bones, calcium ions also participate in the _____ of muscles.

24. The overuse of milk of magnesia can cause _____-magnesemia.
    (hypo or hyper)

25. A deficiency of vitamin _____ can cause hypocalcemia.

26. The overuse of calcium-based antacids can cause _____.

27. Both Ca^{2+} and Mg^{2+} can activate certain _____.

28. From the standpoint of osmosis and dialysis, which is the more concentrated mixture, blood or interstitial fluid? _____

29. In which direction will water naturally have a net tendency to migrate: from a blood capillary into the interstitial compartment or from the interstitial compartment into the bloodstream? _____

30. Besides the forces generated by osmosis and dialysis, what force is present in the circulatory system that is especially important on the arterial side of a capillary loop? _____

31. Materials are taken away from tissues by both veins and the _____ ducts.

32. If fluids accumulate in some tissue (e.g., the lower limbs) a condition of _____ exists.

33. Within the red blood cells, called _____ are molecules of _____, which carry oxygen from the lungs to tissues needing oxygen.

34. Each molecule of _____ in red blood cells has _____ subunits and each subunit can carry _____ molecule(s) of oxygen.

35. The reaction whereby oxygen is picked up may be symbolized as follows: $HHb + O_2 \rightleftharpoons$ _____ + _____

36. To help force the reaction from left to right, the system acts to neutralize the _____ ion.

37. The ion largely responsible for doing this (question 36) has the formula _____, and the product of the neutralizing reaction subsequently breaks up into _____ and water.

38. If 95% of all the hemoglobin in a sample of blood is saturated with oxygen, then the _____ of the sample is 95%.

39. The first molecule of oxygen to bind to deoxygenated hemoglobin has an _____ effect that aids in bringing oxygen to the remaining oxygen-binding sites.

40. The symbol HbO_2^- is our symbol for _____, and that symbol is incorrect to the extent it does not show that each molecule of this substance carries _____ molecules of oxygen.

41. At active tissues needing oxygen, ions with the symbol _____ are generated which help HbO_2^- release oxygen. In other words, at a lower pH hemoglobin has a lower _____.

42. The equation for the formation of carbaminohemoglobin is:

$$\underline{\hspace{4cm}} \rightleftharpoons \underline{\hspace{4cm}}$$

43. The equation of question 42 is one way that newly formed molecules of carbon dioxide are taken up by the bloodstream. The other chemical change to carbon dioxide that occurs when it enters a red blood cell has the equation (an equilibrium):

$$\underline{\hspace{4cm}} \rightleftharpoons \underline{\hspace{4cm}}$$

44. The equations (or equilibria) of questions 42 and 43 occur at actively metabolizing tissue, and their operation shifts what equilibrium involving oxygen release?

$$\underline{\hspace{4cm}} \rightleftharpoons \underline{\hspace{4cm}}$$

As you have written this equilibrium, how does it shift at actively metabolizing cells?

_____
(left or right)

45. To recapitulate, the equilibrium of question 44 shifts to the _____ at cells needing _____. They need it because they have done some chemical work that produces water and _____ which reacts somewhat with the water to give _____ according to the equilibrium of question _____. CO_2 also reacts somewhat with hemoglobin according to the equilibrium of question _____. These last two reactions generate _____ ions that aid in forcing the equilibrium of question 44 to the _____ and thereby help in releasing _____.

46. The use of the hydrogen ions generated in the equilibria of questions 42 and 43 to shift the equilibrium of 44 is called the _____.

47. Bicarbonate ions travel back to the lungs in the serum, not inside _____.

48. When bicarbonate ions leave the erythrocyte,_____ ions move in to replace them. This switch is called the _____.

49. The combined action of H^+ and CO_2 generated at actively metabolizing cells serves to _____ (raise or lower) the oxygen affinity of _____.

50. A hemoprotein at muscles that has a higher oxygen affinity than hemoglobin is called _____.

51. An acidosis brought on by an error in metabolism is called _____.

52. An acidosis caused by a breakdown in the respiratory centers or by some deterioration of the lungs is called _____.

53. Hyperventilation is a method used by a system to expel excess _____, the loss of which should help _____(raise or lower) the pH of the blood.

54. Prolonged vomiting may cause metabolic _____.

55. Shallow breathing, or_____, is the way the system tries to retain _____ which has the effect of retaining a neutralizer of _____ in the carbonate buffer. This helps _____ (raise or lower) the pH of the blood. Thus, shallow breathing may be a response to metabolic _____ (acidosis or alkalosis).

56. If shallow breathing occurs because the respiratory centers are not working, the individual cannot efficiently expel _____ and may experience respiratory _____.

57. The hyperventilation of a patient in hysterics causes an over-removal of_____, a loss of the _____ buffer, and a _____ in the pH of the blood. These responses result in respiratory _____. Rebreathing exhaled air helps suppress this because it supplies more _____ to the lungs and thence to the bloodstream.

58. If air too enriched in oxygen is given to a patient for too long a period, that individual will have trouble removing _____ from metabolizing cells.

59 The technical name for an increase in arterial pCO_2 is_____. The ventilation problem behind this condition has the technical name of _____ and the pH of the blood _____.
                    (increases or decreases)

60. What organ(s), in effect, removes acid from the blood?

_____

61. If the blood pressure drops greatly, the kidneys may not be able to _____ the blood because the blood flow through them is reduced.

62. The kidneys respond to a fall in blood pressure by secreting an enzyme called _____ into the blood which acts on a proenzyme called _____. This proenzyme is changed to _____ which helps to generate _____ the most powerful _____ known.

63. The endocrine gland called the _____ is sensitive to the _____ pressure of the blood. If this pressure goes up, it means that the concentration of dissolved and dispersed substances in blood is too _____(high or low). If this happens, the gland secretes the hormone_____, whose target organ is _____.

64. Secretion of this hormone (in question 63) eventually results in the formation of a _____ (lesser or greater) volume of urine.

65. The hormone that helps the bloodstream to conserve its sodium ions called_____.

MULTIPLE–CHOICE

1. The end products of the digestion of milk sugar are
   - (a) glucose and galactose
   - (c) glucose and fructose
   - (b) only glucose
   - (d) glucose and maltose

2. If gastric juice were completely devoid of its hydrochloric acid, this would impair the digestion in the stomach of
   - (a) lipids
   - (c) proteins
   - (b) carbohydrates
   - (d) chyme

3. Removal of the gall bladder would reduce the efficiency of the digestion of
   - (a) lipids
   - (c) proteins
   - (b) carbohydrates
   - (d) fatty acids

4. The enzyme that catalyzes the conversion of trypsinogen to trypsin is
   - (a) amylase
   - (b) pepsin
   - (c) mucin
   - (d) enteropeptidase

5. The enzyme in saliva is
   - (a) mucin
   - (b) pepsin
   - (c) α-amylase
   - (d) amylose

6. Bile contains
   - (a) a lipase
   - (c) a carbohydrase
   - (b) a protease
   - (d) no enzymes

7. Without bile salts, which substances would not be as easily absorbed from the intestinal tract into the bloodstream?
   - (a) fat-soluble vitamins
   - (c) glucose
   - (b) water-soluble vitamins
   - (d) amino acids

8. The most abundant cation in the blood is
   - (a) Na
   - (b) K
   - (c) K^+
   - (d) Na^+

9. Any injury that causes a large number of cells to break open can lead to
   - (a) hypernatremia
   - (c) hypermagnesemia
   - (b) hyperkalemia
   - (d) hyperchloremia

10. If the intake of K^+ ion is high, the body spontaneously works to lose
    - (a) Cl^-
    - (b) Ca^{2+}
    - (c) Na^+
    - (d) Mg^{2+}

11. The blood can become hypocalcemic in
    - (a) vitamin D deficiency
    - (b) a misfunctioning thyroid gland
    - (c) overdoses of antacids based on $Ca(OH)_2$
    - (d) blood transfusions

12. The blood can become hypermagnesemic
    - (a) in vitamin B_{12} deficiency
    - (b) when it become hypercalcemic
    - (c) if milk of magnesia is overused as a laxative
    - (d) if the thyroid gland's activity becomes impaired

13. A normal value for the level of Cl^- in the blood is
    (a) 2 meq/L   (c) 35.5 mg/L
    (b) 100 meq/L   (d) 100 eq/L

14. If the level of Cl^- ion in blood drops, the body tends to retain
    (a) HCO_3^- (b) H^+ (c) Na^+ (d) H_2O

15. If the level of Cl^- in blood rises, one result can be
    (a) hypochloremia   (c) acidosis
    (b) hyponatremia   (d) alkalosis

16. Of all of the anions in blood, about two-thirds are
    (a) HPO_4^{2-} (b) $H_2PO_4^-$ (c) SO_4^{2-} (d) Cl^-

17. Plasma and interstitial fluids are most unlike in their concentrations of
    (a) electrolytes   (c) lipids
    (b) proteins   (d) carbohydrates

18. Oxygen is transported in the bloodstream chiefly as
    (a) molecules of O_2 (c) oxyhemoglobin ions
    (b) hydronium ions   (d) methemoglobin ions

19. Hemoglobin in blood has a relatively high oxygen affinity in the tissue capillaries of those tissues where
    (a) the pH is dropping   (c) pCO_2 is rising
    (b) the pH is rising   (d) pCO_2 is low

20. Hemoglobin more easily accepts its second, third, and fourth molecules of oxygen than it does its first because the first has
    (a) an allosteric effect   (c) an isohydric effect
    (b) a Bohr effect   (d) a releaser effect

21. The equilibrium $HHb + O_2 \rightleftharpoons HbO_2^- + H^+$ will respond to a drop in pH by
    (a) shifting to the right   (c) remaining unchanged
    (b) shifting to the left   (d) absorbing more O_2

22. If the equilibrium $CO_2 + H_2O \rightleftharpoons H^+ + HCO_3^-$ shift to the right, then the equilibrium of question 21 will tend to
    (a) shift to the right   (c) remain unchanged
    (b) shift to the left   (d) absorb oxygen

23. The equilibrium $HHb + CO_2 \rightleftharpoons Hb{-}CO_2^- + H^+$ shifts to the right in a region where
    (a) the oxygen affinity of HHb is high
    (b) the pO_2 is relatively high
    (c) the pH is relatively high
    (d) the pCO_2 is relatively high

24. When the carbonate buffer system in blood acts, a hydrogen ion is replaced by a water molecule at the expense of a
    (a) hydroxide ion   (c) bicarbonate ion
    (b) hydronium ion   (d) calcium ion

25. Something that has a higher oxygen affinity under identical conditions than adult hemoglobin is
    (a) sickle cell hemoglobin   (c) fetal hemoglobin
    (b) myoglobin   (d) none of these

26. Healthy kidneys respond to acidosis by
    (a) putting H^+ into urine   (c) retaining Na^+
    (b) retaining HCO_3^- (d) removing ketone bodies

27. When respiratory centers are healthy, the body can respond to acidosis by
    (a) hyperventilation   (c) retaining CO_2
    (b) hypoventilation   (d) retaining H^+

28. Hyperventilation aids in controlling acidosis by
    (a) removing CO_2 from blood
    (b) bringing in more O_2
    (c) promoting the chloride shift
    (d) increasing the pCO_2 of blood

29. In severe emphysema, acidosis may develop because
    (a) hyperventilation cannot be stopped
    (b) shallow breathing cannot be used
    (c) oxygen toxicity has become a problem
    (d) the removal of CO_2 from the blood at the lungs is impaired

30. If for any reason hemoglobin molecules leave the lungs not fully saturated with oxygen, the condition is called
    (a) oxygen affinity   (c) hypoxia
    (b) oxygen toxicity   (d) anoxia

31. When a tissue cannot get oxygen, the condition is called
    (a) oxygen affinity   (c) hypoxia
    (b) hypocapnia   (d) anoxia

32. The nitrogen wastes present in urine is (are)
    (a) urea
    (b) creatine
    (c) uric acid (and the urate ion)
    (d) ammonia

33. If the osmotic pressure of the blood increases by even as little as 2%,
    (a) the kidneys release renin
    (b) the hypophysis releases vasopressin
    (c) the adrenal cortex releases aldosterone
    (d) the liver releases fibrinogen

34. The hormone that helps to regulate the level of sodium ions in the blood is
    (a) angiotensin I   (c) renin
    (b) vasopressin   (d) aldosterone

35.   On the arterial side of a capillary loop, the blood pressure is
       (a)   lower than on the venous side
       (b)   equal to that on the venous side
       (c)   lower than the osmotic pressure from the interstitial areas
       (d)   higher than the osmotic pressure from the interstitial areas

ANSWERS

ANSWERS TO SELF–TESTING QUESTIONS

Completion

1.   gastric juice
2.   zymogens
3.   pepsin, pepsinogen
4. $K^+- H^+$; H^+; K^+; Cl^-; hydrochloric; cimetidine (Tagamet); $K^+- H^+$
5.   chyme
6.   mouth, amylase, saliva
7.   hydrolysis (or hydrolytic)
8.   bile salts, detergents (or soaps or steroid-based detergents),
     upper intestine (or duodenum), gall bladder
9.   enteropeptidase
10. chymotrypsinogen, procarboxypeptidase
11. intestinal juice and pancreatic juice
12. bile
13. pancreatic lipase
14. amino acids
     glucose
     glucose, fructose, galactose
     fatty acids and monoacylglycerols (some diacylglycerols)
15. Na^+; 135 to 145 meq/L; hypernatremia; hyponatremia
16. K^+; 125 meq/L
17. 3.5 meq/L; hypokalemia; 5.0 meq/L; hyperkalemia
18. burns, crushing injuries, and heart attacks
19. hyper-; hypo-
20. Mg^{2+}; Ca^{2+}
21. Mg^{2+}
22. Ca^{2+}
23. contraction
24. hyper-
25. D

26. hypercalcemia
27. enzymes
28. blood
29. from the interstitial compartment into the bloodstream
30. simple blood pressure (from the pumping action of the heart)
31. lymph
32. edema
33. erythrocytes, hemoglobin
34. hemoglobin, four, one
35. $HbO_2^- + H^+$
36. hydrogen
37. HCO_3^-, carbon dioxide
38. oxygen affinity
39. allosteric
40. oxyhemoglobin, four
41. H^+ (H_3O^+ is better), oxygen affinity
42. $HHb + CO_2 \rightleftharpoons Hb\!-\!CO_2^- + H^+$
43. $CO_2 + H_2O \rightleftharpoons HCO_3^- + H^+$
44. $HHb + O_2 \rightleftharpoons HbO_2^- + H^+$
    to the left (or right to left)
45. left, oxygen; carbon dioxide, HCO_3^- and H^+, 43; 42 hydrogen (H^+), left, oxygen
46. isohydric shift
47. red blood cells (or erythrocytes)
48. chloride (Cl^-); chloride shift
49. lower, hemoglobin
50. myoglobin
51. metabolic acidosis
52. respiratory acidosis
53. carbon dioxide, raise
54. alkalosis
55. hypoventilation, carbon dioxide, base; lower; alkalosis
56. carbon dioxide, acidosis
57. carbon dioxide, carbonate, rise; alkalosis; carbon dioxide
58. carbon dioxide
59. hypercapnia, hypoventilation, decreases
60. the kidneys
61. filter or cleanse
62. renin, angiotensinogen; angiotensin I, angiotensin II, vasoconstrictor
63. hypophysis (or pituitary), osmotic; high; vasopressin, the kidneys
64. lesser than usual
65. aldosterone

Multiple–Choice

1.	a	13.	b	25.	b and c
2.	c	14.	a	26.	a, b, c, and d
3.	a	15.	c	27.	a
4.	d	16.	d	28.	a
5.	c	17.	b	29.	d
6.	d	18.	c	30.	c
7.	a	19.	b and d	31.	d
8.	d	20.	a	32.	a, b, c, and d
9.	b	21.	b	33.	b
10.	c	22.	b	34.	d
11.	a, b	23.	d	35.	d
12.	c	24.	c		

24

NUCLEIC ACIDS

Heredity is not only involved with substances having certain functions; it is also concerned with molecules having particular structures that carry out these functions. Although the emphasis in this chapter is the relationship between structure and function, you are not expected to memorize the structures of specific compounds. You should, however, be able to name the hydrolysis products of the nucleic acids. You should also be prepared to give some of the condensed structural representations for these products using the symbols for the phosphate-pentose-phosphate-pentose chain and the letters—A, T, G, C, and U—that represent the side chains.

OBJECTIVES

After you have completed your study of this chapter, you should be able to do the following.

1. Give the name and the abbreviation for the chemical of an individual gene.
2. Give the general name for the monomer unit of a nucleic acid.
3. Give the names of the compounds produced when these monomeric units are hydrolyzed.
4. Describe in words the two main structural differences between DNA and RNA.
5. Using simple symbols, describe the features of a DNA strand.
6. Describe what in that structure is the genetic code.
7. Describe in words the contribution of Crick and Watson to the chemistry of heredity.
8. Describe in words the structure and shape of paired strands of DNA and the forces that stabilize them.
9. Explain why, regardless of species, A and T are always found in a ratio of 1:1, and why G and C are found in the same ratio.

10. Name and outline the process by which a gene copies itself.
11. Describe the functions of the four types of RNA and where they work.
12. Using words and simple drawings, explain how a gene specifies a unique amino acid sequence on a polypeptide.
13. Using letter symbols—A, T, C, G, and U—explain what a codon and its anticodon are and name the chemicals that bear them.
14. In general terms, explain how a virus works in a host cell.
15. In general terms, describe some of the things that can be done by recombinant DNA technology.
16. Give four examples of diseases related to genetic disorders.
17. Describe the chief goal of the Human Genome Project.
18. Define each of the terms in the Glossary.

GLOSSARY

Anticodon. A sequence of three adjacent side chain bases on a molecule of tRNA that is complementary to a codon and that fits to its codon on an mRNA chain during polypeptide synthesis.

Base, Heterocyclic. A heterocyclic amine obtained from the hydrolysis of nucleic acids: adenine, thymine, guanine, cytosine, or uracil.

Base Pairing. In nucleic acid chemistry, the association by means of hydrogen bonds of two heterocyclic, side-chain bases—adenine with thymine (or uracil) and guanine with cytosine.

Chromosome. Small threadlike bodies in a cell nucleus that carry genes in a linear array and that are microscopically visible during cell division.

Codon. A sequence of three adjacent side-chain bases in a molecule of mRNA that codes for a specific amino acid residue when the mRNA participates in polypeptide synthesis.

Deoxyribonucleic Acid (DNA). The chemical of a gene; one of a large number of polymers of deoxyribonucleotides and whose sequences of side-chain bases constitute the genetic messages of genes.

Double Helix DNA. A spiral arrangement of two intertwining DNA molecules held together by hydrogen bonds between side-chain bases; duplex DNA.

Duplex DNA. (See *Double Helix DNA.*)

Enzyme Induction. The process of switching on a gene to direct the synthesis of an enzyme.

Exon. A segment of a DNA strand that eventually becomes expressed as a corresponding sequence of aminoacyl residues in a polypeptide.

Gene. A unit of heredity carried on a cell's chromosomes and consisting of DNA.

Genetic Code. The set of correlations that specify which codons on mRNA chains are responsible for which aminoacyl residues when the latter are steered into place during the mRNA-directed synthesis of polypeptides.

Genetic Engineering. The use of recombinant DNA to make genes and the products of such genes.

Genome. The entire complement of the genetic information of a species; all of the genes of an individual.

Heterogeneous Nuclear RNA (hnRNA). RNA made directly at the guidance of DNA and from which messenger RNA (mRNA) is made.

Inducer. A substance whose molecules remove repressor molecules from operator genes and so open the way for structural genes to direct the overall syntheses of particular polypeptides.

Intron. A segment of a DNA strand that separates exons and that does not become expressed as a segment of a polypeptide.

Messenger RNA (mRNA). RNA that carries the genetic code as a specific series of codons for a specific polypeptide from the cell's nucleus to the cytoplasm.

Mitochondria. Cellular bodies in which a cell's ATP is made.

Nucleic Acid. A polymer of nucleotides in which the repeating units are pentose phosphate esters, each pentose unit bearing a side-chain base (one of four heterocyclic amines); polymeric compounds that are involved in the storage, transmission, and expression of genetic messages.

Plasmid. A circular molecule of supercoiled DNA in a bacterial cell.

Radiomimetic Substance. A substance whose chemical effect in a cell mimics the effect of ionizing radiation.

Recombinant DNA. DNA made by combining the natural DNA of plasmids in bacteria or the natural DNA in yeasts with DNA from external sources, such as the DNA for human insulin, and made as a step in a process that uses altered bacteria or yeasts to make specific proteins (e.g., interferons, human growth hormone, or insulin).

Replication. the reproductive duplication of a DNA double helix.

Repressor. A substance whose molecules can bind to a gene and prevent the gene from directing the synthesis of a polypeptide.

Ribonucleic Acids (RNA). Polymers of ribonucleotides that participate in the transcription and the translation of the genetic messages into polypeptides. (See also *Heterogeneous Nuclear RNA, Messenger RNA, Ribosomal RNA,* and *Transfer RNA.*)

Ribosomal RNA (rRNA). RNA that is incorporated into cytoplasmic bodies called ribosomes.

Ribosome. A granular complex of rRNA that becomes attached to a mRNA strand and that supplies some of the enzymes for mRNA-directed polypeptide synthesis.

Ribozyme. An enzyme whose molecules consist of ribonucleic acid rather than polypeptide.

Transcription. The synthesis of messenger RNA under the direction of DNA.

Transfer RNA (tRNA). RNA that serves to carry an aminoacyl group to a specific acceptor site of a mRNA molecule at a ribosome where the aminoacyl group is placed into a growing polypeptide chain.

Translation. The synthesis of a polypeptide under the direction of messenger RNA.

Virus. One of a large number of substances that consist of nucleic acid (usually RNA) surrounded (usually) by a protein overcoat and that can enter host cells, multiply, and destroy the host.

SELF-TESTING QUESTIONS

COMPLETION

1   The smallest unit of life in an organism is the _____. Everything it holds is called _____, which includes discrete bodies called _____, the principal sites of the synthesis of _____, a source of chemical energy.

2. The part of a cell outside its nucleus is the _____ and its liquid portion is the _____. Also present, however, are particles made of nucleoprotein called the _____.

3. Intertwined filaments of nucleoprotein in a cell nucleus make up a material called
    _____. Parts of this necklace-like material (the "pearls") consist of proteins called
    _____ which are wrapped with coils of one of the nucleic acids called _____
    for short.

4. Prior to cell division, the cell's chromatin thickens and bodies called _____ become
    visible under a microscope. What is taking place to cause the thickening is the duplication of
    _____.

5. Nucleic acids are polymers whose monomers have the general name of_____. These
    monomers can be hydrolyzed to give one or the other of two sugars named_____and
    _____, an inorganic_____ion and a set of heterocyclic_____.

6. Nucleic acids that are made with ribose have the full name of _____ which is
    usually abbreviated _____. The four bases usually obtained from this kind of
    nucleic acid have the names and one-letter symbols of

    _____ _____   _____ _____

    _____ _____   _____ _____

7. Nucleic acids made with deoxyribose have the full name of_____ which is
    usually abbreviated_____. The four bases obtained from this kind of nucleic
    acid have the names and one-letter symbols of

    _____ _____   _____ _____

    _____ _____   _____ _____

8. The "backbones" of all nucleic acids contain a chain of diesters of_____ and
    the particular kind of sugar molecule. The bases are attached to the backbone, one base at each
    _____ unit.

9. The bases have functional groups and molecular geometries that permit them to form base-pairs
    with each other by means of _____ bonds. Base A always pairs with either
    _____ or with _____; G always pairs with _____.

10. Two strands of DNA form a twisting _____ according to evidence cited by
    _____ and _____. Base A of one strand pairs to base _____ opposite it on
    the other strand; and base C pairs to base _____.

11. An individual hereditary unit called a _____ consists of a particular series of triplets of
    nucleotides in one of the kinds of nucleic acids, _____.

12. In higher organisms, complete genes generally come in interrupted sequences of triplets. The
    interrupting segments in DNA molecules are called_____, and segments that make
    up a full gene are called _____.

13. The process whereby a gene becomes reproduced exactly, just prior to cell division, is called
    _____. The faithfulness of the copying depends on _____.

14. When DNA is used to direct the synthesis of a polypeptide, the DNA first directs the synthesis
    of a specific form of RNA called_____, abbreviated _____.
    This product is then processed to delete the triplets in its chain that correspond to the
    _____ segments of DNA. Then the remaining triplets are "knitted" together to give
    another form of RNA called _____, abbreviated _____.

15. Each triplet in mRNA is called a _____, and each is able to specify a particular
    _____ residue in a completed _____.

16. The overall process of using DNA to direct the formation of mRNA is called _____.

17. Following this process is another complicated process called _____, and its
    final product is a specific _____. When the latter is made, specific substances

called _____ help the product to adopt its final, correct native configuration.

18. To accomplish this last process, the cell needs two other kinds of RNA. One kind is used to make ribosomes and is called _____, abbreviated _____. The other kind is called _____, abbreviated _____, and its function is to carry _____ to polypeptide assembly sites on _____.

19. One particular triplet of bases on a tRNA molecule can match a complementary triplet on mRNA. This tRNA triplet is called _____.

20. In some organisms at least, genes are in a switched-off status because a _____ molecule has become bound to a segment of the gene. A molecule that can combine with this and remove it is called _____. Several drugs called _____ kill bacteria by interfering with bacterial gene-directed polypeptide synthesis.

21. Radiations such as X rays or gamma rays cause the most damage to a cell when they strike _____. Those that cause cancer are called _____. If a birth defect is the result, the agent is called a _____.

22. Substances that can invade particular "host" cells and take over the genetic machinery are called _____. To enter a cell, this substance uses an _____ to catalyze the breakdown of the _____ of the host cell.

23. Some RNA viruses carry an enzyme called _____ that can catalyze the synthesis of new RNA from directions encoded on the old viral _____.

24. Some RNA viruses carry a DNA polymerase, an enzyme called _____. This enzyme has the unusual ability to use _____ to direct the synthesis of _____, a flow of genetic information opposite the normal flow.

25. A family of viruses that uses its RNA and reverse transcriptase to make duplex DNA is called the _____. The duplex DNA than directs the synthesis of viral _____. This family of viruses includes oncogenic RNA viruses which can change normal genes to _____. Another virus in this family attacks the immune system, specifically the _____ lymphocytes, and so this virus has the abbreviated name of _____, the cause of _____.

26. In a technology called _____ DNA technology, particles called _____ in a bacterium are modified and given new genetic material. Then the bacteria will manufacture some _____ that corresponds to its additional genes.

27. To amplify (clone) small amounts of DNA, the _____ reaction is used.

28. Four diseases attributed to defective genes are
    (1) Associated with the overproduction of thick mucus in the lungs:_____
    (2) Associated with an impairment in the metabolism of the amino acid phenylalanine:

    _____
    (3) Associated with a blood disorder: _____
    (4) Associated with poor pigmentation of the eyes and the skin:_____

29. The defective gene in cystic fibrosis is one that directs the synthesis of a transmembrane _____ in cells of the lungs and the digestive tract that controls the movement of _____ ion through the cell membrane to the outside. When the movement of this ion is impaired, the movement of molecules of _____ is also impaired, leading to a thickening of the _____.

30. In a technology called _____, attempts are made to insert proper DNA into cells carrying defective _____.

MULTIPLE–CHOICE

1. What is transmitted from parents to offspring is a complete set of
    (a) DNA molecules   (c) enzymes
    (b) polypeptides   (d) hormones

2. The site of polypeptide synthesis in a cell is
    (a) a chromosome   (c) a ribosome
    (b) a gene   (d) a nuclear membrane

3. If DNA were fully hydrolyzed, the products would be
    (a) ribose   (c) phosphoric acid
    (b) deoxyribose   (d) a few heterocyclic amines

4. Molecules of tRNA differ from molecules of mRNA in being
    (a) longer   (c) shorter
    (b) triple helices   (d) inside ribosomes

5. The overall process of transcription proceeds in which order?
    (a) exon to intron to polypeptide
    (b) mRNA to polypeptide
    (c) DNA to hnRNA to mRNA
    (d) DNA to rRNA to tRNA to mRNA

6. DNA segments that appear to be uninvolved in polypeptide synthesis are called
    (a) introns   (b) exons   (c) triplets   (d) anticodons

7. Human insulin can be made by bacteria or yeasts by a method called
    (a) recombinant bacteria   (c) recombinant plasmids
    (b) recombinant RNA   (d) recombinant DNA

8. Gene-directed polypeptide synthesis proceeds in which order of events?
    (a) gene to mRNA to hnRNA to tRNA
    (b) gene to hnRNA to mRNA to polypeptide
    (c) gene to rRNA to tRNA to hnRNA
    (d) gene to replicated gene to polypeptide

9. According to the Crick-Watson theory, the genetic message carried by a gene is related most particularly to
    (a) the kinds of heterocyclic amines projecting from the phosphate-pentose chain in the gene
    (b) the sequence in which the heterocyclic amines are lined up along the "backbone" of the gene
    (c) the absence of one of the OH groups normally found in RNA
    (d) the sequence of amino acids in gene molecule

10. The functional groups in adenine are geometrically arranged to enable adenine to pair by hydrogen bonding with
    (a) adenine   (b) guanine   (c) thymine   (d) uracil

11. The molecular basis of a mutation is most closely linked to a
    (a) defect in the transcription of a genetic message to mRNA
    (b) change in the sequence or identity of heterocyclic amines on a DNA molecule
    (c) defect in the arrival sequence of tRNA molecules at mRNA codon sites
    (d) defect in the rRNA of ribosomes

12. If a codon triplet were U–C–G, the anticodon would be
    (a) A–C–G   (b) C–G–A   (c) T–G–C   (d) A–G–C
13. The entire complement of genetic information of a species is called its
    (a) exons   (c) chromatin
    (b) chromosomes   (d) genome
14. To clone DNA in the lab, scientists can use
    (a) the polymerase chain reaction
    (b) restriction enzymes
    (c) interferons
    (d) chaperonines
15. A viral enzyme that uses RNA information to make DNA is
    (a) RNA replicase   (c) restriction enzyme
    (b) reverse transcriptase   (d) DNA replicase

ANSWERS

ANSWERS TO SELF-TESTING QUESTIONS

Completion

1. cell; protoplasm; mitochondria; ATP
2. cytoplasm; cytosol; ribosome
3. chromatin; histones; DNA
4. chromosomes; DNA
5. nucleotides; ribose and deoxyribose; phosphate; bases (or amines)
6. ribonucleic acids; RNA

adenine	A	guanine	G
uracil	U	cytosine	C

7. deoxyribonucleic acids; DNA

adenine	A	guanine	G
thymine	T	cytosine	C

8. phosphoric acid; sugar (or pentose)
9. hydrogen; T or U; C
10. double helix; Crick and Watson; T; G
11. gene; DNA
12. introns; exons
13. replication; base pairing of A to T and of G to C
14. heterogeneous nuclear RNA; hnRNA; intron; messenger RNA; mRNA
15. codon; amino acid; polypeptide
16. transcription
17. translation; polypeptide; chaperonines
18. ribosomal RNA; rRNA; transfer RNA; tRNA; aminoacyl units; a ribosome (or at an mRNA site at a ribosome)

19. an anticodon
20. repressor; an inducer; antibiotics
21. DNA in a cell nucleus; carcinogens; teratogen
22. viruses; enzyme; membrane
23. RNA replicase; RNA
24. reverse transcriptase; RNA; DNA
25. retroviruses; RNA; oncogenes; T_4; HIV, AIDS
26. recombinant; plasmids; polypeptide (or protein)
27. polymerase chain
28. (1) cystic fibrosis
    (2) PKU (phenylketonuria)
    (3) sickle cell anemia
    (4) albinism
29. protein; Cl⁻; water; mucous
30. gene therapy; genes

Multiple–Choice

1. a
2. c
3. b, c, d
4. c
5. c
6. a
7. d
8. b
9. b
10. c, d
11. b
12. b
13. d
14. a
15. b

25

BIOCHEMICAL ENERGETICS

This chapter has two broad objectives—to provide an overview of the major metabolic pathways that the body can tap for chemical energy, and to go into detail about how the cell makes ATP by the citric acid cycle coupled to the respiratory chain. As minimum goals, be sure to be able to name the major pathways introduced in this chapter, name their starting and ending materials, and describe their overall place in the scheme of biochemical energetics.

Pay careful attention to what your instructor tells you concerning what details must be learned and what can be skimmed over. Don't worry about any details, however, until you have the broad picture well in hand.

OBJECTIVES

After you have studied this chapter and worked the Exercises in it, you should be able to do the following.

1. Name the two products of digestion that are most frequently used for chemical energy in living systems.
2. Name the end products of the complete catabolism of carbohydrates and simple lipids.
3. Write the structures of the triphosphate and diphosphate networks.
4. Explain the basis for classifying organophosphates as high or low energy.
5. Name the principal triphosphate used as an immediate source of chemical energy in cells.
6. Outline (by a flow sheet) the principal pathways in biochemical energetics between products of digestion and the synthesis of ATP.
7. Describe the place acetyl coenzyme A has in biochemical energetics.
8. Give the general purpose of the citric acid cycle (Kreb's Cycle; Tricarboxylic Acid Cycle).

9. Give the symbols for the chief hydride-accepting coenzymes and write equations (in two ways) illustrating their activity.

10. In general terms, explain what kinds of gradients are forced into existence by the operation of the respiratory chain, and where they occur.

11. In general terms, describe the connections between these gradients and the synthesis of ATP (using the chemiosmotic theory).

13. Define the terms in the Glossary.

GLOSSARY

Acetyl Coenzyme A. The molecule from which acetyl groups are transferred into the citric acid cycle or into the fatty acid synthesis.

$$CH_3\overset{\overset{\displaystyle O}{\|}}{C}-S-CoA$$

Adenosine Diphosphate (ADP). A high-energy diphosphate ester obtained from adenosine triphosphate (ATP) when part of the chemical energy in ATP is tapped for some purpose in a cell.

Adenosine Monophosphate (AMP). A low-energy phosphate ester that can be obtained by the hydrolysis of ATP or ADP; a monomer for the biosynthesis of nucleic acids.

Adenosine Triphosphate (ATP). A high-energy triphosphate ester used in living systems to provide chemical energy for metabolic needs.

Aerobic Sequence. An oxygen-consuming sequence of catabolism that starts with glucose or with glucose units in glycogen, and proceeds through glycolysis, the citric acid cycle, and the respiratory chain.

Anaerobic Sequence. The oxygen-independent catabolism of glucose or of glucose units in glycogen to lactate ion.

Catabolism. Metabolic reactions that break up larger molecules.

Chemiosmotic Theory. An explanation of how oxidative phosphorylation is related to a flow of protons in a proton gradient that is established by the respiratory chain, and that extends across the inner membrane of a mitochondrion.

Citric Acid Cycle. A series of reactions that dismantle acetyl units and send electrons (and protons) into the respiratory chain; a major source of metabolites for the respiratory chain.

Fatty Acid Cycle. (See *β-Oxidation Pathway*.)

Glycolysis. A series of chemical reactions that break down glucose or glucose units in glycogen until pyruvate remains (when the series is operated aerobically) or lactate forms (when the conditions are anaerobic).

High-Energy Phosphate. An organophosphate with a phosphate group transfer potential equal to or higher than that of ADP or ATP.

β-Oxidation Pathway. The catabolism of a fatty acid by a series of steps that produce acetyl units (in acetyl CoA).

Oxidative Phosphorylation. The synthesis of high energy phosphates such as ATP from lower energy phosphates and inorganic phosphate by the reactions that involve the respiratory chain.

Phosphate Group Transfer Potential. The relative ability of an organophosphate to transfer a phosphate group to some acceptor.

Proton-Pumping ATPase. The enzyme in the inner mitochondrial membrane that catalyzes the formation of ATP from ADP and P_i under the influence of a flow of protons across the membrane through a tubular part of this enzyme.

Respiratory Chain. The reactions that transfer electrons from the intermediates made by other pathways to oxygen; the mechanism that creates a proton gradient across the inner membrane of a mitochondrion and that leads to ATP-synthesis; the enzymes that handle these reactions.

Respiratory Enzymes. The enzymes of the respiratory chain.

Substrate Phosphorylation. The direct transfer of a phosphate unit from an organophosphate to a receptor molecule.

SELF-TESTING QUESTIONS

COMPLETION

1. When glucose is burned in air, the elements present in the glucose emerge in molecules of _____ and _____.

2. When glucose is carried through both the anaerobic and aerobic sequences of metabolism in the body, its elements emerge in molecules of _____ and _____.

3. The energy produced by the combustion of glucose appears largely as _____.

4. Some of the energy produced by the breakdown of glucose in the body appears as _____, but of greater importance to the body, it also appears in the form of molecules of _____.

5. The structure of ATP in its electrically neutral, un-ionized form is (complete the following):

$$\boxed{\text{adenosine}} -$$

6. When adenosine triphosphate reacts, provides energy for some chemical change, and loses one phosphate, the remainder of its molecule is called _____ and has the symbol
_____.

7. The symbol, P_i, stands for a mixture having (give the formulas) _____ and _____ as its two principal ions. The exact proportion of these ions in the mixture is largely a function of the _____ of the medium.

8. If structure II in the following reaction has a higher negative phosphate group transfer potential than structure I, where should the arrowhead be placed on the incomplete arrow?

$$\text{R—O—PO}_3^{2-} + \text{R'OH} \qquad\qquad\qquad \text{ROH} + \text{R'—O—PO}_3^{2-}$$
$$\text{I} \qquad\qquad \text{(incomplete arrow)} \qquad\qquad \text{II}$$

9. When proteins of a relaxed muscle interact with ATP, the muscle contracts as _____ an _____ are produced.

10. In a cell receiving an insufficient supply of oxygen, fresh ATP can be made from glucose by a series of reactions called _____, also called the _____ sequence, for which lactate is an end product.

11. In a cell receiving a sufficient supply of oxygen, the catabolism of glucose can occur by the _____ sequence, which changes glucose to _____, which is then converted to _____ coenzyme A. The latter is catabolized by the _____ cycle, and intermediates of this cycle interact with the _____ chain.

12. The respiratory chain is a series of reactions whereby intermediates of the _____ cycle send electrons through complexes of enzymes until _____ is reduced to water.

13. The organic group that is joined to coenzyme A has the structure: _____, and the symbol we use for the combination of this with coenzyme A is

_____.

14. The catabolism of fatty acids by a series of reactions called _____ generates a succession of molecules of _____, which enter the _____ and the _____ pathways.

15. The name of the high energy phosphate in muscles that can quickly remake ATP from ADP is

_____.

16. The chief location in the cell for the synthesis of ATP is the _____ of a mitochondrion. When the respiratory chain operates, the net effect is to change MH$_2$ and half a molecule of oxygen to M and _____ and to generate a gradient of _____ ions as well as a gradient of _____ across the _____ of the mitochondrion.

17. As _____ ions move across the inner membrane of the mitochondrion at those places where such movement can occur, other changes are initiated that lead to the synthesis of _____ from _____ and P$_i$.

18. Our symbol for a donor of H:$^-$ units to the respiratory chain is _____, and the metabolic pathway that is the richest supplier of H:$^-$ is called the _____.

19. The first receptor of H:$^-$ in the respiratory chain is an enzyme whose coenzyme has the short symbol of _____; the symbol for its reduced form is _____. This reduced form can pass H:$^-$ to another enzyme with a coenzyme having the short symbol of _____ and whose reduced form is _____.

20. When FMNH$_2$ passes H:$^-$ to the next enzyme in the chain having the short symbol _____, only the electrons in H:$^-$ go to this next enzyme and the hydrogen nuclei, H$^+$, are put into _____. In this way, the first "installment" of the two gradients, the _____ gradient and the _____ gradient that extends from relatively high concentrations of these species in the _____ space to lower concentrations in the mitochondrial _____. The enzyme package that accomplishes this is called _____.

21. Following the iron-sulfur enzyme and the enzyme containing coenzyme Q is a series of enzymes collectively called the _____ that are present in two enzyme packages called _____ and _____. The final acceptor of the electrons being transferred from one of these enzymes to the next is _____, and water forms.

22. The respiratory chain has a "branch," and it involves one acceptor of H:$^-$ from certain kinds of metabolites. The coenzyme for this acceptor has the short symbol of _____, and its reduced form is symbolized as _____. The latter can be reoxidized by interacting with an enzyme of the main respiratory chain with the coenzyme having the symbol _____. The package of enzymes of this branch is called _____.

MULTIPLE–CHOICE

1. Of the following substances, which has the most potential for generating molecules of ATP?
   (a) glucose
   (b) $CH_3(CH_2)_{16}CO_2H$
   (c) glycine
   (d) oxygen

2. Among the substances essential to the aerobic sequence of glucose catabolism is (are)
   (a) NAD^+ (b) O_2 (c) ATP   (d) ADP

3. The product of the operation of the respiratory chain that is most needed by the body is
   (a) ATP
   (b) H_2O
   (c) $[H{:}^- + H^+]$
   (d) FAD

4. Among the accomplishments of the citric acid cycle is (are)
   (a) the synthesis of active acetyl
   (b) supplying $H{:}^-$ and H^+ to the respiratory chain
   (c) glycogenesis
   (d) glycolysis

5. To help get glucose inside cells of certain tissues, the blood should carry
   (a) epinephrine   (b) insulin   (c) cyclic AMP   (d) NAD

6. If a reaction is symbolized by

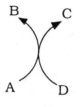

   it could be rewritten as
   (a) $A + B \rightarrow C + D$
   (b) $B + C \rightarrow A + D$
   (c) $A + C \rightarrow B + D$
   (d) $A + D \rightarrow B + C$

7. To complete the following reaction, we should include as a product
   $$ATP + H_2O \rightarrow \underline{\hspace{2cm}} + PP_i$$
   (a) ADP
   (b) AMP
   (c) H_2O
   (d) $CO_2 + H_2O$

8. The chief use of acetyl CoA is to provide "fuel" for
   (a) the citric acid cycle
   (b) glycolysis
   (c) the anaerobic sequence
   (d) homeostasis

9. The chief purpose of the respiratory chain is to
   (a) accept $H{:}^-$
   (b) use up acetyl CoA
   (c) resupply ATP
   (d) use O_2

10. The complete catabolism of pyruvate by the citric acid cycle gives a maximum ATP yield of
    (a) 15   (b) 18   (c) 36   (d) 38

11. Between the respiratory chain and glycolysis in the catabolism of glucose occurs the
    (a) anaerobic sequence
    (b) oxidative phosphorylation
    (c) citric acid cycle
    (d) homeostasis

12. The operation of the respiratory chain establishes two gradients within a mitochondrion. These involve specifically
    (a) OH^- and Cl^-
    (b) H^+ and (+) charge
    (c) NAD^+ and $NADH_2$
    (d) electron pairs and ATP

13.   One of the (incomplete) sequences of enzymes or coenzymes in the respiratory chain is (in the correct order)

(a)   FMN → FAD → Cyt c → Cyt a

(b)   FAD → NAD^+ → FeS—P → Q

(c)   Q → Cyt c_1 → Cyt b → FeS—P

(d) NAD^+ → FMN → Q → Cyt a

14.   The symbol FMN stands for

(a)   an enzyme

(b)   the reduced form of a flavin enzyme

(c)   the oxidized form of a flavoprotein

(d)   a coenzyme

15.   The chemiosmotic theory was proposed by

(a)   Hans Krebs   (c)   Charles MacMunn

(b)   Peter Mitchell   (d)   David Keilin

16.   The proton-pumping ATPase

(a)   is in the outer membrane of the mitochondrion.

(b)   includes a "gate" for protons, which is made of polypeptides.

(c)   is an integral component of complex III of the respiratory chain of enzymes.

(d)   is an enzyme of the citric acid cycle.

17.   One important source of acetyl CoA is

(a)   pyruvate + CoA—SH + NAD^+

(b)   citrate

(c)   the respiratory chain

(d)   oxidative phosphorylation

18.   When glucose is catabolized to CO_2 and H_2O, oxygen atoms from O_2 in the air end up as parts of molecules of

(a) CO_2 (b) H_2O (c)   ATP   (d) P_i

19.   Which of the following types of reactions occur in the citric acid cycle?

(a)   dehydration

(b)   hydrogenation

(c)   dehydrogenation

(d)   addition of water to a double bond

20.   When acetyl CoA adds to the keto group of oxaloacetate, the product is

(a)   pyruvate   (b)   ATP   (c)   lactate   (d)   citrate

ANSWERS

ANSWERS TO SELF–TESTING QUESTIONS

Completion

1.   carbon dioxide, water

2.   carbon dioxide, water

3.   heat

4. heat, ATP

5.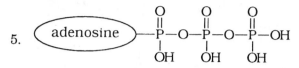

6. adenosine diphosphate, ADP
7. $H_2PO_4^-$, HPO_4^{2-}; pH
8. Place the arrow at the left end of the line
9. ADP; P_i
10. glycolysis; anaerobic
11. aerobic; pyruvate; acetyl; citric acid; respiratory
12. citric acid; oxygen

13. $CH_3-\overset{\overset{\displaystyle O}{\|}}{C}-$; $CH_3-\overset{\overset{\displaystyle O}{\|}}{C}-S-CoA$

14. the β-oxidation pathway; acetyl coenzyme A; citric acid cycle; respiratory chain.
15. creatine phosphate
16. matrix; H_2O; H^+; (+) charge; inner membrane
17. H^+; ATP; ADP
18. MH_2; citric acid cycle
19. NAD^+; NADH; FMN; $FMNH_2$
20. FeS—P; the intermembrane space of the mitochondrion; H^+ ion; (+) charge; intermembrane; matrix; complex I
21. cytochromes; complexes III and IV; oxygen
22. FAD; $FADH_2$; Q (or coenzyme Q); complex II

Multiple–Choice

1.	b	11.	c
2.	a, b, and d	12.	b
3.	a	13.	d
4.	b	14.	d
5.	b	15.	b
6.	d	16.	b
7.	b	17.	a
8.	a	18.	b
9.	c	19.	a, c, and d
10.	a	20.	d

26
METABOLISM OF CARBOHYDRATES

This chapter continues our study of the molecular basis of energy for living and introduces the molecular basis of a widespread disease—diabetes. We cannot go into the molecular basis of very many diseases, but we need to study at least some examples that illustrate the intimate involvement of fundamental chemical principles with life in both wellness and illness. Acid-base theory, buffers, properties of gases, chemical equilibria, organic reactions, enzymes, and chemical messengers all have major or supporting roles in the tragic drama of diabetes. This chapter and the next provide the final acts.

OBJECTIVES

After you have studied this chapter and worked the Review Exercises in it, you should be able to do the following.

1. Discuss the factors that influence the blood sugar level, using the technical terms for high and low values.
2. List some of the effects of hypoglycemia.
3. Describe the glucose tolerance test and its purpose.
4. Describe the influences that the hormones epinephrine, glucagon, insulin, and somatostatin have on glucose metabolism.
5. Describe in general terms what diabetes mellitus is.
6. Outline the Cori Cycle.
7. Write an overall equation for glycolysis—glucose to lactate.
8. Explain the importance of glycolysis.
9. Explain why anaerobic glycolysis ends at lactate, not pyruvate.
10. Give the general purpose of the pentose phosphate pathway of glucose catabolism.

11. Describe in general terms what the liver can do if the brain's chief nutrient is not available in the diet.

12. Define all of the terms in the Glossary.

GLOSSARY

Anaerobic Sequence. The oxygen-independent catabolism of glucose or of glucose units in glycogen to lactate ion.

Blood Sugar Level. The concentration of carbohydrate (mostly glucose) in the blood; usually stated in units of mg/dL.

Cori Cycle. The sequence of chemical events and transfers of substances in the body that describes the distribution, storage, and mobilization of blood sugar, including the reconversion of lactate to glycogen.

Diabetes Mellitus. A disease in which there is an insufficiency of effective insulin and an impairment of glucose tolerance.

Epinephrine. A hormone of the adrenal medulla that activates the enzymes needed to release glucose from glycogen.

Glucagon. A hormone secreted by the α-cells of the pancreas in response to a decrease in the blood sugar level that stimulates the liver to release glucose from its glycogen stores.

Gluconeogenesis. The synthesis of glucose from compounds with smaller molecules or ions.

Glucose Tolerance. The ability of the body to manage the intake of dietary glucose while keeping the blood sugar level from fluctuating widely.

Glucose Tolerance Test. A series of measurements of the blood sugar level after the ingestion of a considerable amount of glucose; used to obtain information about an individual's glucose tolerance.

Glucosuria. The presence of glucose in urine.

Glycogenesis. The synthesis of glycogen.

Glycogenolysis. The breakdown of glycogen to glucose.

Glycolysis. A series of chemical reactions that break down glucose or glucose units in glycogen until pyruvate remains (when the series is operated aerobically) or lactate forms (when the conditions are anaerobic).

Human Growth Hormone. One of the hormones that affects the blood sugar level; a stimulator of the release of the hormone glucagon.

Hyperglycemia. An elevated level of sugar in the blood—above 110 mg/dL in whole blood.

Hypoglycemia. A low level of glucose in blood—below 70 mg/dL of whole blood.

Insulin. A protein hormone made by the pancreas, released in response to a rise in the blood sugar level, and used by certain tissues to help them take up glucose from circulation.

Normal Fasting Level. The normal concentration of something in the blood, such as blood sugar, after about four hours without food.

Oxygen Debt. The condition in a tissue when anaerobic glycolysis has operated and lactate has been excessively produced.

Pentose Phosphate Pathway. The synthesis of NADPH that uses chemical energy in glucose-6-phosphate and that involves pentoses as intermediates.

Renal Threshold. That concentration of a substance in blood above which it appears in the urine.

Somatostatin. A hormone of the hypothalamus that inhibits or slows the release of glucagon and insulin from the pancreas.

SELF-TESTING QUESTIONS

COMPLETION

1. The synthesis of glucose from starting materials that do not include any mono-, di-, or polysaccharides is called_____.

2. The synthesis of glycogen may be called _____.

3. The release of glucose from glycogen is called _____.

4. A hormone that can help release glucose from glycogen in a hurry is _____.

5. Events involved in the distribution, storage, mobilization, and usage of glucose may be summarized by the _____ Cycle.

6. If the _____ rises above normal, a condition of hyperglycemia is said to exist.

7. The appearance of glucose in urine is called _____.

8. Hyperinsulinism or starvation may produce a condition of_____-emia.

9. Clinically, an insufficiency of effective insulin is associated with _____.

10. If the kidneys are releasing glucose into the urine, the _____ for glucose has probably been exceeded.

11. In a situation of sudden stress, the adrenal medulla secretes a trace of the hormone _____. Its target cells are in _____ and to some extent in_____. At these cells it launches a series of enzyme activations that lead finally to the enzyme _____that catalyzes the _____.

12. Because liver cells have an enzyme that catalyzes the hydrolysis of _____ to glucose, the glucose stored as _____ in liver can be made available for release into the _____ and thereby help to raise the _____.

13. A hormone that is an even better than epinephrine as an activator of glycogenolysis at the liver is called _____.

14. The hormone secreted by the pancreas in response to an increase in the blood sugar level is _____, and it stimulates the removal of _____from the bloodstream.

15. The "signal" for the release of insulin is an increase in _____.

16. The ability of the pancreas to respond to glucose is measured by the _____ test.

17. The effect of reduced insulin activity while glucagon activity remains normal is to reduce the supply of _____ inside cells. In this situation, the cells increase their rate of _____.

18. A sequence in glucose catabolism that can be run anaerobically is also called _____. Its end product is _____ which (when there is enough oxygen available) can lose the pieces of the element _____and be thereby oxidized to _____. This, in turn, can be broken down oxidatively to acetyl _____.

19. The anaerobic sequence enables a tissue to make a fresh supply of _____ for energy-demanding processes without oxygen being immediately available.

20. When a tissue is operating anaerobically, we say it is running an oxygen _____, and an accumulation of _____an end-product of _____, occurs.

21. When a tissue is operating aerobically, the change of an NADH-enzyme in glycolysis to its NAD$^+$-enzyme form is accomplished by passing the H:$^-$ from the NADH to _____; but when the tissue is operating anaerobically, the H:$^-$ (plus H$^+$) is transferred to _____ to make _____.

22. The H:$^-$ unit in NADH is used eventually to reduce _____, whereas the H:$^-$ in _____ is used to reduce organic substances that later become fatty acids.

23. The body's chief source of NADPH is the _____.

24. A large fraction of the lactate produced in the anaerobic sequence is converted to _____. The energy for accomplishing this is provided by sending the smaller fraction of the lactate (or some other metabolite) through the _____ sequence.

MULTIPLE-CHOICE

1. The end product of glycolysis under anaerobic conditions is
   (a) phosphoenolpyruvate   (c) lactate
   (b) pyruvate   (d) acetyl CoA

2. The end product of glycolysis under aerobic conditions is
   (a) phosphoenolpyruvate   (c) lactate
   (b) pyruvate   (d) acetyl CoA

3. All dietary monosaccharides undergo anaerobic catabolism in which the steps are for the most part the same as the steps in the catabolism of
   (a) glucose   (c) insulin
   (b) acetyl CoA   (d) pyruvate

4. The principal reducing agent needed to make fatty acids from carbohydrates is
   (a) NADH   (b) NADPH   (c) NAD$^+$ (d) NADP$^+$

5. If lactate is generated by hard work,
   (a) glycolysis has occurred
   (b) an oxygen debt exists
   (c) a fraction is eventually converted back to glycogen
   (d) the blood will become hyperglycemic

6. One important purpose of the pentose phosphate pathway of glucose catabolism is to make
   (a) ATP   (b) NADPH   (c) NADH   (d) glucose-1-phosphate

7. A hormone made in the α-cells of the pancreas that is a powerful activator of adenylate cyclase at liver cells is
   (a) insulin   (c) somatostatin
   (b) epinephrine   (d) glucagon

8. A hormone whose target tissue is the pancreas and that acts to slow down the release of insulin from the pancreas is
   (a) glucagon   (c) epinephrine
   (b) somatostatin   (d) human growth hormone

9. The carbon atoms in glucose most directly made by gluconeogenesis come from
   (a) HCO_3^- (c) acetyl coenzyme A
   (b) lactate   (d) CO_2

10. The breakdown of glucose to lactate is called
    (a) gluconeogenesis   (c) glycolysis
    (b) lactolysis   (d) glycogenolysis

11. The principal site of gluconeogenesis is the
    (a) muscle   (c) pancreas
    (b) liver   (d) adrenal medulla

12. The series of changes that move from glucose to lactate and back to glucose is called the
    (a) Cori Cycle   (c) Krebs' Cycle
    (b) citric acid cycle   (d) tricarboxylic acid cycle

13. The concentration of monosaccharides in blood is called
    (a) diabetes mellitus   (c) the blood sugar level
    (b) the renal threshold   (d) the normal fasting level

14. Hormones that tend to raise the blood sugar level include
    (a) insulin   (c) glucagon
    (b) epinephrine   (d) somatostatin

15. If too much insulin somehow appears in the bloodstream,
    (a) glucosuria will result
    (b) the blood will become hypoglycemic
    (c) the blood will become hyperglycemic
    (d) the renal threshold for glucose will be exceeded

ANSWERS

ANSWERS TO SELF–TESTING QUESTIONS

Completion

1. gluconeogenesis
2. glycogenesis
3. glycogenolysis
4. epinephrine
5. Cori
6. blood sugar level
7. glucosuria
8. hypoglycemia
9. diabetes mellitus
10. renal threshold
11. epinephrine; muscles; liver; phosphorylase kinase; conversion of glycogen into glucose-1-phosphate
12. glucose-6-phosphate; glycogen; bloodstream; blood sugar level
13. glucagon
14. insulin; glucose

15. the blood sugar level
16. glucose tolerance
17. glucose; gluconeogenesis
18. glycolysis; lactate, hydrogen, pyruvate; coenzyme A
19. ATP
20. debt, lactate, glycolysis
21. the respiratory chain (or, to FMN in the respiratory chain); pyruvate, lactate
22. oxygen, NADPH
23. pentose phosphate pathway of glucose catabolism
24. glucose; aerobic

Multiple–Choice

1. c
2. b
3. a
4. b
5. a, b, and c
6. b
7. d
8. b

9. b
10. c
11. b
12. a
13. c
14. b and c
15. b

27

METABOLISM OF LIPIDS

Our study of the molecular basis of the energy required for living is essentially completed in this chapter, as is our study of the molecular basis of diabetes.

OBJECTIVES

When you have finished studying the chapter and have answered the Review Exercises, you should be able to do the following.

1. Describe how lipids are transported in the bloodstream.
2. State the function of chylomicrons.
3. Describe what occurs to chylomicrons in adipose tissue and muscle.
4. Name the ways in which cholesterol is used outside of the liver.
5. Give the names and symbols of the lipoprotein complexes that handle endogenous lipids.
6. Describe the function of VLDL complexes.
7. Explain how VLDL changes to IDL.
8. State how IDL changes to LDL.
9. Explain the uses of LDL and how it becomes HDL.
10. Describe the function of HDL.
11. Explain the function of the liver receptors for IDL and LDL and how they help the body regulate the blood cholesterol level.
12. Contrast human lipid reserves and carbohydrate reserves in terms of roughly how long they would last during a period of starvation.
13. Outline the steps in the mobilization of the energy reserves in adipose tissue.

14. Using palmitic acid as an example, describe the overall result of the degradation of such an acid by the β-oxidation pathway.
15. Describe by equations how acetyl CoA is converted to butyryl ACP.
16. Describe by equations how acetyl CoA is used to lengthen the chain of butyryl ACP.
17. Explain how cholesterol participates in the feedback control of its own synthesis.
18. Explain how lovastatin (or compactin) work to inhibit cholesterol synthesis.
19. Name the ketone bodies and explain how they are produced in greater than normal amounts when effective insulin is missing.
20. Explain the relations between (a) ketonemia and ketonuria, (b) ketonemia and ketone breath, and (c) ketonemia and ketoacidosis.
21. Discuss the step-by-step progression of events from a condition in which effective insulin is lacking to the coma that results if the condition remains untreated.

GLOSSARY

β-Oxidation Pathway. The catabolism of a fatty acid by a series of repeating steps that produce acetyl units (in acetyl CoA).

Fatty Acid Cycle. (See *β-Oxidation Pathway.*)

Ketoacidosis. The acidosis caused by untreated ketonemia.

Ketone Bodies. Acetoacetate, β-hydroxybutyrate, or their parent acids, and acetone.

Ketonemia. An elevated concentration of ketone bodies in the blood.

Ketonuria. An elevated concentration of ketone bodies in the urine.

Ketosis. The combination of ketonemia, ketonuria, and acetone breath.

Lipoprotein Complex. A combination of a lipid molecule with a protein molecule that serves as the vehicle for carrying the lipid in the bloodstream.

SELF-TESTING QUESTIONS

COMPLETION

1. After triacylglycerols have been digested, the products are largely a mixture of _____ and _____. As these migrate out of the digestive tract they are changed into _____ that then become incorporated into particles called _____, which are carried in the blood.
2. The principal storage site for triacylglycerols is _____, but when they are in the bloodstream they are carried by complexes called _____.
3. In muscle and adipose tissue, chylomicrons unload some of their molecules of _____, and this leaves the chylomicron remnants richer in molecules of the more dense, nonhydrolyzable lipid, _____.
4. The organ that has receptors that can recognize chylomicron remnants is the _____.
5. When these receptors are defective or absent, the individual is likely to have _____.
✱ 6. The lipoprotein complex that the liver makes to export endogenous cholesterol into circulation is symbolized as VLDL, which stands for _____.
7. Tissues that can remove triacylglycerols from VLDL are _____ and _____.

8. This removal transforms the VLDL into _____, which stands for _____.

9. The IDL can be reabsorbed by the _____, but some experiences further loss of _____ so that the IDL changes into _____, which stands for _____.

✗ 10. The chief purpose of LDL is to carry cholesterol to _extra hepatic ___ tissue and to glands that make _steroid hormones_____.

11. Left-over cholesterol is carried back to the liver as _____, which stands for _____.

12. Storing chemical energy as lipid rather than as wet glycogen or dissolved glucose is advantageous because lipids have a particularly low _____, which means a low quantity of _____ for each calorie stored. In a 70-kg adult male, there is roughly _____ of triacylglycerol, enough to last about _____ if it has to serve as the sole source of caloric needs.

13. When insulin is in circulation, the activity of the cellular _____ that catalyzes the release of fatty acids from adipose tissue is _____(suppressed or activated). Otherwise the hormone _____can act to activate this enzyme.

14. When the acyl group of a fatty acid is catabolized inside a mitochondrion, it is attached to _____, a coenzyme. The first step in the oxidation is the loss of _____ from the α- and β-carbon atoms to give a functional group adjacent to the carbonyl group having the name _____. Then a molecule of _____adds to this functional group to give a β-_____ acyl system. This is then oxidized in the third step to give the _____-group. Finally a molecule of coenzyme A interacts with this compound to split out _____ and leaves an acyl-CoA system having _____fewer carbon atoms than it originally had. Then this shorter version is subjected to the same series of steps, and the process is called the _____.

15. The hydrogen removed from the acyl CoA in the β-oxidation pathway to give the α, β-unsaturated acyl CoA derivative is accepted by an enzyme having as its coenzyme _____whose reduced form is _____. This enzyme is part of the _____.

16. The hydrogen removed in the oxidation of the 2° alcohol group in the third step of the β-oxidation pathway is accepted by an enzyme having the coenzyme _____, whose reduced form is symbolized as _____.

17. The acetyl CoA units produced by the β-oxidation pathway enter the metabolic pathway having the name _____.

18. If glycolysis produces acetyl CoA that the cell doesn't need for energy, this excess acetyl CoA can be made into _____ by a series of reactions catalyzed by the enzyme of a complex called _____ and fatty acid synthesis takes place in the _____ of the cell.

19. In fatty acid synthesis, one acetyl CoA molecule first combines with HCO_3^- to give _____, which has the structure:

_____

Another molecule of acetyl CoA is hooked to a unit called _____ of the synthase complex. The malonyl unit of malonyl CoA is joined to another part of the synthase and become malonyl ACP, where ACP stands for _____. Malonyl ACP now reacts with acetyl-E to give _____which has the structure:

_____

20. The keto group of this compound is next _____ by NADPH + H$^+$, which changes the keto group into _____.

21. In the next step this group is removed to leave the ACP derivative of an unsaturated acid with the structure:

_____

22. This unsaturated acyl derivative of coenzyme A is now hydrogenated by the action of an enzyme with _____ as its coenzyme. We now have the ACP derivative of a simple fatty acid with the name _____.

23. The raw material for making the steroid nucleus is _____. One principal end product in steroid synthesis is an alcohol called _____ from which such other steroids as the_____hormones are made.

24. One way that the body controls how much cholesterol it makes is by regulating the activity of an enzyme called _____. One of the inhibitors of this enzyme is _____, so if the diet is rich in this substance, the body itself makes little if any more. A drug that successfully lowers the cholesterol level of the blood is _____ and it acts by _____.

25. An enhanced rate of fatty acid oxidation in the liver may produce excessive amounts of _____ in the blood, a condition known as _____. This will slowly lower the pH of the blood, a condition known as _____.

26. Both starvation and untreated _____ can lead to acidosis.

27. Efforts by the body to eliminate ketone bodies and associated positive ions, nitrogen wastes, and excess glucose from the bloodstream mean that more _____ than usual is also removed.

28. If insufficient water is drunk per day, the blood may _____, its circulation in the brain in sufficient quantities may become more difficult, and some blood flow may be diverted from the _____ in order to supply the brain. This diversion only makes it more difficult for the body to eliminate wastes.

29. As the anions from ketonemia become part of the urine being made, the chief cation to leave with them has the formula _____.The loss of this cation is sometimes called "the loss of _____," but in reality this ion is not a base. However, each of these cations that is lost represents the neutralization of one _____ ion, so the net effect is the loss of base within the system.

30. A simplified statement of one sequence of events in undetected (and therefore untreated) diabetes mellitus would be as follows. The excessive release of _____ from adipose tissue and the

                                                          (a)

increased rate of catabolism of fatty acids in the _____ cause the production

                                                          (b)

of_____ at a rate faster than can normally be handled. As a result there is a slow

        (c)

increase in the concentration of _____ in the blood, a condition called

                                                          (d)

_____. Because two of them are acids, the _____ of the blood

        (e)   (f)

slowly drops.

MULTIPLE–CHOICE

1. The β-oxidation pathway
   (a) produces lactic acid
   (b) requires the β-form of oxygen
   (c) involves extensive glycogenolysis
   (d) produces units of acetyl CoA

2. If the amount of energy taken into a healthy body in the form of carbohydrates is greater than the body needs for energy, the body will experience
   (a) glucosuria
   (b) a greater rate of fatty acid synthesis
   (c) a greater rate of running the β-oxidation pathway
   (d) an enhanced rate of glycogenolysis

3. The citric acid cycle is fed two carbon units from
   (a) the catabolism of glucose
   (b) the β-oxidation pathway
   (c) the cholesterol degradation
   (d) the Cori Cycle

4. The average, adequately nourished adult male has enough chemical energy in storage as lipids to sustain life for how long:
   (a) 1 day   (b) 1 week   (c) 1 month   (d) 2 months

5. Fatty acids are transported in the bloodstream bound as complexes to molecules of
   (a) protein   (b) triacylglycerol   (c) FFA   (d) cholesterol

6. The densities of the various lipoprotein complexes increase in the order:
   (a) chylomicron < LDL < VLDL < IDL < HDL
   (b) chylomicron < VLDL < IDL < LDL < HDL
   (c) VLDL < chylomicron
   (d) LDL < chylomicron < VLDL < IDL < HDL

7. The chief carriers of exogenous triacylglycerols to adipose tissue are
   (a) chylomicrons (b) HDL   (c) LDL   (d) IDL

8. The chief carrier of cholesterol from peripheral tissue to the liver is
   (a) LDL   (b) IDL   (c) chylomicron   (d) HDL

9. During each "turn," the β-oxidation pathway produces
   (a) $FADH_2$, NADH, acetyl CoA
   (b) $FADH_2$, NADH, acetoacetyl CoA
   (c) $FADH_2$, NADP, ADP
   (d) $FADH_2$, NADH, β-hydroxybutyrate

10. Once the substance $R-\overset{\overset{\displaystyle O}{\|}}{C}-S-CoA$ has been formed, the next step in the β-oxidation pathway is
    (a) the addition of water   (c) dehydration
    (b) an attack by CoASH   (d) dehydrogenation

11. Once the substance $R-CH=CH-\overset{\displaystyle O}{\overset{\displaystyle \|}{C}}-S-CoA$ has formed in the β-oxidation pathway, the next step is
    (a) the addition of water (c) dehydration
    (b) an attack by CoASH   (d) dehydrogenation

12. The β-oxidation pathway degrades fatty acids by how many carbons per "turn"?
    (a) 1   (b) 2   (c) 3   (d) 4

13. To make the butyryl-ACP needed for the synthesis of fatty acids, acetoacetyl-ACP is first made from
    (a) acetoacetic acid
    (b) two molecules of acetyl-ACP
    (c) butyric acid
    (d) malonyl-ACP and acetyl-E

14. A fat-free, high carbohydrate diet promotes
    (a) the synthesis of fatty acids.
    (b) an elevation of the serum VLDL level.
    (c) the β-oxidation pathway.
    (d) lipolysis.

15. Which one of these structures is not a ketone body?

    (a) $CH_3\overset{\displaystyle O}{\overset{\displaystyle \|}{C}}CH_2\overset{\displaystyle O}{\overset{\displaystyle \|}{C}}O^-$

    (c) $CH_3\overset{\displaystyle O}{\overset{\displaystyle \|}{C}}CH_3$

    (b) $CH_3\overset{\displaystyle O}{\overset{\displaystyle \|}{C}}O^-$

    (d) $CH_3\overset{\displaystyle HO}{\overset{\displaystyle |}{C}}HCH_2\overset{\displaystyle O}{\overset{\displaystyle \|}{C}}O^-$

16. Which one of the conditions given is most closely linked to acidosis?
    (a) acetone breath   (c) ketonuria
    (b) ketonemia   (d) glycosuria

17. The uses of acetyl CoA in the body include
    (a) the synthesis of fatty acids
    (b) the synthesis of cholesterol
    (c) the synthesis of certain amino acids
    (d) fuel for the citric acid cycle

ANSWERS

ANSWERS TO SELF–TESTING QUESTIONS

Completion

1. fatty acids; monoacylglycerols; triacylglycerols; lipoprotein complexes
2. adipose tissue; lipoprotein complexes
3. triacylglycerols; cholesterol
4. liver
5. hypercholesterolemia
6. VLDL; very low density lipoprotein complex
7. adipose tissue; muscle tissue
8. IDL; intermediate density lipoprotein complex
9. liver; triacylglycerol; LDL; low density lipoprotein complex
10. peripheral (extrahepatic); steroid hormones
11. HDL; high density lipoprotein complexes
12. energy density; material mass (in grams); 12 kg; 43 days
13. lipase; suppressed; epinephrine
14. coenzyme A; hydrogen; alkene group; water; hydroxy; keto; acetyl CoA; two; fatty acid; β-oxidation pathway
15. FAD; FADH$_2$; respiratory chain
16. NAD$^+$, NADH
17. citric acid cycle
18. fatty acids; fatty acid synthase; cytosol
19. malonyl CoA; $^-$OCCH$_2$C—S—CoA ; E; acyl carrier protein

    $$\overset{O}{\underset{||}{}}\quad\overset{O}{\underset{||}{}}$$

    acetoacetyl ACP; CH$_3$CCH$_2$C—S—ACP

    $$\overset{O}{\underset{||}{}}\quad\overset{O}{\underset{||}{}}$$

20. reduced (or hydrogenated); a 2° alcohol group
21. CH$_3$CH=CHC—S—ACP

    $$\overset{O}{\underset{||}{}}$$

22. NADPH; butyryl ACP
23. acetyl CoA; cholesterol; sex
24. HMG-CoA reductase; cholesterol; lovastatin (or compactin); inhibiting HMG-CoA synthase
25. ketone bodies; ketonemia; acidosis (or ketoacidosis)
26. diabetes
27. water
28. thicken (or become more viscous); kidneys

29. Na$^+$; base; H$^+$
30. (a) fatty acids
    (b) liver
    (c) ketone bodies
    (d) hydrogen ions (or, hydronium ions)
    (e) acidosis (or, in this case, ketoacidosis)
    (f) pH

Multiple–Choice

1.	d	9.	a
2.	b	10.	d
3.	a and b	11.	a
4.	c	12.	b
5.	a	13.	d
6.	b	14.	a
7.	a	15.	b
8.	d	16.	b
		17.	a, b, c, and d

28

METABOLISM OF NITROGEN COMPOUNDS

Although the catabolism of amino acids inevitably helps generate ATP and therefore contributes to the molecular basis of energy for living, this chapter brings us back to the molecular basis of materials for living.

OBJECTIVES

After you have studied the material in this chapter and have answered the Review Exercises, you should be able to do the following.

1. List the four main fates of amino acids in the body.
2. Describe the nitrogen pool.
3. By means of illustrative equations, show how reductive amination and transamination contribute to the synthesis of some amino acids.
4. Name the principal end products of the catabolism of amino acids.
5. Write an equation illustrating a specific example for each of the catabolic reactions of oxidative deamination, direct deamination, and decarboxylation.
6. Describe the overall result of the urea cycle.
7. Describe an origin of hyperammonemia and state the principal problem associated with it.
8. Describe the overall result of the catabolism of the purine bases (A or G).
9. In general terms, explain how gout and kidney stones are related to purine metabolism.
10. Give the relations between: (a) heme and biliverdin, (b) biliverdin and bilirubin, (c) bilirubin and bilinogen, and (d) bilirubin and jaundice.
11. Define each of the terms in the Glossary.

GLOSSARY

Bile Pigments. Colored products of the partial catabolism of heme that are transferred from the liver to the gall bladder for secretion via the bile.

Bilin. The brownish pigment that is the end product of the catabolism of heme and that contributes to the characteristic colors of feces and urine.

Bilinogen. A product of the catabolism of heme that contributes to the characteristic colors of feces and urine and some of which is oxidized to bilin.

Bilirubin. A reddish-orange substance that forms from biliverdin during the catabolism of heme and which enters the intestinal tract via the bile and is eventually changed into bilinogen and bilin.

Biliverdin. A greenish pigment that forms when partly catabolized hemoglobin (as verdohemoglobin) is further broken down, and which is changed in the liver to bilirubin.

Deamination, Direct. The removal of an amino group from an amino acid.

Decarboxylation. The removal of a carboxyl group.

Hyperammonemia. An elevated level of ammonia in blood.

Nitrogen Pool. The sum total of all nitrogen compounds in the body.

Oxidative Deamination. The change of an amino group to a keto group with loss of nitrogen.

Reductive Amination. The conversion of a keto group to an amino group by the action of ammonia and a reducing agent.

Transamination. The transfer of an amino group from an amino acid to a receptor with a keto group such that the keto group changes to an amino group.

Urea Cycle. The reactions by which urea is made from amino acids.

SELF-TESTING QUESTIONS

COMPLETION

1. Amino acids and other nitrogenous substances in the body, wherever they are, make up the _____.

2. Nitrogen enters the system largely as nitrogen compounds that are products of the digestion of _____.

3. Nitrogen leaves the system largely in the form of compounds called _____, _____, and a trace of _____.

4. The reducing agent in reductive amination has the short formula of _____, and

   the source of nitrogen is _____. If the compound: $^-O_2CCH_2\overset{\overset{O}{\|}}{C}CO_2^-$ underwent

   reductive amination, the following amino acid would form: _____

5. The same amino acid could be made by _____ using the same keto acid but using glutamate instead of NH_4^+ as the source of nitrogen. It leaves glutamate in the form of the

   following: _____

6. The reverse of reductive amination is called _____. The nitrogen of the amino acids undergoing this process emerges in the form of the _____, which can be changed to the chief nitrogen waste, _____.

7. When serine undergoes the following change:

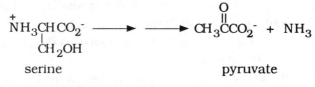

serine   pyruvate

the overall reaction is called _____.

8. When tyrosine undergoes the following change:

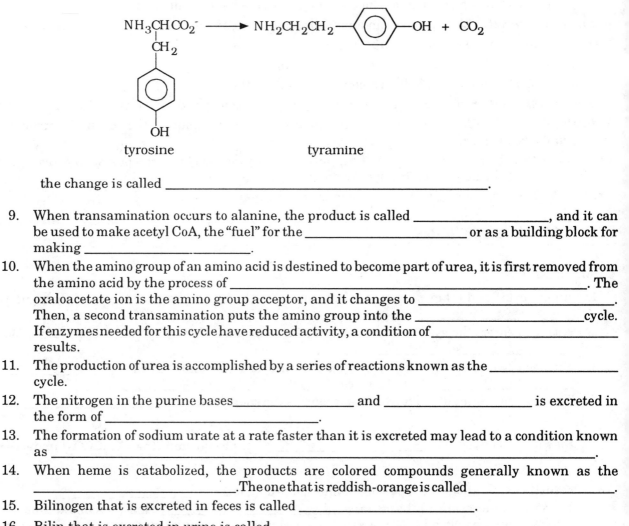

tyrosine   tyramine

the change is called _____.

9. When transamination occurs to alanine, the product is called _____, and it can be used to make acetyl CoA, the "fuel" for the _____ or as a building block for making _____.

10. When the amino group of an amino acid is destined to become part of urea, it is first removed from the amino acid by the process of _____. The oxaloacetate ion is the amino group acceptor, and it changes to _____. Then, a second transamination puts the amino group into the _____cycle. If enzymes needed for this cycle have reduced activity, a condition of_____ results.

11. The production of urea is accomplished by a series of reactions known as the _____ cycle.

12. The nitrogen in the purine bases_____ and _____ is excreted in the form of _____.

13. The formation of sodium urate at a rate faster than it is excreted may lead to a condition known as _____.

14. When heme is catabolized, the products are colored compounds generally known as the _____. The one that is reddish-orange is called _____.

15. Bilinogen that is excreted in feces is called _____.

16. Bilin that is excreted in urine is called _____.

MULTIPLE–CHOICE

1. The following reaction is an example of

$$CH_3\overset{O}{\overset{\|}{C}}CO_2H + HO_2CCH_2CH_2\underset{\underset{NH_2}{|}}{CH}CO_2H \longrightarrow$$

$$CH_3\underset{\underset{NH_2}{|}}{CH}CO_2H + HO_2CCH_2CH_2\overset{O}{\overset{\|}{C}}CO_2H$$

   (a) oxidative deamination   (c) decarboxylation
   (b) transamination   (d) gluconeogenesis

2. The following reaction is an example of

$$CH_3\underset{\underset{NH_2}{|}}{CH}CO_2H \xrightarrow[\;H_2O\;]{NAD^+} \longrightarrow CH_3\overset{O}{\overset{\|}{C}}CO_2H + NH_3 + NADH$$

   (a) oxidative deamination   (c) decarboxylation
   (b) transamination   (d) gluconeogenesis

3. The following reaction illustrates

$$\underset{\underset{OH}{|}}{CH_2}-\underset{\underset{NH_3^+}{|}}{CH}-CO_2^- \longrightarrow CH_3-\overset{O}{\overset{\|}{C}}-CO_2^- + NH_4^+$$

   (a) oxidative deamination   (c) decarboxylation
   (b) direct deamination   (d) transamination

4. If transamination occurred to $CH_3CH_2\underset{\underset{NH_3^+}{|}}{CH}\overset{\overset{CH_3}{|}}{CH}CO_2^-$, it would become

   TYPO

   (a) $CH_3CH_2\overset{\overset{CH_3}{|}}{CH}CH_2NH_3^+$ (c) $CH_3CH_2\underset{\underset{H_3C\ \ NH_3^+}{|\ \ \ \ |}}{CH}CH CO_2^-$

   (b) $CH_3CH_2\overset{\overset{CH_3}{|}}{CH}\underset{\underset{O}{\|}}{C}CO_2^-$ (d) $CH_3CH_2\underset{\underset{CH_3}{|}}{CH}CH_2CO_2^-$

5. The nitrogen waste made from the purine bases of nucleic acids is
   (a) ammonia   (b) urea   (c) uric acid   (d) bilinogen

Exam   6. The end products in the catabolism of proteins are
   (a) amino acids
   (b) nitrogen, water, and carbon dioxide
   (c) ammonia, water, and carbon dioxide
   (d) urea, water, and carbon dioxide

7. In a dietary sense, alanine is classified as a nonessential amino acid. This is because
   (a) the body can make its own alanine
   (b) the body has no need for alanine
   (c) the body excretes alanine as fast as it can be ingested
   (d) alanine cannot be catabolized

8. A non-protein nitrogen compound made from molecules of amino acids is
   (a) triacylglycerol   (c) nucleic acid
   (b) creatine   (d) heme

9. Intermediates in the catabolism of amino acids may be used to make
   (a) glucose   (c) ketone bodies
   (b) fatty acids   (d) other amino acids

10. The major site of the catabolism of amino acids is the
   (a) liver   (b) kidneys   (c) adipose tissue   (d) gall bladder

11. In a condition of hyperammonemia, the level of concentration of what substance rises in the blood?
   (a) ammonia   (b) amino acids   (c) uric acid   (d) DOPA

12. The greenish pigment produced from heme is called
   (a) urobilinogen   (c) chlorophyll
   (b) urobilin   (d) biliverdin

ANSWERS

ANSWERS TO SELF–TESTING QUESTIONS

Completion

1. nitrogen pool
2. protein
3. urea, uric acid, ammonia
4. NADPH; ammonium ion; $^-O_2CCH_2CHCO_2^-$ with NH_3^+ on the CH
5. transamination: $^-O_2CCH_2CH_2\overset{\text{O}}{\overset{\|}{C}}CO_2^-$
6. oxidative deamination; ammonium ion; urea
7. direct deamination

8. decarboxylation
9. pyruvate; citric acid cycle; fatty acids
10. transamination; aspartate; urea; hyperammonemia
11. urea (or Krebs' ornithine)
12. adenine, guanine, uric acid (or urate ions)
13. gout (also, kidney stones or the aggravation of arthritis)
14. tetrapyrrole pigments (or bile pigments); bilirubin
15. stercobilinogen
16. urobilin

Multiple–Choice

1. b
2. a
3. b
4. b
5. c
6. d
7. a
8. b, c, and d
9. a, b, c, and d
10. a
11. a
12. d

29

NUTRITION

Health, happiness, and life are all greatly influenced by what we eat and drink. When most people learn *why* various things must be in the diet in their proper proportions, they usually make an effort to ensure that they have a balanced diet.

OBJECTIVES

The objectives that follow, which you should be able to do once you have studied the chapter and have worked its Exercises and Review Questions, are designed to emphasize the knowledge that will help you have the best physical well-being possible.

1. Explain why the recommended daily allowances of the National Academy of Sciences are higher than the minimum daily requirements.
2. Explain why the best nutrition is obtained from a variety of foods.
3. Explain why food energy should come from a mix of lipids and carbohydrates.
4. Explain why several amino acids, but not all, are called "essential."
5. Compare meat, cereal, and fruit proteins in their digestibility.
6. Give both the positive and negative consequences of milling grains.
7. Compare the proteins of meats, dairy products, cereals, and nuts in their biological values.
8. Describe the major factor affecting the biological values of proteins.
9. Explain why one could not eat enough maize (corn) or cassava per day to satisfy one's needs for amino acids.
10. Describe the problems vegetarians must solve in order to have good nutrition.
11. Name the essential fatty acids and tell why they are important.

12. In general ways, explain how vitamins are different from other nutrients.
13. Name the vitamins and, where known, identify the human deficiency diseases or syndromes associated with each.
14. Give one good source for each vitamin.
15. Name and give the chemical formulas of the six minerals needed at levels above 100 mg/day.
16. Name and give the principal functions of the ten chief trace elements.
17. Define the terms in the Glossary.

GLOSSARY

Adequate Protein. A protein that, when digested, makes available all of the essential amino acids in suitable proportions to satisfy both the amino acid and total nitrogen requirements of good nutrition without providing excessive calories.

Biological Value. In nutrition, the percentage of the nitrogen of ingested protein that is absorbed from the digestive tract and retained by the body when the total protein intake is less than normally required.

Biotin. A water-soluble vitamin needed to make enzymes used in fatty acid synthesis.

Choline. A compound needed to make complex lipids and acetylcholine; classified as a vitamin.

Coefficient of Digestibility. The proportion of an ingested protein's nitrogen that enters circulation rather than elimination (in feces); the difference between the nitrogen ingested and the nitrogen in the feces divided by the nitrogen ingested.

Dietetics. The application of the findings of the science of nutrition to the feeding of individual humans, whether well or ill.

Essential Amino Acid. An α-amino acid that the body cannot make from other amino acids and that must be supplied by the diet.

Essential Fatty Acid. A fatty acid that must be supplied by the diet.

Folate. A vitamin supplied by folic acid or pteroylglutamic acid and that is needed to prevent megaloblastic anemia.

Food. A material that supplies one or more nutrients without contributing materials that, either in kind or quantity, would be harmful to most healthy people.

Limiting Amino Acid. The essential amino acid most poorly provided by a dietary protein.

Minerals. Ions that must be provided in the diet at levels of 100 mg/day or more; Ca^{2+}, Mg^{2+}, Na^+, K^+, Cl^-, and phosphate.

Niacin. A water-soluble vitamin needed to prevent pellagra and essential to the coenzymes in NAD^+ and $NADP^+$; nicotinic acid or nicotinamide.

Nutrients. Chemical substances that take part in normal, healthy metabolism.

Nitrogen Balance. A condition of the body in which it excretes as much nitrogen as it receives in the diet.

Nutrition. The science of the substances of the diet that are necessary for growth, operation, energy, and repair of bodily tissues.

Pantothenic Acid. A water-soluble vitamin needed to make coenzyme A.

Recommended Dietary Allowance (RDA). The level of intake of a particular nutrient as determined by the Food and Nutrition Board of the National Research Council of the National Academy of Sciences to meet the know nutritional needs of most healthy individuals.

Riboflavin. A B vitamin needed to give protection against the breakdown of tissue around the mouth, the nose, and the tongue, as well as to aid in wound healing.

Thiamin. A B vitamin needed to prevent beri beri.

Trace Element. Any element that the body needs each day in an amount of no more than 20 mg.

Vitamin. An organic substance that must be in the diet; whose absence causes a deficiency disease; which is present in foods in trace concentrations; and that isn't a carbohydrate, lipid, protein, or amino acid.

Vitamin A. Retinol; a fat-soluble vitamin in yellow-colored foods and needed to prevent night blindness and certain conditions of the mucous membranes.

Vitamin B_6. Pyridoxine, pyridoxal, or pyridoxamine; a vitamin needed to prevent hypochromic microcytic anemia and used in enzymes of amino acid catabolism.

Vitamin B_{12}. Cobalamin; a vitamin needed to prevent pernicious anemia.

Vitamin C. Ascorbic acid; a vitamin needed to prevent scurvy.

Vitamin D. Cholecalciferol (D_3) or ergocalciferol (D_2); a fat-soluble vitamin needed to prevent rickets and to ensure the formation of healthy bones and teeth.

Vitamin Deficiency Diseases. Diseases caused not by bacteria or viruses but by the absence of specific vitamins, such as pernicious anemia (B_{12}), hypochromic microcytic anemia (B_6), pellagra (niacin), the breakdown of certain tissues (riboflavin), megaloblastic anemia (folate), beri beri (thiamin), scurvy (C), hemorrhagic disease (K), rickets (D), and night blindness (A).

Vitamin E. A mixture of tocopherols; a fat-soluble vitamin apparently needed for protection against edema and anemia (in infants) and possibly against dystrophy, paralysis, and atherosclerosis.

Vitamin K. The antihemorrhagic vitamin that serves as a cofactor in the formation of a blood clot.

SELF-TESTING QUESTIONS

COMPLETION

1. With respect to the terms "nutrient" and "food," we may say that bread is a _____ and the wheat protein in bread is a _____.

2. The symbol RDA stands for _____.

3. A quantitative measure of the digestibility of a given protein is its _____, and the equation that defines it is _____.

4. The extent to which a given protein has a high biological value is determined by the extent to which it supplies _____.

5. A protein with little if any lysine would have a low _____.

6. The essential amino acid most poorly supplied by a given protein is called the _____ of that protein.

7. A protein with all of the essential amino acids in approximately the right proportions for humans is called an _____.

8. An individual whose intake of nitrogen in the diet equals the quantity of nitrogen excreted is said to have a _____.

9. In order to grow and develop an infant should have a _____ nitrogen balance.

10. The fatty acids about which all are agreed is an essential fatty acid is _____.

11. List four criteria that must be satisfied by a substance if it is to be considered a vitamin.

(a) _____

(b) _____

(c) _____

(d) _____

12. The two broad classes of vitamins are the _____ vitamins and the _____ vitamins.

13. The four vitamins that are most hydrocarbon-like are vitamins _____, _____, _____, and _____.

14. Because the molecules of some of the hydrocarbon-like vitamins have carbon-carbon _____ bonds, these vitamins can be slowly destroyed by contact with air.

15. Lack of vitamin D leads to _____, a disorder of _____.

16. Lack of vitamin _____ may lead to impaired vision in dim light.

17. Lack of vitamin _____ may lead to problems in controlling hemorrhaging.

18. In the absence of ascorbic acid, vitamin _____, the disease known as _____ would develop.

19. Because thiamin is a part of an enzyme essential to the catabolism of _____, the daily requirement for it is related to the daily intake of _____.

20. Beri-beri is a disease that occurs when _____ is lacking in the diet.

21. Pantothenic acid is needed to make coenzyme _____.

22. The principal minerals in the body are (6) _____, _____, _____, _____, _____, and _____. (Give their correct formulas.)

23. To qualify as a trace element, the mass that the element contributes to the total mass of the body does not exceed _____.

24. The names of eleven trace elements known or believed to be needed by the body are (in any order)

_____   _____   _____

_____   _____   _____

_____   _____   _____

_____   _____

25. All trace metal elements occur as their _____, not as their atoms.

26. The central ion in hemoglobin has the name _____ and the formula _____.

MULTIPLE–CHOICE

1. A zero-carbohydrate diet will cause the body to make its own
   (a) linoleic acid   (c) glucose
   (b) sucrose   (d) nonessential amino acids

2. The proteins with the highest digestibility coefficients are generally those of
   (a) vegetables   (b) meat   (c) fruit   (d) cereals

3. One of the essential amino acids that often is a limiting amino acid is
   (a) lysine   (b) alanine   (c) glycine   (d) hydroxyproline

4. If 102 g of wheat protein has to be eaten to result in 80.4 g being actually digested and absorbed, the digestibility coefficient of wheat protein is
   (a) 80.4   (b) 82   (c) 1.27   (d) 0.79

5. The vegetarian diet supplies sufficient and adequate protein each day without also furnishing large amount of calories provided that the diet emphasizes
   (a) brown rice
   (b) beans
   (c) two different vegetables about equally
   (d) cassava

6. Even though phosphate is essential in the diet, it is not classified as a vitamin because it is not
   (a) organic
   (b) required for normal growth
   (c) present in foods
   (d) a carbohydrate

7. The vitamin supplied by yellow-colored vegetables is vitamin
   (a) A   (b) B   (c) C   (d) D

8. A vitamin that can be stored in adipose tissue is
   (a) vitamin K   (c) vitamin D
   (b) vitamin B_6 (d) thiamine

9. A vitamin that detoxifies peroxides and so inhibits the oxidation of the lipids of lipoprotein complexes is
   (a) vitamin K   (c) vitamin D
   (b) vitamin B_6 (d) vitamin E

10. The trace element that serves as a cofactor for the action of insulin is
    (a) Cr^{3+} (b) K^+ (c) F^- (d) Mn^{2+}

11. The trace element needed to make heme is
    (a) Cu^{2+} (b) Na^+ (c) Fe^{2+} (d) K^+

ANSWERS

ANSWERS TO SELF–TESTING QUESTIONS

Completion

1. food, nutrient
2. recommended dietary allowances
3. coefficient of digestibility,
   coefficient of digestibility = ([N in food eaten - N in feces]/(N in food eaten)
4. essential amino acids
5. biological value
6. limiting amino acid
7. adequate protein
8. nitrogen balance
9. positive

10. linoleic acid
11. (a) an organic compound that cannot be made in the body
    (b) its absence causes a deficiency disease
    (c) its presence is required for growth and health
    (d) found only in trace concentrations in foods and is not a carbohydrate, a lipid, or a protein
12. fat-soluble, water-soluble
13. A, D, E, and K
14. double
15. rickets, bone metabolism
16. A
17. K
18. C, scurvy
19. carbohydrate, calories
20. thiamin
21. A
22. Ca^{2+}, Mg^{2+}, Na^+, K^+, Cl^-, and inorganic phosphate ion (P)
23. 20 mg
24. iron, cobalt, zinc, chromium, molybdenum, copper, manganese, nickel, tin, vanadium, and silicon
25. ions
26. iron(II) ion (or the ferrous ion); Fe^{2+}

Multiple–Choice

1. c
2. b
3. a
4. d
5. c
6. a
7. a
8. c
9. d
10. a
10. c

ANSWER BOOK

INTRODUCTION

This *Answer Book* is a supplement to *Fundamentals of General, Organic, and Biological Chemistry,* 5th edition by John R. Holum. Although the text itself supplies answers to many Exercises, this supplement provides answers for all simply for the convenience of having them all in one place.

If not used wisely, an answer book will give a false sense of security that will be revealed all too sadly at the time of an examination. *The mistake many students make is to go to the answer book too soon.* Consult this supplement only after you have tried your best to determine the answer *in writing.* Then the answer book can supply positive reinforcement by showing you that you are right, or it can get you over those "impossible" spots.

The answers have been checked by me and by Dr. Melinda Lee of St. Cloud State University. From many years of experience, however, I am sure that some errors have still slipped by. Feel free to write me about them. Don't be concerned by small differences between your answers and mine to problems having numerical, calculated results. Unless there are parts to a question, separately labeled as (a), (b), etc., I always use a chain calculation. This might causes differences attributable to rounding off answers at times other than mine. Be sure to follow the guidelines of the text concerning the rules for rounding. Also remember that in calculations involving atomic masses, the rule in the text is to round all atomic masses to their first decimal place *before* using them (except round the atomic mass of H to 1.01).

John R. Holum
3352 47th Ave. S
Minneapolis, MN 55406

Chapter 1

Practice Exercises, Chapter 1

1. 310 K
2. (a) 5.45×10^8
   (b) 5.67×10^{12}
   (c) 6.454×10^3
   (d) 2.5×10^1
   (e) 3.98×10^{-5}
   (f) 4.26×10^{-3}
   (g) 1.68×10^{-1}
   (h) 9.87×10^{-12}
3. (a) 10^{-6}
   (b) 10^{-9}
   (c) 10^{-6}
   (d) 10^3
4. (a) mL   (b) μL   (c) dL
   (d) mm   (e) cm   (f) kg
   (g) μg   (h) mg
5. (a) kilogram
   (b) centimeter
   (c) deciliter
   (d) microgram
   (e) milliliter
   (f) milligram
   (g) millimeter
   (h) microliter
6. (a) 1.5 Mg   (b) 3.45 μL (c) 3.6 mg
   (d) 6.2 mL   (e) 1.68 kg (f) 5.4 dm
7. (a) 275 kg   (b) 62.5 μL (c) 82 nm or 0.082 μm
8. (a) 95
   (b) 11.36
   (c) 0.0263
   (d) 1.3000
   (e) 16.1
   (f) 3.8×10^2
   (g) 9.31
   (h) 9.1×10^2

9. (a) $\dfrac{1\,g}{1000\,mg}$ or $\dfrac{1000\,mg}{1\,g}$

(b) $\dfrac{1\,kg}{2.205\,lb}$ or $\dfrac{2.205\,lb}{1\,kg}$

10.   0.324 g of aspirin
11.   (a)   324 mg of aspirin
       (b) 3.28×10^{4} ft
       (c)   18.5 mL
       (d)   17.72 g
       (e) 4.78×10^{3} μL
12.   40 °C
13.   59 °F (Quite cool.)
14.   20.7 mL
15.   32.1 g

Review Exercises, Chapter 1

1.1   The substances in nature, their compositions, structures, and their abilities to be changed into other substances.
1.2   Living systems from a huge variety of species, both plant and animal, can either nourish or receive nourishment from each other.
1.3   At the *molecular* level of life *molecules* are exchanged.
1.4   The questions that ask "How does nature work?"
1.5   Other people can independently observe the fact and do so at almost any time they wish.
1.6   Unhappiness can indeed be a fact of one's life. Yet it is not a *reproducible* fact because its intensity cannot be measured, and no one else, especially anyone unfamiliar with you, can gauge it.
1.7   To construct a testable hypothesis (or a diagnosis).
1.8   To show how the set of facts might have a common cause or explanation.
1.9   The better question is (a). Choice (b) begins with a bias toward the hypothesis being true, not false.
1.10   The call has been cut off by some equipment failure is one likely hypothesis. Another is that the person on the other end of the line hung up. Although both hypotheses are extremely logical, neither is *necessarily* true. (The mere fact that *two* logical hypotheses can be advanced makes this so.) To test them, you probably will redial your friend. If this does not work, you will dial the operator. If neither is possible, then maybe a tree fell on the line (another hypotheses)! None of these hypotheses qualifies as a theory because it encompasses too few experiences.
1.11   (a)   It encompassed a number of deficiency diseases involving several difference sets of symptoms that could not be explained by transmitting agents, like bacteria.

(b)   The specific vitamins were isolated, purified, and found to be agents that could prevent the vitamin-deficiency diseases.

1.12   To construct hypotheses and theories from facts and observations.

1.13   The "How...?" question gets at mechanism and does not try to address an ultimate cause.

1.14   Characteristics by means of which the object can be identified and called by its name again.

1.15   The observation of a *chemical* property necessarily converts the substance into a different substance. The observation or measurement of a physical property does not do this.

1.16   A physical *quantity* gives a description of a physical property in terms of a number and a unit.

1.17   Measurement

1.18   The resistance of the object to a change in its position or its motion. *Mass* is the quantitative measure of inertia.

1.19   Your *weight* is a measure of the gravitational attraction experienced by your mass, and this attraction is much less on the moon. Your mass (your inertia), however, does not change.

1.20   When we use a two-pan balance, we have both pans at almost identical locations so the gravitational attractions are the same for the objects on both pans when balanced. Therefore, their masses are the same, too.

1.21   Base quantity. Mass, length, time, temperature degree, and quantity of chemical substance (mole).

1.22   A base unit

1.23   (a) meter (b) second (c) kilogram (d) kelvin (e) mole

1.24   A *reference* standard. The General Conference of Weights and Measures

1.25   It can be defined (or *derived)* from a base quantity, length. Volume = (length)^3

1.26   Meter. SI standard meter

1.27   Kilogram. SI standard kilogram mass

1.28   The standard mass is a specific, one-of-its-kind object, stored at SOAL(e,')vres, France, and is thus at risk to corrosion, fire, or theft. The standard meter is defined in terms of a characteristic of light, which is accessible to all.

1.29   (a)   meter (b) inch
        (c)   ounce (d) centimeter
        (e)   kilogram   (f) ton
        (g)   liter   (h) milliliter
        (i)   pound (j)   kilogram

1.30   1000 mL

1.31   1000 µg

1.32   1000 g

1.33   (a) 0 °C   (b) 32 °F

          (c)   273 K (rounded from 273.15, our usual practice)

1.34   (a)   100 °C   (b) 212 °F   (c) 373 K

1.35   (a)   100   (b) 180   (c) 100

1.36   Celsius degree by a factor of 9/5 (180/100)

1.37   The kelvin, by a factor of 9/5 (180/100)

1.38   −273 °C

1.39   This is the lowest degree of coldness obtainable.

1.40   −40 °F

1.41   41 °F (5 °C); too cold without a coat or heavy sweater for most people.

1.42   160 °C

1.43   20 °C

1.44   104 °F (The patient has a fever.)

1.45   (a)   2.5 dL (b) 31 mg
          (c)   46 cm (d) 110 km
          (e)   35 µL (f)   75 µg
          (g)   25 mm

1.46   (a)   110 milliliters   (b) 150 milligrams
          (c)   16 kilometers   (d) 50 micrograms
          (e)   1.5 deciliters (f)   2.5 kilograms
          (g)   75 microliters

1.47   (a) 5.230×10^3 g   (b) 4.50×10^{-2} L
          (c) 1.562×10^3 m   (d) 9.3×10^{-6} g

1.48   (a) 1.30×10^{-1} L   (b) 3.5685×10^3 m
          (c) 4.2×10^{-6} g   (d) 4.5×10^{-3} g

1.49   (a)   5.230 kg   (b) 4.50 cL
          (c)   1.562 km   (d) 9.3 µg

1.50   (a)   1.30 dL   (b) 3.5685 km
          (c)   4.2 µg   (d) 4.5 mg

1.51 2.53×10^4 tickets

1.52 5.2×10^6 people

1.53   (a)   A, B, D
          (b)   E, F, G
          (c)   C, H, I

1.54   (a) 2×10^7 (b) 1.7×10^7 (c) 1.66×10^7 (d) 1.656×10^7 (e) 1.6560×10^7
          (f) 1.65600×10^7

1.55   (a) 2.00×10^5 (b) 1.999×10^5 (c) 1.9990×10^5 (d) 1.99899×10^5 (e)
          1.9989891×10^5 (f) 1.99898909×10^5

1.56   An infinite number

1.57   (a) 1.5×10^{-4} (b) 3.5×10^4 (c) 2.50×10^{24}
          (d) 6.65×10^1 (e) 2.8   (f) 4.5025×10^1
          (g) 3.0×10^1 (h) 1×10^{-1} (i) 2.00

1.58   (a) 3.00000×10^1 (b) 3.00×10^1 (c) 4.65×10^1
         (d) 6.75×10^1 (e) 4.35×10^1 (f) 1×10^{-5}

1.59   (a)   They are accurate; the average is 59.84. They are close to the   t r u e
         value.
         (b)   Evidently the numbers could be read to within one unit of the
         second decimal place, so the uncertainty is small.

1.60   The measuring instrument is inadequate; it is not giving true values. Human
         error might be involved, such as misreading the instrument.

1.61   (a) $\dfrac{39.37\,\text{in.}}{1\,\text{m}}$ and $\dfrac{1\,\text{m}}{39.37\,\text{in.}}$

         (b) $\dfrac{1\,\text{L}}{1.057\,\text{quart}}$ and $\dfrac{1.057\,\text{quart}}{1\,\text{L}}$

         (c) $\dfrac{1\,\text{g}}{1000\,\text{mg}}$ and $\dfrac{1000\,\text{mg}}{1\,\text{g}}$

         (d) $\dfrac{1\,\text{kg}}{2.205\,\text{lb}}$ and $\dfrac{2.205\,\text{lb}}{1\,\text{kg}}$

         (e) $\dfrac{1\,\text{kg}}{2.205\,\text{lb}}$ and $\dfrac{2.205\,\text{lb}}{1\,\text{kg}}$

1.62   (a)   20 in. (b)   0.23 kg   (c)   0.25 oz   (d)   4.5 g
1.63   (a)   200 mL   (b)   1.6 km   (c)   0.25 in.   (d)   1 L
1.64   (a)   64.2 in.   (b)   69.8 kg
1.65   (a)   50.6 kg   (b)   75.6 in.
1.66   355 mL
1.67   10.0 liquid ounces
1.68   45.4 L
1.69   No. The vehicle has a mass of 2.0×10^3 kg, too much for the bridge.
1.70   2 tablets
1.71   3 tablets
1.72   150 mL
1.73   7.00 mL
1.74   29028 ft
1.75   6194.2 m
1.76   3.54 g/pat

1.77   0.500 g

1.78   The mass of something is related directly to the size of the sample, but the density is the *ratio* of the mass to the volume of the material. (The density of water is the same, 1.00 g/mL regardless of how much water you have.)

1.79   Density = 0.787 g/cm^3 (on a mass of 1.70×10^3 g and a volume of 2.16×10^3 cm^3). 24.8 kg (if lead) or 54.7 lb. (Answers can vary slightly depending on the timing of rounding.)

1.80   675 g. 1.49 lb

1.81   13.6 mL

1.82   0.911 g/mL. 2.7×10^2 mL

1.83   (a) No. (b) Decrease

1.84   Dividing a substance's density in g/mL by the density of water in g/mL is like dividing something by 1. The units cancel but the number is unchanged.

1.85   Its density approaches that of water itself, so the urine contains little if any dissolved substances.

1.86   High density

1.87   1.03

1.88   (a) 1.1×10^4 mg/6.0 pt; 3.9×10^3 mg/L

        (b) 2.4×10^3 mg/6.0 pt; 8.5×10^2 mg/L

Chapter 2

Practice Exercises, Chapter 2

1. Na_2S

2.   2 atoms potassium to 1 atom carbon to 3 atoms oxygen

3.   (a) $\dfrac{1\,\text{cal}}{4.184\,\text{J}}$ and $\dfrac{4.184\,\text{J}}{1\,\text{cal}}$

        (b) 333 J or 3.33×10^{-1} kJ

4.   The temperature *increase* is 4.53 °C, so the final temperatue is 24.5 °C

5.   In terms of *kilocalories* equation 2.3 becomes

$$\text{heat capacity (in kcal/}^\circ\text{C)} = \frac{\text{kcal}}{\Delta t} \text{ so, } 50\,\text{kcal}/^\circ\text{C} = \frac{1200\,\text{kcal}}{\Delta t} \quad \text{Therefore, } \Delta t$$

    = 24 °C

6. 5.8×10^2 kcal

7. 2.99×10^4 cal or 29.9 kcal

8.   8.86 kcal

Review Exercises, Chapter 2

2.1   (a) Gas, liquid, and solid

        (b) Elements, compounds, and mixtures

2.2   States of matter (because the distinctions among them concern volume and shape, which are physical properties).

2.3   The fundamental particles of water (its molecules) are identical in all three states.

2.4   That in frozen water, the molecules are much more strongly attracted to each other than they are at a higher temperature, where water is in the liquid state.

2.5   Nonmetal. (Nonconductivity is the key.)

2.6   Metal

2.7   Metal, mostly because it is a conductor, but it is unusual for a metal to be a liquid at room temperature. (This element is mercury.)

2.8   In *chemical* changes, substances change into other substances. This inevitably is accompanied by changes in physical appearances and properties, because different substances differ from each other in at least one physical way.

2.9   (a) Chemical (b) Physical (c) Physical   (d) Chemical

2.10   To the water only. In chemistry we restrict the word *substance* to elements and compounds, not to mixtures like sugar in water.

2.11   Two, elements and compounds

2.12   Elements, because they cannot be broken down into anything less complex and stable.

2.13   Radioactive elements emit streams of radiation that affect photographic film.

2.14   Solid state

2.15   Alloys are mixtures or solutions of two of more metals in each other.

2.16   Carbon

2.17   2

2.18   Roughly, 100

2.19   Compounds are composed elements and the elements of each compound are combined in a definite proportion by mass that is unique for that compound.

2.20   Mixtures consist of substances that can be made in a variety of proportions. Each compound is a unique substance in which the elements are combined in a fixed and definite proportion by mass.

2.21   A *mixture* consists of two or more *substances* (elements or compounds) combined physically in no particular ratio by mass.

2.22   (a) Because both the elements sodium and chlorine "disappear" and b e - come part of a new and different substance, sodium chloride.
       (b) The reactants are sodium and chlorine; the product is sodium chloride
       (c) The ratio is a *fixed* ratio.

2.23   Law of definite proportions

2.24   Law of definite proportions

2.25   (1) Matter consists of definite particles called atoms.

(2)   Atoms are indestructible.

(3)   All atoms of one particular element are identical in mass.

(4)   Atoms of different elements have different masses.

(5)   By becoming stuck together in different ways, atoms form compounds in definite ratios by atoms.

2.26   Law of definite proportions

2.27   The atoms of different elements have different masses.

2.28   Their relative masses would be equal.

2.29   Law of multiple proportions.

2.30   Yes, the ratio, $\dfrac{7.94454}{3.97265} = 1.99981$, is extremely close to the whole number 2.

2.31   According to the law of multiple proportions, the answer has to be 15.8731, because only this number, when divided by 7.93655, gives a whole number, 2.

$\dfrac{15.8731}{7.93655} = 2.00000$, whereas, $\dfrac{9.45386}{7.93655} = 1.19118$ and $\dfrac{13.0521}{7.93655} = 1.64446$

2.32   No is the symbol of an element, nobelium, because the second letter is lower case. NO is the symbol of a compound, nitric oxide, made of the elements nitrogen (N) and oxygen (O).

2.33   (a)   P   (b) Ca (c) Br   (d) Pt   (e) C   (f) Ba

2.34   (a)   Pb (b) Hg (c) F   (d) K   (e) H   (f) Fe

2.35   (a)   S   (b) I   (c) Mn (d) Na (e) Cu (f) Mg

2.36   (a)   N   (b) O   (c) Ag (d) Zn (e) Li   (f) Cl

2.39   One atom of iron

2.40 NO_2

2.41   (a) The subscripts, 2 and 2 are in a ratio of 1:1, the correct ratio for sodium chloride.

(b)   This formula violates only a convention about writing formulas that the lowest whole numbers are generally used to represent the ratios of the atoms present.

(c)   Empirical formula

(d)   Formula unit

2.42   (a)   One (b) Two (c) Coefficients (d) Two

2.43   (a) $Ca + S \rightarrow CaS$

(b) $2Na + S \rightarrow Na_2S$

2.44   Matter is any *thing* that occupies space *and has mass*. Energy is an ability possessed by "things," the ability to cause some kind of change.

2.45   Kinetic energy. $KE = f_{(1,2)}\, mv^2$

2.46   The joule, J

2.47   The kinetic energy is doubled; KE is directly proportional to the mass of the moving object.

2.48   The kinetic energy is multiplied by four. Notice that the velocity is doubled, and KE is directly proportional to the *square* of the velocity, so if the velocity is multiplied by 2, the KE is multiplied by 2^2, or 4.

2.49   (a) $kg \times \dfrac{m^2}{s^2}$

        (b) 6.25×10^5 J

        (c) 1.49×10^5 cal or 1.49×10^2 kcal

        (d)   35.4 m/s (about 80 mi/hr) (Notice that the velocity does not have to double to double the associated kinetic energy.)

2.50   (a)   67.1 mi/hr

        (b)   22.4 times the speed of walking

        (c)   31.5 kJ in the vehicle versus 6.28×10^{-2} kJ for walking

2.51   Most of it become heat energy, but some sound is released and some mechanical energy (movement of masses).

2.52   As reactive chemicals within the battery, so it is in the form of chemical energy (a potential energy)

2.53   As chemical energy in the substances of the muscle.

2.54   They must be at the same temperature.

2.55   (a)   From A to B.

        (b)   B is either melting or boiling.

2.56   (a)   Melting point   (b) Boiling point

2.57   The calorie. No, the calorie is an extremely small amount of energy.

2.58   The kilocalorie

2.59   The water sample; water has a higher specific heat.

2.60   The specific heat of granite as well as the mass of the sample.

2.61   The olive oil sample. Olive oil has a higher specific heat, so more heat is released per gram per degree of temperature change.

2.62   12.5 kcal; 52.3 kJ

2.63   3.00 kcal; 12.6 kJ

2.64   When it is melting or when it is boiling.

2.65   The high heat of fusion of ice means that much heat can be withdrawn from the fevered area without warming up the contents of the ice bag.

2.66   When the steam condenses to the liquid state, the high heat of vaporization of water is released where the condensation occurs.

2.67   We reserve the word *vapor* to the gaseous form of something that ordinarily is a liquid at room temperature (which air is not).

2.68   The heat is released to the surroundings.

2.69   Evaporation or vaporization.

2.70   Condensation

2.71   It is water vapor if its temperature is below 100 °C and steam above 100 °C.

2.72   (a) exothermic (b) exothermic (c) endothermic (d) endothermic
(e) endothermic (f) exothermic. Remember that these refer to the flow of
heat into or out of the *system*. If heat must flow in, as in the evaporation of
water (part c), the change is endothermic. If heat must flow out, as in the
condensing of water (part a), the change is exothermic.

2.73   199 °C (Δt = 174 °C)

2.74   86 °C (Δt = 66 °C)

2.75   14 °C (Δt = −23 °C; *minus* because the temperature is lowered)

2.76   That considerable quantities of heat can move into or out of the body with only
a small effect on the body temperature. The high specific heat of water makes
this true.

2.77   The heat capacity

2.78   *Basal metabolism* refers to activities; *basal metabolic rate* refers to how
rapidly they occur.

2.79   Other activities are over and above those needed just to maintain normal body
functions when it is at complete rest.

2.80   Maintenance of body tone, control of body temperature, circulation of the
blood, breathing, chemical reactions associated with all of these activities,
including the operation of tissues and glands.

2.81   (a) 0.9 – 1.1 kcal/min.   (b) 1.0 – 1.2 kcal/min

2.82 1.44×10^3 kcal/24.00 hr

2.83   Liquids (48%), food (40%), and metabolism, 12%)

2.84   Evaporation (40%), urine (56%), and feces (4%)

2.85   Skin and lungs

2.86   Heat (carried away by water vapor that absorbed heat of vaporization from the
body)

2.87   Radiation, conduction, and convection

2.88   Conduction

2.89   Air is a poor conductor of heat. By trapping air, the fabrics inhibit loss of heat
by convection.

2.90   Radiation (but also convection)

2.91   Hypothermia

2.92   More rapid breathing brings in extra oxygen to sustain the increased rate of
metabolism caused by the higher body temperature.

2.93   The increased heart beat helps to deliver oxygen needed wherever metabolism
has accelerated.

2.94 3.3×10^2 kcal (rounded from 332 kcal)

2.95 2.0×10^2 kcal (rounded from 201 kcal)

2.96   (a) 3.9×10^2 kcal (rounded from 385 kcal)

       (b) 1.3 hr; 4.6 mi

Chapter 3[1]

Practice Exercises, Chapter 3

1. 8.68×10^{22} atoms of gold per ounce

2.   (a) 180 (b) 58.3 (c) 858.6

3.   408 g of NH_3

4.   0.0380 mol of aspirin

5. $3O_2 \rightarrow 2O_3$

6. $4Al + 3O_2 \rightarrow 2Al_2O_3$

7.   (a) $2Ca + O_2 \rightarrow 2CaO$

      (b) $2KOH + H_2SO_4 \rightarrow 2H_2O + K_2SO_4$

      (c) $Cu(NO_3)_2 + Na_2S \rightarrow CuS + 2NaNO_3$

      (d) $2AgNO_3 + CaCl_2 \rightarrow 2AgCl + Ca(NO_3)_2$

      (e) $2Al + 3H_2SO_4 \rightarrow Al_2(SO_4)_3 + 3H_2$

      (f) $CH_4 + 2O_2 \rightarrow 2H_2O + CO_2$

8.   0.500 mol of H_2O.   500 mmol of H_2O

9.   4.20 mol of N_2 and 4.20 mol of O_2

10.   450 mol of H_2 and 150 mol of N_2

11.   11.5 g of O_2

12.   18.4 g of Na

13.   (a) 2.45 g of H_2SO_4

      (b) 9.01 g of $C_6H_{12}O_6$

14.   156 mL of 0.800 M Na_2CO_3 solution

15.   9.82 mL of 0.112 M H_2SO_4, when calculated step-by-step with rounding after each step.

      9.84 mL of 0.112 M H_2SO_4, when found by a chain calculation.

16.   Dilute 20.0 mL of 0.200 M $K_2Cr_2O_7$ to a final volume of 100 mL.

17.   Dilute 14 mL of 18 M H_2SO_4 to a final volume of 250 mL.

---

[1] If your calculated answers differ slightly from the answers given here, remember that it may be caused by a conceptually unimportant difference in handling the calculation. All answers to computational problems given here were obtained by *chain* calculations. The formula masses needed for these calculations, were first computed in the usual way from atomic masses rounded to the first decimal place (H to 1.01), and then they were rounded to the number of significant figures allowed by the given data *before* they were used in the calculations.

Review Exercises, Chapter 3

3.1   It is the study of the ratios by atoms in pure substances and the ratios by formula units of the participants in chemical reactions.

3.2   We need to know *numbers* because it is in a whole-number ratio of *numbers* of particles that substances interact, not in whole-number ratios of their masses. The problem is that the particles are too tiny to count directly (and so obtain them directly in whole-number ratios). Thus we must use an indirect method to count them, and Avogadro's number is the basis for solving this problem.

3.3 6×10^{23}

3.4   Mole

3.5   The ratio by atoms is 2 Al atoms to 3 O atoms; or, the ratio by moles, is 2 mol Al to 3 mol O.

3.6   Electrons, protons, and neutrons. Protons and neutrons.

3.7   16 protons. Sulfur, S. By scanning through the table of the elements inside the front cover to find the element of atomic number 16.

3.8   Elements usually consist of a mixture of isotopes in which all atoms have identical atomic numbers but, because of small variations in numbers of neutrons, slightly different mass numbers.

3.9   Lithium-7. Mass number = 7

3.10   They exhibit the same chemical reactions.

3.11   It is the average of the atomic masses of the individual isotopes of the element allowing for the percentage abundances of the isotopes.

3.12   The percentage abundances of the isotopes in an element are generally the same all over the world.

3.13   (a) Neither. (b) The isotope with the larger mass. (c) 23.0 (the average of 24.0 and 22.0 can be taken because the ratio of 1:1).

3.14 10^{-23} g

3.15   Because then the total mass of this many atoms of an element numerially comes out equal to something familiar about the element, its atomic mass expressed in grams.

3.16   Avogadro's number of helium atoms or 6.02×10^{23} atoms of helium.

3.17 6.02×10^{22} atoms of cobalt.

3.18 1.58×10^{23} atoms of silver.

3.19   The law of conservation of mass in chemical reactions. (Because no loss in mass occurs when atoms combine to form compounds, the sum of the atomic masses gives the formula mass.)

3.20   (a) 36.5   (b) 56.1   (c) 184.1
       (d) 63.0   (e) 84.0   (f) 261.3
       (g) 132.1   (h) 158.2   (i) 180.1

3.21   (a) 106.0   (b) 98.1   (c) 149.1

(d) 262.9   (e) 204.1   (f) 239.1

(g) 116.2   (h) 294.2   (g) 737.7

3.22   Formula masses vary from substance to substance, so the formula mass *taken in grams* must also vary accordingly. What is constant about 1 mole of all substances is that they all have identical numbers of formula units, Avogadro's number.

3.23   The reactants of a reaction interact in whole number ratios by *formula units*, but we cannot count these units directly. By taking substances in ratios by *moles*, which can be weighed as an equivalent number of grams, we get them in the same ratios by formula units, so mole calculations let us count particles indirectly.

3.24   By computing the substance's formula mass and writing *grams* (or g) after it.

3.25   A separate balance for each possible value of formula mass likely to be encountered in laboratory work would have to be manufactured if balances read in moles.

3.26 $$\frac{40.0 \, g \, NaOH}{1.00 \, mol \, NaOH} \quad \text{and} \quad \frac{1.00 \, mol \, NaOH}{40.0 \, g \, NaOH}$$

3.27   (a) 4.56 g HCl   (b) 7.01 g KOH   (c) 23.0 g $MgBr_2$
(d) 7.88 g HNO_3 (e) 10.5 g $NaHCO_3$ (f) 32.7 g $Ba(NO_3)_2$
(g) 16.5 g $(NH_4)_2HPO_4$
(h) 19.8 g $Ca(C_2H_3O_2)_2$
(i) 22.5 g $C_6H_{12}O_6$

3.28   (a) 79.5 g Na_2CO_3 (b) 73.6 g H_2SO_4 (c) 112 g $(NH_4)_3PO_4$
(d) 197 g $Mg_3(PO_4)_2$ (e) 153 g $Al(C_2H_3O_2)_3$ (f) 179 g $Ca(ClO_4)_2$
(g) 87.2 g $(NH_4)_2SO_3$ (h) 221 g $K_2Cr_2O_7$ (i) 553 g $Fe_4(OH)_2(SO_4)_5$

3.29   (a) 1.37 mol HCl   (b) 0.891 mol KOH   (c) 0.272 mol $MgBr_2$
(d) 0.794 mol HNO_3 (e) 0.595 mol $NaHCO_3$ (f) 0.191 mol $Ba(NO_3)_2$
(g) 0.379 mol $(NH_4)_2HPO_4$
(h) 0.316 mol $Ca(C_2H_3O_2)_2$
(i) 0.277 mol $C_6H_{12}O_6$

3.30   (a) 1.42×10^{-2} mol Na_2CO_3
(b) 1.53×10^{-2} mol H_2SO_4
(c) 1.01×10^{-2} mol $(NH_4)_3PO_4$
(d) 5.71×10^{-3} mol $Mg_3(PO_4)_2$
(e) 7.35×10^{-3} mol $Al(C_2H_3O_2)_3$
(f) 6.27×10^{-3} mol $Ca(ClO_4)_2$
(g) 1.29×10^{-2} mol $(NH_4)_2SO_3$
(h) 5.10×10^{-3} mol $K_2Cr_2O_7$
(i) 2.03×10^{-3} mol $Fe_4(OH)_2(SO_4)_5$

3.31 2.15×10^{22} molecules N_2

3.32 2.09×10^{21} molecules H_2O

3.33 6×10^{15} molecules O_3

3.34 9.99×10^{-4} mol aspirin; 6.02×10^{20} molecules aspirin

3.35   One atom of sulfur reacts with one molecule of oxygen to give one molecule of sulfur dioxide.

3.36   Two molecules of nitrogen monoxide react with one molecule of oxygen to give two molecules of nitrogen dioxide.

3.37 $H_2SO_4 + 2NaOH \rightarrow Na_2SO_4 + 2H_2O$

3.38   (a) $N_2 + O_2 \rightarrow 2NO$

　　　(b) $MgO + 2HNO_3 \rightarrow Mg(NO_3)_2 + H_2O$

　　　(c) $CaBr_2 + 2AgNO_3 \rightarrow Ca(NO_3)_2 + 2AgBr$

　　　(d) $2HI + Mg(OH)_2 \rightarrow MgI_2 + 2H_2O$

　　　(e) $CaCO_3 + 2HBr \rightarrow CaBr_2 + CO_2 + H_2O$

3.39   (a) $4P + 5O_2 \rightarrow P_4O_{10}$

　　　(b) $Fe_3O_4 + 4H_2 \rightarrow 3Fe + 4H_2O$

　　　(c) $Al_2S_3 + 3H_2SO_4 \rightarrow Al_2(SO_4)_3 + 3H_2S$

　　　(d) $2HNO_3 \rightarrow N_2O_5 + H_2O$

　　　(e) $2KHCO_3 + H_2SO_4 \rightarrow K_2SO_4 + 2CO_2 + 2H_2O$

3.40   (a) $CH_4 + 2O_2 \quad f(\quad,)> \quad CO_2 + 2H_2O$

　　　(b) $\dfrac{1\,mol\,CH_4}{2\,mol\,O_2} \quad \dfrac{2\,mol\,O_2}{1\,mol\,CH_4}$

$\dfrac{1\,mol\,CH_4}{1\,mol\,CO_2} \quad \dfrac{1\,mol\,CO_2}{1\,mol\,CH_4}$

$\dfrac{1\,mol\,CH_4}{2\,mol\,H_2O} \quad \dfrac{2\,mol\,H_2O}{1\,mol\,CH_4}$

3.41 $\dfrac{1\,mol\,Ca(OH)_2}{2\,mol\,HCl} \quad \dfrac{2\,mol\,HCl}{1\,mol\,Ca(OH)_2}$

3.42   (a) $\dfrac{2\,mol\,Al}{3\,mol\,H_2SO_4} \quad \dfrac{3\,mol\,H_2SO_4}{2\,mol\,Al}$

　　　(b) $\dfrac{2\,mol\,Al}{3\,mol\,H_2} \quad \dfrac{3\,mol\,H_2}{2\,mol\,Al}$

　　　(c) $\dfrac{3\,mol\,H_2SO_4}{1\,mol\,Al_2(SO_4)_3} \quad \dfrac{1\,mol\,Al_2(SO_4)_3}{3\,mol\,H_2SO_4}$

3.43   (a)   1.5 mol N_2/mol TNT   (b) 3.5 mol CO/mol TNT

　　　(c)   2.5 mol H_2O vapor/mol TNT

    (d)   7.5 mol gases/mol TNT

    (e) $1.7 \times 10^3 \dfrac{\text{L gases}}{\text{LTNT}}$ (Note that this is nearly a 2000-fold expansion.)

3.44   (a) $C_6H_{12}O_6 + 6O_2 \rightarrow 6CO_2 + 6H_2O$

         (b) $\dfrac{1\,\text{mol}\,C_6H_{12}O_6}{6\,\text{mol}\,O_2} \qquad \dfrac{6\,\text{mol}\,O_2}{1\,\text{mol}\,C_6H_{12}O_6}$

3.45   (a) $C_2H_6O_2 + 3O_2 \rightarrow 2CO_2 + 3H_2O$
         (b) 15.0 mol O_2
         (c) 10.0 mol CO_2

3.46   (a) 0.417 mol O_2 (b) 0.278 mol Fe_2O_3

3.47   (a) 0.462 mol C_4H_{10} (b) 0.288 mol C_4H_{10}, 1.87 mol O_2

3.48   (a) $2Al_2O_3 \rightarrow 4Al + 3O_2$
         (b) 52.9 g Al   (c) 47.1 g O_2 (d) 100.0 g (Al + O_2), which is identical to the initial mass of Al_2O_3 used. Law of conservation of mass in chemical reactions.

3.49   (a) 524 g Fe   (b) 395 g CO   (c) 620 g CO_2

3.50   (a) 0.740 mg H_2S (b) 5.38 mg Ag_2S

3.51   (a) 15.9 g $Mn(NO_3)_2$ (b) 62.2 g $NaBiO_3$ (c) 39.2 g HNO_3 (d) 87.7 g $Bi(NO_3)_3$

3.52   32.4 g Na_2CO_3

3.53   To be a solution the substances must be subdivided to their atomic, ionic, or molecular sizes. Even powdered sand is not that finely divided. Moreover, once the stirring stops, the sand will settle to the bottom of the container. Solutions do not separate spontaneously.

3.54   Water is the *solvent,* sugar is the *solute,* and solutions in which water is the dispersing medium can be called *aqueous solutions.*

3.55   (a) Saturated   (b) Concentrated

3.56   Barium sulfate

3.57   The solubility in water of sodium hydroxide *increases* with temperature, so a saturated solution can become supersaturated by cooling the solution, provided that the excess solute does not precipitate. If the saturated solution is heated, it becomes unsaturated.

3.58   Add sodium chloride to the desired amount of water, as the solution is stirred, until no more solute dissolves and some excess solute persists indefinitely as undissolved solid at the bottom of the solution. (Portions of this solution can easily be poured off the undissolved material.)

3.59   Molarity

3.60   Molar concentration and molarity are exact synonyms. Each refers to a *concentration* in units of moles per liter. A *mole* is that mass of a substance that equals its formula mass in the unit of grams. A *molecule* is just one of the 6.02

$\times\ 10^{23}$ formula units in a molecular substance, so it is an exceedingly tiny *particle*.

3.61   Moles per liter of solution

3.62   (a)   0.0625 mol or 3.66 g NaCl
       (b)   0.0250 mol or 4.50 g $C_6H_{12}O_6$
       (c)   0.0250 mol or 2.45 g H_2SO_4
       (d)   0.0625 mol or 6.63 g Na_2CO_3

3.63   (a)   0.100 mol or 8.20 g $NaC_2H_3O_2$
       (b)   0.0313 mol or 1.97 g HNO_3
       (c)   0.0100 mol or 0.400 g NaOH
       (d)   0.0125 mol or 1.05 g $NaHCO_3$

3.64   66.7 mL

3.65   284 mL

3.66   400 mL

3.67   0.0500 mol HCl

3.68   0.300 mol Na_2CO_3

3.69   0.0100 mol $C_6H_{12}O_6$

3.70   79.4 mL

3.71   20.4 mL

3.72   22.8 mL

3.73 $\dfrac{0.250\ \text{mol HCl}}{1000\ \text{mLHCl solution}}$ and $\dfrac{1000\ \text{mL HCl solution}}{0.250\ \text{mol HCl}}$

3.74   28.6 mL of 0.150 M Na_2SO_4 solution and 42.9 mL of 0.100 M $Ba(NO_3)_2$ solution

3.75   26.9 mL of 16.0 M HNO_3 solution and 47.8 mL of 12.0 M HCl solution

3.76   33.5 mL of 0.500 M Na_2CO_3. 2.22 g of Na_2CO_3

3.77   823 mL of 0.100 M HCl

3.78   1.04 L of 0.120 M Na_2CO_3

3.79   33.3 mL of 15 M H_3PO_4. You would place some water into a 500-mL volumetric flask, slowly add the 15 M H_3PO_4, and then make up the final volume to the 500-mL mark.

3.80   3.00 M NH_3

3.81   0.50 mol of NH_3

3.82   1.00 mol iodine (I)

3.83   4.79 g Na, 0.210 g H, 10.0 g O

3.84   (a)   Yes; 0.307 mol HNO_3 was spilled and half this or 0.154 mol of Na_2CO_3 is needed. But 0.189 mol of Na_2CO_3 is provided in the 20.0 g of Na_2CO_3.
       (b) HNO_3 (the reactant that can be all used up)
       (c)   0.035 mol of Na_2CO_3 remained
       (d)   0.154 mol or 6.78 g of CO_2 was produced

Chapter 4

Practice Exercises, Chapter 4

1.   (a) Sn   (b) Cl (c) Rb (d) Mg   (e) Ar
2.   (a) $1s^2 2s^2 2p^6 3s^2 3p_x^1$
      (b) $1s^2 2s^2 2p^6 3s^2 3p_x^2 3p_y^2 3p_z^1$
      (c) $1s^2 2s^2 2p^6 3s^2 3p_x^1 3p_y^1$
      (d) $1s^2 2s^2 2p^6 3s^2 3p^6 4s^2$
3.   (a) 1   (b) 6   (c) 5   (d) 7

Review Exercises, Chapter 4

4.1   They go from a low value to a high value and then swing through this cycle again. (In other words, they do not steadily increase. They vary in a periodic manner as the atomic number increases.)

4.2   *First ionization energy* is the energy needed to remove one electron from each of the atoms in one mole of the element. This energy cycles through low and high values as the atomic number increases. (In other words, it does not steadily increase with increasing atomic number.)

4.3   The number of H atoms that combine with the atoms of an element moves from a low value (0) through a maximum of 4 and then back down again. (In other words, the number of H atoms does not steadily increase with increasing atomic number.)

4.4   (a) KH   (b) CaH_2 (c) GaH_3 (d) GeH_4
       (e) AsH_3 (f) SeH_2 (usually written as H_2Se)
       (g) BrH (usually written as HBr)

4.5   The same *group* or *family*. A *period*

4.6   (a) IVA   (b) Representative
       (c) Metals   (d) Representative

4.7   Te (#52) and I (#53) would be switched in positions because Te has the higher atomic mass. Mendeleev made his decision because the *chemical* properties of I are more like those in group VIIA, however, and the *chemical* properties of Te are more like those of group VIA.

4.8   (a) IA
       (b) base
       (c) $XOH + HBr \rightarrow XBr + H_2O$
       (d) acid-base neutralization

4.9   (a) IA, alkali metals

(b)   VIIA, halogens
(c)   VIA, oxygen family
(d)   IIA, alkaline earth metals

4.10   (a)   VIIA, halogens
(b)   VA, nitrogen family
(c)   IIA, alkaline earth metals
(d)   IA, alkali metals

4.11   (a)   subatomic particles
(b)   electron, 1– charge; proton, 1+ charge; neutron, 0 charge
(c)   Electrons and protons attract each other.
(d)   Like charges repel; unlike charges attract.

4.12   (a)   1+   (b) 1–
(c)   Attract; they have opposite charges
(d) X, 23; Y, 35

4.13   Ernest Rutherford. He concluded that essentially all of the mass of an atom is concentrated in its nucleus and that the atom as a whole is mostly empty space.

4.14   The protons. Whole numbers of protons, each with a whole-number charge of 1+ must result in a whole number for the nuclear charge.

4.15   Its *electron configuration*.

4.16   Electrons are confined in atoms in certain allowed energy states.
As long as electrons remain in their allowed states, the atom neither gives off nor absorbs energy.
These two postulates are still true.

4.17   Electrons move from states of higher energy to states of lower energy in the atoms. One unit of light is a *quantum of energy* or a *photon*.

4.18   The light emerged only with certain values of energy, not with all possible values.

4.19   The solar system; electrons are like planets orbiting the sun (the nucleus). The analogy is no longer used.

4.20   The location and the energy of an electron. Heisenberg. Efforts to describe precise electron *orbits* were abandoned.

4.21   Principal energy level or shell.

4.22   Ground state

4.23   The number assigned to a principal energy level. This number also equals the number of the sublevels associated with the principal energy level.

4.24

Pr incipal Energy Level Number	Number of Sublevels	Number of Orbitals
1	1	1
2	2	4
3	3	9
4	4	16

4.25   (a) $1s$ (b) $2s$ (c) $2p$ (d) $3p$

4.26 $3s^1$

4.27   (a)   It is the volume of space near the atomic nucleus in which the probability of finding the $1s$ electron is very high.
(b)   The probability of finding the $1s$ electron at any one place on the surface is identical to the probability of finding it anywhere else on the surface. (The surface is an equi-probability surface.)
(c)   Yes, but the probability of finding the $1s$ electron outside the $1s$ sphere becomes increasingly small as the distance outward increases.

4.28   A figure eight.

4.29   Only the *direction* in which they are oriented.

4.30   Many chemical properties of the elements are correlated with their outside-level electron configurations.

4.31   (a)   Level 1, 2 electrons. Level 2, 8 electrons, Level 3, 18 electrons
(b)   At both levels 2 and 3, the p orbitals can hold up to 6 electrons, two in each of the three p orbitals.
(c)   At any principal energy level, the s orbital can hold up to 2 electrons.
(d)   The d orbitals can hold a maximum of 10 electrons
(e)   The f orbitals can hold a maximum of 14 electrons.

4.32   Electrons at the same sublevel spread out among the sublevel's orbitals as much as possible. The likely reason is that electrons repel each other.

4.33   Hund's rule.

4.34   We can place two electrons in the same orbital only if their spins are opposite.

4.35   (a) 8. oxygen   (b) 13. aluminum

4.36   (a) 13, aluminum   (b) 20, calcium

4.37   (a) $1s^22s^22p^63s^23p_x^13p_y^13p_z^1$ (b) [Ne] $3s^2\,3ps(1,x)3ps(1,y)3ps(1,z)$

4.38   (a) $1s^22s^22p^63s^23p^64s^1$ (b) [Ar] $4s^1$

4.39   (a)   30; its number of electrons, 30, equals its number of protons,   which is its atomic number.
(b)   Yes, it has 18 electrons.
(c)   No, all occupied orbitals are *filled* orbitals (each with 2 electrons), and the Pauli exclusion principle tells us that orbitals can hold 2 electrons only if their spins are opposite or paired.
(d)   [Ar] $4s^23d^{10}$. (Argon has no $3d$ electrons so the $3d^{10}$ electrons must be shown as part of the condensed electron configuration.)
(e)   [Ar] $4s^23d^{10}4ps(2,x)4ps(1,y)4ps(1,z)$ Atomic no. = 34. Atomic symbol = Se
(f)   Three of the four $4p$ electrons spread out among the three $4p$ orbitals.
(g)   The fourth $4p$ electron pairs up with another electron in the $4p_x$ orbital, and we assume that the spins of these two are opposite.

4.40   [He] $2s^22p^6$

4.41   (a)   The same element; they have identical numbers of electrons and so identical atomic numbers.

(b)   Configuration **1**; its electrons are in the lowest available energy states.

(c)   Configuration **2**. Configuration **2** has an electron in the $4s$ orbital while having empty $3p$ orbitals.

(d)   The atom has to be given energy to change it from **1** to **2**. (The change from **2** to **1** would release the identical amount of energy.)

4.42   (a) $1s^2 2s^2$ or [He] $2s^2$

(b) $1s^2 2s^2 2ps(1,x)2ps(1,y)$ or [He] $2s^2 2ps(1,x)2ps(1,y)$ (or [He] $2s^2 2p^2$)

(c) $1s^2 2s^2 2p^6 3s^2$ or [Ne] $3s^2$

(d) $1s^2 2s^2 2p^6 3s^2 3ps(2,x)3ps(1,y)3ps(1,z)$ or [Ne] $3s^2 3ps(2,x)3ps(1,y)3ps(1,z)$ (or [Ne] $3s^2 3p^4$)

4.43   (a) $1s^2 2s^2 2ps(1,x)$ or [He] $2s^2 2ps(1,x)$

(b) $1s^2 2s^2 2ps(1,x)2ps(1,y)2ps(1,z)$ or [He] $2s^2 2ps(1,x)2ps(1,y)2ps(1,z)$ (or [He] $2s^2 2p^3$)

(c) $1s^2 2s^2 2p^6 3s^2 3ps(1,x)3ps(1,y)$ or [Ne] $3s^2 3ps(1,x)3ps(1,y)$

(d) $1s^2 2s^2 2p^6 3s^2 3ps(2,x)3ps(2,y)3ps(1,z)$ or [Ne] $3s^2 3ps(2,x)3ps(2,y)3ps(1,z)$ (or [Ne] $3s^2 3p^5$)

4.44   (a)   VA. Levels 1, 2, and 3 are full and the highest occupied principal energy level (4) has 5 electrons, like all elements in VA.

(b) Nonmetal. The highest occupied energy level has more than 4 electrons, like most nonmetals.

4.45   (a)   IVA. All inner levels, 1-3, are full and the outer level (5) has 4 electrons, like all elements in group IVA.

(b)   [Kr] $5s^2 4d^{10} 5p^2$

(c)   [Kr] $5s^2 4d^{10} 5p^3$

(d)   [Kr] $5s^2 4d^{10} 5p^1$

(e)   [Ar] $4s^2 3d^{10} 4p^2$ (Notice that only the numbers of the principal energy levels change in shifting from element 50 to the element immediately above it in the periodic table.)

4.46   (a) 13, 14, 15, 16, 17

(b)   6, 14, 32

(c)   9, 17, 35

(d)

IIIA	IVA	VA	VIA	VIIA
5	6	7	8	9

(e)   2 (The element would be in group IIA, so has two outside shell electrons.)

(f)   6 (The element is in the same family as d, group VIA, so it has six outside shell electrons, just like d.)

(g) XH_3 and ZH_3

(h)   9 (It stands high up in a group with more than 4 outside-level electrons.)

Chapter 5

Practice Exercises, Chapter 5

1. (a) AgBr (b) Na_2O (c) Fe_2O_3 (d) $CuCl_2$
2. (a) Copper(II) sulfide (cupric sulfide)
    (b) Sodium fluoride
    (c) Iron(II) iodide (ferrous iodide)
    (d) Zinc bromide
    (e) Copper(I) oxide (cuprous oxide)
3. (a) 3+ (b) 2+ (c) 2+
4. (a) $1s^2 2s^2 2p^6 3s^2 3p^6 4s^1$. 1+ charge on the ion
    (b) $1s^2 2s^2 2p^6 3s^2 3ps(2,x)3ps(1,y)3ps(1,z)$. 2– charge on the ion
    (c) $1s^2 2s^2 2p^6 3s^2 3ps(1,x)3ps(1,y)$. No ion is predicted (or exists).
5. (a) $1s^2 2s^2 2p^6 3s^2 3p^6$
    (b) $1s^2 2s^2 2p^6 3s^2 3ps(2,x)3ps(2,y)3ps(2,z)$
    (c) No ion exists
6. (a) Cs^+ (b) F^- (c) No ion is predicted. (d) Sr^{2+}
7. (a) Mg is oxidized; S is reduced
        Mg is the reducing agent; S is the oxidizing agent
    (b) Zn is oxidized; Cu^{2+} is reduced
        Zn is the reducing agent; Cu^{2+} is the oxidizing agent

8. Na·   ·Mg·   ·Al·   ·S̈i·   ·P̈·   ·S̈·   :C̈l·   :Är :

9. ·S̈b·

10. ·Ca· + ·Ö· ⟶ Ca^{2+} + :Ö:²⁻

11.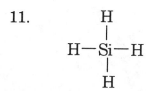

12. (a) $KHCO_3$
     (b) Na_2HPO_4
     (c) $(NH_3)_3PO_4$

13.   (a)   Sodium cyanide
       (b)   Potassium nitrate
       (c)   Sodium hydrogen sulfite
       (d)   Ammonium carbonate
       (e)   Sodium acetate

14.

O   O

H O S O H   H O P O H

O   O

                           H

15.   32

16.

O

H O Cl O   26 valence electrons $H-\ddot{O}-\overset{\overset{\displaystyle\ddot{\ddot{O}}}{|}}{Cl}-\ddot{O}:$

17.

$:\ddot{O}:\overset{\overset{\displaystyle :\overset{..}{O}:}{\|}}{S}:\ddot{O}:$

18.   (a) $\left[\begin{matrix} H \\ H:\overset{..}{O}:H \end{matrix}\right]^{+}$ (b) $\left[H:\overset{..}{\underset{..}{O}}:\right]^{-}$

19.   (a) $\left[:\overset{..}{\underset{..}{O}}:\overset{\overset{\displaystyle :O:}{\|}}{C}:\overset{..}{\underset{..}{O}}:\right]^{2-}$ (b) $\left[:\overset{..}{\underset{..}{O}}:\overset{\overset{\displaystyle :O:}{\|}}{N}:\overset{..}{\underset{..}{O}}:\right]^{-}$

20.

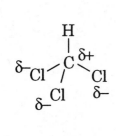

Review Exercises, Chapter 5

5.1   Unlike charges attract.

5.2   The electrons and nuclei of the two atoms are reorganized relative to their previous arrangements. Once the bond forms, it is improper to say that the atoms themselves are present; only their parts are present. We *define* an atom as an electrically neutral particle with *one* nucleus. One the bond forms, two nuclei are present in the product.

5.3   Molecular and ionic compounds.

5.4   Molecule

5.5   Nonmetals

5.6   They must lose too many electrons.

5.7

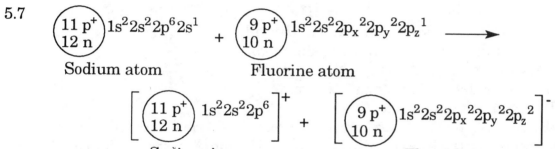

5.8   They differ by one electron. The sodium *atom* is electrically neutral; the sodium *ion* carries a charge of 1+.

5.9   (a) I^- (b) Na^+
            (c) Ag^+ (d) Ca^{2+}
            (e) Zn^{2+} (f) Al^{3+}
            (g) S^{2-} (h) Li^+
            (i) Br^- (j) Cl^-
            (k) K^+ (l) Ba^{2+}
            (m) O^{2-} (n) Cu^{2+}
            (o) F^- (p) Cu^+
            (q) Fe^{3+} (r) Mg^{2+}
            (s) Fe^{2+}

5.10   (a) potassium ion   (b) sulfide ion
         (c) aluminum ion   (d) iron(II) ion, ferrous ion
         (e) bromide ion   (f) iron(III) ion, ferric ion
         (g) barium ion   (h) sodium ion
         (i) chloride ion   (j) magnesium ion
         (k) lithium ion   (l) copper(I) ion, cuprous ion

(m) zinc ion   (n) calcium ion
(o) silver ion   (p) oxide ion
(q) iodide ion   (r) fluoride ion
(s) copper(II) ion, cupric ion

5.11 Sn^{2+} is the stannous ion and Sn^{4+} is the stannic ion.

5.12   (a) lead(II) ion   (b) gold(III) ion   (c) mercury(I) ion. The charge *per* Hg is
        1+. (d) lead(IV) ion

5.13   (a) Cu_2S (b) BaO
        (c) Al_2O_3 (d) $CaCl_2$
        (e) $FeBr_2$ (f) NaI

5.14   (a) MgF_2 (b) Li_2O
        (c) CuS (d) $FeCl_3$
        (e) $NaBr$ (f) CaO

5.15   (a) silver iodide   (b) iron(II) chloride, ferrous chloride
        (c) aluminum oxide   (d) barium chloride
        (e) calcium sulfide   (f) potassium iodide

5.16   (a) sodium fluoride   (b) lithium oxide
        (c) copper(II) bromide, cupric bromide
        (d) magnesium chloride
        (e) zinc oxide   (f) iron(III) bromide, ferric bromide

5.17   The atom has the larger radius because it has more electrons than a positively
        charged ion and so needs more space.

5.18   The S atom is larger. It has the higher atomic number and more electrons
        needing more space.

5.19 O^{2-} has the larger radius because it has more electrons that the O atom and
        so needs more room.

5.20   Ionic compounds. To be an electrolyte, the compound has to furnish ions, and
        these pre-exist in ionic compounds.

5.21   To the potassium *ion* level, not the potassium *atom* or the potassium *metal*
        level.

5.22

$$\left(\begin{matrix}20\ p^+ \\ 20\ n\end{matrix}\right)1s^2 2s^2 2p^6 3s^2 3p^6 4s^2 \ +\ 2\left(\begin{matrix}17\ p^+ \\ 18\ n\end{matrix}\right)1s^2 2s^2 2p^6 3s^2 3p_x{}^2 3p_y{}^2 3p_z{}^1 \longrightarrow$$

Calcium atom   Two chlorine atoms (Cl-35 isotope)

$$\left[\left(\begin{matrix}20\ p^+ \\ 20\ n\end{matrix}\right)1s^2 2s^2 2p^6 3s^2 3p^6\right]^{2+} +\ 2\left[\left(\begin{matrix}17\ p^+ \\ 18\ n\end{matrix}\right)1s^2 2s^2 2p^6 3s^2 3p_x{}^2 3p_y{}^2 3p_z{}^2\right]^{-}$$

Calcium ion   Two chloride ions

5.23

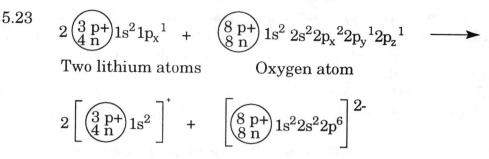

2 $\left(\begin{smallmatrix}3\ p+\\ 4\ n\end{smallmatrix}\right)1s^2 1p_x{}^1$ + $\left(\begin{smallmatrix}8\ p+\\ 8\ n\end{smallmatrix}\right)1s^2\ 2s^2 2p_x{}^2 2p_y{}^1 2p_z{}^1$ $\longrightarrow$

Two lithium atoms   Oxygen atom

2 $\left[\left(\begin{smallmatrix}3\ p+\\ 4\ n\end{smallmatrix}\right)1s^2\right]^+$ + $\left[\left(\begin{smallmatrix}8\ p+\\ 8\ n\end{smallmatrix}\right)1s^2 2s^2 2p^6\right]^{2-}$

Two lithium ions   Oxide ion

5.24   IIA

5.25   VA

5.26   (a) 1+ (b) 2+ (c) 3+ (d) 1– (e) 2–

5.27   Group 0. The helium configuration with 2 electrons in the outside level (level 1), and the outer octet of the remaining group 0 elements.

5.28   Yes, 1–

5.29   Yes, 1+

5.30   Yes, 2–

5.31   No. Charges of 4+ or of 4– are not reasonable (but, in special circumstances, not impossible).

5.32   No. The atom has an outer octet.

5.33   Positively charged ion. Most are metals whose atoms have 1, 2, or 3 outer-level electrons.

5.34   (a) M^+ $1s^2 2s^2 p^6 3s^2 3p^6$
        (b) Q^+ $1s^2$
        (c) Z^{2-} $1s^2 2s^2 2p^6 3s^2 3p^6$

5.35   Its charge is 1–. Its electron configuration is $1s^2$. When principal energy level 1 is the *outside* level, it has the helium configuration when it holds 2 electrons, and the helium configuration is also an octet rule configuration.

5.36   (a) 1+   (b) 3+ (c) 2–
        (d) 2+   (e) 1– (f) 2+

5.37   (a) 3+   (b) 3+ (c) 3+
        (d) 4+   (e) 4+ (f) 5+

5.38 Mn_2O_7

5.39 W_2O_5

5.40   (a) O_2 (b) Al (c) Al (d) O_2

5.41   (a) Ca   (b) Cl_2 (c) Cl_2 (d) Ca

5.42   (a) H   (b) Fe^{3+} (c) Fe_2O_3 (specifically the Fe^{3+} ion in this)
        (d) H_2 (e) H_2 (f) Fe_2O_3 (specifically the Fe^{3+} ion in this)

5.43   Both atoms and molecules are small particles and both are electrically neutral. A molecule, however, has two or more atomic nuclei and an atom has just one.

5.44   An ion and a molecule are both small particles, but the ion is electrically charged and a molecule is electrically neutral. (It is possible for ions to have more than one nucleus; molecules *always* do.)

5.45   In molecular elements, like O_2, all atomic nuclei have identical atomic numbers. In molecular compounds, the nuclei of two or more elements are present.

5.46   Molecular compounds consist of electrically neutral particles, molecules, each capable of independent existence. Ionic compounds consist of oppositely charged ions.

5.47   An *electrical* force of attraction. Its special name here is *covalent bond*.

5.48   When two hydrogen atoms approach each other closely enough, the electron of each senses an attraction for *both* nuclei, so the electrons spend most of their time between these nuclei. The nuclei are attracted toward this concentration of opposite charge and so a covalent bond develops.

5.49   Both electrons of a shared pair in a covalent bond are counted toward an outer octet for each atom held by the bond when one checks to see that each atom has an outer octet.

5.50   Helium has atomic number 2. Its electron configuration is therefore $1s^2$, and it already has one of the two conditions of extraordinary stability specified by the octet rule. Its outside level, level 1, can hold no more than two electrons.

5.51   (a) Rb·   (b) ·Sr·   (c) ·G̈a·   (d) ·T̈e·

5.52   :C̈l· + ·Ca· + ·C̈l: $\longrightarrow$ $2\left[:\ddot{C}l:\right]^-$ + Ca^{2+}

5.53   (a) H· + ·F̈: $\longrightarrow$ H:F̈:

        (b) H· + ·S̈· + ·H $\longrightarrow$ H:S̈:H

        (c)   H
                   ·
                   +
        H· + ·S̈i· + ·H $\longrightarrow$ H :S̈i: H
                   +
                   ·
                   H

5.54   In ethylene. There is twice as much electron density between the nuclei, so they are more strongly attracted toward this region and thus closer together.

5.55   (a)   hydroxide ion   (b) ammonium ion
        (c)   cyanide ion   (d)   permanganate ion
        (e)   hydrogen sulfate ion   (f)   hydrogen sulfite ion
        (g)   dihydrogen phosphate ion   (h) hydronium ion
        (i)   acetate ion   (j) bicarbonate ion
        (k)   sulfate ion   (l) nitrate ion
        (m) monohydrogen phosphate ion   (n) chromate ion
        (o)   carbonate ion   (p) nitrite ion
        (q)   phosphate ion   (r)   dichromate ion

5.56   (a) SO_3^{2-} (b) $C_2H_3O_2^-$
        (c) NO_2^- (d) HCO_3^-
        (e) OH^- (f) NH_4^+
        (g) CO_3^{2-} (h) NO_3^-
        (i) PO_4^{3-} (j) CN^-
        (k) H_3O^+ (l) HPO_4^{2-}
        (m) HSO_4^-(n) $H_2PO_4^-$
        (o) $Cr_2O_7^{2-}$ (p) HSO_3^-
        (q) CrO_4^{2-} (r) SO_4^{2-}

5.57   (a) K_3PO_4 (b) Na_2CO_3
        (c) $CaSO_4$ (d) NH_4CN
        (e) $LiNO_2$ (f) $NaHSO_3$
        (g) $CaCr_2O_7$ (h) $Mg(C_2H_3O_2)_2$

5.58   (a) Na_2HPO_4 (b) $(NH_4)_2CO_3$
        (c) $NaHSO_4$ (d) $NH_4H_2PO_4$
        (e) $NaMnO_4$ (f) $Al(OH)_3$
        (g) $LiHCO_3$ (h) $Ca(NO_3)_2$

5.59   (a)   sodium carbonate   (b) ammonium nitrate
        (c)   magnesium hydroxide   (d) barium sulfate
        (e)   potassium bicarbonate   (f)   calcium acetate
        (g)   sodium nitrite   (h) ammonium phosphate

5.60   (a)   potassium hydrogen sulfate   (b) lithium monohydrogen
                                                              phosphate

        (c)   calcium cyanide   (d) sodium dichromate
        (e)   sodium sulfite   (f)   barium chromate
        (g)   aluminum sulfate   (h) potassium permanganate

5.61   (a) 14   (b) 22   (c) 15
5.62   (a) 14   (b) 9   (c) 20
5.63   49
5.64   Hydrogen ion, H^+.
5.65 HNO_3. Hydrogen ion, H^+, and nitrate ion, NO_3^-

5.66 H_2SO_4. Hydrogen ion, H^+, and sulfate ion, $SO_4{}^{2-}$. (Some hydrogen sulfate ion, $HSO_4{}^-$, is also present.)

5.67   Hydrogen ion, H^+, and chloride ion, Cl^-

5.68   Tartness and the ability to corrode metals. The hydrogen ion, H^+.

5.69   Bases. They react with the hydrogen ion, the positive ion.

5.70

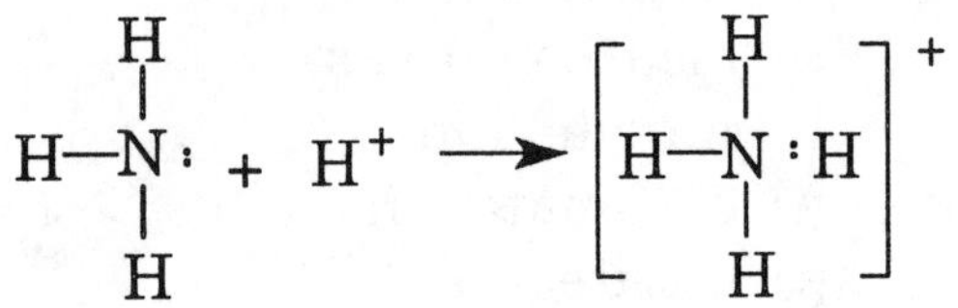

5.71

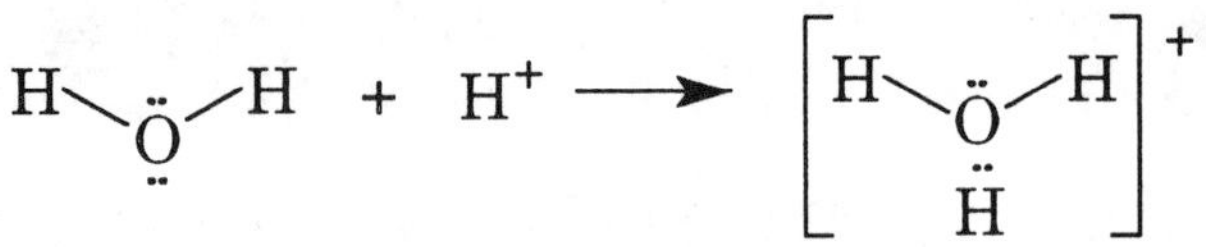

5.72   Arsenic is in group VA and so an As atom has five outer-level electrons. It needs three more for an octet and so can form three bonds to hydrogens. The molecular formula is AsH_3. An atom of selenium, in group VIA, has six outer level electrons, needs two more for an octet, and so can form single bonds to two hydrogens. The formula is SeH_2. A germanium atom, from group IVA, has four outer level electrons, needs four more, so can form four bonds to hydrogens to give GeH_4. The Lewis structures are the following.

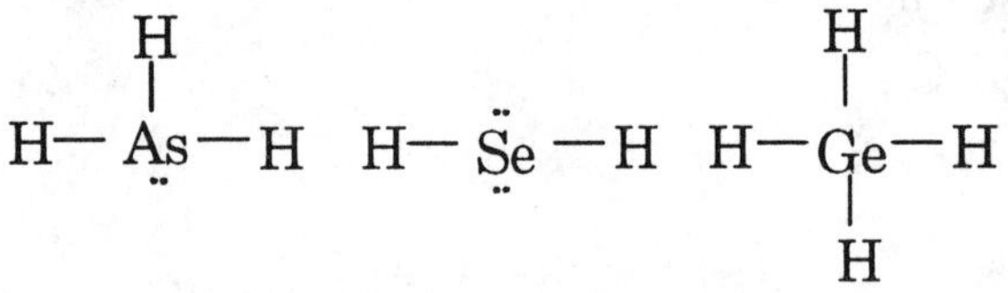

5.73 (a)

```
       Cl
    Cl Pb Cl
       Cl
```

(b) F O F

(c)

```
       Cl
    Cl N Cl
```

(d)

```
       H
    H N H
```

(e)

```
          O
    H O S O
          O
```

(f)

```
          O
    H O S O
```

5.74　(a) 32　(b) 20　(c) 26　(d) 8　(e) 32　(f) 26

5.75 (a)

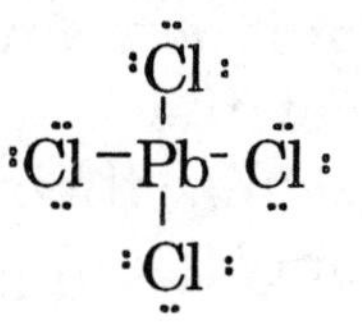

```
        ··
      :Cl:
       |
  ··   |   ··
 :Cl─Pb─Cl:
  ··   |   ··
      :Cl:
        ··
```

(b) $:\ddot{F}-\ddot{O}-\ddot{F}:$

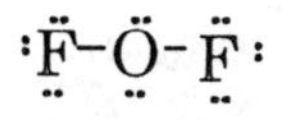

(c)
$$
\begin{array}{c}
\ddot{\underset{\cdot\cdot}{C}l}\text{:} \\
| \\
\text{:}\ddot{C}l\text{--}N\text{--}\ddot{\underset{\cdot\cdot}{C}l}\text{:}
\end{array}
$$

(d)
$$
\begin{array}{c}
H \\
| \\
H\text{--}\underset{\cdot\cdot}{N}\text{--}H
\end{array}
$$

(e)
$$
\left[
\begin{array}{c}
\text{:}\ddot{\underset{\cdot\cdot}{O}}\text{:} \\
| \\
H\text{--}\ddot{\underset{\cdot\cdot}{O}}\text{--}S\text{--}\ddot{\underset{\cdot\cdot}{O}}\text{:} \\
| \\
\text{:}\ddot{O}\text{:}
\end{array}
\right]^{-}
$$

(f)
$$
\left[
H\text{--}\ddot{\underset{\cdot\cdot}{O}}\text{--}\underset{\underset{\cdot\cdot}{\overset{||}{O}}\text{:}}{\overset{\text{:}\ddot{O}\text{:}}{S}}\text{--}\ddot{\underset{\cdot\cdot}{O}}\text{:}
\right]^{-}
$$

5.76 $\left[\text{:}C\text{:::}C\text{:} \right]^{2-}$

5.77   (a) NO_2

(b)
$$
\begin{array}{c}
\text{:}O\text{:} \quad \text{:}O\text{:} \\
|| \qquad || \\
\text{:}\ddot{O}\text{:}N\text{:}\;\text{:}N\text{:}\ddot{O}\text{:}
\end{array}
$$

5.78   The molecules at the molecular level of life all have unique geometries, and molecular shape is as important to the properties of these molecules as anything else about them. Hormones, for example, recognize their target cells because their molecules have shapes that let them fit only to uniquely shaped receptor molecules on these cells.

5.79   Valence-shell electron-pair repulsion theory. The electron clouds of the electron pairs in the valence shell of an atom in a molecule repel each other.

5.80   (a)   The four axes point to the corners of a regular tetrahedron and so make angles of 109.5° with respect to each other.
(b)   There are three axes, they lie in the same plane, they point to the corners of a regular (equilateral) triangle, and they make angles of 120°.
(c)   There are two axes, they are colinear, and so they make an angle of 180°.

5.81   (a)   In $BeCl_2$, 180°, and in H_2O, 104.5°.

(b)   The Be atom in $BeCl_2$ has no unshared electron pairs to force the angle to any other value. The O atom in H_2O has two such pairs, and VSEPR theory predicts a bond angle of 109.5°. The electron clouds of the two *unshared* pairs squeeze the angle slightly.

5.82   The same as in methane, CH_4, 109.5°.

5.83   The atoms held by the bond have different electronegativities.

5.84   *X* has the higher electronegativity *because* it has the larger nuclear charge. (Being in the same period, *X* and *Y* have the same inner level electrons that screen their nuclei, so the atom with the higher nuclear charge has a higher *unscreened* ability to draw electrons of a covalent bond toward it.)

5.85   (a) Yes.   (b) δ+ is near *X* and δ– is near *Y*.

5.86   (a)   Within the same family, electronegativities increase from bottom to top.

(b)   Within the same period, electronegativies increase from left to right.

(c)   Electronegativities increase generally in moving from the lower left corner of the periodic table to the upper right corner.

5.87   The molecular orbital encompasses more than one atomic nucleus. The molecular orbital is the basis for a covalent bond because the electrons within a molecular orbital are what the atomic nuclei are attracted to and so held near each other.

5.88   Both kinds of orbitals are regions of space in which electrons can be and both kinds can hold a maximum of two electrons (and then only if their spins are opposite).

5.89   By the partial overlapping of two atomic orbitals.

5.90   By the partial overlapping of the two $1s$ atomic orbitals, each with one electron and one such atomic orbital from each of the two hydrogen atoms.

5.91   By the partial overlapping of two $3p_z$ atomic orbitals, each with one electron and one such atomic orbital from each of the two chlorine atoms.

5.92   A $1s$ orbital of the H atom (with one electron) partially overlaps with the $2p_z$ orbital of the F atom (also with one electron).

5.93   The $1s$ orbitals of the two H atoms must take up positions for partial overlapping with the $3p_y$ and the $3p_z$ orbitals of the S atom *where they are*, and they are at right angles. Hence, the resulting bond angle, H-S-H, must be 90° (or very close to it).

5.94   The bond angle would be 90° if this occurred, but the true bond angle (104°) is closer to the tetrahedral angele (109.5˚).

5.95   The four atomic orbitals at level two of each of these atoms, the $2s$, $2p_x$, $2p_y$, and the $2p_z$, are "mixed" to form four new, hybrid orbitals, called sp^3 hybrid orbitals, each holding one electron and all four of equivalent energy and stability. The axes of these four orbitals make angles of 109.5° with each other and point to the corners of a regular tetrahedron.

5.96   The molecular orbital for this bond has the symmetry of a cylinder or a long sausage.

5.97   Each pair is in an sp^3 hybrid orbital of the central atom (N or O).

5.98   Probably the simple $3p$ orbitals, because this would result in a bond angle equal to or close to 90°.

5.99   At each carbon atom in ethylene, one $2s$ and two $2p$ orbitals are mixed to give three sp^2 hybrid orbitals, and one $2p$ orbital remains unhybridized.

5.100   The axes of the three sp^2 hybrid orbitals are in the same plane and make angles of 120° with each other. The axis of the unhybridized $2p$ atomic orbital is perpendicular to this plane and passes through it where the axes in the plane meet.

5.101   One sigma bond and one pi bond.

5.102   The pi bond is the result of the partial, side-by-side overlap of unhybridized p orbitals.

5.103 $$O_2 \xrightarrow[\lambda\,=\,242\ nm\ or\ lower]{UV\ radiation} 2O$$

5.104 $$O^* + O_2 + M \rightarrow O_3 + M + heat$$

$$O_3 + UV\ energy \xrightarrow[\lambda\,=\,240\,-\,320\,nm]{} O_2 + O^*$$

The two reactions constitute a chemical chain reaction because one product (O^*) of the second reaction is a necessary reactant for the first reaction.

5.105   It is converted into heat.

5.106 $$CFCl_3 \xrightarrow{UV\ radiation} CFCl_2 + Cl \quad \text{(This generates Cl, which then}$$

participates in the following ozone-consuming chain reaction.)
$$Cl + O_3 \rightarrow ClO + O_2$$
$$ClO + O \rightarrow Cl + O_2$$

Net: $O_3 + O \rightarrow 2O_2$

5.107   The polar vortex is a circulating wind pattern over the pole. The Antarctic ozone hole is a column of the atmosphere around the south pole in which the ozone level is somewhat depleted.

5.108   Chlorine atoms (Cl) from the ozone-destroying cycle help make HCl as follows from methane (which is present): $CH_4 + Cl \rightarrow HCl + CH_3$.
HCl combines with $ClNO_3$ to produce Cl_2 as follows: $HCl + ClNO_3 \rightarrow Cl_2 +$ HNO_3. [The $ClNO_3$ originates by a reaction of ClO (from the ozone-destroying cycle) with NO_2, which is present: $ClO + NO_2 \rightarrow ClNO_3$]. The molecules of Cl_2 adhere to polar stratospheric clouds, which consist largely of the trihydrate of nitric acid, $HNO_3 \cdot 3H_2O$.

5.109 Cl_2 molecules are broken into Cl atoms by the UV radiation from the rising spring sun at the Antarctic.

5.110   (a) X^{2+}, $1s^22s^22p^63s^23p^6$
        (b) Y^-, $1s^22s^22p^63s^23p^6$
        (c) Z has no ions.

5.111   ·In·   Its electrovalence is 3+.

5.112   (a) $1s^22s^22ps(1,x)$
        (b)   The axes of the three sp^2 orbitals would lie in a plane and make angles of 120° with each other.
        (c)   No
        (d)   All atoms lie in the same plane and all Cl–B–Cl angles are 120°.

Chapter 6

Practice Exercises, Chapter 6

1.   2.6 L
2.   547 mL
3.   794 mm Hg
4.   214 mL
5.   98.1 g O_2
6.   159 mm Hg
7.   52 mm Hg
8. $P_{nitrogen}$ = 732 mm Hg. 283 mL at STP

Review Exercises, Chapter 6

6.1   State of matter. The three *kinds* of matter are elements, compounds, and mixtures. The three *states* are gas, liquid, and solid.
6.2   Gases generally obey the same set of physical laws, the gas laws. There are no comparable sets of laws for liquids or solids.
6.3   The pressure, volume, temperature, and number of moles.
6.4   The gas will entirely occupy whatever container it is in.
6.5   To the force with which the object is attracted to the earth by gravitational attraction. (The mass of an object is the quantitative measure of its resistance to any change in its motion.)
6.6   As the force exerted by an object divided by the area on which the object acts; pressure is force per unit area.)

6.7   With gases, a given *mass* can be made to have a large range of pressures.

6.8   The atmosphere has weight and so is gravitationally attracted to the earth with a definite force per unit area of the earth's surface.

6.9   The column of air supported by the earth is shorter at the mountain top, so it exerts less weight on a unit of the earth's area.

6.10   14.7 lb

6.11   The weight doubles; the pressure stays the same because pressure is the *ratio* of weight to area.

6.12   Although the weight of mercury in a larger diameter tube will be greater than that in a tube of smaller diameter, the weight *per unit area* , the pressure, exerted by the mercury stays the same. The *height* of the column of mercury in a Torricelli barometer thus depends solely on how much air pressure is available to hold the mercury up.

6.13   Something else defines the standard atmosphere, a column of mercury 760 mm tall when measured at 0 °C. (The sea level pressure varies daily with the weather conditions.)

6.14   33.9 ft

6.15   They are the same.

6.16   Pascal. 1 Pa is much smaller than 1 mm Hg; 1 mm Hg = 133 Pa.

6.17 1×10^5 Pa. (1 atm = 101,325 Pa or 1.01325×10^5 Pa)

6.18   0.329 atm. 250 torr. 33.3 kPa

6.19 1.5×10^2 mm Hg or 1.5×10^2 torr. 20 kPa

6.20   666 mm Hg

6.21   (a)   21.3 kPa   (b) 79.3 kPa   (c) 5.07×10^{-2} kPa

6.22   (a)   Boyle's law. The volume of a given amount of gas held at constant temperature varies inversely with the pressure.
$$P_1 V_1 = P_2 V_2$$
(b)   Gay-Lussac's law. The pressure of a given amount of gas held at constant volume is directly proportional to the Kelvin temperature.
$$\frac{P_1}{T_1} = \frac{P_2}{T_2}$$
(c)   Charles' law. The volume of a given amount of gas held at constant pressure is directly proportional to the Kelvin temperature.
$$\frac{V_1}{T_1} = \frac{V_2}{T_2}$$
(d)   Dalton's law of partial pressures. The total pressure of a mixture of nonreacting gases is the sum of their individual partial pressures.
$$P_{total} = P_a + P_b + P_c + ... +$$

6.23   (a)   Constant composition of the gas mixture
         (b)   Moles of gas and volume

   (c) Moles of gas and temperature

   (d) Moles of gas and pressure

   (e) Temperature and pressure

   (f) Moles of gas

6.24 That the inverse relationship between pressure and volume for a given amount of gas at a given temperture might be true of *all* gases.

6.25 The volume is decreased to one-third of its initial value.

6.26 By $\dfrac{745}{730}$. Boyles law tells us that if we *reduce* the pressure (at constant temperatures), the volume *increases*, so we must use the ratio of pressures that is greater than 1.

6.27 2.59 L

6.28 16.1 L

6.29 740 mm Hg

6.30 The gas pressure had to change, to a new value of 799 mm Hg.

6.31 2.66 L

6.32 241 mL

6.33 272 atm

6.34 12.0 atm

6.35 740 mm Hg

6.36 5.36 L

6.37 257 mL

6.38 106 °C

6.39 668 mm Hg

6.40 68.0 °C

6.41 24.1 L

6.42 4.81 atm

6.43 64.9 mol O_2; 2.08 kg O_2

6.44 $P = 218$ atm, so the cylinder is not in danger.

6.45 4.74 kg N_2

6.46 1.3 mol O_2 removed

6.47 Standard temperture and pressure; 273.15 K (which we round to 273 K) and 1 atm (760 mm Hg)

6.48 (a) 2.98×10^{-2} mol He

   (b) 2.98×10^{-2} mol H_2. Avogadro's principle tells us that when measured at the same temperature and pressure, equal volumes of gases contain equal numbers of moles.

6.49 30.2 mmol O_2

6.50 317 mL

6.51 (a) 0.0354 mol of the gas

   (b) 32.0

(c)   oxygen

(d)   0.0708 mol H_2

(e)   0.143 g H_2

6.52   (a)   4.00 mol NH_3

(b)   500 L of NH_3

(c)   16.2 g H_2 and 91.1 g NH_3 (If the law of conservation of mass in a chemical reaction is used for the calculation of the mass of NH_3, the result is 91.2 g NH_3; the discrepancy between 91.2 and 91.1 is caused by rounding.)

6.53   (a) 9.82×10^{-3} mol CO_2

(b) 9.82×10^{-3} mol $CaCO_3$

(c)   0.983 g $CaCO_3$

(d)   0.551 g CaO

6.54   To a *mixture* of gases. Both the air we breathe in and what we breathe out is a mixture of gases of which one, oxygen, is an essential substance for life and another, carbon dioxide, is a waste product we must remove from the body.

6.55   The individual gases in the mixture act independently in contributing to the total pressure so that the total pressure is the sum of the partial pressures.

6.56   601 mm Hg. (This is what *partial pressure* means, the pressure that a component of a gas mixture would exert if it were all alone in the container and all other gases were removed.)

6.57   Yes. The sum of the partial pressures is only 725 mm Hg, so something else must be present to account for the "missing" 20 mm Hg of partial pressure.

6.58   20 °C. (At this temperatue, the vapor pressure of water is 17.5 mm Hg, which corresponds to the "missing" mm Hg of pressure when the water vapor is removed from the water-saturated gas mixture.)

6.59   (a)   0.729 g Zn

(b)   288 mL

6.60   The postulates that describe an ideal gas:, the postulates of the kinetic theory of gases.

6.61   It obeys all of the gas laws exactly.

6.62   The particles of a gas neither attract nor repel each other.

6.63   Gas pressure is the net result of the innumerable forces exerted on the fixed area of the container by the collisions made at the walls by the gas particles.

6.64   When the volume of the container is reduced, the area of its walls also decreases, so if *area* becomes smaller in the equation that defines pressure, pressure = force/area, the pressure must increase.

6.65   (a)   The Kelvin temperature

(b)   The Kelvin temperature is proportional to the average kinetic energy.

6.66   They cease.

6.67   A higher temperature means a higher average kinetic energy, and this means a higher average velocity. In a fixed-volume container, this would mean a higher pressure, so if the pressure is to be kept constant (a condition of Charles' law), the volume must be allowed to expand with increasing temperature.

6.68   Because a higher temperature means a higher average velocity of the gas particles, they beat on the fixed walls of the container with greater average force. This means a higher pressure, since pressure = force/area.

6.69   The distances between particles in liquids and solids are virtually zero, so physical properties of liquids and solids are much more sensitive to the chemical natures of the particles.

6.70   London forces arising from transient dipoles provide net forces of attraction.

6.71   Octane; its molecules are larger than those of butane but both are compounds of carbon and hydrogen so have roughly the same (very small) permanent polarity).

6.72   (a)   Rapidly moving molecules of the liquid escape into the space above the liquid and thus create a partial pressure called the vapor pressure.
(b)   Vaporization is endothermic, so the addition of heat (by raising the temperature) shifts the following equilibrium to the right (Le Chatelier's principle):

$$\text{liquid} + \text{heat} \rightleftharpoons \text{vapor}$$

The extra vapor in a closed space exerts a higher pressure.

6.73   (a)   Less volatile. With a higher boiling point than water, DMSO will at any given temperature have a lower vapor pressure than that of water. Lower vapor pressure, in this context, means a lower volatility.
(b)   A $\delta+$ on S and a $\delta-$ on O. O is more electronegative than S.
(c)   Dipole-dipole attraction.

6.74   (a)   B   (b)   B   (c)   A   (d)   C   (e)   A, B   (f)   100 °C
(g)   Their rates are equal.   (h)   Equilibrium

6.75   The rate of evaporation equals the rate of condensation.

6.76   The vapor pressure of the liquid can equal the external pressure at a lower and lower temperature as the external pressure is reduced.

6.77   If a system in equilibrium is upset by a stress, the system shifts in whichever direction most directly absorbs the stress and restores equilibrium.

6.78   (a)   Condensation of alcohol vapor to alcohol liquid occurs.
(b)   Forward change
(c)   Shift to the left
(d)   Shift to the right; this supplies vapor to compensate for the loss of vapor and tends to restore equilibrium.
(e)   Yes, the equilibrium will shift to the left because this releases heat and so tends to compensate for the heat loss caused by the cooling.

6.79   (a)   Nitrogen and oxygen absorb heat and change to nitric oxide in mole proportions of 1:1:2.
(b)   Nitric oxide breaks up into N_2 and O_2 as heat is liberated.

(c)   Forward

(d)   Forward

6.80   (a)   Forward. $2NO_2 \rightleftharpoons N_2O_4 + heat$

(b)   Forward. The forward reaction is the conversion of 2 mol of gas (NO_2) into 1 mol (N_2O_4). Increasing the pressure favors this volume-reducing effect.

6.81   (a)   Covalent bond

(b)   It is a nonpolar molecule and there is no $\delta+$ or $\delta-$ on H.

6.82   The relative electronegativities of C and H are so similar that the C–H bonds are nearly nonpolar. Hence there is no significant $\delta+$ or $\delta-$ anywhere.

6.83   The ionic bond between the ions, Na^+ and OH^+ and the covalent bond that holds H and O together in the hydroxide ion.

6.84

$$\delta+ \quad \delta- \quad H-O \quad H\cdots O \underset{H}{\overset{H}{<}}$$

6.85

$$\delta+ \quad \delta- \quad H-N \quad H\cdots N \underset{H}{\overset{H}{<}}$$

6.86   (a)   The boiling point of ammonia is much less than that of water. Because the sizes of ammonia and water molecules are about the same, we cannot explain the difference in boiling points by differences in London forces between the molecules. Instead, there must be differences in the sizes of partial charges that exist more permanently than those of the London forces.

(b)   Both $\delta+$ and $\delta-$ are larger in the water molecule than in the ammonia molecule.

(c)   Oxygen is more electronegative than nitrogen.

6.87   About 5% the strength of a covalent bond or about 5 kcal/mol.

6.88   (a)   A relatively large quantity of energy is needed to overcome the relatively strong forces of attraction between the molecules in these states.

(b)   The relatively large forces of attraction between water molecules in the liquid state make for a strong jamming together of these molecules at the surface.

6.89   On a waxy surface, wax molecules do not attract water molecules so the latter jam in on each other to form a bead. On a glass surface, the polar particles in the glass attract water molecules more strongly than the water molecules can attract each other, so this attraction by the glass for the water molecules makes the water spread out and form a film rather than beads.

6.90   Reduces it.

6.91   Detergents and soaps.

6.92   The vibrate about fixed points.

6.93   Heat increases the violence of the vibrations of the particles in the crystal until they no longer can hold to fixed positions.

6.94   The melting point.

6.95   Electrical forces between the particles are weakest between nitrogen molecules and strongest between sodium and chloride ions.

6.96 $CO_2(s)$ + heat $\rightleftharpoons$ $CO_2(g)$

6.97   (a)   Water molecules in the liquid state cannot return to the liquid state when they are blown away by the breeze.
(b)   Crushing the ice greatly increases the surface area from which water molecules can go into the liquid state, so the water molecules in ice can escape into their liquid state at many more places at the same time.
(c)   Water molecules can pass directly from the solid to the vapor state.

6.98   The temperature of the boiling water is lower in Denver, and the rate of a reaction (like cooking) is therefore slower in Denver. Hence the reaction takes longer there.

6.99   547 mL

6.100   737 mm Hg. 260 mL

6.101   0.759 mol

6.102   1.85 g $CaCO_3$; 4.63 mL HCl

Chapter 7

Practice Exercises, Chapter 7

1.   1.47 mg N_2/100 g H_2O

2.   10.2 g of 96 % H_2SO_4

3.   1.25 g of glucose and 499 g of water (rounded from 498.75, and assuming that the density of water is 1.00 g/mL)

4.   1.67 x 10^4 mm Hg

5.   (a)   0.020 Osm   (b) 0.015 Osm   (c) 0.100 Osm   (d) 0.150 Osm

Review Exercises, Chapter 7

7.1   An exceptionally small sample of hydrogen, for example, which might conceivably consist of ten molecules, could have an isotopic composition that is not the same observed for samples that can be manipulated in the lab.

7.2   For measurements of physical properties, the sample of the mixture would have to include enough molecules so that the average composition would be consistent with the experimentally determined ratio of the various isotopes. For studies of chemical properties (of the type we are studying), the isotope composition is unimportant because isotopes have the same chemical properties.

7.3   Because particles having at least one dimension within the range defining the particular kind of homogeneous mixture give all such mixtures some common properties. As the size becomes larger, the particles take on the ability to reflect light (Tyndall effect), exhibit Brownian movement, and (at large enough sizes) be influenced by gravity in such a way as to settle out of the mixture.

7.4   The must be stirred continuously to remain homogeneous

7.5   (a)   Stirred suspensions
      (b)   Colloidal dispersions
      (c)   Colloidal dispersions
      (d)   Solutions
      (e)   Unstirred suspensions

7.6   Those whose dispersed particles have the same kind of electrical charge, because they repel each other and can't coalesce into larger particles that would separate out.

7.7   Dissolved ions and small molecules make it a solution; dispersed protein molecules make it a colloidal dispersion; and various kinds of blood cells make blood a suspension.

7.8   The solute particles in a solution are too small to scatter light.

7.9   The uneven motions of colloidal particles suggested that random motions of other smaller particles actually occur, as postulated by the kinetic theory.

7.10   Test for the Tyndall effect.

7.11   It is a colloidal dispersion of one liquid in another. Examples are cream, mayonnaise, and milk.

7.12   A colloidal dispersion of a solid in a liquid. Examples are jellies, paints, and starch in water.

7.13   A sol that has adopted a semisolid, semirigid form. Examples are gelatin desserts and fruit jellies.

7.14   The $\delta+$ ends of polar water molecules.

7.15   It is surrounded by polar water molecules with their $\delta-$ ends pointing at a sodium ion. (The drawing should be like that in the upper right corner of Figure 7.2.)

7.16   Water molecules are strongly attracted to each other and they find nothing in molecules of CF_4 with which to establish forces of attraction of comparable strength, so the water molecules stay together.

7.17 (a) This increases the surface area against which the solvent molecules can simultaneously attack and dissolve the solid.
(b) This moves freshly dissolved solute molecules away from the surfaces of the solid, which continuously exposes the surfaces to dissolving action.
(c) This increases the violence with which solvent molecules hit the solid's surface and cause the solid particles to go into solution.

7.18 (a) $KBr(s) \rightarrow K^+(aq) + Br^-(aq)$
(b) The rates at which solid dissolves and at which solid reforms from the ions are equal. $KBr(s) \rightleftharpoons K^+(aq) + Br^-(aq)$

7.19 Make sure that the solution has undissolved $NaNO_3$ present.

7.20 The dissolving of a solid and a liquid is usually an endothermic change, so heat shifts the following equilibrium to the right, in favor of more solute being in solution.

$$NH_4Cl(s) + heat \rightleftharpoons NH_4^+(aq) + Cl^-(aq)$$

The removal of heat (by lowering the temperature) shifts this equilibrium to the left and more solid NH_4Cl forms.

7.21 $MgSO_4 \cdot 7H_2O(s) \rightleftharpoons MgSO_4(s) + H_2O(g)$

7.22 They obey the law of definite proportions.

7.23 $Na_2SO_4(s) + 10H_2O \rightarrow Na_2SO_4 \cdot 10H_2O(s)$

7.24 It can remove moisture from the air by forming a hydrate. Yes.

7.25 The pellets can draw enough moisture from the air to form a solution of sodium hydroxide that coats every exposed pellet.

7.26 $y = 3$. The formula is $Y \cdot 3H_2O$

7.27 $Z \cdot 2H_2O$

7.28 0.035 g/L

7.29 0.0191 g/L

7.30 Carbon dioxide molecules can form hydrogen bonds with water molecules. Moreover, a (small) percentage of the carbon dioxide molecules in solution in water have reacted with the water to give carbonic acid. This reaction also increases the solubility of CO_2 in water over that of oxygen.

7.31 SO_2 molecules can form hydrogen bonds with water molecules.

7.32 Using oxygen as an example, the equilibrium between its gaseous (undissolved) state and its solution is:

$$O_2(g) + pressure \rightleftharpoons O_2(aq)$$

When the pressure is increased, this equilibrium shifts to the right in favor of more oxygen in solution.

7.33 The air in contact with this blood under a total pressure of 1 atm has a partial pressure of O_2 equal to 80 mm Hg.

7.34 The first region (where the gas tension is 79 mm Hg).

7.35 $\dfrac{0.915 \text{ g NaOH}}{100 \text{ g NaOH soln}}$ and $\dfrac{100 \text{ g NaOH soln}}{0.915 \text{ g NaOH}}$

7.36 $\dfrac{1.42 \text{ g KCl}}{100 \text{ mL KCl soln}}$ and $\dfrac{100 \text{ mL KCl soln}}{1.42 \text{ g KCl}}$

7.37   2.0 mg/L

7.38 $\dfrac{30 \text{ mL alcohol}}{100 \text{ mL alcohol soln}}$ and $\dfrac{100 \text{ mL alcohol soln}}{30 \text{ mL alcohol}}$

7.39   (a)   2.25 g NaCl
       (b)   16.1 g $NaC_2H_3O_2$
       (c)   8.44 g NH_4Cl
       (d)   3.13 g Na_2CO_3

7.40   (a)   1.56 g NaI
       (b)   0.469 g NaBr
       (c)   1.00 g glucose
       (d)   4.25 g H_2SO_4

7.41   (a)   31.3 g NaCl
       (b)   7.50 g KBr
       (c)   1.12 g $CaCl_2$
       (d)   4.50 g NaCl

7.42   (a)   7.50 g $Mg(NO_3)_2$
       (b)   5.63 g NaBr
       (c)   5.00 g KI
       (d)   0.938 g $Ca(NO_3)_2$

7.43   100 mL ethyl alcohol

7.44   46.9 mL methyl alcohol

7.45   (a)   75.0 mL 4.00% NaOH solution
       (b)   3.25 mL 10% Na_2CO_3 solution
       (c)   6.38 mL 4.00% glucose solution
       (d)   115 mL 4.00% NaOH solution
       (e)   901 mL 4.00% glucose solution

7.46   (a)   3.33 mL 3.00% KOH solution
       (b)   33.3 mL 0.600% HCl solution
       (c)   673 mL 1.00% NaCl solution
       (d)   234 mL 3.00% KOH solution

7.47   16.3 g of the trihydrate

7.48   30.8 g of the decahydrate. (30.9 g by a chain calculation)

7.49   62.5 g 10.0% NaOH solution

7.50   12.5 g (11.9 mL) 10.0% HCl solution

7.51   (a)   35.9% (w/w) HCl
       (b)   88.1 mL (104 g) of 35.9% (w/w) HCl. (88.5 mL by a chain calculation)

7.52   (a)   71.0% (w/w) HNO_3
       (b)   29.8 mL (42.3 g) of 71.0% (w/w) HNO_3. (28.7 mL by a chain calculation)

7.53   −1.86 °C

7.54   The solute in the second solution breaks up (ionizes) into two ions per formula unit when it dissolves, so the effective concentration is 2.00 mol/1000 g H_2O.

7.55   The rate at which water can move *into* the solution is greater than the rate at which it can return, because solute particles tend to block the return. The figure should resemble part *b* of Figure 7.6.

7.56   The osmotic membrane doesn't let anything in the dissolved state go through, but the dialyzing membrane lets solutes through and blocks colloidally dispersed particles.

7.57   The blocking action of the solute particles is a function of their *presence* and *relative numbers,* not their chemical properties.

7.58   A higher temperature gives greater average velocities to the solvent molecules. They therefore can move more rapidly through the membrane, but this increase in rate is greater from the side of the dilute solution into the concentrated solution than the increase in the rate of return.

7.59   This solution is 2.0 M in all solute particles, and osmolarity is a function of the molar concentrations of all osmotically active solute particles.

7.60   0.080 M Na_2SO_4 solution, because it is $3 \times 0.080\ M = 0.240\ M$ in its osmolarity.

7.61   5.0% NaCl, which has 0.085 mol solute/100 g solution versus only 0.030 mol solute/100 g solution for 5% KI

7.62   Solution A. While the osmolarities of A and B are identical with respect to their dissolved salts and sugars, A has the higher concentration of the colloidally dispersed starch.

7.63   186 mm Hg

7.64   457 mm Hg

7.65   The shrivel.

7.66   (a)   Hypertonic
            (b)   (1) Hemolysis (2) Crenation

7.67   The loss of large molecules lowers the colloidal osmotic pressure of the blood to a value less than the osmotic pressure of the fluids just outside of the blood vessels. As a result, there is a net flow of water from the blood to the outside of the blood vessels, and the blood volume decreases.

7.68   Nitrogen and oxygen. Their partial pressures are greater, so in accordance with Henry's law their solubilities in water are greater.

7.69   The excess gases come out of solution as microbubbles in the blood stream, and these can block blood flowage through fine capillaries.

7.70   The gases come out much more slowly. Excess oxygen gets a chance to be used by metabolism and excess nitrogen gets a chance to be vented at the lungs.

7.71   For each atmosphere of pressure above normal pressure to which the individual was exposed, about 20 minutes of decompression time should be allowed.

7.72 The use of dialysis to cleanse the blood of wastes.

7.73 The solution that circulates around the dialyzing tubes and into which blood wastes enter.

7.74 (a) the same (b) the same (c) less concentrated

7.75 $Ca(NO_3)_2(s) \rightarrow Ca^{2+}(aq) + 2NO_3^-(aq)$

7.76 0.0194 g/L

7.77 7.12 M H_2SO_4

7.78 229 mm Hg

7.79 0.33 osmol. (0.12 osmol NaCl + 0.060 osmol $NaHCO_3$ + 0.040 osmol KCl + 0.11 osmol glucose)

7.80 (a) $MgCO_3(s) + 2HCl(aq) \rightarrow MgCl_2(aq) + CO_2(g) + H_2O$

    (b) 26.9 mL of 15.0% HCl

    (c) 1.46×10^3 mL CO_2

Chapter 8

Practice Exercises, Chapter 8

1.

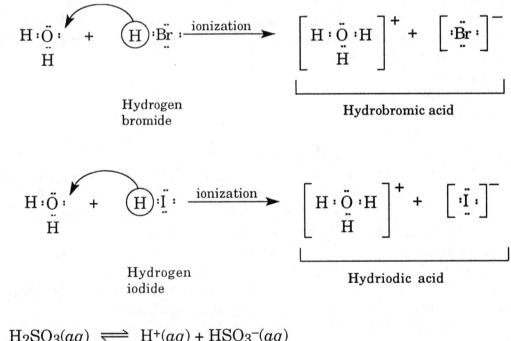

2. $H_2SO_3(aq) \rightleftharpoons H^+(aq) + HSO_3^-(aq)$

    $HSO_3^-(aq) \rightleftharpoons H^+(aq) + SO_3^{2-}(aq)$

3. $HNO_3(aq) + KOH(aq) \rightarrow KNO_3(aq) + H_2O$

$$H^+(aq) + NO_3^-(aq) + K^+(aq) + OH^-(aq) \rightarrow K^+(aq) + NO_3^-(aq) + H_2O$$
$$H^+(aq) + OH^-(aq) \rightarrow H_2O$$

4. $$Mg(OH)_2(s) + 2HCl(aq) \rightarrow MgCl_2(aq) + 2H_2O$$
$$Mg(OH)_2(s) + 2H^+(aq) \rightarrow Mg^{2+}(aq) + 2H_2O$$

5. K_2SO_4

6. $$2NaHCO_3(aq) + H_2SO_4(aq) \rightarrow Na_2SO_4(aq) + 2CO_2(g) + 2H_2O$$
$$2Na^+(aq) + 2HCO_3^-(aq) + 2H^+(aq) + SO_4^{2-}(aq) \rightarrow$$
$$2Na^+(aq) + SO_4^{2-}(aq) + 2CO_2(g) + 2H_2O$$
$$HCO_3^-(aq) + H^+(aq) \rightarrow CO_2(g) + H_2O$$

7. $$K_2CO_3(aq) + H_2SO_4(aq) \rightarrow K_2SO_4(aq) + CO_2(g) + H_2O$$
$$2K^+(aq) + CO_3^{2-}(aq) + 2H^+(aq) + SO_4^{2-}(aq) \rightarrow$$
$$2K^+(aq) + SO_4^{2-}(aq) + CO_2(aq) + H_2O$$
$$CO_3^{2-}(aq) + 2H^+(aq) \rightarrow CO_2(g) + H_2O$$

8. $$MgCO_3(s) + 2HNO_3(aq) \rightarrow Mg(NO_3)_2(aq) + CO_2(g) + H_2O$$
$$MgCO_3(s) + 2H^+(aq) + 2NO_3^-(aq) \rightarrow$$
$$Mg^{2+}(aq) + 2NO_3^-(aq) + CO_2(g) + H_2O$$
$$MgCO_3(s) + 2H^+(aq) \rightarrow Mg^{2+}(aq) + CO_2(g) + H_2O$$

9. (a) $$NH_3(aq) + HBr(aq) \rightarrow NH_4Br(aq)$$
$$NH_3(aq) + H^+(aq) \rightarrow NH_4^+(aq)$$
   (b) $$2NH_3(aq) + H_2SO_4(aq) \rightarrow (NH_4)_2SO_4(aq)$$
$$NH_3(aq) + H^+(aq) \rightarrow NH_4^+(aq)$$

10. $$Mg(s) + 2HCl(aq) \rightarrow MgCl_2(aq) + H_2(g)$$
$$Mg(s) + 2H^+(aq) \rightarrow Mg^{2+}(aq) + H_2(g)$$

11. (a) HNO_3 (b) HSO_3^- (c) HCO_3^- (d) HSO_4^-
    (e) HCl (f) H_3O^+ (g) H_2O

12. (a) CO_3^{2-} (b) PO_4^{3-} (c) HSO_4^- (d) SO_4^{2-}
    (e) Br^- (f) H_2O (g) OH^-

13. (a) Weak acid   (b) Weak acid   (c) Weak acid

14. (a) Weak base   (b) Weak base   (c) Strong base   (d) Strong base

15. $$NO_2^-(aq) + H^+(aq) \rightleftharpoons HNO_2(aq).$$ The product is favored because we know that HNO_2 is a weak acid (not being on the list of strong acids).

16. $$Na_2S(aq) + Cu(NO_3)_2(aq) \rightarrow CuS(s) + 2NaNO_3(aq)$$
$$S^{2-}(aq) + Cu^{2+}(aq) \rightarrow CuS(s)$$

17. The acetate ion combines with (neutralizes) the hydrogen ion. In the following equilibrium, the product is favored.

$$H^+(aq) + C_2H_3O_2^-(aq) \rightleftharpoons HC_2H_3O_2(aq)$$

18. (a) AgCl precipitates. $$Ag^+(aq) + Cl^-(aq) \rightarrow AgCl(s)$$
    (b) CO_2 evolves. $$CaCO_3(s) + 2H^+(aq) \rightarrow Ca^{2+}(aq) + CO_2(g) + H_2O$$
    (c) No reaction occurs.

Review Exercises

8.1 $HCl(g) + H_2O \rightarrow H_3O^+(aq) + Cl^-(aq)$
This *ionization* is a chemical reaction in which bonds break and form and molecules change into ions. When NaCl dissolves in water, the *dissociation* of preformed ions that already exist in the solid occurs.

8.2   (a)   It forms separated ions when dissolved in water and the solution conducts electricity.
(b)   Dissociation

8.3   Ionization. The fact that SO_3 is a *gas* tells us that SO_3 contains no preformed ions, so it must react with water as it dissolves to generate ions.

8.4   Aqueous solutions of electrolytes conduct electricity. Molten forms of electrolytes conduct electricity.

8.5   Anode

8.6   Negative

8.7   Anions

8.8   Cations take electrons from the cathode simultaneously as anions deliver electrons to the anode, so the net effect is just as if electrons transferred directly from the cathode to the anode—an electron flow.

8.9   Ethyl alcohol does not furnish any ions of any kind in water.

8.10   Strong electrolyte

8.11   It is a molecular compound. It does not consist of ions in the liquid state.

8.12   (a) $Na^+(l) + e^- \rightarrow Na(l)$
(b) $2Cl^-(l) \rightarrow Cl_2(g) + 2e^-$
(c) $2Na^+(l) + 2Cl^-(l) \rightarrow 2Na(l) + Cl_2(g)$

8.13   Acids, bases, and salts

8.14   (a)   No
(b)   Yes, any polyatomic ion such as SO_4^{2-}
(c)   No
(d)   No

8.15 $2H_2O \rightleftharpoons \underset{\text{ion}}{\underset{\text{hydronium}}{H_3O^+(aq)}} + \underset{\text{ion}}{\underset{\text{hydroxide}}{OH^-(aq)}}$

8.16   (a)   Acidic (b) Neutral (c) Basic

8.17   They consist of oppositely charged ions, and between these are strong forces of attraction that set up rigid solids.

8.18   Acids are compounds that supply hydrogen ions in water. Bases are compounds that supply hydroxide ions in water.

8.19   They furnish hydronium ions in water.

8.20   Proton and hydronium ion

8.21   Salts do not supply a *common* ion in solution, whereas aqueous acids furnish hydrogen ions and aqueous bases supply hydroxide ions.

8.22   In an acidic solution, litmus is red. In a basic solution it is blue.

8.23   An acid is a proton-donor. A base is a proton-acceptor.

8.24   Hydrofluoric acid, $HF(aq)$. Hydrochloric acid, $HCl(aq)$. Hydrobromic acid, $HBr(aq)$. Hydroiodic acid, $HI(aq)$.

8.25   Hydrochloric acid is the aqueous solution of the gas, hydrogen chloride.

8.26   In H_3O^+, because the weaker bond in $H–I(g)$ breaks to form the stronger bond in the hydronium ion by the following reaction.

$$HI(g) + H_2O \rightarrow H_3O^+(aq) + I^-(aq)$$

8.27 $HClO_4(aq) + H_2O \rightarrow H_3O^+(aq) + ClO_4^-(aq)$

8.28 $HNO_3(aq) + H_2O \rightarrow H_3O^+(aq) + NO_3^-(aq)$

8.29   Both H's in H_2SO_4 can react with a base, but only one H in $HC_2H_3O_2$ can neutralize a base.

8.30 $H_2A + H_2O \rightleftharpoons H_3O^+(aq) + HA^-(aq)$

$HA^-(aq) + H_2O \rightleftharpoons H_3O^+(aq) + A^{2-}(aq)$

8.31   With greater difficulty. The second H^+ ion has to pull away from a particle that has more negative charge than the first H^+ ion. Unlike charges attract, so the more unlike the charges are, the more energy is needed to separate particles bearing them.

8.32 $H_2SO_4(aq) + H_2O \rightarrow H_3O^+(aq) + HSO_4^-(aq)$

hydrogen sulfate ion

$HSO_4^-(aq) + H_2O \rightarrow H_3O^+(aq) + SO_4^{2-}(aq)$

sulfate ion

8.33 $H_3PO_4(aq) + H_2O \rightarrow H_3O^+(aq) + H_2PO_4^-(aq)$

dihydrogen phosphate ion

$H_2PO_4^-(aq) + H_2O \rightarrow H_3O^+(aq) + HPO_4^{2-}(aq)$

monohydrogen phosphate ion

$HPO_4^{2-}(aq) + H_2O \rightarrow H_3O^+(aq) + PO_4^{3-}(aq)$

phosphate ion

8.34   Sulfuric acid. The extra oxygen atom provides more electron-withdrawing action, and this weakens the H–O bonds more.

8.35   Chloric acid is the stronger acid. Its molecules have one more oxygen to exert electron-withdrawing action on the electron pair of the H–O bond.

8.36 $CO_2(aq) + H_2O \rightleftharpoons H_2CO_3(aq)$

8.37 $H_2CO_3(aq) + H_2O \rightarrow H_3O^+(aq) + HCO_3^-(aq)$

$HCO_3^-(aq) + H_2O(aq) \rightleftharpoons H_3O^+(aq) + CO_3^{2-}(aq)$

8.38   In the case of an ionic compound like KOH, both terms mean a high percentage dissociation as it dissolves in water.

8.39   What little does dissolve in water still ionizes 100 percent.

8.40   Only a very low percentage of all ammonia molecules in solution react with water to generate hydroxide ions in the equilibrium:

8.41   Sodium hydroxide, NaOH, and potassium hydroxide, KOH

8.42 $CO_2(aq) + NaOH(aq) \rightarrow NaHCO_3(aq)$

8.43   A solution of ammonia in water. Because it contains only a very low percentage of ammonium and hydroxide ions, it's inappropriate to call it ammonium hydroxide (although some chemical suppliers do).

8.44   Hydrochloric acid, $HCl(aq)$
        Hydrobromic acid, $HBr(aq)$
        Hydriodic acid, $HI(aq)$
        Nitric acid, $HNO_3(aq)$
        Sulfuric acid. $H_2SO_4(aq)$

8.45   Sodium hydroxide, NaOH (very soluble)
        Potassium hydroxide, KOH (very soluble)
        Magnesium hydroxide, $Mg(OH)_2$ (slightly soluble)
        Calcium hydroxide, $Ca(OH)_2$ (slightly soluble)

8.46   (a) Yes   (b) No; it's not balanced.

8.47   (a) $HNO_3(aq) + KOH(aq) \rightarrow KNO_3(aq) + H_2O$
             $H^+(aq) + OH^-(aq) \rightarrow H_2O$
        (b) $HCl(aq) + NaHCO_3(aq) \rightarrow NaCl(aq) + CO_2(aq) + H_2O$
             $H^+(aq) + HCO_3^-(aq) \rightarrow CO_2(g) + H_2O$
        (c) $2HBr(aq) + MgCO_3(s) \rightarrow MgBr_2(aq) + CO_2(g) + H_2O$
             $2H^+(aq) + MgCO_3(s) \rightarrow Mg^{2+}(aq) + CO_2(g) + H_2O$
        (d) $HNO_3(aq) + KHCO_3(aq) \rightarrow KNO_3(aq) + CO_2(g) + H_2O$
             $H^+(aq) + HCO_3^-(aq) \rightarrow CO_2(g) + H_2O$
        (e) $HBr(aq) + NH_3(aq) \rightarrow NH_4Br(aq)$
             $H^+(aq) + NH_3(aq) \rightarrow NH_4^+(aq)$
        (f) $2HNO_3(aq) + Ca(OH)_2(s) \rightarrow Ca(NO_3)_2(aq) + 2H_2O$
             $2H^+(aq) + Ca(OH)_2(s) \rightarrow Ca^{2+}(aq) + 2H_2O$
        (g) $2HCl(aq) + Mg(s) \rightarrow MgCl_2(aq) + H_2(g)$
             $2H^+(aq) + Mg(s) \rightarrow Mg^{2+}(aq) + H_2(g)$

8.48   (a) $2NaOH(aq) + H_2SO_4(aq) \rightarrow Na_2SO_4(aq) + 2H_2O$
             $OH^-(aq) + H^+(aq) \rightarrow H_2O$
        (b) $K_2CO_3(aq) + 2HNO_3(aq) \rightarrow 2KNO_3(aq) + CO_2(g) + H_2O$
             $CO_3^{2-}(aq) + 2H^+(aq) \rightarrow CO_2(g) + H_2O$
        (c) $NaHCO_3(aq) + HBr(aq) \rightarrow NaBr(aq) + CO_2(g) + H_2O$
             $HCO_3^-(aq) + H^+(aq) \rightarrow CO_2(g) + H_2O$
        (d) $CaCO_3(s) + 2HI(aq) \rightarrow CaI_2(aq) + CO_2(g) + H_2O$
             $CaCO_3(s) + 2H^+(aq) \rightarrow Ca^{2+}(aq) + CO_2(g) + H_2O$
        (e) $NH_3(aq) + HI(aq) \rightarrow NH_4I(aq)$
             $NH_3(aq) + H^+(aq) \rightarrow NH_4^+(aq)$

(f) $Mg(OH)_2(s) + 2HBr(aq) \rightarrow MgBr_2(aq) + 2H_2O$
     $Mg(OH)_2(s) + 2H^+(aq) \rightarrow Mg^{2+}(aq) + 2H_2O$

(g) $2Al(s) + 6HCl(aq) \rightarrow 2AlCl_3(aq) + 3H_2(g)$
     $2Al(s) + 6H^+(aq) \rightarrow 2Al^{3+}(aq) + 3H_2(g)$

8.49 (a) $OH^-(aq) + H^+(aq) \rightarrow H_2O$

(b) $HCO_3^-(aq) + H^+(aq) \rightarrow CO_2(g) + H_2O$

(c) $CO_3^{2-}(aq) + 2H^+(aq) \rightarrow CO_2(g) + H_2O$

(d) $NH_3(aq) + H^+(aq) \rightarrow NH_4^+(aq)$

8.50 $MCO_3(s) + 2H^+(aq) \rightarrow M^{2+}(aq) + CO_2(g) + H_2O$

8.51 $M(OH)_2(s) + 2H^+(aq) \rightarrow M^{2+}(aq) + 2H_2O$

8.52 $M(s) + 2H^+(aq) \rightarrow M^{2+}(aq) + H_2(g)$

8.53 (a) To be higher in the activity series means, in a qualitative sense, that the atoms of the element have a greater tendency to become ions than those of elements lower in the series.

(b) The lower ionization energies of sodium and potassium also indicate this greater tendency to become ions.

8.54 Zinc reacts more rapidly with $1\,M$ HCl. The reaction is with the hydronium ion, and the molar concentration of this ion is much higher in $1\ M$ HCl (which is 100% ionized) than in $1\ M$ H_3PO_4, which is a moderate acid and only moderately ionized in water.

8.55 0.355 mol $KHCO_3$

8.56 0.512 mol of NaOH

8.57 7.61 g Na_2CO_3

8.58 6.34 g $CaCO_3$

8.59 5.10 g $NaHCO_3$

8.60 0.989 g K_2CO_3

8.61 36.7 mL NaOH solution

8.62 40.9 mL KOH solution

8.63 (a) $CaCO_3(s) + 2HCl(aq) \rightarrow CaCl_2(aq) + CO_2(g) + H_2O$
           $CaCO_3(s) + 2H^+(aq) \rightarrow Ca^{2+}(aq) + CO_2(g) + H_2O$

(b) 54.4 g $CaCO_3$; 235 mL HCl solution

8.64 $Na_2CO_3(s) + 2HCl(aq) \rightarrow 2NaCl(aq) + CO_2(g) + H_2O$
      $CO_3^{2-}(aq) + 2H^+(aq) \rightarrow CO_2(g) + H_2O$
      23.9 L of CO_2; 101 g Na_2CO_3

8.65 Any stronger base can take H^+ from H_2O, thus be neutralized and so be replaced by OH^-.

8.66 Any acid stronger than this gives up a proton to H_2O, and thus it is replaced by H_3O^+ and the conjugate base of the stronger acid.

8.67 (a) H_2SO_3 (b) HBr   (c) H_3O^+ (d) $HC_2H_3O_2$

8.68 (a) H_2SO_4 (b) H_2CO_3 (c) HI   (d) HNO_2

8.69 (a) NH_2^- (b) NO_2^- (c) SO_3^{2-} (d) HSO_3^-

8.70   (a) HCO_3^- (b) HPO_4^{2-} (c) NH_3 (d) O^{2-}

8.71   (a) NH_2^- (b) OH^- (c) S^{2-}

8.72   (a) HCO_3^- (b) $H_2PO_4^-$ (c) NO_2^-

8.73   (a) HCl (b) H_2O (c) HSO_4^-

8.74 $H_2PO_4^-$ (b) H_2SO_3 (c) NH_4^+

8.75   The reactants are favored because they include the weaker acid and the weaker base.

8.76   The products are favored because they include the weaker acid and the weaker base.

8.77   An aqueous solution of NaOH or KOH, when added to the solution to be tested releases ammonia, which has a characteristic odor, if the solution in the test tube is ammonium chloride.
$$NH_4^+(aq) + OH^-(aq) \rightarrow NH_3(aq) + H_2O$$

8.78   (a) $Na_2O(s) + H_2O \rightarrow 2NaOH(aq)$
       (b) $KNH_2(s) + H_2O \rightarrow KOH(aq) + NH_3(aq)$
       (c) $LiH(s) + H_2O \rightarrow LiOH(aq) + H_2(g)$

8.79   Potassium hydroxide, KOH
       $KOH(aq) + HCl(aq) \rightarrow KCl(aq) + H_2O$
       Potassium bicarbonate, $KHCO_3$
       $KHCO_3(aq) + HCl(aq) \rightarrow KCl(aq) + CO_2(g) + H_2O$
       Potassium carbonate, K_2CO_3
       $K_2CO_3(aq) + 2HCl(aq) \rightarrow 2KCl(aq) + CO_2(g) + H_2O$

8.80   Sodium hydroxide, NaOH
       $NaOH(aq) + HBr(aq) \rightarrow NaBr(aq) + H_2O$
       Sodium bicarbonate, $NaHCO_3$
       $NaHCO_3(aq) + HBr(aq) \rightarrow NaBr(aq) + CO_2(g) + H_2O$
       Sodium carbonate, Na_2CO_3
       $Na_2CO_3(aq) + 2HBr(aq) \rightarrow 2NaBr(aq) + CO_2(g) + H_2O$

8.81   Compounds c and d are insoluble in water.

8.82   Compounds d and e are insoluble in water.

8.83   Compounds a and d are insoluble in water.

8.84   Compounds b and c are insoluble in water.

8.85   (a) $Cl^-(aq) + Ag^+ \rightarrow AgCl(s)$
       (b) no reaction
       (c) $OH^-(aq) + H^+(aq) \rightarrow H_2O$
       (d) $Pb^{2+}(aq) + 2Cl^-(aq) \rightarrow PbCl_2(s)$
       (e) no reaction
       (f) $S^{2-}(aq) + Cu^{2+}(aq) \rightarrow CuS(s)$
       (g) $SO_4^{2-}(aq) + Ba^{2+}(aq) \rightarrow BaSO_4(s)$
       (h) $OH^-(aq) + H^+(aq) \rightarrow H_2O$
       (i) $S^{2-}(aq) + Ni^{2+}(aq) \rightarrow NiS(s)$

(j)　$Ag^+(aq) + Br^-(aq) \rightarrow AgBr(s)$
(k)　$HCO_3^-(aq) + H^+(aq) \rightarrow CO_2(g) + H_2O$
(l)　$Mg^{2+}(aq) + 2OH^-(aq) \rightarrow Mg(OH)_2(s)$

8.86　(a)　$S^{2-}(aq) + Cu^{2+}(aq) \rightarrow CuS(s)$
(b)　$OH^-(aq) + H^+(aq) \rightarrow H_2O$
(c)　$SO_4^{2-}(aq) + Ba^{2+}(aq) \rightarrow BaSO_4(s)$
(d)　$SO_4^{2-}(aq) + Pb^{2+}(aq) \rightarrow PbSO_4(s)$
(e)　no reaction
(f)　$HCO_3^-(aq) + H^+(aq) \rightarrow CO_2(g) + H_2O$
(g)　$S^{2-}(aq) + Cd^{2+}(aq) \rightarrow CdS(s)$
(h)　$OH^-(aq) + H^+(aq) \rightarrow H_2O$
(i)　no reaction
(j)　$HCO_3^-(aq) + H^+(aq) \rightarrow CO_2(g) + H_2O$
(k)　no reaction
(l)　$Pb^{2+}(aq) + CrO_4^{2-}(aq) \rightarrow PbCrO_4(s)$

8.87　(a)　$Na(Ste) \rightleftharpoons Na^+(aq) + (Ste)^-(aq)$
(b)　The equilibrium would shift to the left and solid sodium stearate would precipitate.
(c)　The presence of the common ion, Na^+, suppresses the solubility of the soap in water and so renders the soap less effective.

8.88　3.5 - 5.0 meq K^+/L
8.89　4.2 - 5.2 meq Ca^{2+}/L
8.90　5.01 meq of K^+
8.91　2.00 meq Mg^{2+}
8.92　Both are solids so there is none of the mobility of ions or molecules necessary for a reaction.
8.93　$HCO_3^-(aq) + H^+(aq) \rightarrow CO_2(g) + H_2O$
8.94　Water that is difficult to use with ordinary soap because precipitates form between the "hardness ions" and the soap.
8.95　$Ca^{2+}, Mg^{2+}, Fe^{3+} (Fe^{2+})$
8.96　The hardness ions form insoluble compounds with the anions of ordinary soap.
8.97　Hard water in which the chief anion is HCO_3^-. Its hardness is lost when such water is heated because HCO_3^- changes to CO_3^{2-}, which forms a carbonate precipitate with any of the hardness ions.
8.98　Hard water in which the anions do not include much HCO_3^-.
8.99　The removal of the hardness ions.
8.100　(a)　$Na_2CO_3 \cdot 10H_2O$
(b)　The CO_3^{2-} ion.
(c)　$Ca^{2+}(aq) + CO_3^{2-}(aq) \rightarrow CaCO_3(s)$
　　　$Mg^{2+}(aq) + CO_3^{2-}(aq) \rightarrow MgCO_3(s)$

8.101   (a) $PbSO_4(s) \rightleftharpoons Pb^{2+}(aq) + SO_4{}^{2-}(aq)$
      (b) $K_{sp} = [Pb^{2+}][SO_4{}^{2-}]$
      (c)   In a saturated solution
      (d) 6.2×10^{-7}

8.102   Carbon dioxide—from respiration, decay, and combustion
      Methane—from bacterial action and oil field releases
      Dinitrogen monoxide—from bacterial action and uses of fertilizers
      Chlorofluorocarbons—released from space conditioners and (formerly) aerosol cans

8.103   Heat radiation leaving the earth for outer space is caught by molecules of the greenhouse gases and partly radiated back to the earth.

8.104   The increased combustion of fossil fuels.

8.105   By photosynthesis and by the formation of insoluble carbonates in the world's oceans.

8.106   Largely the haze is caused by colloidal sized particles consisting of microscopic droplets of sulfuric acid formed from gases ejected by volcanoes and the combustion of sulfur-containing fossil fuels.

8.107   Anion gap = 19 meq/L. This is above the normal range of 5 - 14 meq/L, so this anion gap suggests a disturbance in metabolism.

8.108   (a)   We look for the salt with the anion having the highest charge to be least soluble. This salt would involve the strongest attraction between cation and anion and so would be least able to release the ions from the crystal.
      (b) $Ca(H_2PO_4)_2$
      (c) $Ca_3(PO_4)_2$

8.109   Whichever aqueous solution is a nonconductor contains a molecular compound, unless the molecular compound reacts with water (ionizes) to give ions.

8.110   Make a solution of the unknown. If it is K_2O, you will notice that the temperature increases, because K_2O reacts exothermically with water to give KOH ($K_2O + 2H_2O \rightarrow 2KOH$). The solution can be tested with litmus. If the unknown is K_2O, red litmus will turn blue. KNO_3 will not do this.

8.111 $NaHCO_3$

8.112   0.232 g K_2CO_3

Chapter 9

Practice Exercises, Chapter 9

1.   (a) 2.5×10^{-6} mol OH⁻/L. Basic
      (b) 9.1×10^{-8} mol OH⁻/L. Acidic
      (c) 1.1×10^{-7} mol OH⁻/L. Basic

2.   (a)   1.60   (b) 10.40   (c) 10.70

3.   7.14. Basic

4.   (a) 4.6×10^{-7} mol/L, acidic   (b) 1.3×10^{-8} mol/L, basic

5. 5.2×10^{-8} mol/L

6. 3.6×10^{-10} mol/L

7. $HC_2H_3O_2(aq) \rightleftharpoons H^+(aq) + C_2H_3O_2^-(aq)$

$$K_a = \frac{[H^+][C_2H_3O_2{}^-]}{[HC_2H_3O_2]}$$

8. $HCO_3^-(aq) \rightleftharpoons H^+(aq) + CO_3^{2-}(aq)$

$$K_a = \frac{[H^+][CO_3{}^{2-}]}{[HCO_3{}^-]}$$

9. $NH_4^+(aq) \rightleftharpoons H^+(aq) + NH_3(aq)$

$$K_a = \frac{[H^+][NH_3]}{[NH_4{}^+]}$$

10.   ascorbic acid

11.   cyanide ion

12.   (a) $CO_3^{2-}(aq) + H_2O \rightleftharpoons HCO_3^-(aq) + OH^-(aq)$

$$K_b = \frac{[HCO_3{}^-][OH^-]}{[CO_3{}^{2-}]}$$

       (b) $C_2H_3O_2^-(aq) + H_2O \rightleftharpoons HC_2H_3O_2(aq) + OH^-(aq)$

$$K_b = \frac{[HC_2H_3O_2][OH^-]}{[C_2H_3O_2{}^-]}$$

       (c) $NH_3(aq) + H_2O \rightleftharpoons NH_4^+(aq) + OH^-(aq)$

$$K_b = \frac{[NH_4{}^+][OH^-]}{[NH_3]}$$

13.   (a) Yes, basic   (b) Yes, basic
       (c) Yes, basic   (d) Yes, acidic
       (e) Yes, basic   (e) Yes, basic

14.   Basic

15.   Acidic

16.   Yes, decrease the pH because NH_4^+ hydrolyzes to give some H^+.

17.   10.33

18.   acetic acid

19.   6.80

20. NH_3, $K_b = 1.8 \times 10^{-5}$
21. 4.8

$$CN^-(aq) + H_2O \rightleftharpoons HCN(aq) + OH^-(aq)$$

$$K_b = \frac{[HCN][OH^-]}{[CN^-]}$$

22. 3.89
23. 3.86
24. (a) $pH = pK_a + 1$
    (b) $pH = pK_a - 1$
25. (a) 7.00
    (b) 7.18
    (c) Buffer *capacity* depends on the *absolute* values of [anion] and [acid].
26. 7.75. No
27. 0.105 M NaOH
28. 0.125 M H_2SO_4

Review Exercises, Chapter 9

9.1 The rates of reactions, the factors that govern the rates, and the explanations for the facts.

9.2 (a) $\dfrac{\text{change in concentration}}{\text{time}}$ (b) $\dfrac{\text{mol}/\text{L}}{\text{s}}$

9.3 The nature of the reactants; the concentrations of the reactants, the temperature of the reaction mixture; and the presence or absence of a catalyst. In a homogeneous reaction all substances are in the *same* phase (gas or liquid).

9.4 (a) The concentrations of the reactants are highest at the start.
    (b) Higher concentrations mean higher collision frequencies, and colliding molecules is a postulate of the kinetic theory.

9.5 C and D

9.6 At a higher temperature, both the frequency of all collisions increases and an increase in the *fraction* of successful collisions occurs.

9.7 About 10 °C

9.8 The higher temperature increases the rates of reactions of metabolism so the rate at which oxygen is needed increases. The heart (and also the lungs) must work harder to distribute this oxygen.

9.9 Increase concentrations

9.10 (a) No effect (b) Reduces it (c) No effect (d) Increases

9.11 Enzymes

9.12   Catalase : $2H_2O_2 \xrightarrow{\text{catalase}} 2H_2O + O_2$

Carbonicanhydrase : $CO_2 + OH^- \xrightarrow{\text{carbonic anhydrase}} HCO_3{}^-$

9.13   (a)   A catalyst can also make a reaction go at the same rate as in its absence, but do so at a lower temperature and so under milder conditions.
(b)   A catalyst can enable a synthesis at lower energy costs.

9.14   Two reactant particles must collide so that deformations of their electron clouds leading to rearrangements of electrons relative to nuclei can occur. Collisional kinetic energy is converted to potential energy, which helps the reaction take place.

9.15   Collision frequency refers to the *total* number of collisions (of every amount of collisional energy) per unit of volume per second. The rate of a reaction is the frequency of *successful* collisions per unit of volume per second.

9.16   By increasing the collision frequency and by increasing the *fraction* of successful collisions.

9.17   (a) E_{act}
(b)   heat of reaction
(c)   If the reaction has both a large E_{act} and a large (evolving) heat of reaction.
(d)   The reaction is instantaneous (an explosion).
(e) E_{act}

9.18   For a collision to be *successful*, there must be sufficient conversion of molecular kinetic energy into potential energy. What is "sufficient" constitutes the energy of activation.

9.19   (a)   CO and O_2
(b) CO_2
(c)   C
(d)   B
(e)   Exothermic. The energy of the product D is less than that of the reactants at A and the difference in energy *evolves* as the heat of reaction.
(f)   E

9.20

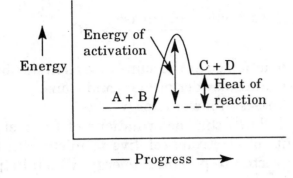

9.21

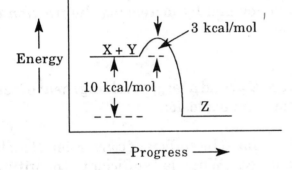

9.22   That at a given temperature for a given equilibrium the equilibrium constant does not change as the equilibrium shifts in response to the common ion effect or other stresses.

9.23   (a)   mol/L

(b)   As exponents for their associated molar concentration terms

(c)   Reactants

(d)   Values of K_{eq} change with temperature.

9.24   (a) $K_{eq} = \dfrac{[NH_4^+][OH^-]}{[NH_3][H_2O]}$

(b) $K_{eq} = \dfrac{[H_2O]^2}{[H_2]^2[O_2]}$

(c) $K_{eq} = \dfrac{[NH_3]^2}{[N_2][H_2]^3}$

9.25   The product is favored because K_{eq} is (much) greater than 1.

9.26 K_w = [H+][OH-]. The *equilibrium law* is $K_{eq} = \dfrac{[H^+][OH^-]}{[H_2O]}$

9.27 1.00×10^{-14}

9.28   Acid-base neutralization is exothermic. This neutralization is the *reverse* reaction in the equilibrium

$$H_2O \;\rightleftharpoons\; H^+(aq) + OH^-(aq)$$

so the *forward* reaction must be endothermic. Thus the addition of heat shifts the equilibrium to the right in accordance with Le Châtelier's principle.

9.29 2.43×10^{-14}. Neutral, because [H+] = [OH−]

9.30 9.0×10^{-16}

9.31   [H+] = 1×10^{-pH}. pH = −log [H+]

9.32   Acidic

9.33   Basic

9.34   3.0

9.35   pH = 11 (pOH = 3)

9.36   Because in water at pH = 7.00 (25 °C), [H+] = [OH−]

9.37 4.5×10^{-6} mol/L. Slightly acidic

9.38 1.5×10^{-5} mol/L.

9.39   Strong. At a pH of 2, the value of [H+] is 1×10^{-2} mol/L, which is numerically identical to the initial concentration of the acid, so all of the acid is ionized.

9.40   Weak. At a pH of 5.72, [H+] is between 1×10^{-5} to 1×10^{-6} mol/L, but the initial concentration of the acid is much higher (1×10^{-3} mol/L). Therefore, only a small percentage of the acid molecules can be ionized.

9.41   Basic (pH = 7.76)

9.42   pOH = 1.433; pH = 12.567

9.43 $HNO_2(aq) \rightleftharpoons H^+(aq) + NO_2^-(aq)$

$$K_{eq} = \frac{[H^+][NO_2^-]}{[HNO_2]}$$

9.44 $HSO_4^-(aq) \rightleftharpoons H^+(aq) + SO_4^{2-}(aq)$

$$K_{eq} = \frac{[H^+][SO_4^{2-}]}{[HSO_4^-]}$$

9.45 $NH_3(aq) \rightleftharpoons NH_2^-(aq) + H^+(aq)$

$$K_{eq} = \frac{[NH_2^-][H^+]}{[NH_3]}$$

9.46   barbituric acid

9.47   ammonium ion

9.48 $HCO_2^-(aq) + H_2O \rightleftharpoons HCO_2H(aq) + OH^-(aq)$

$$K_b = \frac{[HCO_2H][OH^-]}{[HCO_2]}$$

9.49 $NO_2^-(aq) + H_2O \rightleftharpoons HNO_2(aq) + OH^-(aq)$

$$K_b = \frac{[HNO_2][OH^-]}{[NO_{2^-}]}$$

9.50 $HPO_4^{2-}(aq) + H_2O \rightleftharpoons H_2PO_4^-(aq) + OH^-(aq)$

$$K_b = \frac{[H_2PO_4^-][OH^-]}{[HPO_4{}^{2-}]}$$

9.51   ammonia

9.52   The ammonium ion, but not the bromide ion, hydrolyzes. The hydrolysis of NH_4^+ generates a small excess of H^+ over OH^-.

9.53   The sulfide ion reacts with water as follows, which produces an excess of hydroxide ions in the solution.
$S^{2-}(aq) + H_2O \rightarrow HS^-(aq) + OH^-(aq)$

9.54   (a) Neutral   (b) Acidic (c) Basic   (d) Acidic   (e) Basic

9.55   (a) Neutral   (b) Basic (c) Basic   (d) Acidic   (e) Basic

9.56   Basic. Aspirin is a weak acid, so its conjugate base is a relatively strong base, and such anions hydrolyze to give basic solutions.

9.57   Basic.

9.58   (a) 3.17   (b) 7.52

9.59   (a) 10.85   (b) 10.25

9.60   (a) 1.5×10^{-11}, 10.83   (b) 3.3×10^{-7}. 6.48

9.61   (a) 7.1×10^{-4}, 3.15   (b) 1.8×10^{-4}. 3.75

9.62 X is the stronger acid. Y has the stronger conjugate base.

9.63 N is the stronger base and it has the weaker conjugate acid.

9.64   Without rigid control of blood pH, the processes of respiration break down. Moreover, enzymes work best only at particular pHs.

9.65   Acidosis is a decrease in the pH of blood. Alkalosis is an increase in the pH of blood.

9.66   Either causes interferences with the process of respiration.

9.67   More alkaline. Alkalosis

9.68   More acidic. Acidosis

9.69   pH = 7.18. This means acidosis because 7.18 is less (so more acidic) than 7.35, the normal pH of blood.

9.70   The pH will stay quite close to 7.45 even if small quantities of acid or base are added.

9.71 $H_2PO_4^-$ and HPO_4^{2-}

9.72 $H_2PO_4^-(aq) + OH^-(aq) \rightarrow HPO_4^{2-}(aq) + H_2O$

9.73 $HPO_4^{2-}(aq) + H^+(aq) \rightarrow H_2PO_4^-(aq)$

9.74 $CO_2(aq)$ and $HCO_3^-(aq)$. (It's all right to write H_2CO_3 for CO_2 here, but follow the leading of your instructor.)

9.75   Acid is neutralized by: $H^+(aq) + HCO_3^-(aq) \rightarrow CO_2(aq) + H_2O$
       Base is neutralized by: $OH^-(aq) + CO_2(aq) \rightarrow HCO_3^-(aq)$

9.76   The permanent removal of $CO_2(g)$ at the lungs means that the following equilibrium shifts to the right. The shift is forced by the removal of one of its products, $CO_2(aq)$ in the form of $CO_2(g)$. Thus one H^+ disappears for each $CO_2(g)$ that is lost.

$H^+(aq) + HCO_3^-(aq) \rightleftharpoons CO_2(aq) + H_2O$
Then, $CO_2(aq) \rightarrow CO_2(g)$

9.77   The movement of air into and out of the lungs. Hyperventilation is ventilation at an accelerated rate. Hypoventilation is ventilation as a reduced rate.

9.78   To hyperventilate so as to remove the excess CO_2 more rapidly.

9.79   Involuntary hypoventilation forces the system to retain CO_2, which is equivalent to the retention of acid, causing acidosis.

9.80   (a)   Alkalosis
       (b)   For each CO_2 lost at the lungs, one H^+ ion is permanently neutralized (as described in the answer to Review Exercise 9.76). The loss of H^+ ion, of course, means an increase in the value of the pH of the blood.

9.81   A decrease in the blood's pH (acidosis). The hyperventilation helps to remove acid.

9.82   The concentrations after equilibrium has been established.

9.83   If HA is the acid component of the buffer and A^- its conjugate base, is the base component, then the presence of A^- from the *salt* used to supply the base suppresses the ionization of HA. Thus $[HA]_{eq} = [HA]_{initial} = [acid]$. However, because so little A^- is lost because of hydrolysis, we can set $[A^-]_{eq} = [A^-]_{initial} = [anion]$

9.84   pH = 4.83

9.85   pH = 7.26

9.86   (a)   pH = 5.10   (b) pH = 4.96   (c) pH = 5.24
       (d)   After the addition of acid to 500 mL water, pH = 1.40
             After the addition of base to 500 mL water, pH = 12.60

9.87   Because virtually all of the dissolved CO_2 exists as $CO_2(aq)$ instead of as $H_2CO_3(aq)$.

9.88   6.1

9.89   (a)   24 mmol/L (b) 1.2 mmol/L

9.90   (a)   pH = 6.1

(b)   pH = 7.1

(c)   Hyperventilation expels additional CO_2.

(d)   A net synthesis of HCO_3^- for the blood is performed by the kidneys.

9.91   The molarity of the solution is accurately known.

9.92   The indicator changes color.

9.93   The indicator is picked so that its color change occurs at or very close to the pH of the solution that forms when the stoichiometric amount of base has been matched by that of the acid.

9.94   The titration of any strong acid (e.g., HCl) with any strong base (e.g., NaOH) produces a salt whose ions do not hydrolyze.

9.95   The titration of any strong base (e.g., NaOH) against acetic acid or any weak acid gives a solution whose salt has an ion, the anion, that would hydrolyze to give a slightly basic solution.

9.96   The titration of a strong acid against aqueous ammonia would produce an ammonium salt whose cation, NH_4^+ would hydrolyze to give a slightly acidic pH. The anion would not hydrolyze.

9.97   (a)   0.3781 M HCl

　　　 (b)   0.4000 M HBr

9.98   (a)   0.3407 M HI

　　　 (b)   0.2000 M H_2SO_4

9.99   400.0

9.100   64.00

9.101   (a)   7.292 g HCl

　　　 (b)   4.845 g HNO_3

　　　 (c)   0.5518 g H_2SO_4

9.102   (a)   1.279 g HI

　　　 (b)   14.71 g H_2SO_4

　　　 (c)   59.62 g Na_2CO_3

9.103   (a)   0.05206 M Na_2CO_3

　　　 (b)   5.518 g Na_2CO_3/L

9.104   (a)   0.2240 M NaOH

　　　 (b)   8.96 g NaOH/L

9.105 $K_a = 1.34 \times 10^{-3}$; $pK_a = 2.87$

9.106 K_a 1.10×10^{-4}; $pK_a = 3.96$

9.107   pH = 3.22

9.108   pH = 1.93

9.109 SO_2, from the combustion of fossil fuels that contain sulfur. SO_3, from the oxidation of SO_2 in the atmosphere. NO, from vehicle exhaust. NO_2, from the oxidation of NO in air. Acid *deposition* is better than acid *rain* as a label for the problem because the gaseous oxides are often adsorbed on the surfaces of particulate matter, which settles (deposits) like a dust.

9.110   Acid rain lowers the pH of lakes and streams making it more difficult for game fish to survive. Acid rain corrodes limestone building materials and leaches calcium and magnesium ions from soil. Acid rain corrodes things made of metal.

9.111   0.939

9.112   10.65

9.113   3.92

9.114   0.055 mol acetic acid

9.115   (a)   The ammonium ion: $NH_4^+(aq) + OH^-(aq) \rightarrow NH_3(aq) + H_2O$
         (b)   Ammonia: $NH_3(aq) + H^+(aq) \rightarrow NH_4^+(aq)$
         (c)   9.24

Chapter 10

Practice Exercises, Chapter 10

1.   (a) H, +1 (b) S, +4   (c) H, +1   (d) O, –2   (e) H, +1   (f) O, –2
            S, –2   O, –2   O, –2   S, +6   O, –2   S, +6
                                             S, +4   S, +6

2.   (a) H, +1 (b) H, +1   (c) H, +1   (d) H, +1   (e) H, +1
            C, –4   C, –2   C, 0   C, +2   C, +4
                         O, –2   O, –2   O, –2   O, –2

3.   (a) –1 (b) –2 (c) –3. Reduction

4. $Cu(s) + 4H^+(aq) + 2NO_3^-(aq) \rightarrow Cu^{2+}(aq) + 2NO_2(g) + 2H_2O$

5. $3C_2H_6O + 4MnO_4^-(aq) \rightarrow$
$$3C_2H_3O_2^-(aq) + 4MnO_2(s) + OH^-(aq) + 4H_2O$$

6. $Zn(s) + Fe^{2+}(aq) \rightarrow Zn^{2+}(aq) + Fe(s)$

7.   No, the reduction potential for $2H^+/H_2$ is not more positive that that of $Cu^{2+}/$ Cu.

8. $ES_{(o,cell)} = +0.29$ V. $K_{eq} = 6.3 \times 10^9$

Review Exercises, Chapter 10

10.1   (a)   An reaction in which an oxidation number becomes more positive.
         (b)   An reaction in which an oxidation number becomes more negative.
         (c)   A substance that causes an oxidation and is itself reduced.
         (d)   A substance that causes a reduction and is itself oxidized.
         (e)   A chemical reaction in which oxidation numbers change.

10.2   (a)   N, –3; H, +1 (b) N, +3; F, –1   (c) N,+4; O, –2
         (d)   N, +3; O, –2 (e) N, +5; O, –2

10.3   (a)   H, +1; I, +7; O, –2   (b) H, +1; I, +5; O, –2   (c) H, +1; I, +1; O, –2
10.4   (a)   H, +1; S, –2   (b) H, +1; S, +4; O, –2   (c) H, +1; S, +6; O, –2
10.5   (a)   Mn +4; O, –2 (b) Mn, +3; O, –2
       (c)   Mn, +7; O, –2   (d) Mn, +2; Cl, –1
10.6   Oxidation. An oxidation number has become more positive (or less negative)
       Half-reactions with electrons as reactants are reductions. Reducing agents
       are oxidized.
10.7   (a) $MnO_4^- + 8H^+ + 5e^- \rightarrow Mn^{2+} + 4H_2O$ (reduction)
       (b) $2Fe^{2+} + 3H_2O \rightarrow Fe_2O_3 + 6H^+ + 2e^-$ (oxidation)
       (c) $H_2C_2O_4 \rightarrow 2CO_2 + 2H^+ + 2e^-$ (oxidation)
       (d) $2NO_2 + 8H^+ + 8e^- \rightarrow N_2 + 4H_2O$ (reduction)
10.8   (a) $CH_3OH + H_2O \rightarrow CO_2 + 6H^+ + 6e^-$ (oxidation)
       (b) $CH_4 + H_2O \rightarrow CO + 6H^+ + 6e^-$ (oxidation)
       (c) $CH_3OH \rightarrow CH_2O + 2H^+ + 2e^-$ (oxidation)
       (d) $CO + 2H^+ + 2e^- \rightarrow C + H_2O$ (reduction)
10.9   (a) $2I^- + 2HNO_2 + 2H^+ \rightarrow I_2 + 2NO + 2H_2O$
       (b) $3Sn + 4NO_3^- + 4H^+ \rightarrow 3SnO_2 + 4NO + 2H_2O$
       (c) $Mg + SO_4^{2-} + 4H^+ \rightarrow Mg^{2+} + SO_2 + 2H_2O$
       (d) $PbO_2 + 4Cl^- + 4H^+ \rightarrow PbCl_2 + Cl_2 + 2H_2O$
10.10 (a) $Ag + NO_3^- + 2H^+ \rightarrow Ag^+ + NO_2 + H_2O$
       (b) $C_2O_4^{2-} + 2HNO_2 + 2H^+ \rightarrow 2CO_2 + 2NO + 2H_2O$
       (c) $2MnO_4^- + 5HNO_2 + H^+ \rightarrow 2Mn^{2+} + 5NO_3^- + 3H_2O$
       (d) $3H_3PO_2 + 2Cr_2O_7^{2-} + 16H^+ \rightarrow 3H_3PO_4 + 4Cr^{3+} + 8H_2O$
10.11 (a) $4MnO_4^- + 3CH_2O \rightarrow 4MnO_2 + 3CO_2 + 4OH^- + H_2O$
       (b) $2CrO_4^{2-} + 3S^{2-} + 4H_2O \rightarrow 2CrO_2^- + 3S + 8OH^-$
10.12 (a) $2MnO_4^- + 3SO_3^{2-} + H_2O \rightarrow 2MnO_2 + 3SO_4^{2-} + 2OH^-$
       (b) $C_6H_5CH_3 + 2CrO_4^{2-} \rightarrow C_6H_5CO_2^- + 2CrO_2^- + H_2O + OH^-$
10.13 $2H^+ + 2e^- \rightleftharpoons H_2$
       $[H^+] = 1\ M$, Temperature = 25 °C, Pressure of H_2 = 1 atm
10.14 (a) $Ca^{2+}(aq) + 2e^- \rightleftharpoons Ca(s)$
       (b)   Lesser
       (c) H^+
10.15 (a) $I_2(s) + 2e^- \rightarrow 2I^-(aq)$
       (b)   The $I_2/2I^-$ system
       (c) I_2
10.16 (a) $I_2 < Br_2 < Cl_2 < F_2$
       (b) $F^- < Cl^- < Br^- < I^-$
10.17 Low. We can tell from how hard it is to reduce these ions (they have very
       negative reduction potentials) that the metals are easily oxidized. This means

they easily lose electrons, which is what their low ionization potentials also tell us.

10.18   Au. Gold, the metal with the highest reduction potential, would have the lowest potential for becoming oxidized to a metal ion and so is the least reactive of all metals.

10.19   The metals are arranged in the activity series, from bottom to top, in their order of decreasing reduction potential.

10.20 $4I^- + O_2 + 4H^+ \rightarrow 2I_2 + 2H_2O$

10.21 $2Fe^{2+} + Cl_2 \rightarrow 2Fe^{3+} + 2Cl^-$

10.22   No

10.23   (a) No   (b) No

10.24   1.51 V

10.25   0.11 V

10.26 1.0×10^{51}

10.27 5.2×10^3. Yes

10.28   When the temperature is 25 °C, all concentrations are 1 M, and all gas pressures are 1 atm.

10.29   After equilibrium has been reached.

10.30

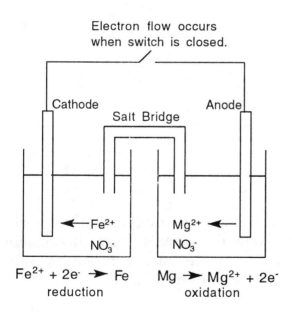

10.31   To supply ions that will balance charges as other ions, those invoved in the redox reaction, enter or leave the electrolytes.

10.32   1.93 V

10.33 $PbO_2 + 4H^+ + SO_4{}^{2-} + 2e^- \rightarrow PbSO_4 + 2H_2O$

   $Pb + SO_4{}^{2-} \rightarrow PbSO_4 + 2e^-$

10.34 $PbO_2 + Pb + 4H^+ + 2SO_4{}^{2-} \rightarrow 2PbSO_4 + 2H_2O$

10.35   As H_2SO_4 is consumed while the battery runs down, the electrolyte becomes less dense, which the hydrometer can detect.

10.36

   $Zn + 2OH^- \rightarrow Zn(OH)_2 + 2e^-$

   $Ag_2O + H_2O + 2e^- \rightarrow 2Ag + 2OH^-$

   _____

   Sum: $Zn + Ag_2O + H_2O \rightarrow Zn(OH)_2 + 2Ag$

10.37   (a) Br_2 (b) F_2

10.38   19.1 g Na_2SO_3

10.39   (a) $2I^- + HSO_4{}^- + 3H^+ \rightarrow I_2 + SO_2 + 2H_2O$

   (b) $2Mn^{2+} + 5BiO_3{}^- + 14H^+ \rightarrow 2MnO_4{}^- + 5Bi^{3+} + 7H_2O$

10.40   (a) $4Au + 8CN^- + O_2 + 2H_2O \rightarrow 4Au(CN)_2{}^- + 4OH^-$

   (b) $4ClO_3{}^- + 3N_2H_4 \rightarrow 4Cl^- + 6NO + 6H_2O$

Chapter 11

Practice Exercises, Chapter 11

1. $^{131}_{53}I \rightarrow {}^{131}_{54}Xe + {}^{0}_{-1}e + {}^{0}_{0}\gamma$

2. $^{239}_{94}Pu \rightarrow {}^{235}_{92}U + {}^{4}_{2}He + {}^{0}_{0}\gamma$

3.   10,000 units

4.   8.5 m

Review Exercises, Chapter 11

11.1   *Radioactive decay* is a change the occurs to radionuclides whereby they spontaneously emit radiation and change to other isotopes. In becoming other isotopes, the radionuclides have undergone *transmutation* as well. Thus radioactive decay is accompanied by transmutation.

11.2 $^{4}_{2}He$, ${}^{0}_{-1}e$, and ${}^{0}_{0}\gamma$ (or simply γ)

11.3   Gamma radiation

11.4   (a) By comparing the sum of the mass numbers of the isotopes on one side of the arrow with the sum of the mass numbers of the isotopes on the opposite side of the arrow.

(b)   Any electrically charged product particles soon lose their charges as they give up or acquire electrons. (When beta particles are products, they are absorbed by surrounding matter.)

(c)   There must be a balance of the nuclear charges on opposite sides of the arrow by comparing the sums of the atomic numbers, (For this, we consider that the electron has an atomic number of –1.)

11.5   It is the most massive of the particles and it carries the largest charge. Therefore, it collides very quickly with a molecule in the air or other matter that it enters and so travels the shorter distance (is least penetrating).

11.6   The mass number is reduced by 4 units and the atomic number is reduced by 2 units.

11.7   There is no change in mass number, because the mass number of the beta particle is 0. The atomic number increases by one because the loss of $_{-1}^{0}e$ has the effect of changing a neutron into a proton.

11.8   140

11.9   Isotope. A radionuclide is a radioactive *isotope* than consists of *atoms*.

11.10   A neutron changes into a proton as an electron is ejected.

11.11   (a) $_{83}^{211}Bi$ (b) $_{84}^{216}Po$ (c) $_{57}^{140}La$

11.12   (a) $_{60}^{145}Nd$ (b) $_{94}^{241}Pu$ (c) $_{10}^{22}Ne$

11.13   (a) $_{60}^{144}Nd \rightarrow _{58}^{140}Ce + _{2}^{4}He$

(b) $_{19}^{40}K \rightarrow _{20}^{40}Ca + _{-1}^{0}e$

(c) $_{62}^{149}Sm \rightarrow _{63}^{149}Eu + _{-1}^{0}e$

(d) $_{98}^{251}Cf \rightarrow _{96}^{247}Cm + _{2}^{4}He + _{0}^{0}\gamma$

11.14   (a) $_{75}^{187}Re \rightarrow _{76}^{187}Os + _{-1}^{0}e$

(b) $_{94}^{242}Pu \rightarrow _{92}^{238}U + _{2}^{4}He + _{0}^{0}\gamma$

(c) $_{53}^{131}I \rightarrow _{54}^{131}Xe + _{-1}^{0}e$

(d) $_{95}^{243}Am \rightarrow _{93}^{239}Np + _{2}^{4}He$

11.15   Lead-214 forms by successive decays of uranium-238. The quantity of lead-214 in the sample diminishes by half each 26.8 minutes.

11.16   The beta and gamma emitter, because its radiation is more penetrating.

11.17   1.500 ng

11.18 2.930×10^{-3} ng (rounding only after the last calculation)

11.19   The ions that radiation produces are strange, unstable, highly reactive ions that initiate undesirable reactions in the body.

11.20   Any particle with an unpaired electron. The particle lacks an outer octet and so is reactive.

11.21   Radiation can cause birth defects.

11.22   Its radiation can cause cancer.

11.23   Radiation intensity diminishes with the square of the distance; and the radiation can be blocked by dense absorbing materials, like lead.

11.24   There is no level of exposure below which no damage is possible.

11.25   In low doses over a long period, radiation can initiate cancer. In well-focused, massive doses over a short period, radiation can kill cancer cells.

11.26   A factor of 4 (meaning that the intensity at the greater distance is one-fourth the intensity at the lesser distance).

11.27   Radiation moves in straight lines and spread out in the way that light from a light bulb spreads out.

11.28   Radionuclides in natural materials such as the soil, fallout from nuclear testing, cosmic rays, medical X rays, radioactive wastes released from nuclear power plants, television tubes, and medical radionuclides.

11.29   Cosmic rays are more intense at higher altitudes.

11.30   15.1 m

11.31 2.0×10^3 millirad

11.32   The becquerel

11.33   The sample is undergoing 1.5×10^{-3} Ci $\times$ $(3.7 \times 10^{10}$ disintegrations/Ci$) = 5.6 \times 10^7$ disintegrations per second.

11.34   The roentgen is the older unit. In the SI, the intensity is described by a ratio,

$$X = \frac{\text{total charge}}{\text{kg dry air}} \text{ (with the charge given in the SI unit of charge, the coulomb).}$$

11.35   The gray, Gy. The older unit is the rad.

11.36   The dose equivalent (the *sievert* in the SI) is the absorbed dose in gray multiplied by one or more *quality factors* that take into account biologically significant properties of the radiation in a given tissue. Alpha radiation has a higher quality factor (meaning that it is more dangerous in tissue) because of its relatively high mass and charge (compared with the electron, for example).

11.37   600 rad. They are roughly the same.

11.38   Different kinds of tissue have different responses to the same quantity of rads.

11.39   The rad doses are adjusted for the kinds of tissues and radiations and expressed as rems or sieverts.

11.40   295 mrem

11.41   The electron-volt

11.42   100 keV or less

11.43   Radiations can cause cancer, so for diagnosis the lowest usable energies are in order.

11.44   Radiations fog the film, and the degree of fogging is proportional to the exposure.

11.45   Radiations enter the tube and generate ions in the low-pressure gas in the tube. This makes the gas a conductor, so a circuit is thereby closed, which leads to a count or a click. Alpha particles can't penetrate the tube's window.

11.46   Iron-55. $^{55}_{25}Mn + ^{1}_{1}p \rightarrow ^{1}_{0}n + ^{55}_{26}Fe$

11.47   Indium-113 $^{109}_{47}Ag + ^{4}_{2}He \rightarrow ^{113}_{49}In$

11.48   Neutrons $^{113}_{49}In \rightarrow ^{111}_{49}In + 2^{1}_{0}n$

11.49   Gallium-67 $^{66}_{30}Zn + ^{1}_{1}p \rightarrow ^{67}_{31}Ga$

11.50 $^{19}_{9}F + ^{4}_{2}He \rightarrow ^{23}_{11}Na \rightarrow ^{22}_{11}Na + ^{1}_{0}n$

11.51 $^{10}_{5}B + ^{4}_{2}He \rightarrow ^{13}_{7}N + ^{1}_{0}n$

11.52 $^{14}_{7}N + ^{2}_{1}H \rightarrow ^{15}_{8}O + ^{1}_{0}n$

11.53   A lithium-6 nucleus. $^{27}_{13}Al + ^{6}_{3}Li \rightarrow ^{32}_{15}P + ^{1}_{1}p$

11.54   A neutron $^{32}_{16}S + ^{1}_{0}n \rightarrow ^{32}_{15}P + ^{1}_{1}p$

11.55   10 J/kg

11.56   A product produced by the action of the ionizing radiation.

11.57   A product produced by the ionizing radiation that is not present in the food or produced either by cooking of digestion.

11.58   Yes. Yes. Benzene

11.59   Cooking and digestion

11.60   Botulinum bacillus

11.61   The shorter the half-life, the more active is the radionuclide and hence the smaller is the dose that is needed to get results.

11.62   Gamma radiation can penetrate the entire body and reach a detector and thereby serve a diagnostic purpose. Alpha and beta radiation would be absorbed in the body, causing harm, without giving diagnostic value.

11.63   It emits only gamma radiation, and it has a shorter half-life.

11.64   It has a more intense radiation and it involves only gamma radiation.

11.65   As phosphate ion, because the hydroxyapatite in bone contains this ion.

11.66   The splitting apart of a large nucleus, following neutron capture, into two smaller nuclei and neutrons.

11.67   In decay, only a tiny part of the atom breaks away. In fission, the whole atom splits roughly in half.

11.68   Each fission event produces more neutron initiators than were needed to cause the fission event.

11.69   Uranium-235

11.70   About 3% to 5%. Essentially 100% in the bomb.

11.71   By the coolant, usually water. To generate steam to drive electrical turbines.

11.72   Unless the heat is carried away, the reactor will melt.

11.73   An emergency supply of coolant is used and the reactor is shut down.

11.74   The thick-walled structure that holds the reactor. In the event of a loss-of-coolant emergency, the containment vessel retains radioactive materials.

11.75   Strontium-90 is a bone seeker. Iodine-131 is taken up by the thyroid gland. Cesium-137 gets as widely distributed as the sodium ion.

11.76   It tends to take the place of radioactive iodine which would otherwise be taken up into thyroxine in a higher concentration.

11.77   Some radioactive isotopes in wastes have very long half lives.

11.78   The sun

11.79   Protons

11.80   They collide with air molecules and produce many other particles.

11.81   As a product in the uranium-238 disintegration series.

11.82   Alpha and gamma

11.83   Its decay products, which are not gases but are also radioactive, stay in the lungs.

11.84   4 picocuries/L

11.85   Neutron bombardment of molybdenum-98 in the device changes some of it to molybdenum-99, which then decays to technetium-99m.

11.86   Initially as the pertechnitate ion, TcO_4^-, but this can be changed into a number of other chemical forms to suit a particular radiological purpose.

11.87   By bombarding a metal surface with high-energy electrons, which are able to expel $1s$ orbital electrons from the metal atoms. As higher level orbital electrons drop into the $1s$ "holes," X rays are emitted.

11.88   It consists of a large array of X-ray generators that can all be focused onto an area of the body. Brief pulses are sent through the body, and the emerging radiation is processed into an image on a film.

11.89   Same masses, but the charge on the positron is 1+, not 1− as on the electron.

11.90   A nuclear proton breaks into a neutron and a positron:

$$_1^1 p \rightarrow {}_0^1 n + {}_1^0 e$$

11.91   In any collision with an electron it is annihilated, and electrons are abundant in matter.

11.92   Gamma radiation (annihilation radiation).

11.93   The radionuclide is incorporated into molecules of some substance, like glucose, that can be taken up by the target cell of the tissue.

11.94   No ionizing radiation or alien chemicals are used.

11.95   Bones do not obscure the MRI scan. Soft, water-abundant tissues are imaged easily.

11.96   The inorganic ions in bone, like calcium ion, do not have magnetic nuclei that give off signals that would confuse signals from water molecules or others with hydrogen nuclei.

11.97   An *acute effect* is one produced at the time of the exposure or soon thereafter. Cancer (particularly leukemia) and gene alteration are *latent effects*.

11.98   The material of the control rods captures neutrons and so reduces the rate at which neutrons can be captured by uranium-235 nuclei and cause fission.

11.99   Despite being neutral, the radical lacks an octet on oxygen and so is a chemically reactive species.

11.100   The atomic number is reduced by one unit.

$$\underset{23}{\overset{50}{}}V + \underset{-1}{\overset{0}{}}e \xrightarrow{\text{electron capture}} \underset{22}{\overset{50}{}}Ti$$

Chapter 12

Practice Exercises, Chapter 12

1.   (a) $CH_3-CH_2-CH_3$ (b) $CH_3-\underset{\underset{CH_3}{|}}{CH}-CH_3$

(c) $CH_3-\underset{\underset{CH_3}{|}}{\overset{\overset{CH_3}{|}}{C}}-\underset{\overset{CH_3}{|}}{CH}-\underset{\overset{CH_3}{|}}{CH}-CH_3$

2.   (a) $CH_3CH_2CH_3$ (b) CH_3CHCH_3
                                              |
                                             CH_3

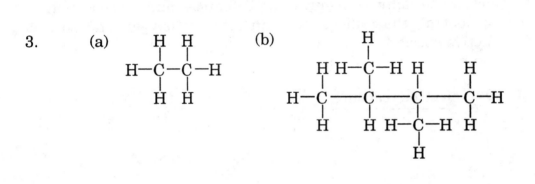

        (c) CH_3C——CH—$CHCH_3$
              with CH_3, CH_3, CH_3 above and CH_3 below

3.   (a)   (b)

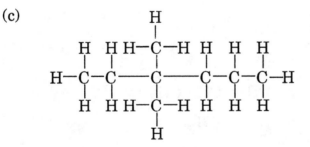

        (c)

4.   Structure (b) and (c) violate the tetravalences of carbon at one point.

5.   (a)

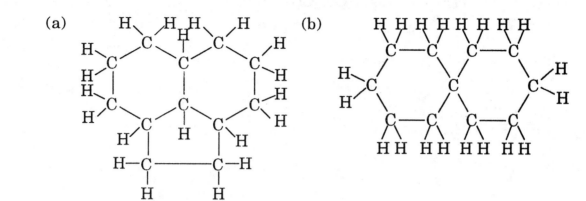

6.

CH₃CH₂-

7.   (a)   identical
     (b)   isomers
     (c)   identical
     (d)   isomers
     (e)   different in another way
8.   2-methyl-1-butanol (less polar)
9.   (a)   3-methylhexane
     (b)   4-ethyl-2,3-dimethylheptane
     (c)   5-ethyl-2,4,6-trimethyloctane

10.   (a) $BrCH_2CHCH_2CH_2CH_3$
                         |
                        NO_2

      (b)
      $$CH_3C-C-C-CHCH_2CH_2CH_3$$

(c)

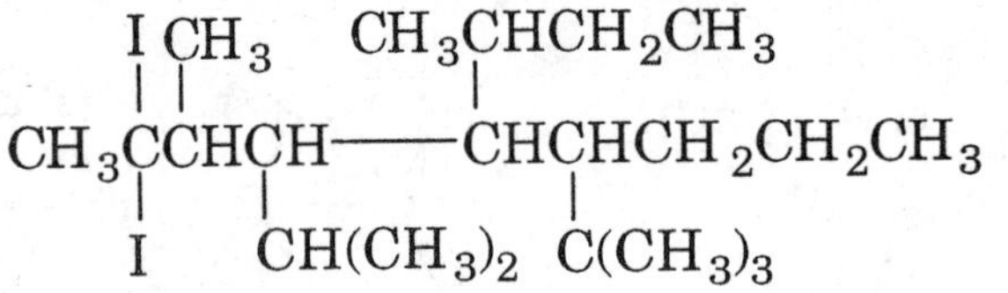

$$\underset{\substack{|\\I}}{\overset{\substack{I\ CH_3\\|\ \ |}}{CH_3CCHCH}}\!\!-\!\!\!\!\underset{\substack{|\\CH(CH_3)_2}}{\overset{\substack{CH_3CHCH_2CH_3\\|}}{CHCHCH_2CH_2CH_3}}$$

(d) $\underset{\substack{|\ \ \ |\\Cl\ \ CH_3}}{BrCHCHCH_3}$

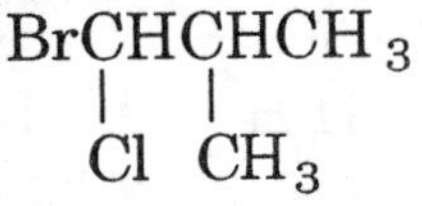

(e)

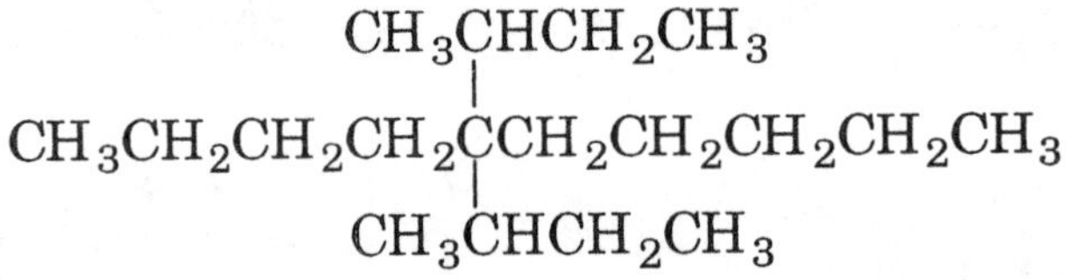

$$\underset{\substack{CH_3CHCH_2CH_3\\|}}{\overset{\substack{CH_3CHCH_2CH_3\\|}}{CH_3CH_2CH_2CH_2CCH_2CH_2CH_2CH_2CH_3}}$$

11.

$$\underset{\substack{CH_3CHCH_2CH_3\\\uparrow}}{\overset{\substack{CH_3CHCH_2CH_3\\\downarrow}}{CH_3CH_2CH_2CH_2CCH_2CH_2CH_2CH_2CH_3}}$$

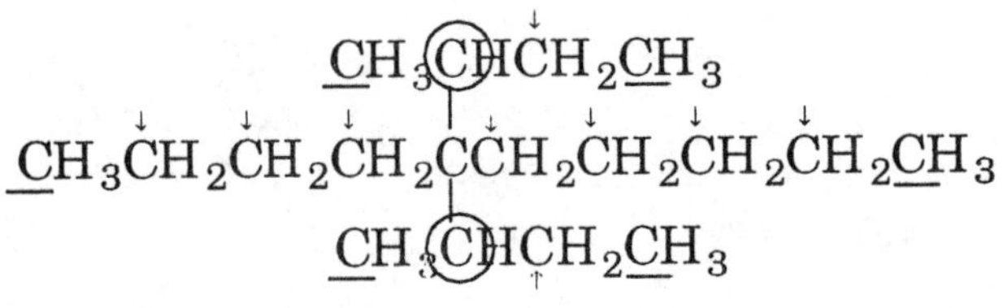

12. (a) ethyl chloride
    (b) butyl bromide
    (c) isobutyl chloride
    (d) *t*-butyl bromide

13. (a) butyl chloride, 1-chlorobutane
    sec-butyl chloride, 2-chlorobutane
    (b) isobutyl chloride, 2-methyl-1-chloropropane
    t-butyl chloride, 2-methyl-2-chloropropane

Review Exercises, Chapter 12

12.1 Carbon atoms are able to form strong bonds to each other while also forming strong bonds to other nonmetal atoms. Carbon atoms can join to each other in an infinite number of ways—by single, double, or triple bonds; by chains (straight and branched) and rings of three or more carbon atoms in size.

12.2   Chemists had been unable to synthesize organic compounds from minerals. The vital force theory held that such a synthesis was inherently impossible without the presence of a "vital force."

12.3   To prepare crystalline ammonium cyanate. He obtained an organic compound, urea, from an inorganic compound and this contradicted the vital force theory.

12.4   Covalent bonds

12.5   (a) 4   (b) 2   (c) 3   (d) 1   (e) 1

12.6   Compounds b, d, and e are considered to be inorganic.

12.7   Ionic and inorganic

12.8   Organic compounds generally consist of *molecules*, not ions, and their molecules generally do not react with water to give ions.

12.9   (a)   Molecular; low melting and flammable
       (b)   Ionic; water-soluble (and likely a carbonate or a bicarbonate)
       (c)   Molecular; no ionic compound is a gas (or a liquid) at room temperature.
       (d)   Ionic; high melting and nonflammable
       (e)   Molecular; most liquid organic compounds are insoluble in water but will burn.
       (f)   Molecular; no ionic compound is a liquid at room temperature.

12.10 Straight chain. It has no 3° carbons as do all branched-chain, open-chain compounds.

12.11 (a)   Compounds a, d, and e are possible

12.12 (a)

$$\begin{array}{c} H \\ | \\ H-C-O-H \\ | \\ H \end{array}$$

(b)

$$\begin{array}{c} Cl \\ | \\ H-C-H \\ | \\ Cl \end{array}$$

(c)

$$\begin{array}{c} H \quad H \\ | \quad | \\ H-N-N-H \end{array}$$

(d)

$$\begin{array}{c} H \quad H \\ | \quad | \\ H-C-C-H \\ | \quad | \\ H \quad H \end{array}$$

(e)

$$\begin{array}{c} O \\ \| \\ H-C-H \end{array}$$

(f)

$$\begin{array}{c} O \\ \| \\ H-C-O-H \end{array}$$

(g)

$$H-N-O-H$$
with H on top of N

(h)

$$H-C=C-H$$
with H, H on top of each C

(i)

$$H-\underset{\underset{Cl}{|}}{\overset{\overset{Cl}{|}}{C}}-Cl$$

(j) $H-C\equiv N$

(k)

$$H-\underset{\underset{H}{|}}{\overset{\overset{H}{|}}{C}}-C\equiv N \text{ or } H-\overset{\overset{H}{|}}{C}=C=N-H$$

(l)

$$H-\underset{\underset{H}{|}}{\overset{\overset{H}{|}}{C}}-\overset{\overset{H}{|}}{N}-H$$

12.13

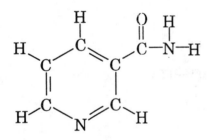

12.14

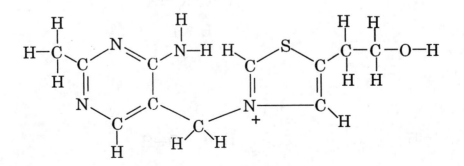

12.15   (a) $CH_3CH_2CH_2CH_2CH_3$

(b)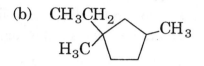

(c)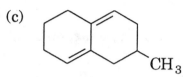

12.16   The geometry of a molecule is as important to the ability of an enzyme to work as other aspects of structure.

12.17 sp^3 hybrid orbitals

12.18   The rotation does not reduce the degree of the overlap of the hybrid atomic orbitals and so does not weaken the molecule.

12.19   Unsaturated compounds are (b), (c), and (d).

12.20 C_4H_{10} (c) and cyclohexanol (d) are saturated. (C_4H_{10} can only be butane or isobutane.)

12.21   Identical compounds are a, b, e, f, and m
Isomers are d, g, h, i, j, k, and l.
Structures that are unrelated occur at c and n.

12.22   (a)   alkane
(b)   alcohol
(c)   thioalcohol
(d)   alkyne
(e)   aldehyde
(f)   ester
(g)   ester
(h)   ketone
(i)   amine
(j)   ether

12.23   (a)   alcohol
(b)   alcohol
(c)   both thioalcohols
(d)   first, alkene; second, cycloalkane

(e)   ketone
(f)   alkane
(g)   both amines
(h)   first, carboxylic acid; second, alcohol + ketone
(i)   first, ester; second, carboxylic acid. (If you called the first an aldehyde, instead of an ester, don't worry about it now. Why it is an ester sill be explained later.)
(j)   first, ester + alcohol; second, alcohol + carboxylic acid
(k)   first, ether + ketone; second, ester
(l)   both alkanes
(m) ketone

12.24   B. It consists of larger molecules and so there would be larger London forces of attraction between molecules.

12.25   B. Its molecules have water-like OH groups.

12.26   Add a drop of the liquid to water. If it does not dissolve, it is pentane.

12.27   Add a drop of the liquid to water. If it dissolves, it is methyl alcohol.

12.28

$CH_3CH_2CH_2CH_2CH_2CH_3$ hexane

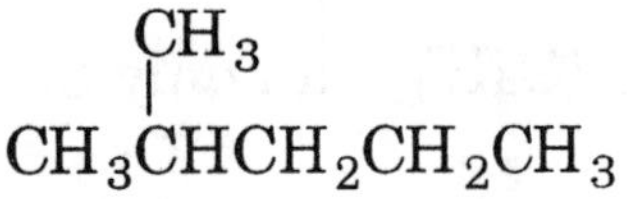

$$\underset{\displaystyle CH_3CHCH_2CH_2CH_3}{\overset{\displaystyle CH_3}{\vert}} \qquad \text{2-methylpentane}$$

$$\underset{\displaystyle CH_3CH_2CHCH_2CH_3}{\overset{\displaystyle CH_3}{\vert}} \qquad \text{3-methylpentane}$$

$$\underset{\displaystyle \underset{\displaystyle CH_3}{\overset{\displaystyle \vert}{CH_3CCH_2CH_3}}}{\overset{\displaystyle CH_3}{\vert}} \qquad \text{2,2-dimethylbutane}$$

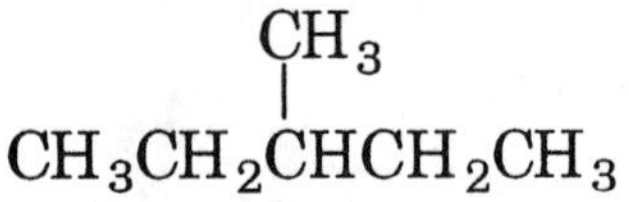

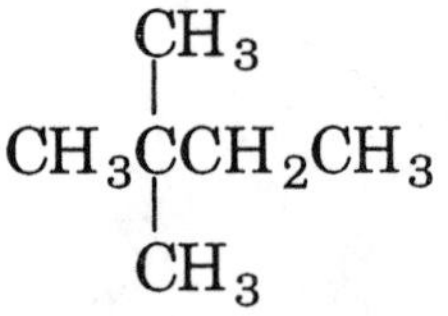

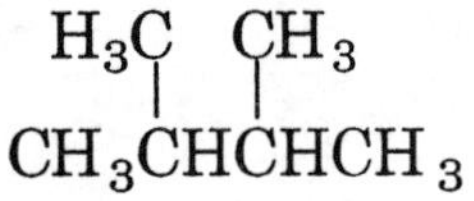

$$\underset{\displaystyle CH_3CHCHCH_3}{\overset{\displaystyle H_3C \quad CH_3}{\vert \qquad \vert}} \qquad \text{2,3-dimethylbutane}$$

12.29

$CH_3CH_2CH_2CH_2CH_2CH_3$ hexane

12.30

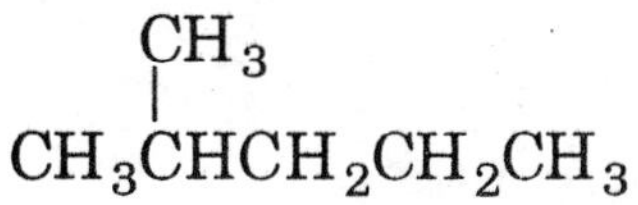

$$\begin{array}{c} CH_3 \\ | \\ CH_3CHCH_2CH_2CH_3 \end{array}$$ 2-methylpentane

12.31

$CH_3CH_2CH_2CH_2CH_2CH_2CH_3$ heptane

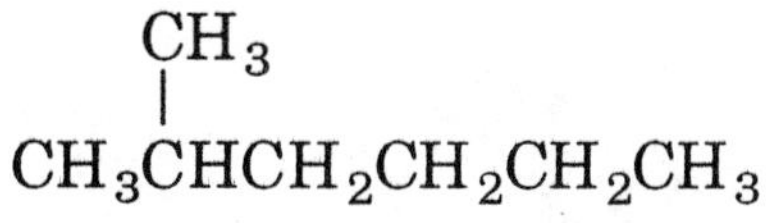

$$\begin{array}{c} CH_3 \\ | \\ CH_3CHCH_2CH_2CH_2CH_3 \end{array}$$ 2-methylhexane

$$\begin{array}{c} CH_3 \\ | \\ CH_3CH_2CHCH_2CH_2CH_3 \end{array}$$ 3-methylhexane

$$\begin{array}{c} CH_2CH_3 \\ | \\ CH_3CH_2CHCH_2CH_3 \end{array}$$ 3-ethylpentane

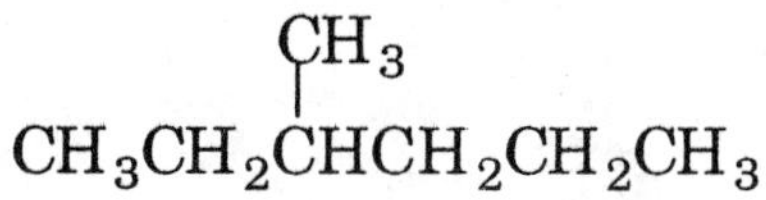

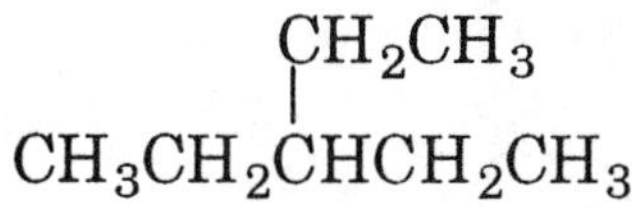

$$\begin{array}{c} CH_3 \\ | \\ CH_3CCH_2CH_2CH_3 \\ | \\ CH_3 \end{array}$$ 2,2-dimethylpentane

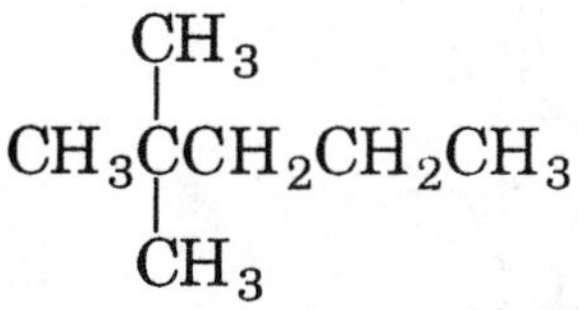

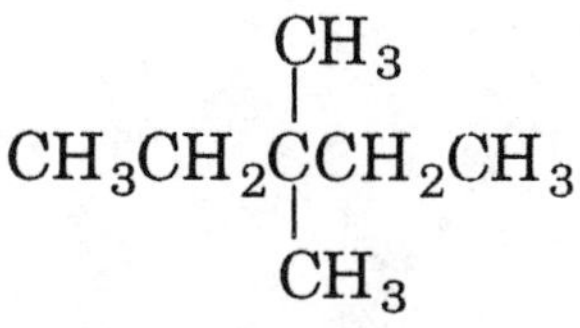

$$\begin{array}{c} CH_3 \\ | \\ CH_3CH_2CCH_2CH_3 \\ | \\ CH_3 \end{array}$$ 3,3-dimethylpentane

$$\underset{CH_3CHCHCH_2CH_3}{\overset{H_3C \quad CH_3}{| \quad |}}$$ 2,3-dimethylpentane

$$\underset{CH_3CHCH_2CHCH_3}{\overset{CH_3 \quad CH_3}{| \quad |}}$$ 2,4-dimethylpentane

$$\underset{\underset{CH_3}{|}}{\overset{H_3C \quad CH_3}{\underset{CH_3C-CHCH_3}{| \quad |}}}$$ 2,2,3-trimethylbutane

12.32   (a) $CH_3CH_2CH_2CH_2CH_2CH_2CH_3$

   (b) $$\underset{CH_3CHCH_2CH_2CH_2CH_3}{\overset{CH_3}{|}}$$

12.33   (a)   5-sec-butyl-5-ethyl-2,3,3,9-tetramethyldecane
   (b)   7-t-butyl-5-isobutyl-2-methyl-6-propyldecane

12.34   (a) $CH_3CH_2CH_2CH_2Br$ (b) $$\underset{CH_3CHCH_2CH_2CH_2I}{\overset{CH_3}{|}}$$

   (c) $$\underset{\underset{Cl}{|}}{CH_3CHCH_2CH_3}$$ (d) $(CH_3)_2CH-\hspace{-0.3em}\bigcirc$

12.35   (a) $CH_3CH_2CH_2Cl$

(b) 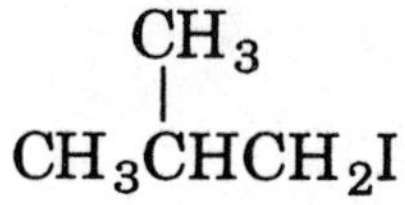
$$\underset{\displaystyle CH_3CHCH_2I}{\overset{\displaystyle CH_3}{|}}$$

(c) 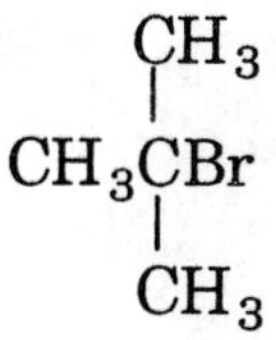
$$\underset{\displaystyle CH_3}{\overset{\displaystyle CH_3}{\underset{|}{\overset{|}{CH_3CBr}}}}$$

(d) CH_3CH_2Br

12.36   (a)

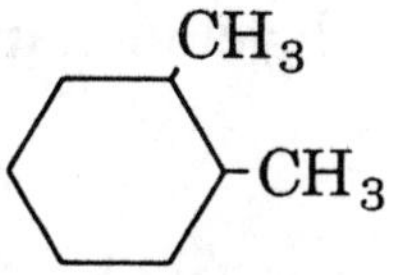

1,2-dimethylcyclohexane

(b) 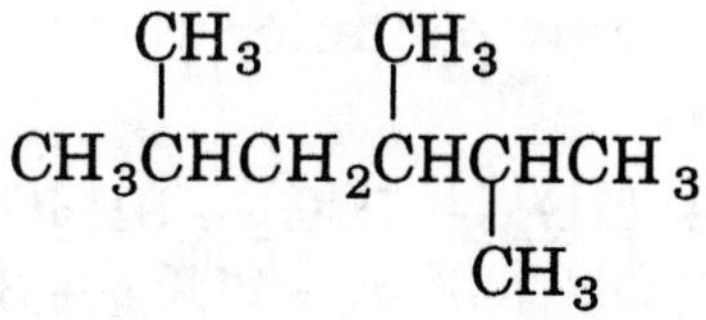
$$\underset{\displaystyle\underset{CH_3}{|}}{CH_3\overset{\overset{\displaystyle CH_3}{|}}{CH}CH_2\overset{\overset{\displaystyle CH_3}{|}}{CH}CHCH_3}$$

2,3,5-trimethylhexane

(c) $CH_3CH_2CH_2CH_2Cl$

1-chlorobutane

(d) 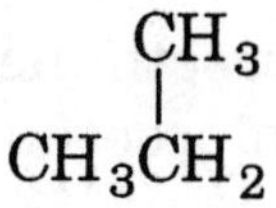
$$\underset{\displaystyle CH_3CH_2}{\overset{\displaystyle CH_3}{|}}$$

propane

12.37 (a)

$$CH_3$$
$$CH_3CHCH_2Cl$$

1-chloro-2-methylpropane

(b)

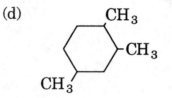

1,3-dichlorocyclopentane

(c)

$$CH_2CH_3$$
$$CH_3CHCH_2CH_3$$

3-methylpentane

(d)

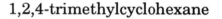

1,2,4-trimethylcyclohexane

12.38 $C_7H_{16} + 11O_2 \rightarrow 7CO_2 + 8H_2O$

12.39 $CH_3CH_2OH + 3O_2 \rightarrow 2CO_2 + 3H_2O$

12.40 CH_3Cl, methyl chloride
        CH_2Cl_2, methylene chloride
        $CHCl_3$, chloroform
        CCl_4, carbon tetrachloride

12.41 CH_3CHCl_2, 1,1-dichloroethane
        $ClCH_2CH_2Cl$, 1,2-dichloroethane

12.42

$CH_3CH_2CHCl_2$ $ClCH_2CH_2CH_2Cl$

1,1-dichloropropane   1,3-dichloropropane

$$Cl$$
$$CH_3CHCH_2Cl$$

1,2-dichloropropane

$$Cl$$
$$CH_3CCH_3$$
$$Cl$$

2,2-dichloropropane

12.43   Coal, oil, and natural gas
12.44   Petroleum is a mixture of liquid (crude oil) and gas.

12.45 The action of increasing pressure as sedimentary rock formations grew in size over the deposits of peat.

12.46 A portion of the liquid material that boils between two temperatures—the range of temperature defining the fraction.

12.47 Alkanes and cycloalkanes having up to 7 carbons per molecule.

12.48 They are able to "crack" large alkanes into those of the C_5 to C_8 range or they take smaller molecules and form them into larger alkanes.

12.49 The atom has one unpaired electron; the molecule has no unpaired electrons.

12.50 (a) Br_2 + UV or heat → 2Br· (bromine atoms, showing only the unpaired electron)

    (b) $Br· + CH_4 → HBr + CH_3·$
       $CH_3· + Br_2 → CH_3Br + Br·$

    (c) $Br· + Br· → Br_2$
       $Br· + CH_3· → CH_3Br$
       $CH_3· + CH_3· → CH_3CH_3$

12.51 (a) $H_2 + Cl_2 → 2HCl$

    (b) Cl_2 + UV or heat → 2Cl·
       $Cl· + H_2 → HCl + H·$
       $H· + Cl_2 → HCl + Cl·$

12.52 A mixture of products (CH_3Cl, CH_2Cl_2, $CHCl_3$, and CCl_4) forms but the *mole* ratios do not bear any constant relationship to the mole ratio of the reactants.

12.53

One, cyclohexyl chloride:

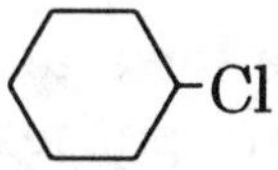

12.54 No reaction with any of the given reactants.

12.55 *t*-Butyl

12.56 11.1 g chlorocyclopentane

Chapter 13

Practice Exercises, Chapter 13

1. (a) 2-methylpropene (or 2-methyl-1-propene)
    (b) 4-isobutyl-3,6-dimethyl-3-heptene
    (c) 1-chloropropene (or 1-chloro-1-propene)
    (d) 3-bromopropene (or 3-bromo-1-propene)
    (e) 4-methyl-1-hexene
    (f) 4-methylcyclohexene

2.   (a)

$$CH_3CH{=}CHCHCH_3$$

with CH_3 on the CH carbon.

(b)

$$CH_2{=}CHCHCH_2CH_2CH_2CH_3$$

with $CH_2CH_2CH_3$ substituent.

(c)

$$CH_2{=}CHCCH_2Cl$$

with CH_3 above and CH_3 below the central carbon.

(d)

$$CH_3C{=}CCH_3$$

with H_3C and CH_3 substituents.

3.   Cis-trans isomerism is possible for a and b. For part (a), cis versus trans is based on the way the main chain passes through the double bond.

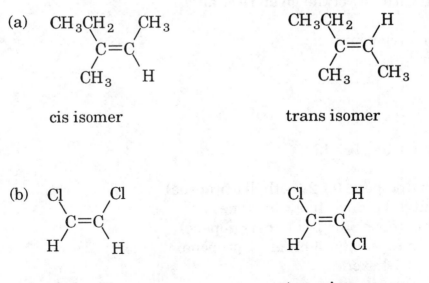

(a)

cis isomer   trans isomer

(b)

cis isomer   trans isomer

4. (a) $CH_3CH_2CH_3$
    (b) No reaction

    (c)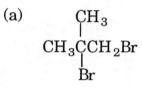

    (d) $CH_3(CH_2)_{16}CO_2H$

5. (a) CH_3
        CH_3CCH_2Br
              Br
        (with CH_3 above and Br below the central carbon)

    (b) No reaction (in the absence of heat or UV radiation)

    (c) $ClCH_2CHCH_2CH_3$
                  Cl

    (d) $CH_3CH_2CH_2CH_3$

6. (a) $CH_3CHCH_2CH_3$
              Cl

    (b) CH_3
        CH_3CCH_3
              Br
        (with CH_3 above and Br below the central carbon)

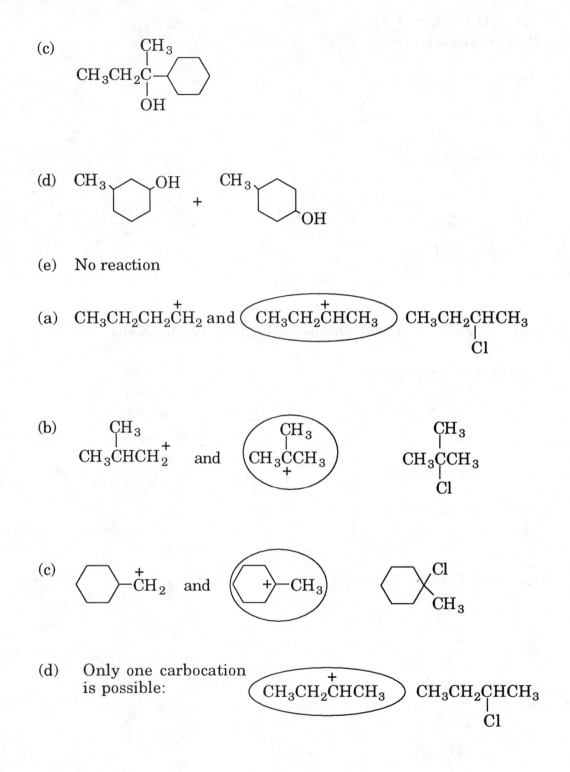

(c)

CH$_3$CH$_2$C(CH$_3$)(OH)—⬡

(d) CH$_3$—⬡—OH + CH$_3$—⬡—OH

(e) No reaction

7. (a) CH$_3$CH$_2$CH$_2$$\overset{+}{\text{C}}H_2$ and ⟨CH$_3$CH$_2$$\overset{+}{\text{C}}HCH_3$⟩ CH$_3CH_2$CHCH$_3$ | Cl

(b) CH$_3$$\overset{CH_3}{\underset{}{\text{C}}}HCH_2^+$ and ⟨CH$_3$$\overset{CH_3}{\underset{+}{\text{C}}}CH_3$⟩ CH$_3$$\overset{CH_3}{\underset{Cl}{\text{C}}}CH_3$

(c) ⬡—$\overset{+}{\text{C}}$H$_2$ and ⟨⬡—$^+$CH$_3$⟩ ⬡(Cl)(CH$_3$)

(d) Only one carbocation is possible: ⟨CH$_3$CH$_2$$\overset{+}{\text{C}}HCH_3$⟩ CH$_3CH_2$CHCH$_3$ | Cl

(e) $CH_3\overset{+}{C}HCH_2CH_2CH_3$ $CH_3CHCH_2CH_2CH_3$
                                                       |
                                                       Cl

and

$CH_3CH_2\overset{+}{C}HCH_2CH_3$ $CH_3CH_2CHCH_2CH_3$
                                                   |
                                                   Cl

(Both carbocations are 2°, so both are equally possible and both form. Thus two isomeric chloropentanes form.)

(f) $CH_3CHCH_2CH_2CH_3$ and $CH_3CH_2CHCH_2CH_3$
           | |
           OH OH

Two 2° carbocations are can form, so two isomeric pentanols form. Only one carbocation can form from propene, namely the more stable isopropyl carbocation

Review Exercises, Chapter 13

13.1 (a) A, B, E
      (b) C
      (c) E (Structure C has "-pent-" in "cyclopentane.")
      (d) All are insoluble in water.
      (e) B, and C. No, C is not an alkene.
      (f) A, D, and E. Only D is an alkyne.
      (g) Not well; the presence of rings or multiple bonds can reduce the ratio of carbon atoms to hydrogen atoms of a hydrocarbon.

13.2 The alkene group is widely present in edible fats and oils and in related compounds that make up every animal cell membrane.

13.3 (a) CH_3 (b) $CH_3CH{=}CH_2$
                 |
           $CH_3C{=}CH_2$

(c)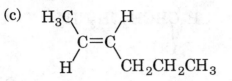

(d)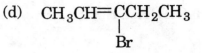

(e)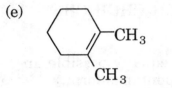

(f)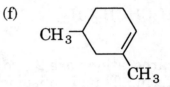

13.4   (a)   1-octene
        (b)   1-bromo-3-methyl-1-butene
        (c)   4-methyl-2-propyl-1-hexene
        (d)   4,4-dimethyl-2-hexene

13.5

CH_2=$CHCH_2CH_2CH_3$ 1-pentene

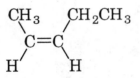   *cis*- 2-pentene

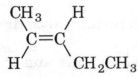   *trans*- 2-pentene

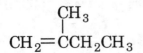   2-methyl-1-butene

$$CH_2{=}CHCHCH_3$$ 3-methyl-1-butene

with CH₃ substituent on the third carbon

$$CH_3\overset{\displaystyle CH_3}{\underset{|}{C}}{=}CHCH_3$$ 2-methyl-2-butene

13.6

1-methylcyclopentene

3-methylcyclopentene

4-methylcyclopentene

13.7

$$HC{\equiv}CCH_2CH_3$$ 1-butyne

$$CH_3C{\equiv}CCH_3$$ 2-butyne

13.8

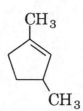

1,2-dimethyl-
cyclopentene

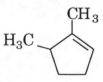

1,3-dimethyl-
cyclopentene

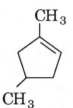

1,4-dimethyl-
cyclopentene

H₃C—

2,3-dimethyl-
cyclopentene

H₃C

cis- 3,4-dimethyl-
cyclopentene

trans- 3,4-dimethyl-
cyclopentene

cis- 3,5-dimethyl-
cyclopentene

trans- 3,5-dimethyl-
cyclopentene

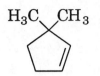

3,3-dimethyl-
cyclopentene

4,4-dimethyl-
cyclopentene

13.9

$CH_2{=}C{=}CHCH_2CH_3$ 1,2-pentadiene

$CH_2{=}CHCH{=}CHCH_3$ 1,3-pentadiene

$CH_2{=}CHCH_2CH{=}CH_2$ 1,4-pentadiene

$CH_3CH{=}C{=}CHCH_3$ 2,3-pentadiene

$$\overset{\overset{\textstyle CH_3}{|}}{CH_2{=}CCH{=}CH_2}$$ 2-methyl-1,3-butadiene

13.10   One electron pair is in a sigma bond; the other pair is in a pi bond.

13.11   The sigma bond results from the overlap of two neighboring sp^2 hybrid orbitals. The pi bond forms by the overlap of two neighboring p orbitals.

13.12   Free rotation would require that the pi bond break, and this costs too much energy. This matters because it gives rise to cis-trans isomers.

13.13   (a)   identical
(b)   identical
(c)   isomers
(d)   identical
(e)   identical

13.14   (a)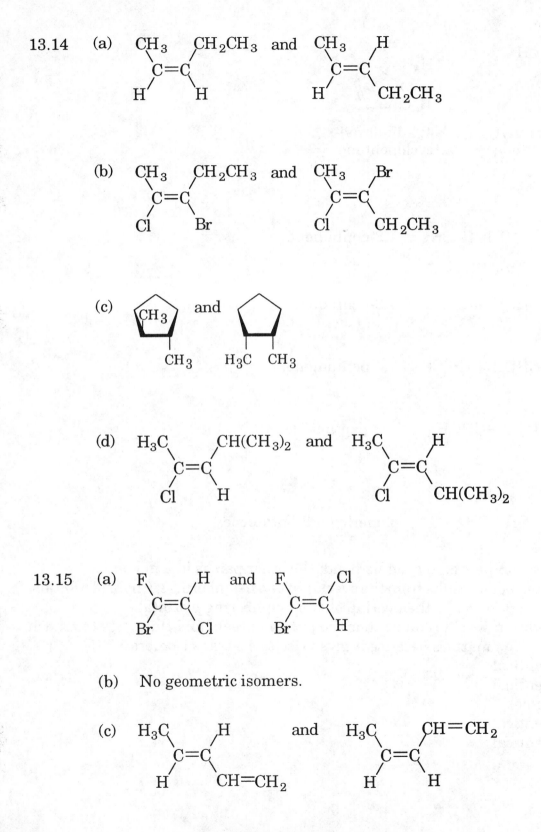

CH₃   CH₂CH₃   and   CH₃   H
   C=C   C=C
H   H   H   CH₂CH₃

(b)   CH₃   CH₂CH₃   and   CH₃   Br
         C=C   C=C
      Cl   Br   Cl   CH₂CH₃

(c)   (CH₃) ⬠   and   ⬠
         CH₃   H₃C   CH₃

(d)   H₃C   CH(CH₃)₂   and   H₃C   H
         C=C   C=C
      Cl   H   Cl   CH(CH₃)₂

13.15   (a)   F   H   and   F   Cl
              C=C   C=C
           Br   Cl   Br   H

(b)   No geometric isomers.

(c)   H₃C   H   and   H₃C   CH=CH₂
         C=C   C=C
      H   CH=CH₂   H   H

13.16 (a)

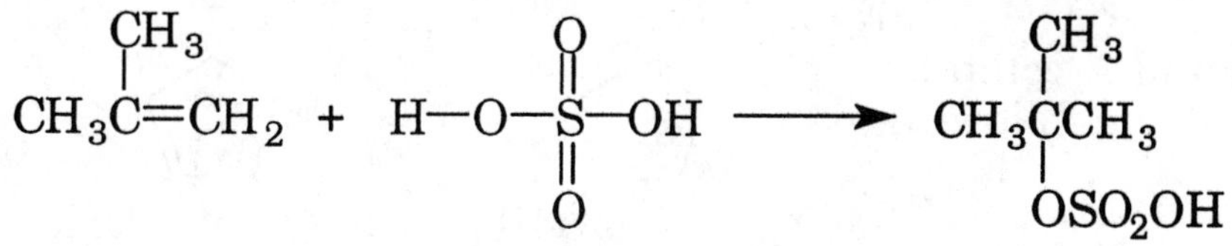

$$CH_3\overset{\overset{\displaystyle CH_3}{|}}{C}=CH_2 \ + \ H\!-\!O\!-\!\overset{\overset{\displaystyle O}{\|}}{\underset{\underset{\displaystyle O}{\|}}{S}}\!-\!OH \ \longrightarrow \ CH_3\overset{\overset{\displaystyle CH_3}{|}}{\underset{\underset{\displaystyle OSO_2OH}{|}}{C}}CH_3$$

(b)

$$CH_3\overset{\overset{\displaystyle CH_3}{|}}{C}=CH_2 \ + \ H_2 \ \xrightarrow{\text{catalyst}} \ CH_3\overset{\overset{\displaystyle CH_3}{|}}{C}HCH_3$$

(c)

$$CH_3\overset{\overset{\displaystyle CH_3}{|}}{C}=CH_2 \ + \ H_2O \ \xrightarrow{H^+} \ CH_3\overset{\overset{\displaystyle CH_3}{|}}{\underset{\underset{\displaystyle OH}{|}}{C}}CH_3$$

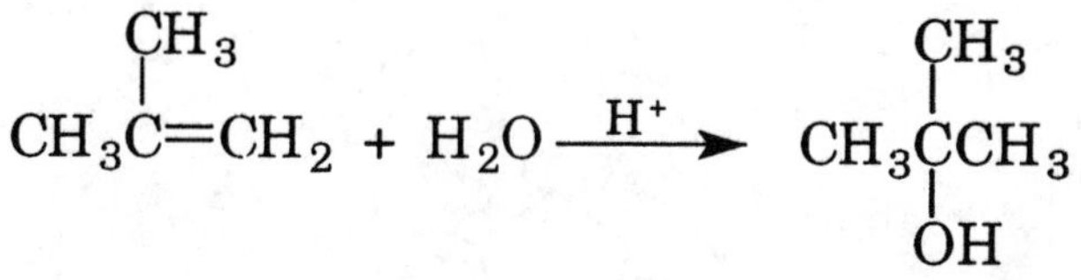

(d)

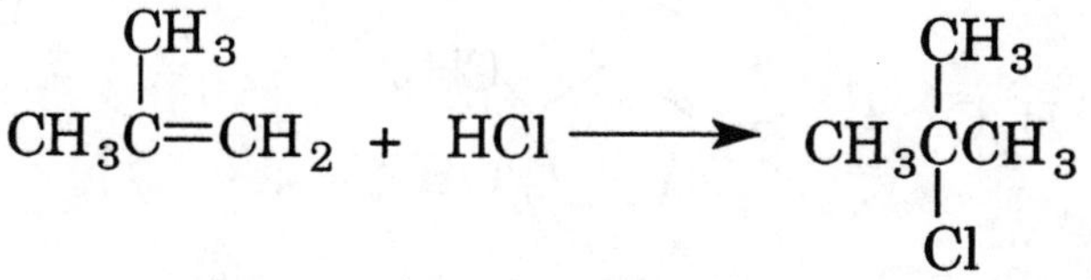

$$CH_3\overset{\overset{\displaystyle CH_3}{|}}{C}=CH_2 \ + \ HCl \ \longrightarrow \ CH_3\overset{\overset{\displaystyle CH_3}{|}}{\underset{\underset{\displaystyle Cl}{|}}{C}}CH_3$$

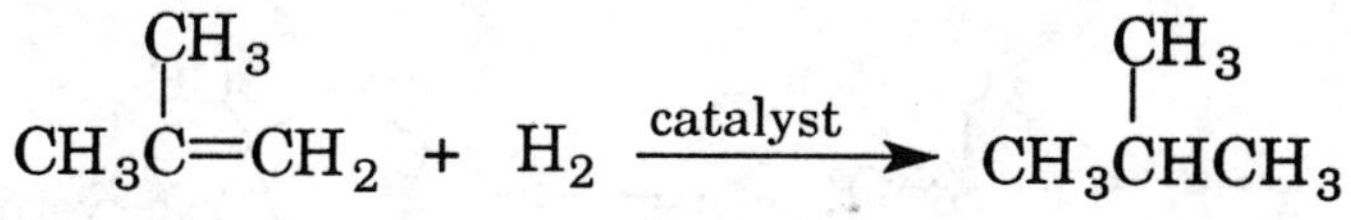

(e)

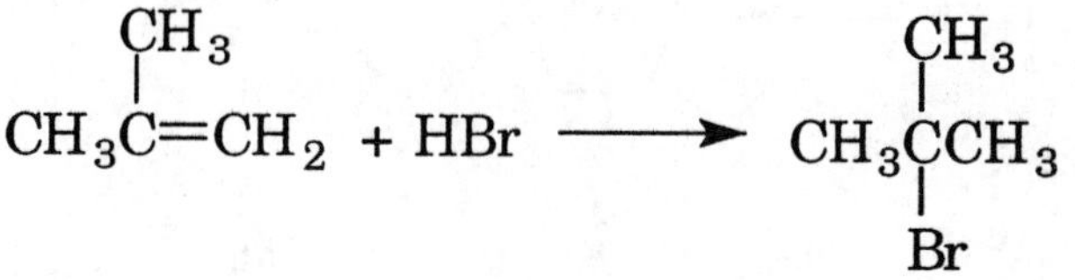

$$CH_3\overset{\overset{\displaystyle CH_3}{|}}{C}=CH_2 \ + \ HBr \ \longrightarrow \ CH_3\overset{\overset{\displaystyle CH_3}{|}}{\underset{\underset{\displaystyle Br}{|}}{C}}CH_3$$

(f)

$$CH_3\overset{\overset{\displaystyle CH_3}{|}}{C}=CH_2 \ + \ Br_2 \ \longrightarrow \ CH_3\overset{\overset{\displaystyle CH_3}{|}}{\underset{\underset{\displaystyle Br}{|}}{C}}CH_2Br$$

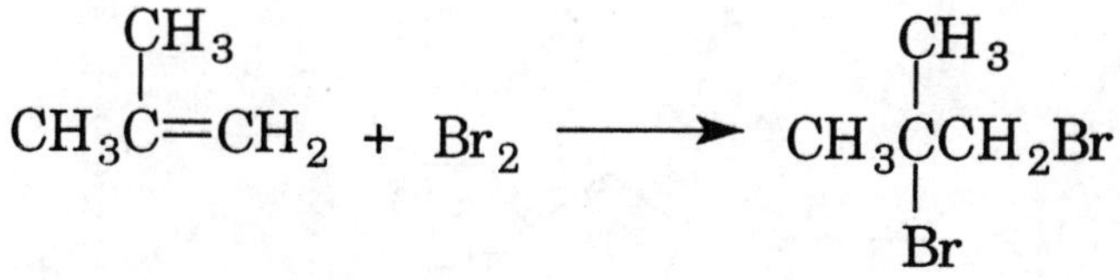

13.17

Compound A could be either of the following:

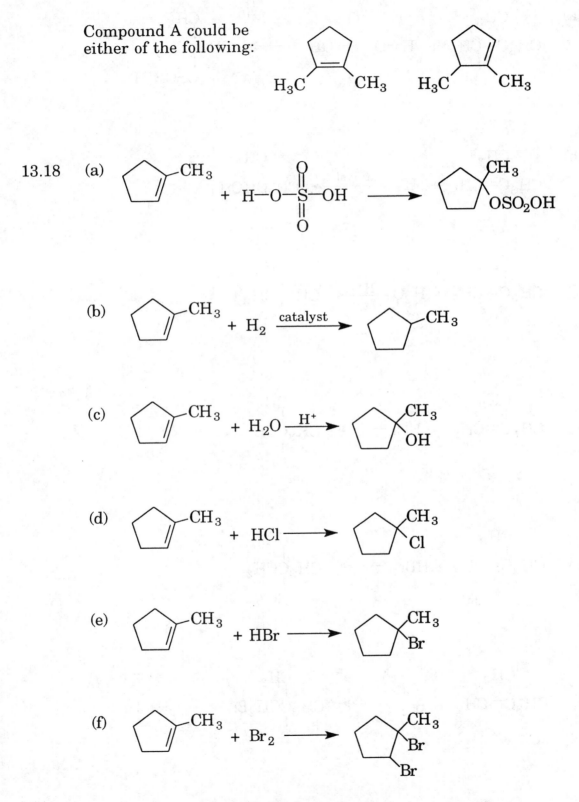

13.18 (a)

(b)

(c)

(d)

(e)

(f)

13.19 (a)

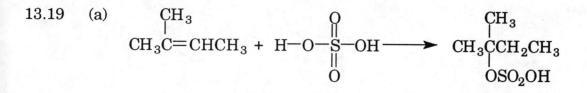

$$\underset{\overset{\displaystyle CH_3}{\textstyle |}}{CH_3C}=CHCH_3 \;+\; H-O-\overset{\overset{\displaystyle O}{\|}}{\underset{\underset{\displaystyle O}{\|}}{S}}-OH \longrightarrow \underset{\underset{\displaystyle OSO_2OH}{|}}{\overset{\overset{\displaystyle CH_3}{|}}{CH_3C}}CH_2CH_3$$

(b)

$$\underset{\overset{\displaystyle CH_3}{\textstyle |}}{CH_3C}=CHCH_3 \;+\; H_2 \;\xrightarrow{\text{catalyst}}\; \overset{\overset{\displaystyle CH_3}{|}}{CH_3CH}CH_2CH_3$$

(c)

$$\underset{\overset{\displaystyle CH_3}{\textstyle |}}{CH_3C}=CHCH_3 \;+\; H_2O \;\xrightarrow{H^+}\; \underset{\underset{\displaystyle OH}{|}}{\overset{\overset{\displaystyle CH_3}{|}}{CH_3C}}CH_2CH_3$$

(d)

$$\underset{\overset{\displaystyle CH_3}{\textstyle |}}{CH_3C}=CHCH_3 \;+\; HCl \longrightarrow \underset{\underset{\displaystyle Cl}{|}}{\overset{\overset{\displaystyle CH_3}{|}}{CH_3C}}CH_2CH_3$$

(e)

$$\underset{\overset{\displaystyle CH_3}{\textstyle |}}{CH_3C}=CHCH_3 \;+\; HBr \longrightarrow \underset{\underset{\displaystyle Br}{|}}{\overset{\overset{\displaystyle CH_3}{|}}{CH_3C}}CH_2CH_3$$

(f)

$$\underset{\overset{\displaystyle CH_3}{\textstyle |}}{CH_3C}=CHCH_3 \;+\; Br_2 \longrightarrow \underset{\underset{\displaystyle Br}{|}}{\overset{\overset{\displaystyle CH_3}{|}}{CH_3C}}-\underset{\underset{\displaystyle Br}{|}}{CH}CH_3$$

13.20   (a)

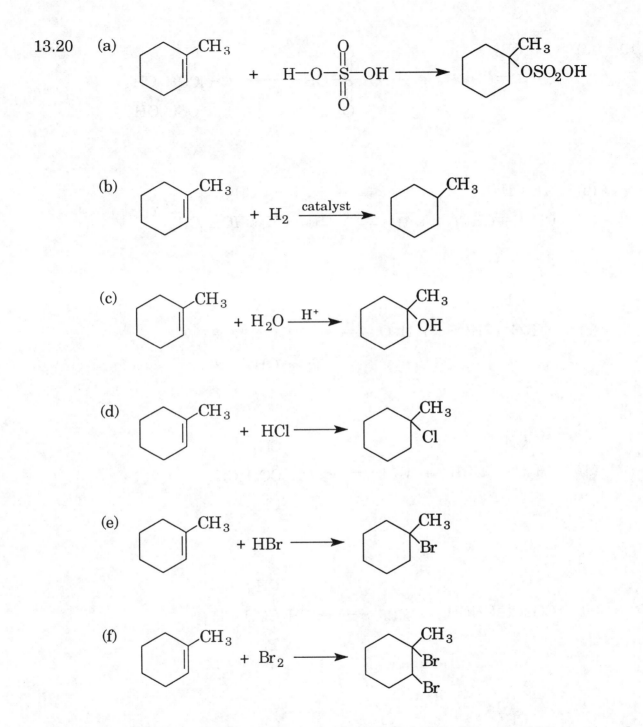

(b)

(c)

(d)

(e)

(f)

13.21 $CH_2{=}CH_2$ + H_2SO_4 → $CH_3CH_2OSO_3H$ (ethyl hydrogen sulfate; very polar)

13.22   Cycloalkanes with the formula C_5H_{10} have no alkene groups and so cannot react with the given reactants. For example,

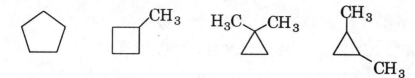

13.23   57.5 g KMnO$_4$

13.24   11.1 g K$_2$C$_6$H$_8$O$_4$

13.25   Of the two possible carbocation intermediates, **A** and **B**, the more stable, 2°
carbocation forms (**B**). When Cl⁻ combines with **B**, the product is 2-chlorobutane.

$$\overset{+}{CH_3CH_2CH_2CH_2} \qquad\qquad CH_3CH_2\overset{+}{C}HCH_3$$

A   **B**

13.26   The two possible carbocation intermediates, **A** and **B**, are both 2° carbocations,
so they are equally stable. Some of each forms from 4-methylcyclohexene.
When Cl⁻ ions combine, some react with **A** and some with **B** to give two isomeric
products.

A   **B**

13.27   (a) etc.—CH$_2$C—CH$_2$C—CH$_2$C—CH$_2$C—etc.
with CH$_3$ groups above and below each C

(b)

$$+(CH_2\overset{\displaystyle CH_3}{\underset{\displaystyle CH_3}{C}})_n$$

13.28   (a)

$$\underset{\underset{\text{etc.}-CH_2CH-CH_2CH-CH_2CH-CH_2CH-\text{etc.}}{|\qquad\quad|\qquad\quad|\qquad\quad|}}{\overset{O}{\overset{\|}{OCCH_3}}\quad \overset{O}{\overset{\|}{OCCH_3}}\quad \overset{O}{\overset{\|}{OCCH_3}}\quad \overset{O}{\overset{\|}{OCCH_3}}}$$

    (b)

$$\underset{-(CH_2CH)_{\overline{n}}}{\overset{\underset{|}{\overset{O}{\overset{\|}{OCCH_3}}}}{}}$$

13.29   Some traces of alkenes are also present.

13.30   The traces of alkenes in the fuel are slowly polymerizing to form sticky, low-formula-mass polymers.

13.31   Dipentene has no benzene ring.

13.32   Sulfanilamide has a benzene ring.

13.33   The products of the reactions are the following where C_6H_5 is the phenyl group.
    (a) $C_6H_5SO_2OH$ (or $C_6H_5SO_3H$, benzenesulfonic acid) + H_2O
    (b) $C_6H_5NO_2$ + H_2O
    (c)   No reaction
    (d)   No reaction
    (e)   No reaction (No iron or iron salt catalyst is specified.)
    (f)   No reaction
    (g) C_6H_5Br + HBr

13.34   Any monoalkylbenzene, like toluene, $C_6H_5CH_3$, or ethylbenzene, $C_6H_5CH_2CH_3$

13.35

13.36   Your discussion should call attention to the following aspects
    (a)   Between each carbon of the ring there is a sigma bond made from the overlap of sp^2 hybrid orbitals on adjacent carbons.

(b)   Each C–H bond are made by the overlap of a carbon sp^2 hybrid orbital with an s orbital of H.

(c)   The unhybridized p orbitals of each carbon have axes that are coparallel with each other and perpendicular to the plane of the ring. These p orbitals overlap side to side to form the pi electron network of the benzene ring. Your figure should have the principal features of Figure 13.9.

13.37   With more space in which to spread out, the pi electrons are in a more stable arrangement.

13.38   An addition reaction would break up circular the pi electron network, which costs more energy than it takes to bring about a substitution reaction.

13.39   (a) $C_6H_5CH_3$ (b) $C_6H_5NH_2$ (c) C_6H_5OH (d) $C_6H_5CO_2H$
(e) C_6H_5CHO (f) $C_6H_5NO_2$

13.40   (a)   (b)   (c)   (d)

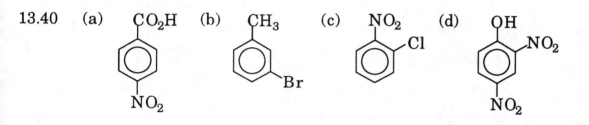

13.41   The have alkene groups that are attacked by the oxygen in air, particularly when heated.

13.42   Vegetable oils have more alkene groups per molecule.

13.43   No

13.44   The energy of the photon causes the disengagement of the side-to-side overlap of the p orbitals used to make the pi bond. In this excited state, free rotation can occur with subsequent re-overlapping of the p orbitals.

13.45   Rods enable the seeing of shades of gray, which characterizes very dim light. The owl cannot see in total blackness.

13.46   Oxygen and nitrogen react: $N_2(g) + O_2(g) \rightarrow 2NO(g)$

13.47   The NO in fresh exhaust reacts with the (cooler) O_2 in air.
$$2NO(g) + O_2(g) \rightarrow 2NO_2(g)$$

13.48   Solar radiation provides the energy to decompose some NO_2 into NO and oxygen atoms, O.

$$NO_2(g) \xrightarrow{\text{UV radiation}} NO(g) + O(g)$$

At the surface of a neutral particle, M, oxygen atoms combine with O_2 to give ozone.
$$O(g) + O_2(g) + M \rightarrow O_3(g) + M$$

13.49   It attacks lung tissue.

13.50   NO can destroy ozone ($O_3 + NO \rightarrow NO_2 + O_2$), so anything that destroys NO leads to increasing levels of O_3. Peroxy radicals (ROO) that form from unburned hydrocarbons in smog can destroy NO:

$$ROO + NO \rightarrow RO + NO_2$$

13.51   (a) $CH_3CH = CHCH_3$

      (b) 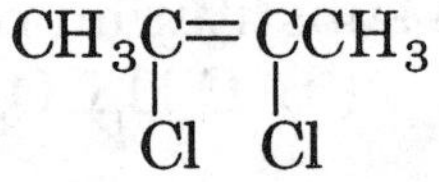
$$CH_3C = CCH_3$$
$$\quad\ \ | \quad\ |$$
$$\quad\ \ Cl \quad Cl$$

      (c) 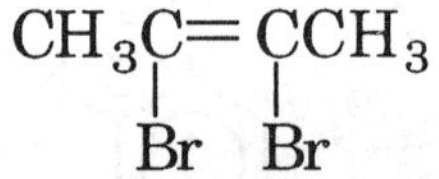
$$CH_3C = CCH_3$$
$$\quad\ \ | \quad\ \ |$$
$$\quad\ Br \quad Br$$

13.52   (a) $CH_3CH_2CH_2CH_3$

      (b) 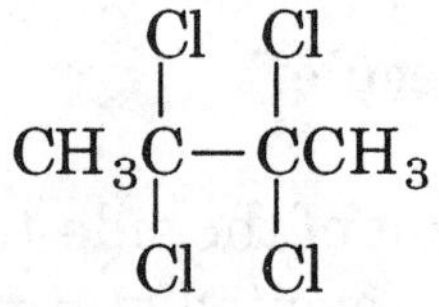
$$\quad\quad\ \ Cl \quad Cl$$
$$\quad\quad\ \ | \quad\ \ |$$
$$CH_3C - CCH_3$$
$$\quad\quad\ \ | \quad\ \ |$$
$$\quad\quad\ \ Cl \quad Cl$$

      (c) 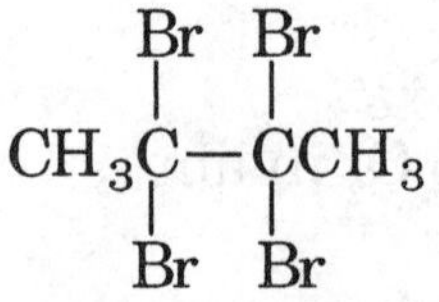
$$\quad\quad\ \ Br \quad Br$$
$$\quad\quad\ \ | \quad\ \ |$$
$$CH_3C - CCH_3$$
$$\quad\quad\ \ | \quad\ \ |$$
$$\quad\quad\ \ Br \quad Br$$

13.53   The addition would disrupt the pi electron network of the benzene ring, which costs too much energy.

13.54   Because the catalyst aids in generating the reactive species, Cl^+, from Cl_2, not from the catalyst itself.

13.55 $FeBr_3$ is able to react with Br_2 as follows to give $Br^+FeBr_4^-$.

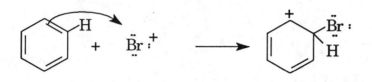

Br⁺ then attacks the ring, taking a pair of electrons from the ring's pi electron network and forming a C–Br bond.

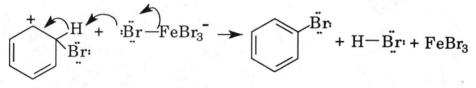

The pair of electrons is restored to the ring as H⁺ transfers away, HBr forms, and the catalyst is recovered.

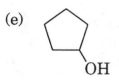

Bromobenzene

13.56   (a) $CH_3CH_2CH_2CHCH_2CH_3$
$\quad\quad\quad\quad\quad\quad\quad\quad |$
$\quad\quad\quad\quad\quad\quad\quad\quad OH$

(b) CH_3
$\quad\quad |$
$CH_3CHCH_2CH_3$

(c) C_6H_5Br + HBr

(d)   No reaction

(e)

(f) $CH_3CH_2CH_2CH_2CH_3$

(g) No reaction

(h) $C_6H_5CH_2CHC_6H_5$
$\qquad\qquad\quad |$
$\qquad\qquad\quad OH$

(i) No reaction

(j) $C_5H_{12} + 8O_2 \rightarrow 5CO_2 + 6H_2O$

(k) No reaction

13.57 (a) $CH_3CH_2CH_2CH_2CH_2CH_3$

(b)

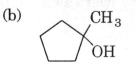

(c) $H_3C\quad CH_3$
$\qquad |\qquad |$
CH_3CHCCH_3
$\qquad\qquad |$
$\qquad\qquad Br$

(d) No reaction

(e)

CH_2Cl

Cl

(f) $2C_8H_{10} + 21O_2 \rightarrow 16CO_2 + 10H_2O$

(g) $C_6H_5Cl + HCl$

(h) No reaction

(i) $\qquad\qquad CH_3$
$\qquad\qquad\quad |$
$CH_3CH_2CCH_2CH_3$
$\qquad\qquad\quad |$
$\qquad\qquad\quad Cl$

(j)   No reaction

(j) $CH_3CHCHCH_2CHCH_2Cl$
          | | |
          Cl Cl   Cl

(k) $C_6H_5CHCHCH_3$
             | |
             Br Br

Chapter 14

Practice Exercises, Chapter 14

1.   (a)   Monohydric, secondary
      (b)   Monohydric, secondary
      (c)   Dihydric, unstable (two OH groups on the same carbon)
      (d)   Dihydric, both are secondary
      (e)   Monohydric, primary
      (f)   Monohydric, primary
      (g)   Monohydric, tertiary
      (h)   Monohydric, secondary
      (i)   Trihydric, unstable (three OH groups on the same carbon)
2.   (a)   Alcohol   (b) Phenol
      (c)   Carboxylic acid   (d) Alcohol (but unstable; an enol)
      (e)   Alcohol   (f) Alcohol
3.   (a)   4-Methyl-1-pentanol
      (b)   2-Methyl-2-propanol
      (c)   2-Ethyl-2-methyl-1-pentanol
      (d)   2-Methyl-1,3-propanediol
4.   In 1,2-propanediol. Its boiling point is 189 °C, much higher than that of 1-butanol (b.p. 117 °C). 1,2-Propanediol is more soluble in water.
5.   (a) $CH_3CH=CH_2$ (b) $CH_3CH=CH_2$

      (b) CH_3 (c)
                        |
          $CH_2=CCH_3$

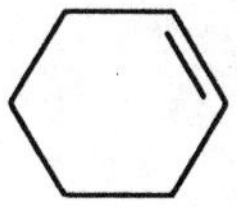

6.

(a) $\underset{\underset{CH_3}{|}}{CH_3CHCH{=}O}$ then $\underset{\underset{CH_3}{|}}{CH_3CHCO_2H}$

(b) $C_6H_5CH{=}O$ then $C_6H_5CO_2H$

7.

(a) $\underset{CH_3\overset{\overset{O}{\|}}{C}CH_2CH_3}{}$ (b) $\underset{C_6H_5\overset{\overset{O}{\|}}{C}CH_3}{}$ (c)

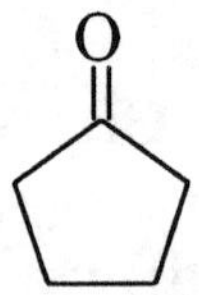

8.

(a) $\underset{CH_3\overset{\overset{O}{\|}}{C}CH_2CHO}{}$ and $\underset{CH_3\overset{\overset{O}{\|}}{C}CH_2CO_2H}{}$

(b)   No reaction

(c) $\underset{\underset{CH_3}{|}}{\overset{\overset{CH_3}{|}}{CH_3CCH{=}O}}$ and $\underset{\underset{CH_3}{|}}{\overset{\overset{CH_3}{|}}{CH_3CCO_2H}}$

(d) $\underset{\underset{CH_3}{|}}{CH_3CH\overset{\overset{O}{\|}}{C}CH_3}$

9.   (a) CH_3OCH_3 (b) $CH_3CH_2CH_2OCH_2CH_2CH_3$

(c)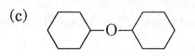

10.

(a) $2 CH_3SH$

(b)
$$\underset{\underset{CH_3}{|}}{CH_3CH}SS\underset{\underset{CH_3}{|}}{CHCH_3}$$

(c)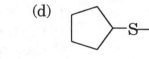

(d)

Review Exercises, Chapter 14

14.1   1, 1°alcohol; 2, ketone; 3, 2°alcohol; 4, ketone; 5, alkene
14.2   1, ketone; 2, carboxylic acid; 3, 2°alcohol; 4, alkene; 5, 2°alcohol
14.3

(a)
$$\underset{\underset{CH_3}{|}}{CH_3CH}CH_2OH$$

(b)
$$\underset{\underset{OH}{|}}{CH_3CH}CH_3$$

(c) $CH_3CH_2CH_2OH$

(d) $\underset{\underset{OH}{|}}{HOCH_2CH}CH_2OH$

14.4

(a) CH_3OH

(b)
$$CH_3\underset{\underset{CH_3}{|}}{\overset{\overset{CH_3}{|}}{C}}OH$$

(c) CH_3CH_2OH

(d) $CH_3CH_2CH_2CH_2OH$

14.5   (a)   Propyl alcohol   (b)   Butyl alcohol
        (c)   *t*-Butyl alcohol   (d)   Isobutyl alcohol
14.6 $HOCH_2CH_2OH$, 1,2-ethanediol. (Remember, no carbon may hold two
        or more OH groups.)
14.7   1,2,3-Propanetriol

$$HOCH_2\underset{\underset{\displaystyle OH}{|}}{C}HCH_2OH$$

14.8   (a)   2-Methyl-1-propanol   (b) 2-Propanol
        (c)   1-Propanol   (d) 1,2,3-Propanetriol
14.9   (a)   Methanol   (b) 2-Methyl-2-propanol
        (c)   Ethanol   (d) 1-Butanol
14.10   (a)   1-Propanol   (b) 1-Butanol
        (c)   2-Methyl-2-propanol   (d) 2-Methyl-1-propanol
14.11   2-Ethyl-1-pentanol
14.12   Hydrogen bonds of the following type form.

14.13

B < D < A < C

14.14

(a) CH_3 (b) $CH_3CH{=}CHCH_3 + CH_2{=}CHCH_2CH_3$
     $CH_3\underset{}{C}{=}CH_2$ mostly   some

(c) CH_3 CH_2 (d) $C_6H_5CH{=}C(CH_3)_2$

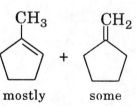

         mostly   some

(e)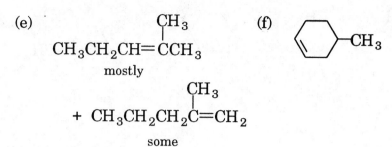

mostly

some

(f)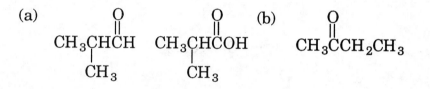

14.15

(a)

O
‖
CH_3CHCH CH_3CHCOH
| |
CH_3 CH_3

(b)

O
‖
$CH_3CCH_2CH_3$

(c)   No reaction

(d)

O
‖
$C_6H_5CCH(CH_3)_2$

(e)   No reaction

(f)

O=⬡-CH_3

14.16

(a) $HOCH_2CH_2CH_3$ or

CH_3CHCH_3
|
OH

(b)   ⬠-OH

(c)   CH₂OH or   CH₃   (d)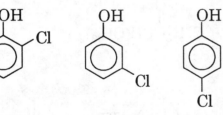

CH₃CHCH₃   CH₃CCH₃

OH

14.17

(a)   HOCH₂CH₂CH₂CH₃   (b)   OH

CH₃CH₂CH₂CHCH(CH₃)₂

(c)   HOCH₂⟨⟩   (d)   C₆H₅CH₂OH

14.18

OH   OH   OH

Cl

Cl

Cl

o-chloro-   m-chloro-   p-chloro-
phenol   phenol   phenol

14.19   **A** reacts with aqueous NaOH; **B** does not. **B** can be dehydrated to an alkene; **A** cannot. (Both react with oxidizing agents, but in different ways.)

14.20   Compound **A**. It is a phenol that changes to a water-soluble salt:.

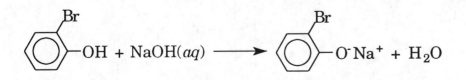

14.21

(a) $CH_3CH_2OCH_2CH_3$ (b) $\begin{matrix} CH_3 & CH_3 \\ | & | \\ CH_3CHOCHCH_3 \end{matrix}$

(c) $CH_3OCH_2CH_2OCH_2CH_2OCH_3$ (d)

14.22

(a) $CH_3CH_2CH_2OH$ (b) $\begin{matrix} CH_3CHCH_2OH \\ | \\ CH_3 \end{matrix}$

(c)      (d)

14.23 $CH_3OCH_3 + CH_3OCH_2CH_3 + CH_3CH_2OCH_2CH_3$
14.24   No reaction occurs. Ethers are stable in base.
14.25

(a) $CH_3CH_2SSCH_2CH_3$ (b) $\begin{matrix} HSCH_2CHCH_3 \\ | \\ SH \end{matrix}$

(c) $\begin{matrix} CH_3CHSH \\ | \\ CH_3 \end{matrix}$ (d) $HSCH_2CH_2CH_3$

14.26

(a) $CH_3CH_2CH_2SSCH_2CH_2CH_3$ (b) $(CH_3)_2CHCH_2SH$

(c)      (d) $(CH_3)_2CHSSCH(CH_3)_2$

14.27   Hydrogen bonding in the thioalcohol family does exist, but the hydrogen bonds are not as strong as those in the alcohol family.

14.28   (a)   Ethanol
          (b)   Ethanol, 2-propanol
          (c)   1,2,3-Propanetriol (glycerol)
          (d)   Methanol
          (e)   1,2-Ethanediol and 1,2-propanediol
          (f)   1,2,3-Propanetriol (glycerol)

14.29   (a)   1,2,3-Propanetriol (glycerol)
          (b)   Ethanol
          (c)   Methanol

14.30 $C_5H_9OH + H_2SO_4 \rightleftharpoons C_5H_9OH_2^+ + HSO_4^-$

14.31

14.32   It must lose H^+. The most abundant and so the most likely proton acceptor is a molecule of cyclopentanol.

14.33   Carbocations have a carbon atom lacking an outer octet, but the sodium ion has such an octet.

14.34   In dilute sulfuric acid, the likeliest proton donor is H_3O^+.

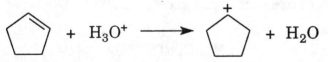

The carbocation reacts with water to give the protonated forı of the alcohol.

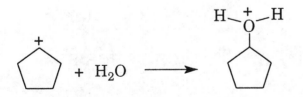

A proton transfers to an acceptor (not shown) and th alcohol forms.

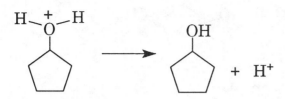

14.35   (a)   vanillin
        (b)   phenol
        (c)   eugenol
        (d)   members of the urushiol family

14.36   Their greater ability to react with oxidizing agents (and thus food-spoiling agents) than key constituents of the food itself.

14.37   It is a general protoplasmic poison and too harmful to healthy tissue.

14.38   Its volatility; it exists in the gas phase at body temperature.

14.39   Its ability to react so rapidly with oxygen in air (given a spark) as to cause an explosion.

14.40   Like cholesterol, methyl *t*-butyl ether is largely hydrocarbon-like and so this ether is able to dissolve cholesterol.

14.41   The dioxins.

14.42   The operation of municipal incinerators.

14.43

(a)

(b) $CH_3CH_2OCH_2CH_3$

(c) $CH_3\overset{\overset{\displaystyle O}{\|}}{C}CH_2CH_3$

(d) CH_3

(e)   No reaction

(f)   No reaction

(g)   No reaction

(h) $CH_3CH_2\underset{\underset{\displaystyle CH_3}{|}}{C}HCH_3$

(i)

(j)

14.44

(a)   No reaction

(b)

$$CH_3CH_2\overset{\overset{\displaystyle Cl}{|}}{\underset{\underset{\displaystyle CH_3}{|}}{C}}CH_3$$

(c)

$$CH_3\overset{\overset{\displaystyle CH_3}{|}}{\underset{\underset{\displaystyle O}{\|}}{C}}CHCH_3$$

(d) $CH_3\overset{\underset{\displaystyle CH_3}{|}}{C}HO\overset{\underset{\displaystyle CH_3}{|}}{C}HCH_3$

(e)

$$\overset{\overset{\displaystyle O}{\|}}{H}CCH_2CH_3$$

(f)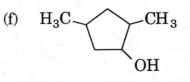

(g)   No reaction

(h)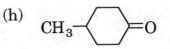

(i) $CH_3CH{=}CH_2$

(j)

$$CH_3\overset{\overset{\displaystyle O}{\|}}{C}CH_2OCH_3$$

14.45   (a)   2.50 mol acetone
          (b)   0.120 mol $KMnO_4$

(c)   22.1 g $KMnO_4$

(d)   12.2 g acetone; 12.1 g MnO_2

14.46   (a) $3C_3H_8O + 2Cr_2O_7{}^{2-} + 16H^+ \rightarrow 3C_3H_6O_2 + 4Cr^{3+} + 11H_2O$

(b) $3C_3H_8O + 2K_2Cr_2O_7 + 16HCl \rightarrow 3C_3H_6O_2 + 4CrCl_3 + 4KCl +$ $11H_2O$

(c)   2/3 mol $K_2Cr_2O_7$

(d) $K_2Cr_2O_7 \cdot 2H_2O$; 2/3 mol

(e)   15.3 g propanoic acid

(f)   53.1 g $K_2Cr_2O_7 \cdot 2H_2O$

14.47 $3C_5H_{10}O + Cr_2O_7{}^{2-} + 8H^+ \rightarrow 3C_5H_8O + 2Cr^{3+} + 7H_2O$

20.5 g cyclopentanol needed; 20.8 g $Na_2Cr_2O_7$ required.

Chapter 15

Practice Exercises, Chapter 15

1.   (a)   2-Methylpropanal

(b)   3-Bromobutanal

(c)   4-Ethyl-2,4,6-trimethylheptanal

2.   2-Isopropylpropanal would have the structure:

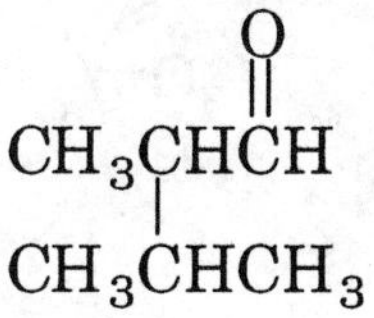

$$\underset{\underset{\displaystyle CH_3CHCH_3}{|}}{CH_3CHCH}{\overset{\displaystyle \overset{O}{\|}}{}}$$

and it should be named 2,3-dimethylbutanal.

3.   (a)   2-Butanone

(b)   6-Methyl-2-heptanone

(c)   2-Methylcyclohexanone

4.

(a) $\underset{\underset{\displaystyle CH_3}{|}}{CH_3CH_2\overset{\overset{\displaystyle O}{\|}}{C}CHCH_3}$

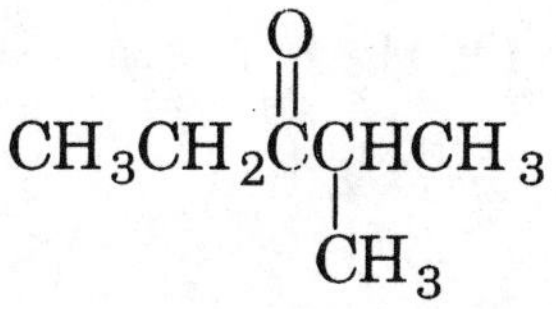

(b) $CH_3\overset{\overset{\displaystyle O}{\|}}{C}C_6H_5$

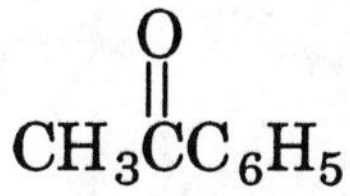

(c) $CH_3CH_2CH_2\overset{\overset{\displaystyle O}{\|}}{C}CH_2CH_2CH_3$ (d) $(CH_3)_3C\overset{\overset{\displaystyle O}{\|}}{C}C(CH_3)_3$

5.

(a)
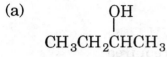
$\underset{\displaystyle CH_3CH_2CHCH_3}{\overset{\displaystyle OH}{|}}$

(b) $CH_3\underset{\displaystyle CH_3}{\overset{|}{C}}HCH_2CH_2OH$

(c)
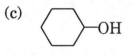

6.

(a)   Not a hemiacetal

(b)   Not a hemiacetal

(c) $HOCH_2OCH_2CH_3$

hemiacetal
position

(d)   hemiketal
position

$CH_3O\!\!-$
HO

7.

(a) $\underset{\displaystyle CH_3CHOCH_3}{\overset{\displaystyle OH}{|}}$

(b) $\underset{\displaystyle CH_3CH_2CH_2CHOCH_2CH_3}{\overset{\displaystyle OH}{|}}$

(c) $\underset{\displaystyle C_6H_5CHOCH_2CH_2CH_3}{\overset{\displaystyle OH}{|}}$

(d) $HOCH_2OCH_3$

8.

(a)

$$CH_3CH_2\overset{\displaystyle O}{\overset{\|}{C}}H + HOCH_3$$

(b)

$$CH_3CH_2OH + H\overset{\displaystyle O}{\overset{\|}{C}}CH_2CH_3$$

9.   (a)   Neither an acetal nor a ketal

(b)   A ketal. Its carbon atom that holds two oxygen atoms
was a keto group carbon. The breakdown products ar

$$2CH_3CH_2OH + CH_3\overset{\displaystyle O}{\overset{\|}{C}}CH_3$$

10.

(a)

$$2CH_3OH + H\overset{\displaystyle O}{\overset{\|}{C}}H$$

(b)   No reaction

(c)

$$2CH_3OH + CH_3\overset{\displaystyle H_3C}{\underset{|}{C}}H\overset{\displaystyle O}{\overset{\|}{C}}CH_3$$

Review Exercises, Chapter 15

15.1   (a)   Ketone   (b)   Aldehyde
          (c)   Ketone   (d)   Carboxylic acid
          (e)   Aldehyde   (f)   Ether + ketone

15.2

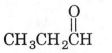

$$CH_3CH_2\overset{\displaystyle O}{\overset{\|}{C}}H \qquad CH_3\overset{\displaystyle O}{\overset{\|}{C}}CH_3 \qquad CH_3CH_2\overset{\displaystyle O}{\overset{\|}{C}}OH \qquad CH_3\overset{\displaystyle O}{\overset{\|}{C}}OCH_3$$

aldehyde   ketone   carboxylic acid   ester

15.3

(a)   CH$_3$CH$_2$CHCHO
            |
           CH$_3$

(b)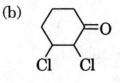

(c)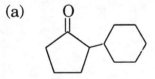
      C$_6$H$_5$CCH$_3$

(d)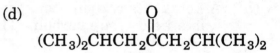
      (CH$_3$)$_2$CHCH$_2$CCH$_2$CH(CH$_3$)$_2$

(e)   CH$_3$CCH$_2$CH$_2$CCH$_3$

15.4

(a)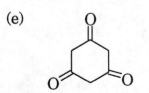

(b)   CH$_3$CH$_2$CH$_2$CH$_2$CHCHO
                              |
                             CH$_3$

(c)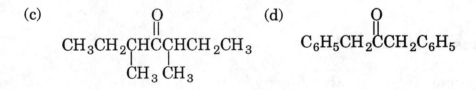
      CH$_3$CH$_2$CHCCHCH$_2$CH$_3$
            | |
           CH$_3$ CH$_3$

(d)   C$_6$H$_5$CH$_2$CCH$_2$C$_6$H$_5$

(e)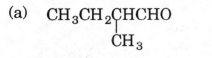

15.5   (a)   2-Methylcyclohexanone   (b) Propionic acid
     (c)   2-Pentanone   (d) Propanal
     (e)   2-Methylpentanal

15.6   (a)   2-Ethyl-3-methylpentanal   (b) 1-Phenylethanone
     (c)   2,3-dimethylcyclopentanone   (d) Acetic acid
     (e)   Butanal

15.7   5-Ketohexanal

15.8   2-Formylbenzoic acid

15.9   (a)   3-Methylbutanal
     (b)   3-Methylpentanal
     (c)   3-Ethyl-5-methylhexanal
     (d)   4-Methyl-2-pentanone
     (e)   3-Propylcyclopentanone

15.10   (a)   3-Isobutyl-5-methyl-2-heptanone
     (b)   4-*t*-Butyl-6-methyloctanal
     (c)   4-Phenyl-2-butanone
     (d)   3,4-Dimethylcyclohexanone
     (e)   2,2-Dimethylcyclooctanone

15.11   Valeraldehyde

15.12   Glyceric acid

15.13

    B < A < D < C

15.14

    C < B < D < A

15.15

    B < A < D < C

15.16

    C < B < D < A

15.17

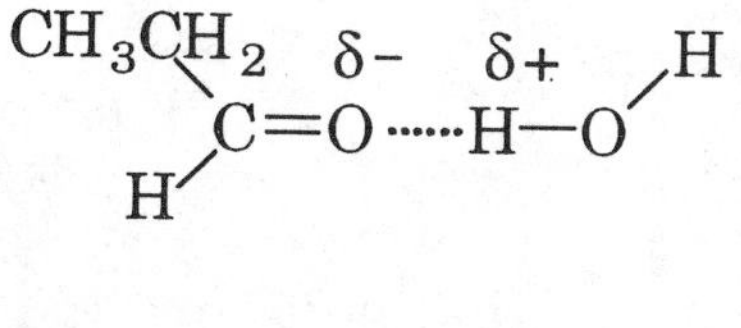

$$CH_3CH_2 \quad \delta- \quad \delta+ \quad H$$
$$\underset{H}{}C=O \cdots H-O$$

15.18

$$\begin{array}{c} H_3C \\ \\ H_3C \end{array} C {=} O \overset{\delta-}{\cdots\cdots} \overset{\delta+}{H} {-} O \begin{array}{c} CH_3 \\ \end{array}$$

15.19

(a)

$$CH_3CH_2\overset{\displaystyle O}{\overset{\|}{C}}CH_3$$

2-Butanone

(b)

$$\overset{\displaystyle CH_3}{\underset{|}{CH_3}}CHCH_2CH_2CHO$$

4-Methylpentanal

(c)   H₃C—⬠=O

3-Methylcyclopentanone

(d) $C_6H_5CH_2\underset{\underset{CH_3}{|}}{C}HCHO$

2-Methyl-3-phenylpropanal

15.20

(a)

$$CH_3\overset{\displaystyle O}{\overset{\|}{C}}CH_2CH_3$$

(b)

$$\overset{\displaystyle O}{\overset{\|}{H}}\overset{\displaystyle CH_3}{\underset{|}{C}}CHCH_3$$

(c)   No oxidation product

(d)   No oxidation product

(e)

$$CH_3OCH_2CH_2\overset{\displaystyle O}{\overset{\|}{C}}CH_3$$

(f)

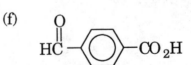

15.21   C₃H₆O is CH₃CH₂CH=O; C₃H₆O₂ is CH₃CH₂CO₂H

15.22

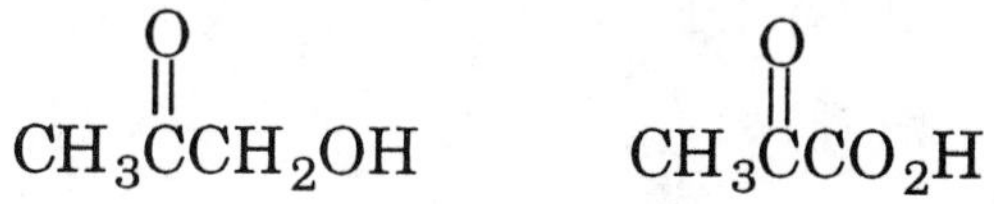

$$CH_3\overset{\overset{\displaystyle O}{\|}}{C}CH_2OH \qquad CH_3\overset{\overset{\displaystyle O}{\|}}{C}CO_2H$$

$$C_3H_6O_2 \qquad\qquad C_3H_4O_3$$

15.23   Positive Benedict's tests are given by a and b.

15.24   Benedict's tests are given by b and d.

15.25   (a)   The cations of transition metals.
   (b)   Electron-rich particles, whether electrically neutral or negatively charged.
   (c) F^-, Cl^-, Br^-, and I^- are four examples in the same family.
   (d) H_2O, which forms $Cu(H_2O)_4{}^{2+}$
         NH_3, which forms $Cu(NH_3)_4{}^{2+}$

15.26   (a) $Ag(NH_3)_2{}^+$. Hydroxide ions are persent, which react with Ag^+ to give Ag_2O, an insoluble compound. Hydroxide ions do not react with $Ag(NH_3)_2{}^+$.
   (b)   It forms a complex ion with Cu^{2+} which retains Cu^{2+} in solution in the presence of base. (Cu^{2+} is otherwise insoluble in base; it forms CuO.)

15.27 Cu_2O

15.28   To test for glucose in urine specimens.

15.29   Manufacture of silvered mirrors.

15.30

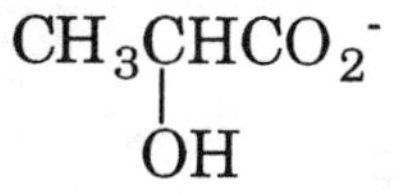

$$CH_3\underset{\underset{\displaystyle OH}{|}}{C}HCO_2{}^-$$

15.31

$$CH_3\overset{\overset{\displaystyle O}{\|}}{C}CH_2CO_2{}^-$$

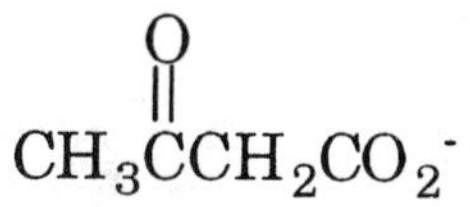

15.32   **B** is oxidized to a compound with the keto group.

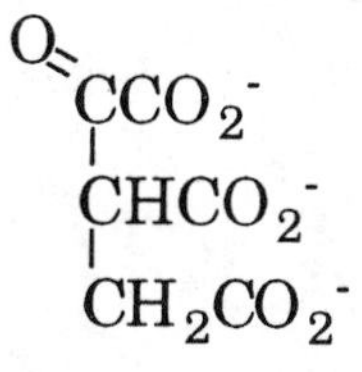

$$\overset{\displaystyle O}{\underset{\underset{\underset{\underset{\displaystyle CH_2CO_2{}^-}{|}}{\displaystyle CHCO_2{}^-}}{|}}{\overset{\diagdown}{C}CO_2{}^-}}$$

15.33 $H{:}^- + CH_3CH_2OH \rightarrow H_2 + CH_3CH_2O^-$

15.34   (a) $CH_3CH_2O^-$

(b) $CH_3CH_2O^- + H_2O \rightarrow CH_3CH_2OH + OH^-$

(c)   Ethanol

15.35

(a)
$$\overset{\displaystyle O^-}{\underset{\textstyle CH_3CHCH_3}{|}}$$

(b)
$$\overset{\displaystyle O^-}{\underset{\textstyle CH_3CHCH_3}{|}} + H_2O \longrightarrow \overset{\displaystyle OH}{\underset{\textstyle CH_3CHCH_3}{|}} + OH^-$$

(c)   2-Propanol

15.36

$$\overset{+}{H_3}\overset{|}{N}CHCO_2^-\qquad \overset{+}{H_3}\overset{|}{N}CHCO_2^-$$
$$\underset{\textbf{A}}{CH_2CH_2O^-}\qquad \underset{\textbf{B}}{CH_2CH_2OH}$$

15.37

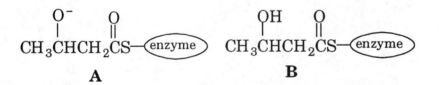

15.38

(a)
$$\overset{\displaystyle O}{\overset{\|}{CH_3CCH_2CH_3}}$$

(b)
$$\overset{\displaystyle O\,CH_3}{\overset{\|\ \ |}{HCCHCH_2CH_3}}$$

(c)

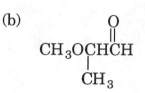

(d)

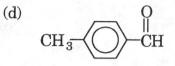

15.39

(a)

$$\underset{\text{O}}{\overset{\text{O}}{\|}}$$
HCCH$_2$OCH$_3$

(b)

$$\underset{\underset{\text{CH}_3}{|}}{\overset{\text{O}}{\overset{\|}{\text{CH}_3\text{OCHCH}}}}$$

(c)

$$\underset{\underset{\text{CH}_3}{|}}{\overset{\text{O}\quad\text{OH}}{\overset{\|}{\text{CH}_3\text{CCH}_2}}\overset{|}{\underset{}{\text{CCH}_2}}}$$

(d)

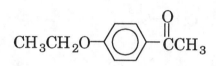

15.40 (a)   Hemiacetal   (b) Acetal
         (c)   Something else (a 1,2-di-ether)   (d) Ketal

15.41 (a)   Acetal   (b) Hemiacetal
         (c)   Hemiacetal   (d) Something else (an ether-
                        alcohol)

15.42

(a)

$$\overset{\text{OH}}{\overset{|}{\text{CH}_3\text{CH}_2\text{CHOCH}_3}}$$

$$\overset{\text{OCH}_3}{\overset{|}{\text{CH}_3\text{CH}_2\text{CHOCH}_3}}$$

(b)

$$\overset{\text{OH}}{\overset{|}{\text{CH}_3\text{CH}_2\text{CHOCH}_2\text{CH}_3}}$$

$$\overset{\text{OCH}_2\text{CH}_3}{\overset{|}{\text{CH}_3\text{CH}_2\text{CHOCH}_2\text{CH}_3}}$$

15.43

(a)

$$CH_3\overset{\displaystyle OCH_3}{\underset{\displaystyle CH_3}{C}}OCH_3$$

(b)

$$CH_3\overset{\displaystyle OCH_2CH_3}{\underset{\displaystyle CH_3}{C}}OCH_2CH_3$$

15.44

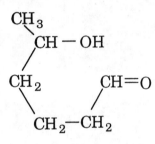

15.45

(a)
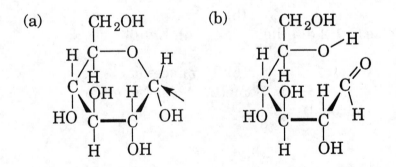
(b)

15.46

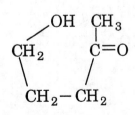

15.47

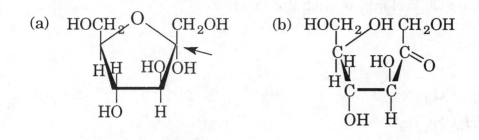

15.48

(a) $CH_3CH_2CHO + 2CH_3OH$ (b)   No reaction

(c)

$$CH_3\overset{\overset{\displaystyle O}{\|}}{C}CH_3 + 2CH_3CH_2OH$$

(d)   cyclopentanone $=O + 2CH_3OH$

15.49

(a) CH_3CH_2CHO

+ $HOCH_2CH_3$

+ $HOCH(CH_3)_2$

(b)   No reaction

(c)

$$\begin{array}{c} CH_2-OH \\ CH_2 \\ CH_2-OH \end{array} + CH_3\overset{\overset{\displaystyle O}{\|}}{C}CH_3$$

(d) $CH_3OCH_2CHO + HOCH_2CH_3$

+ $HOCH_3$

15.50   (a)   Estrone
(b)   Acetone
(c)   Formaldehyde

15.51 (a) sp^2 on C overlapping with s on H

(b) sp^2 on C overlapping with sp^2 on O

(c) $2p_z$ on C overlapping with $2p_z$ on O

15.52 120°. Yes

15.53

(a) 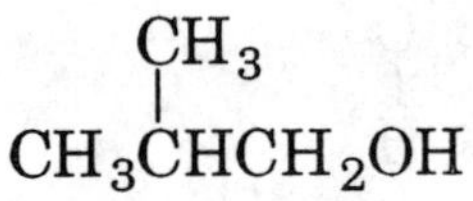 $$\underset{\text{CH}_3\text{CHCH}_2\text{OH}}{\overset{\overset{\displaystyle \text{CH}_3}{|}}{}}$$

(b) 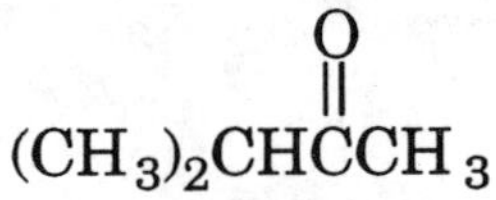 $$\underset{(\text{CH}_3)_2\text{CHCCH}_3}{\overset{\overset{\displaystyle \text{O}}{\|}}{}}$$

(c) No reaction

(d) $CH_3CH_2CH_2CH_2CH_3$

(e) 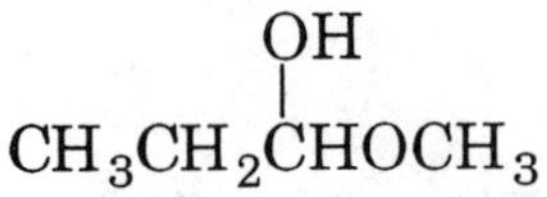 $$\underset{\text{CH}_3\text{CH}_2\text{CHOCH}_3}{\overset{\overset{\displaystyle \text{OH}}{|}}{}}$$

(f) $CH_3CH_2OH + Mtb^+$

(g) 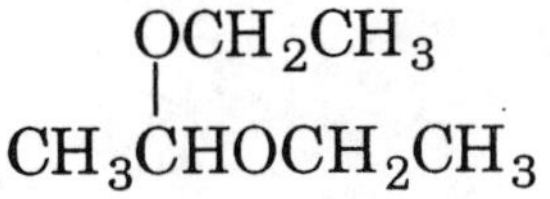 $$\underset{\text{CH}_3\text{CHOCH}_2\text{CH}_3}{\overset{\overset{\displaystyle \text{OCH}_2\text{CH}_3}{|}}{}}$$

(h) $CH_3CHO + 2CH_3OH$

(i)

CO_2H

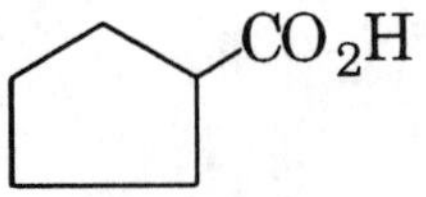

(j) No reaction

15.54

(a) No reaction

(b) No reaction

(c) 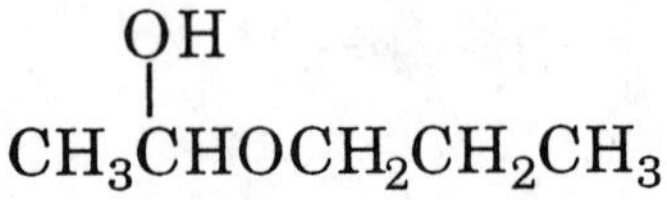 $$\underset{\text{CH}_3\text{CHOCH}_2\text{CH}_2\text{CH}_3}{\overset{\overset{\displaystyle \text{OH}}{|}}{}}$$

(d) No reaction

(e) 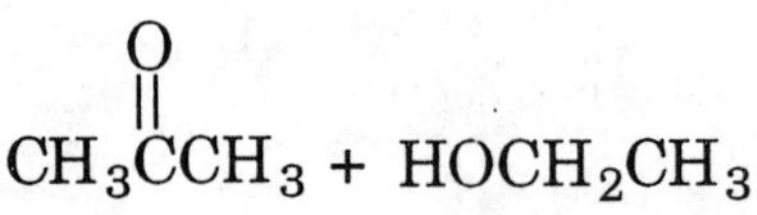 $$\underset{\text{CH}_3\text{CCH}_3 + \text{HOCH}_2\text{CH}_3}{\overset{\overset{\displaystyle \text{O}}{\|}}{}}$$

(f) $CH_3OCH_2CH_2CH_2OH + Mtb^+$

(g)

O
‖
$CH_3CH_2CCH_3$

+ $2HOCH_2CH_3$

(h)

O
‖
$CH_3CC_6H_5$

(i) 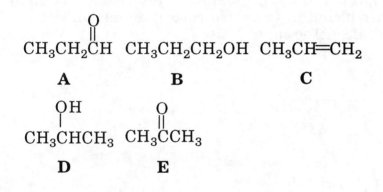 —OCH_3

(j)

OCH_3
|
$C_6H_5CHOCH_3$

15.55

O
‖
CH_3CH_2CH $CH_3CH_2CH_2OH$ $CH_3CH=CH_2$

A   **B**   **C**

OH
|
CH_3CHCH_3

O
‖
CH_3CCH_3

D   **E**

15.56

O   O
‖   ‖
$(CH_3)_2CH_2OH$ $(CH_3)_2CHCH$ $(CH_3)_2CHCOH$

F   **G**   **H**

$(CH_3)_2C=CH_2$ $(CH_3)_3COH$

I   **J**

15.57   (a)   0.173 mol butanal
           (b)   1.23 mol CH_3OH
           (c)   Yes, 11.1 g CH_3OH needed but 39.4 g taken
           (d)   3.11 g H_2O obtained

(e) To ensure that the equilibria involved in the reaction are all shifted as much as possible to the right, in favor of the products.

15.58

(a)

(b)

etc.—CH_2CH—CH_2CH—etc.
with OH groups on each CH

(c)

CH_2=CH The "alcohol" is actually an enol and is unstable. In polyvinyl alcohol, the OH groups are proper alcohol group because all are bound to saturated carbon atoms; all OH groups are 2° alcohol groups.

(d)

etc.—CH_2CH CH—etc.

Chapter 16

Practice Exercises, Chapter 16

1.   (a) 2,2-Dimethylpropanoic acid
      (b) 5-Ethyl-5-isopropyl-3-methyloctanoic acid
      (c) Sodium ethanoate
      (d) 5-Chloro-3-methylheptanoic acid
2.   Pentanedioic acid
3.   9-Octadecenoic acid

4.

(a) $CH_3CH_2CO_2^-$ (b) $CH_3O-\langle\bigcirc\rangle-CO_2^-$ (c) $CH_3CH{=}CHCO_2^-$

5.

(a) $CH_3O-\langle\bigcirc\rangle-CO_2H$ (b) $CH_3CH_2CO_2H$ (c) $CH_3CH{=}CHCO_2H$

6.

(a)
$$\underset{CH_3COCH_3}{\overset{O}{\|}}$$

(b)
$$\underset{CH_3COCH_2CH_2CH_3}{\overset{O}{\|}}$$

(c)
$$\underset{CH_3COCHCH_3}{\overset{O\quad CH_3}{\|\qquad|}}$$

7.

(a)
$$\underset{HCOCH_2CH_3}{\overset{O}{\|}}$$

(b)
$$\underset{CH_3CH_2COCH_2CH_3}{\overset{O}{\|}}$$

(c)
$$\underset{C_6H_5COCH_2CH_3}{\overset{O}{\|}}$$

8.   (a) Methyl propanoate   (b) Propyl 3-methylpentanoate
9.   (a) *t*-Butyl acetate   (b) Ethyl butyrate
10.   (a) $CH_3OH + CH_3CO_2H$ (b) $(CH_3)_2CHOH + CH_3CH_2CO_2H$
      (c) $CH_3CH_2CH_2OH + (CH_3)_2CHCO_2H$

11.   (a) $C_6H_5OH + CH_3CO_2^-$ (b) $CH_3OH + {}^-O_2C-\langle\bigcirc\rangle-OCH_3$

Review Exercises, Chapter 16

16.1   (a) **B**   (b) **A** (c) **B**   (d) **C**
16.2   Fatty acids
16.3   Acetic acid; lactic acid
16.4   (a) $CH_3CH_2CO_2H$ (b) $C_6H_5CO_2H$
       (c) CH_3CO_2H (d) HCO_2H

16.5

(a)
$$CH_3CH_2\overset{\overset{\displaystyle CH_3}{|}}{\underset{\underset{\displaystyle CH_3}{|}}{C}}CO_2^-$$

(b) $CH_3CH_2CH_2\underset{\underset{\displaystyle Cl}{|}}{C}HCH_2\underset{\underset{\displaystyle CH_3}{|}}{C}HCO_2H$

(c)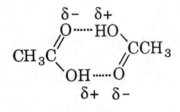

(b) $C_6H_5CO_2^-$

16.6   (a)   2-Methylpropanoic acid   (b)   2,2-Dimethylbutanoic acid
       (c)   Sodium 3-chloropentanoate   (d)   Potassium benzoate

16.7   (a)   2,4-Dimethylpentanoic acid   (b)   3,4-Dimethylpentanoic acid
       (c)   Sodium decanoate   (d)   Potassium 2-bromopropanoate

16.8   sodium 3-hydroxybutanoate   (b)   Sodium β-hydroxybutyrate

16.9   *trans*-Butenedioic acid

16.10

$$CH_3C\overset{\overset{\displaystyle \overset{\delta-\ \ \delta+}{O\cdots\cdots HO}}{\|}}{\underset{\underset{\displaystyle \underset{\delta+\ \ \delta-}{OH\cdots\cdots O}}{\|}}{\ }}CCH_3$$

16.11

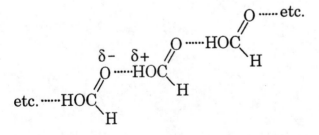

16.12

$$C < A < B$$

16.13

$$B < C < D < A$$

16.14   (a) $CH_3CO_2H + H_2O \rightleftharpoons CH_3CO_2^- + H_3O^+$
(b)   Toward acetic acid. The addition of $HCl(aq)$ makes the concentration of H_3O^+ increase. This puts a stress on the equilibrium, which shifts to the left to relieve the stress.

(c) $$K_a = \frac{[CH_3CO_2^-][H^+]}{[CH_3CO_2H]}$$

(d)   Weaker

16.15   (a) $HCO_2H + H_2O \rightleftharpoons HCO_2^- + H_3O^+$
(b)   Toward the formate ion. The added OH^- (from $NaOH$) neutralizes H_3O^+ and so reduces the concentration of H_3O^+ in the equilibrium. The equilibrium thus must shift to the right to replace the lost H_3O^+.

(c) $$K_a = \frac{[HCO_2^-][H^+]}{[HCO_2H]}$$

(d)   Stronger

16.16

$$A < C < D < B$$

16.17

$$B < A < C < D$$

16.18

(a)

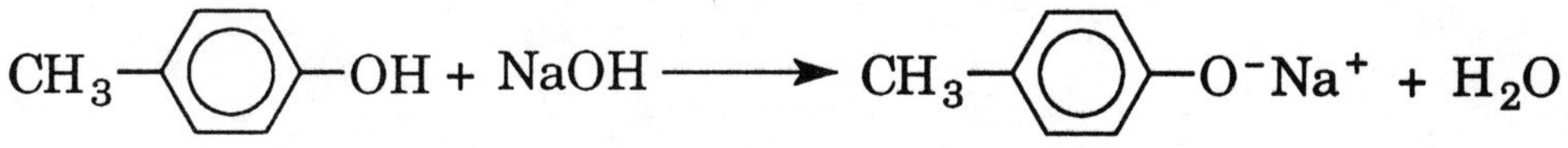

(b) No reaction

(c)  CH_3—⟨○⟩—CO_2H + NaOH $\longrightarrow$ CH_3—⟨○⟩—$CO_2^-Na^+$ + H_2O

(d) HNO_3 + NaOH $\longrightarrow$ $NaNO_3$ + H_2O

16.19

(a) $HO_2CCH_2CH_2CO_2H$ + 2OH$^-$ $\rightarrow$ $^-O_2CCH_2CH_2CO_2^-$ + 2H_2O

(b) $HOCH_2CH_2CH_2CO_2H$ + OH$^-$ $\rightarrow$ $HOCH_2CH_2CH_2CO_2^-$ + H_2O

(c)
$$\overset{O}{\overset{\|}{H}CCH_2CH_2CH_2CO_2H} + OH^- \rightarrow \overset{O}{\overset{\|}{H}CCH_2CH_2CH_2CO_2^-} + H_2O$$

(d) 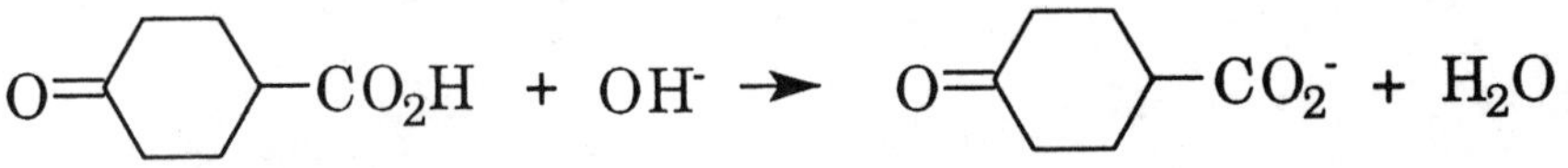
O=⟨○⟩—CO_2H + OH$^-$ $\rightarrow$ O=⟨○⟩—CO_2^- + H_2O

16.20 **B**. The ionic compound, **A**, is very insoluble in a nonpolar solvent. **B** is not ionic.
16.21 **A**, an ionic compound, is much more soluble in water than the molecular compound, **B**.

16.22

(a) $CH_3CH_2CO_2^-$ + H$^+$ $\rightarrow$ $CH_3CH_2CO_2H$

(b) $^-O_2CCH_2CH_2CH_2CO_2^-$ + H$^+$ $\rightarrow$ $HO_2CH_2CH_2CH_2CO_2^-$

(c) $NH_3 + H^+ \longrightarrow NH_4^+$

16.23

(a) $HOCH_2CH_2CO_2^- + H^+ \longrightarrow HOCH_2CH_2CO_2H$

(b)   No reaction

(c) $C_6H_5O^- + H^+ \longrightarrow C_6H_5OH$

16.24

(a) $\underset{\displaystyle CH_3CH_2\overset{\textstyle O}{\overset{\|}{C}}Cl}{}$
(b) $CH_3CH_2\overset{\textstyle O}{\overset{\|}{C}}O\overset{\textstyle O}{\overset{\|}{C}}CH_2CH_3$
(c) $CH_3CH_2\overset{\textstyle O}{\overset{\|}{C}}OH$

16.25

(a) $C_6H_5\overset{\textstyle O}{\overset{\|}{C}}OH + HOCH_3$
(b) $C_6H_5\overset{\textstyle O}{\overset{\|}{C}}Cl + HOCH_3$

(c) $C_6H_5\overset{\textstyle O}{\overset{\|}{C}}O\overset{\textstyle O}{\overset{\|}{C}}C_6H_5 + HOCH_3$

16.26

(a) $CH_3\overset{\textstyle O}{\overset{\|}{C}}OCH_2CH_3$

(b)   The electronegativities of O and Cl place a relatively large δ+ charge on the carbon atom of the carbonyl group in acetyl chloride. This charge is able quite strongly to attract the $\delta-$ charge on the O atom of the alcohol molecule. In addition, the Cl^- ion is a very stable leaving group and so quite readily leaves the carbonyl carbon atom of the acetyl chloride molecule when the alcohol molecule attacks.

16.27   The electronegativies of the O atoms of the anhydride create a sizeable $\delta+$ charge on the carbonyl carbon atoms. This charge is able quite strongly to attract the $\delta-$ charge on the O atom of the alcohol. In addition, the acetate ion is a stable leaving group and so quite readily leaves the carbonyl carbon atom when the alcohol molecule attacks.

16.28

(a)

$$CH_3CH_2\overset{\overset{\displaystyle O}{\|}}{C}OCH_2CH_3 + H_2O$$

(b)

$$(CH_3)_2CH\overset{\overset{\displaystyle O}{\|}}{C}OCH_2CH_3 + H_2O$$

(c)

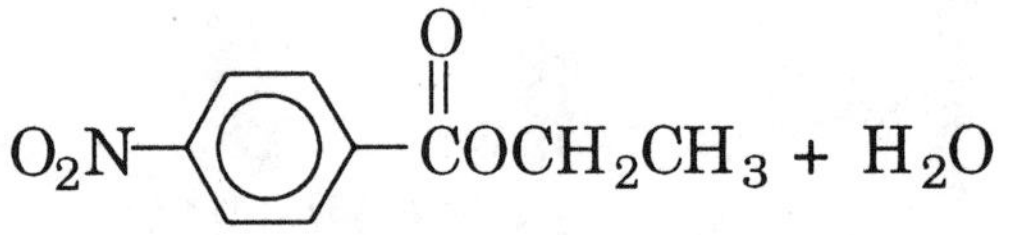

$$O_2N-\!\!\left\langle\bigcirc\right\rangle\!\!-\overset{\overset{\displaystyle O}{\|}}{C}OCH_2CH_3 + H_2O$$

(d)

$$CH_3CH_2O\overset{\overset{\displaystyle O}{\|}}{C}-\!\!\left\langle\bigcirc\right\rangle\!\!-\overset{\overset{\displaystyle O}{\|}}{C}OCH_2CH_3$$

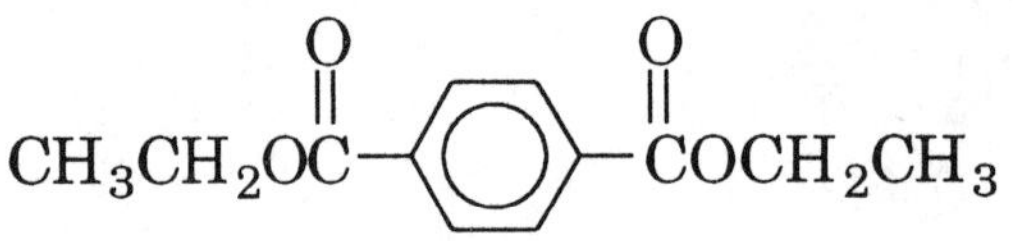

16.29

(a)

$$CH_3\overset{\overset{\displaystyle O}{\|}}{C}OCH_3$$

(b)

$$CH_3\overset{\overset{\displaystyle O}{\|}}{C}OCH_2CH(CH_3)_2$$

(c)
$$CH_3\overset{O}{\overset{\|}{C}}OC_6H_5$$

(d)
$$CH_3\overset{O}{\overset{\|}{C}}OCH_2CH_2O\overset{O}{\overset{\|}{C}}CH_3$$

16.30   In the first step, H⁺ transfers from the hydronium ion to form a bond to oxygen in **I** to make **II**.

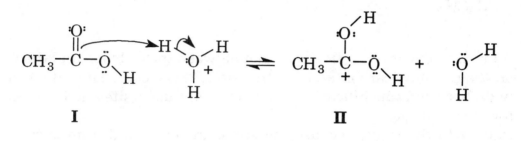

I   **II**

II now attracts a molecule of ethyl alcohol to form **III**. Then a proton transfers from one O atom to another in **III** to create a stable leaving group, H₂O, in the product, **IV**.

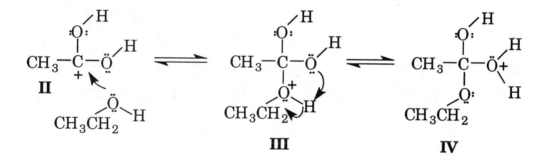

II   **III**   **IV**

In the next step, **IV** drops off a water molecule and **V** forms.

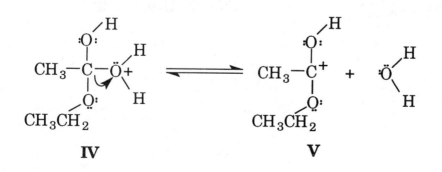

IV   **V**

Finally, **V** drops off the proton and electrons relocate to reestablish an outer octet for the carbonyl carbon atom as the ester forms.

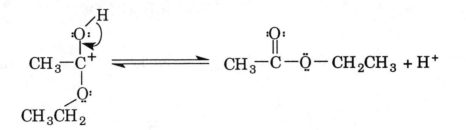

16.31   A much stronger attraction can exist between the OH^- ion and the $\delta+$ charge on the carbonyl carbon atom of the ester, the specific site attacked in both hydrolysis and saponification, than between this $\delta+$ site and the $\delta-$ charge on a water molecule.

16.32   Shift it to the right, because the stress in the equilibrium is the loss of a *product*. In accordance with Le Châtelier's principle, the equilibrium must shift in the direction that tries to replace this loss.

16.33   The acid chloride has a more stable leaving group (the weakly basic Cl^- ion) than the ester, for which the leaving group is a very strongly basic anion of an alcohol

16.34

(a) $$\underset{HCOCH_2CH_3}{\overset{O}{\underset{||}{}}}$$

(b)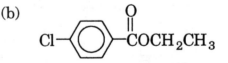

16.35

(a) $$\underset{CH_3CH_2COC(CH_3)_3}{\overset{O}{\underset{||}{}}}$$

(b) $$\underset{CH_3CH_2\underset{}{CH}COCH(CH_3)_2}{\overset{H_3C\ \ \ O}{\underset{|\ \ \ \ ||}{}}}$$

16.36

C < A < B < D

16.37

D < B < C < A

16.38

(a)

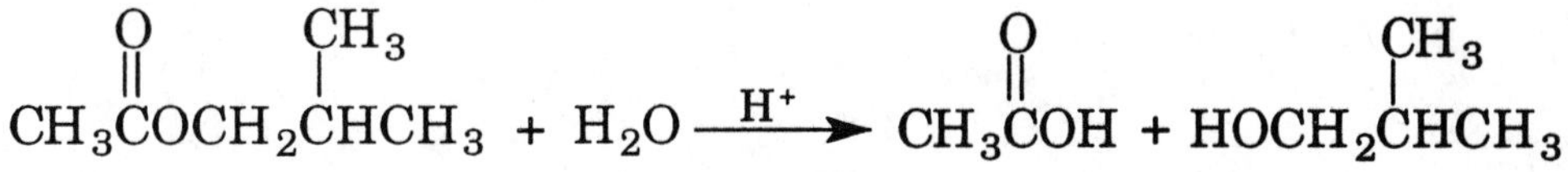

$$CH_3\overset{O}{\overset{\|}{C}}OCH_2\overset{CH_3}{\overset{|}{C}}HCH_3 + H_2O \xrightarrow{H^+} CH_3\overset{O}{\overset{\|}{C}}OH + HOCH_2\overset{CH_3}{\overset{|}{C}}HCH_3$$

(b)

$$CH_3CH_2O\overset{O}{\overset{\|}{C}}\!-\!\bigcirc + H_2O \xrightarrow{H^+} HO\overset{O}{\overset{\|}{C}}\!-\!\bigcirc + HOCH_2CH_3$$

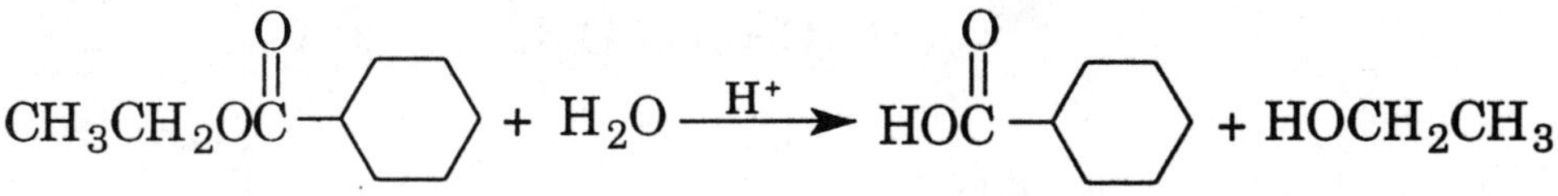

(c)   No reaction   (d)   No reaction

16.39

(a)

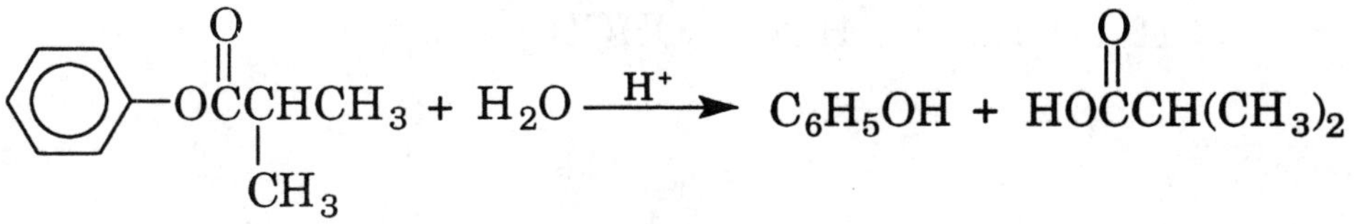

$$\bigcirc\!-\!O\overset{O}{\overset{\|}{C}}\underset{\underset{CH_3}{|}}{C}HCH_3 + H_2O \xrightarrow{H^+} C_6H_5OH + HO\overset{O}{\overset{\|}{C}}CH(CH_3)_2$$

(b)

$$\bigcirc\!-\!\overset{O}{\overset{\|}{C}}O\underset{\underset{CH_3}{|}}{C}HCH_3 + H_2O \xrightarrow{H^+} C_6H_5\overset{O}{\overset{\|}{C}}OH + HOCH(CH_3)_2$$

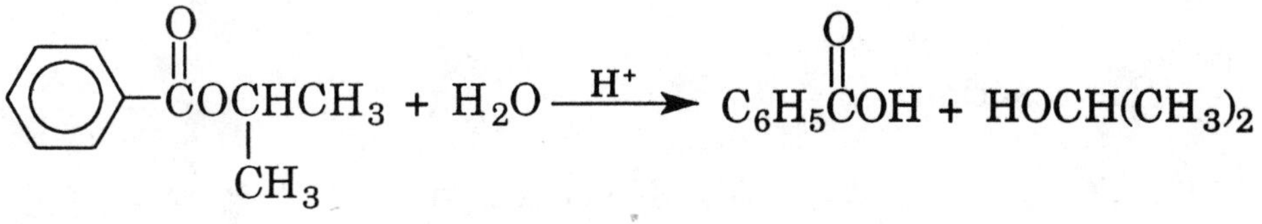

(c)   No reaction

(d)

$$CH_3CH_2OCCH_2CH_2COCH_2CH_3 + 2H_2O \xrightarrow{H^+}$$

$$HOCCH_2CH_2COH + 2CH_3CH_2OH$$

16.40

$$HOCH_2CHCH_2OH + CH_3(CH_2)_{12}CO_2H + CH_3(CH_2)_{14}CO_2H$$
$$\overset{|}{OH} \quad\quad + CH_3(CH_2)_{10}CO_2H$$

16.41 $HOCH_2CH_2CH_2CO_2H$

16.42

(a)

$$CH_3CO^-Na^+ + HOCH_2\overset{\overset{\displaystyle CH_3}{|}}{C}HCH_3$$

(b)

$$Na^{+\,-}OC-\bigcirc + HOCH_2CH_3$$

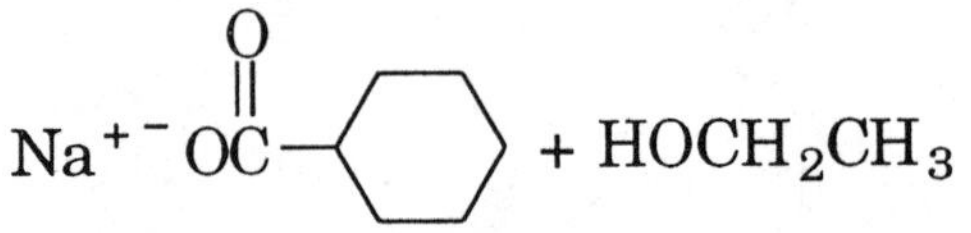

(c)

No reaction

(d)   No reaction

16.43

(a) $C_6H_5O^-K^+ + K^{+\,-}O_2CCH(CH_3)_2$

(b)

$$C_6H_5CO^-\,K^+ + HOCH(CH_3)_2$$

(d)

$$K^+{}^-OCCH_2CH_2CO^-\,K^+ + 2\,CH_3CH_2OH$$

(with two C=O groups shown above the two carbonyls)

16.44

$$HOCH_2CHCH_2OH + CH_3(CH_2)_{12}CO_2^-\,Na^+ + CH_3(CH_2)_{14}CO_2^-\,Na^+$$
$$\underset{OH}{\big|} \qquad + CH_3(CH_2)_{10}CO_2^-\,Na^+$$

16.45 $HOCH_2CH_2CH_2CO_2^-$

16.46   If a large mole excess of ethyl alcohol is used, the following equilibrium will lie so much on the side of the products that essentially all of the expensive acid will be converted to the ester.

$$RCO_2H + CH_3CH_2OH \rightleftharpoons RCO_2CH_2CH_3 + H_2O$$

16.47   The ester, **I**, accepts a proton from the acid catalyst.

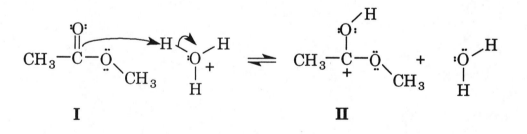

The protonated ester, **II**, reacts with a water molecule to give **III**, which undergoes an internal proton transfer to give **IV**.

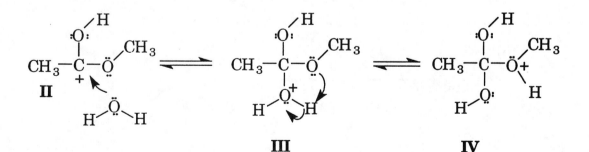

IV drops off a water molecule to give **V**.

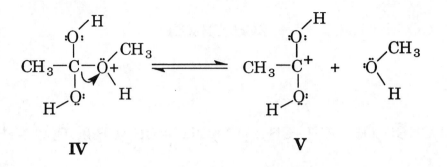

IV   V

The proton is transferred from **V** as an internal shift of an electron pair occurs to give the carbonyl group of the carboxylic acid.

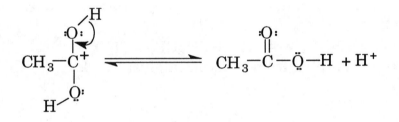

16.48

(a)

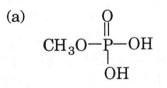

$$CH_3O-\overset{\overset{\displaystyle O}{\|}}{\underset{\underset{\displaystyle OH}{|}}{P}}-OH$$

(b)

$$CH_3CH_2O-\overset{\overset{\displaystyle O}{\|}}{\underset{\underset{\displaystyle OH}{|}}{P}}-O-\overset{\overset{\displaystyle O}{\|}}{\underset{\underset{\displaystyle OH}{|}}{P}}-OH$$

(c)

$$CH_3CH_2CH_2O-\overset{\overset{\displaystyle O}{\parallel}}{\underset{\underset{\displaystyle OH}{|}}{P}}-O-\overset{\overset{\displaystyle O}{\parallel}}{\underset{\underset{\displaystyle OH}{|}}{P}}-O-\overset{\overset{\displaystyle O}{\parallel}}{\underset{\underset{\displaystyle OH}{|}}{P}}-OH$$

16.49   The phosphate esters are more soluble in water.
16.50   The phosphoric anhydride system. The breakup of this system releases considerable energy, but the breakup reaction is very slow in the absence of the appropriate enzyme.
16.51   In acetyl chloride, the attack by water occurs at the carbonyl carbon atom, which is very open and exposed. The site of attack in the phosphoric anhydride group is P, which is surrounded by electron-rich O atoms that tend to repel a water molecule.
16.52   (a)   Acetic acid
        (b)   Acetic acid
        (c)   Sorbic acid and sorbate salts
16.53   Parabens. As mold-inhibiting additives in cosmetics, pharmaceuticals, and food.
16.54   Two (or more) monomers are combined to give the polymer.
16.55   Dacron
16.56   An analgesic is a pain suppressant; an antipyretic is a fever reducer.
16.57   Salicylic acid is a stomach irritant.
16.58   (a)   Phenol group and the carboxylic acid group.
        (b)   The phenol group.
        (c)   The carboxylic acid group.
16.59   (a)   **A**
        (b) $C_6H_5CO_2^-$ and $C_6H_5O^-$
        (c) $C_6H_5O^-$
16.60   (a)   6.29 g methyl benzoate
        (b)   1.48 g CH_3OH; 1.88 ml CH_3OH
        (c)   The reaction involves an equilibrium. By using a large excess of methyl alcohol, the equilibrium shifts in accordance with Le Châtelier's principle so that essentially all of the benzoic acid is converted to the ester.
16.61

        (a) $CH_3\overset{\underset{\displaystyle CH_3O}{|}}{C}HCO_2^-\ Na^+$

(b) $CH_3CH_2CO_2H$ + CH_3OH

(c) CH_3CO_2H

(d)

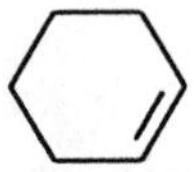

(e) $(CH_3)_2CHCH_2CO_2^- Na^+$ + CH_3OH

(f)
$$(CH_3)_2CH\overset{\overset{\displaystyle O}{\|}}{C}CH_3$$

(g)
$$CH_3CH_2\overset{\overset{\displaystyle O}{\|}}{C}OCH_2CH_3$$

(h) CH_3CH_2CHO + $2CH_3OH$

(i) No reaction

(j)
$$C_6H_5\overset{\overset{\displaystyle O}{\|}}{C}OCH_2CH_3$$

(k) $CH_3\underset{\underset{\displaystyle Cl}{|}}{C}HCH_2CH_3$

(l) No reaction

16.62

(a)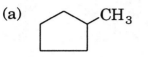

(b)

$$CH_3\overset{\displaystyle O}{\overset{\displaystyle \|}{C}}OCH_2CH_2CH_3 + CH_3\overset{\displaystyle O}{\overset{\displaystyle \|}{C}}OH$$

(c) $(CH_3)_2CHCH_2CO_2H$

(d)   No reaction

(e)

$$CH_3CH_2OH + Na^+\ ^-O\overset{\displaystyle O}{\overset{\displaystyle \|}{C}}CH_2CH_2\overset{\displaystyle O}{\overset{\displaystyle \|}{C}}O^-\ Na^+ + HOCH_3$$

(f)

$$\overset{\displaystyle O}{\overset{\displaystyle \|}{}}$$
cyclohexyl$-\overset{\displaystyle O}{\overset{\displaystyle \|}{C}}OCH_3$

(g)

$$CH_3CH_2OH + Na^+\ ^-O\overset{\displaystyle O}{\overset{\displaystyle \|}{C}}CH_2CH_2OH + Na^+\ ^-O\overset{\displaystyle O}{\overset{\displaystyle \|}{C}}CH_2CH_3$$

(h)

$$C_6H_5\overset{\displaystyle O}{\overset{\displaystyle \|}{C}}H + 2CH_3OH$$

(i) $Na^+\ ^-O_2CCH_2CH_2CH_2CH_3$

(j)

$$CH_3CH_2CH_2OH + HO\overset{O}{\overset{\|}{C}}CH_2CH_2OH + HO\overset{O}{\overset{\|}{C}}CH_3$$

(k)

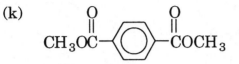

$$CH_3O\overset{O}{\overset{\|}{C}}-\langle\bigcirc\rangle-\overset{O}{\overset{\|}{C}}OCH_3$$

(l) $CH_3OCH_2CH_2CO_2H$

Chapter 17

Practice Exercises, Chapter 17

1.   (a) Isopropyldimethylamine
      (b) Cyclohexylamine
      (c) *t*-Butylisobutylamine

2.

   (a) $(CH_3)_3CNHCHCH_2CH_3$
                        $\overset{|}{\underset{}{CH_3}}$

   (b) $NO_2-\langle\bigcirc\rangle-NH_2$

   (c) $NH_2-\langle\bigcirc\rangle-CO_2H$

3.

   (a) $C_6H_5NH_3{}^+$ (b) $(CH_3)_3NH^+$ (c) $^+NH_3CH_2CH_2NH_3{}^+$

4.

(a)

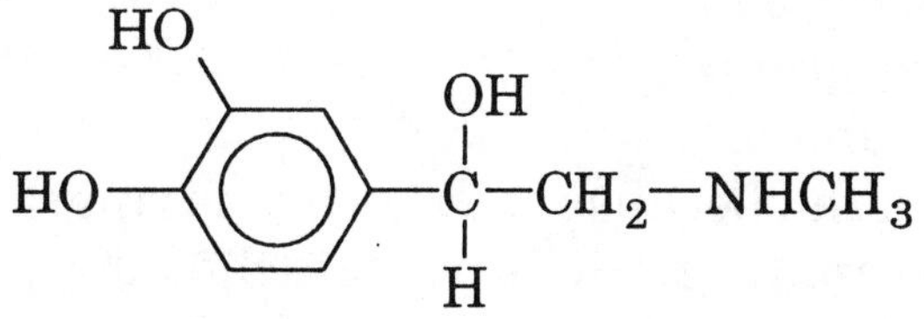

(b)

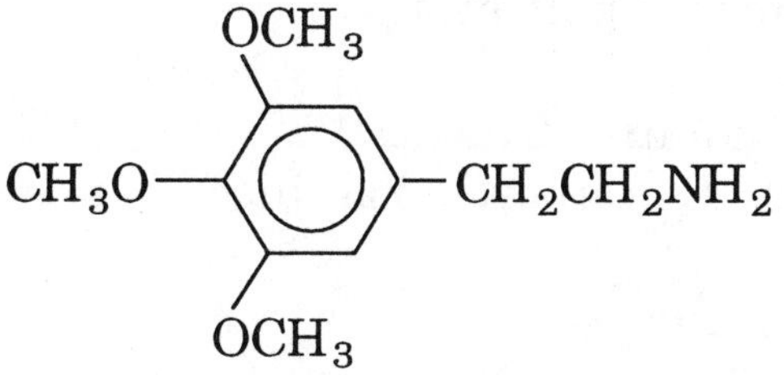

5. (a) 4-Methylhexanamide
   (b) 2-Ethylbutanamide

6.

(a)

$$(CH_3)_2CHCNHCH_3$$
(with O double-bonded above the C)

(b)

$$CH_3CNHC_6H_5$$
(with O double-bonded above the C)

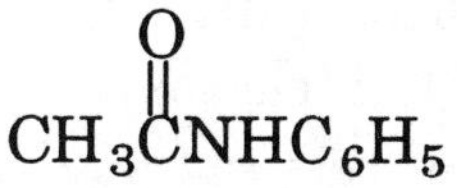

(c) No amide forms.

(d) No amide forms.

7.

(a) $C_6H_5CO_2H + NH_2CH_3$

(b) No hydrolysis occurs.

(c) $C_6H_5NH_2 + HO_2CCH_3$

(d) $NH_2CH_2CH_2NH_2 + 2CH_3CO_2H$

8.

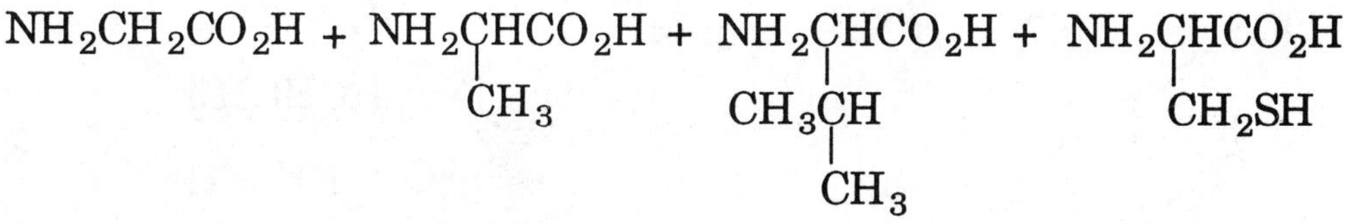

$$NH_2CH_2CO_2H + NH_2CHCO_2H + NH_2CHCO_2H + NH_2CHCO_2H$$
$$CH_3 \qquad CH_3CH \qquad CH_2SH$$
$$CH_3$$

Review Exercises, Chapter 17

17.1   (a)   Aliphatic amide + ether group
       (b)   Aliphatic amine + ester group
       (c)   Aliphatic, heterocyclic amide
       (d)   Aromatic *compound* overall because of the benzene ring, but the 2° amine
       is an *aliphatic* amine. (The amino group is not attached directly to the ring.)

17.2   (a)   Aliphatic, heterocyclic amine + keto group
       (b)   Aliphatic, heterocyclic amide
       (c)   Aliphatic, heterocyclic amide
       (d)   Aliphatic, heterocyclic amine + keto group

17.3   (a)   2° Amine and heterocyclic
       (b)   1, 3° Amine; 2, ester; 3, 1° amine (aromatic)
       (c)   1, Heterocyclic amine; 2, 2° (heterocyclic) amine
       (d)   1, 2° Alcohol; 2, 2° amine

17.4   (a)   1, Alkene; 2, ester; 3, 3° amine
       (b)   1, 3° Amine; 2, 1° alcohol; 3, ester
       (c)   1, Alkene; 2, 2° alcohol; 3, ether; 4, heterocyclic amine
       (d)   1, Amide; 2, 3° amine; 3, alkene; 4, 2° (aliphatic, heterocyclic) amine

17.5   (a)   Isopropylpropylamine   (b)   Ethylmethylpropylamine
       (c)   *p*-Bromoaniline   (d)   Dipropylamine

17.6   (a)   Trimethylammonium chloride   (b)   Cyclohexylmethylamine
       (c)   3,5-Dichloroaniline   (d)   Triisopropylamine

17.7   (a) $CH_3CH_2CH_2NH_3^+$ (b) $CH_3CH_2CH_2NH_2$
       (c)   No reaction   (d)   No reaction

17.8   (a)

       (b)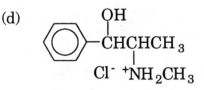

       (c)

       (d)

(e)

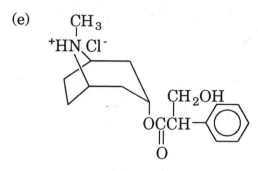

17.9   **A** is the stronger base; it is an amine (plus a ketone) **B** is an amide.
17.10   **B** is the stronger proton acceptor; it's a 3° amine. **A** has no space on N to accept
        a proton.
17.11   (a)   Butanamide
        (b)   3-Methylbutanamide
17.12   Caproamide
17.13 $C_6H_5CON(CH_3)_2$
17.14

$$NH_2CCH_2CH_2CNH_2$$

with two $\overset{O}{\underset{\parallel}{C}}$ groups

17.15

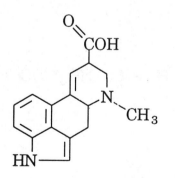

17.16

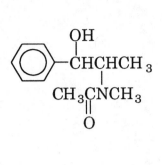

17.17

$$CH_3\overset{\overset{\displaystyle O}{\|}}{C}Cl \;+\; 2NH_3 \longrightarrow CH_3\overset{\overset{\displaystyle O}{\|}}{C}NH_2 \;+\; NH_4{}^+Cl^-$$

$$CH_3\overset{\overset{\displaystyle O}{\|}}{C}O\overset{\overset{\displaystyle O}{\|}}{C}CH_3 \;+\; 2NH_3 \longrightarrow CH_3\overset{\overset{\displaystyle O}{\|}}{C}NH_2 \;+\; NH_4{}^{+\;-}OCCH_3$$

17.18

$$CH_3\overset{\overset{\displaystyle O}{\|}}{C}Cl \;+\; 2NH_2CH_3 \longrightarrow CH_3\overset{\overset{\displaystyle O}{\|}}{C}NHCH_3 \;+\; CH_3NH_3{}^+Cl^-$$

$$CH_3\overset{\overset{\displaystyle O}{\|}}{C}O\overset{\overset{\displaystyle O}{\|}}{C}CH_3 \;+\; 2NH_2CH_3 \longrightarrow CH_3\overset{\overset{\displaystyle O}{\|}}{C}NHCH_3 \;+\; CH_3NH_3{}^{+\;-}OCCH_3$$

17.19

(a)

$$NH_2CH_2\overset{\overset{\displaystyle O}{\|}}{C}NHCHC\overset{\overset{\displaystyle O}{\|}}{\underset{\underset{\displaystyle CH_3}{|}}{}}-$$

(b) Two

17.20

$$CH_3CH_2\overset{\overset{\displaystyle O}{\|}}{C}NH_2 + CH_3\overset{\overset{\displaystyle O}{\|}}{C}NH_2$$

17.21 (a) $CH_3CH_2NH_2 + CH_3CO_2H$
      (b) $(CH_3)_2CHNH_2 + CH_3CH_2CO_2H$
      (c) $CH_3NH_2 + (CH_3)_2CHCO_2H$
      (d) Does not hydrolyze.

17.22

(a)
$$\underset{\displaystyle NH_2CHCH_2CO_2H}{\overset{\displaystyle CH_3}{|}} + NH_2CH_2CO_2H$$

(b)
$$2NH_3 + \underset{}{HO_2CCH_2\overset{\overset{\displaystyle CH_3}{|}}{C}HCO_2H}$$

(c)
$$CH_3\underset{\underset{\displaystyle NH_2}{|}}{C}HCH_2CH_2CH_2CO_2H$$

(d) $2NH_3 + (H_2CO_3)$. The latter breaks up into $CO_2 + H_2O$.

17.23 Compounds that the body makes in special glands to serve as chemical messengers.
17.24 Adrenergic agents
17.25 Epinephrine and norepinephrine
17.26 Adrenergic drugs
17.27 The 1,2-hydroxybenzene ring system (the catechol system).
17.28 Yes
17.29 The β-phenylethylamines
17.30 (a) Dexidrin   (b) Amphetamines
17.31 The amide group
17.32 The hydrogen bond
17.33 (a) Water reacts quantitatively with alkenes, acetals or ketals, esters, and

amides. (Not shown are the hydrolyses of acid chlorides, acid anhydrides, and esters of phosphoric acid.) The R groups can be alike or different. (H)R means that the group can be H or R.

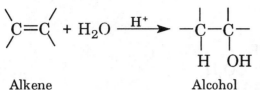

$$\begin{array}{ccc} \diagdown\text{C}=\text{C}\diagup & + \text{ } H_2O & \xrightarrow{\text{H}^+} & -\underset{\text{H}}{\overset{|}{\text{C}}}-\underset{\text{OH}}{\overset{|}{\text{C}}}- \\ \diagup \qquad \diagdown & & \end{array}$$

Alkene   Alcohol

$$\underset{\text{(H)R}}{\overset{\text{(H)R}}{\text{(H)RC(OR)}_2}} + H_2O \xrightarrow{\text{H}^+} \overset{\text{O}}{\overset{||}{\text{(H)RCR(H)}}} + \text{2HOR}$$

Acetal or   Aldehyde   Alcohol
ketal   or ketone

$$\overset{\text{O}}{\overset{||}{\text{(H)RCOR}}} + H_2O \xrightarrow{\text{H}^+} \overset{\text{O}}{\overset{||}{\text{(H)RCOH}}} + \text{HOR}$$

Ester   Carboxylic   Alcohol
                acid

$$\overset{\text{O}}{\overset{||}{\text{(H)RCNH}_2}} + H_2O \xrightarrow{\text{H}^+} \overset{\text{O}}{\overset{||}{\text{(H)RCOH}}} + \text{NH}_3$$

Amide   Carboxylic   Ammonia
                acid

(The Hs on N of the amide can be replaced by one or two alkyl groups.
(b) The groups that can be hydrogenated are alkenes, aldehydes and ketones, and disulfides.

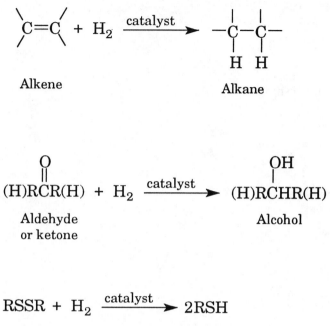

Alkene   Alkane

Aldehyde
or ketone

Alcohol

RSSR + H₂ $\xrightarrow{\text{catalyst}}$ 2RSH

Disul-   Thioalcohol
fide

(c)   Oxidizable groups in our study are 1° and 2° alcohols, aldehydes, a n d thioalcohols.

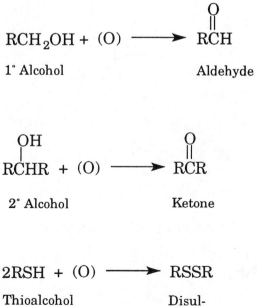

1° Alcohol   Aldehyde

2° Alcohol   Ketone

2RSH + (O) ⟶ RSSR

Thioalcohol   Disul-
                                fide

17.34   Acetal (or ketal) group in carbohydrates; ester group in fats and oils; and the amide group in proteins.

17.35   (a)   1.66 g benzoic acid
        (b)   28.3 mL 0.482 M HCl

17.36

(a) $CH_3CO_2H + CH_3OH$

(b)
$$\begin{array}{c} OH \\ | \\ CH_3CHCH_2CH_3 \end{array}$$

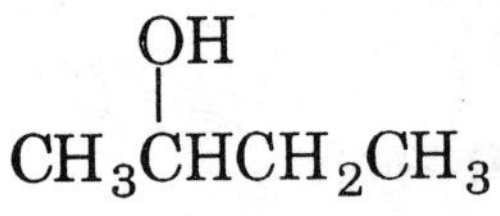

(c)   No reaction

(d)
$$\begin{array}{c} O \\ || \\ CH_3CH_2CNH_2 \end{array}$$

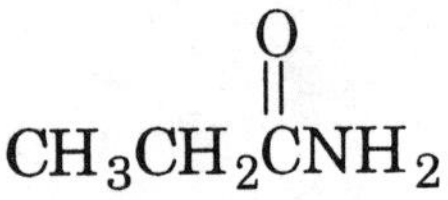

(e)   No reaction

(f)   No reaction

(g) $CH_3CHO + 2HOCH_2CH_3$

(h) $CH_3CH_2CO_2H$

(i)   No reaction

(j)
$$\begin{array}{c} O \\ || \\ CH_3CH_2COCH_3 \end{array}$$

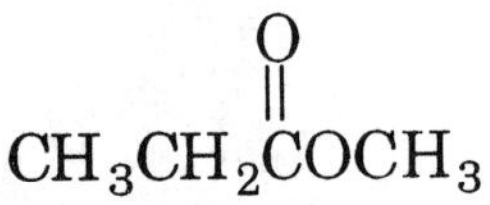

(k) $CH_3CH_2CO_2^- Na^+ + NH_3$

(l)

$$OCH_3$$
$$CH_3CH_2CHOCH_3$$

(m) $CH_3CH_2SSCH_2CH_3$

(n) $C_6H_5CO_2^- Na^+ + HOCH_2CH(CH_3)_2$

(o) $Cl^- {}^+NH_3CH_2CH_2CH(CH_3)_2$

(p) $CH_3CH_2CH_2CH_2OCH_3$

17.37

(a) $Na^{+-}O_2CCH_2CH_2CH_3$

(b)   No reaction

(c) $CH_3CH_2OCH_2CH_2CO_2H$

(d) $Cl^- {}^+NH_3CH_2CH_2NH_3^+ Cl^-$

(e)

$$OH$$
$$\langle \ \rangle - CHCH_2CH_3$$

(f)   No reaction

(g)

$$OCH_3$$
$$CH_3 - \langle \bigcirc \rangle - CHOCH_3$$

(h)

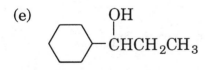
$CH_3 - \langle \bigcirc \rangle - CO_2^- Na^+ + HOCH_2CH(CH_3)_2$

(i) $CH_3\overset{\overset{O}{\|}}{C}CH_2CH_3$

(j) $CH_3\overset{\overset{O}{\|}}{C}CH_3 + 2HOCH_2CH_3$

(k) $HO_2C(CH_3)_3CO_2H + 2CH_3CH_2OH$

(l) $CH_3CH_2CHO + 2CH_3OH$

(m) $CH_3\overset{\overset{O}{\|}}{C}NH_2 + NH_4{}^{+}\,{}^{-}O\overset{\overset{O}{\|}}{C}CH_3$

(n) $2CH_3SH$

(o) $CH_3(CH_2)_5CO_2CH_3$

(p) $CH_3NH_2 + HO_2CCH_2CH_2NH_2 + HO_2CCH_2CH_3$

17.38 (a) methyl butanoate
(b) 1-bromo-2-methylpropane
(c) 3-methylbutanal
(d) 2-pentene
(e) 2,2,4-trimethylpentane
(f) 2-methyl-3-hexanone
(g) 2-methyl-2-propanol
(h) pentanoic acid
(i) sodium ethanoate

17.39   (a)   sodium benzoate
        (b)   propylamine
        (c)   aniline
        (d)   propionic acid
        (e)   butyraldehyde
        (f)   isobutyl alcohol
        (g)   phenol
        (h)   diethyl ether
        (i)   ethyl butyrate
        (j)   acetamide
        (k)   acetone

17.40   **B**. It is a carboxylic acid that will become an anion at the basic pH and so more soluble in water. (**A** is an ester and **C** is an amine.)

17.41   **B**. It is an amine (plus a ketone), and so will form a water-soluble salt in acid. (**A** is an amide; **C** is a carboxylic acid)

Chapter 18

Practice Exercises, Chapter 18

1.

(a)

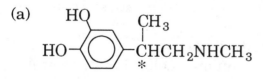

(b) $CH_3\overset{*}{C}HCO_2H$
          |
          OH

(c) $CH_3\overset{*}{C}H\overset{*}{C}HCO_2^-$
          | |
          HO NH_3^+

(d)

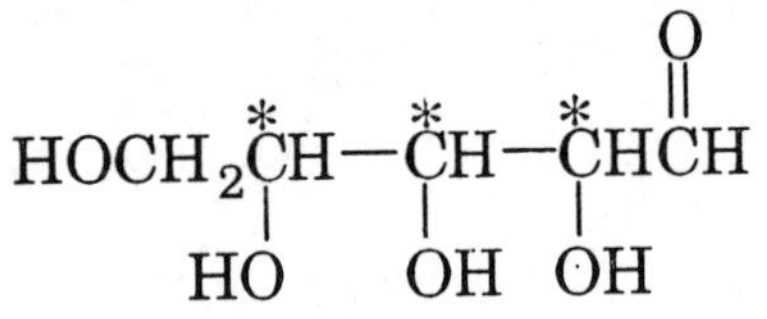

$$\text{HOCH}_2\overset{*}{\text{C}}\text{H}-\overset{*}{\text{C}}\text{H}-\overset{*}{\text{C}}\text{HCH}\overset{\displaystyle\text{O}}{\|}$$

with HO, OH, OH substituents

2.   (a) 3   (b) 8   (c) 4

3.

$$\text{CH}_3\overset{*}{\text{C}}\text{H}\overset{*}{\text{C}}\text{HCH}_3$$
$$\text{HO}\quad\text{OH}$$

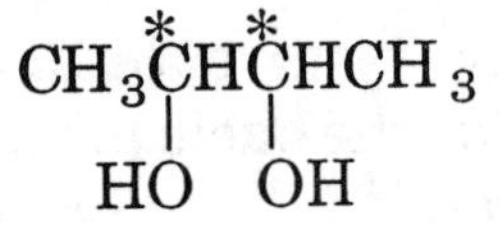

The two tetrahedral stereocenters are identical; they hold identical sets of four different groups, CH_3, OH, H, and $CH_3CH(OH)$.

Review Exercises

18.1   Their molecular structures must have different atom-to-atom sequences.

18.2 $CH_3CH_2CH_2OH$ and $(CH_3)_2CHOH$

18.3   The must have identical constitutions—identical molecular formulas, functional groups, and heavy-atom skeletons—but display different geometries.

18.4   *Enantiomers* are substances whose molecules are related as object to mirror image that cannot be superimposed. *Diastereomers* are stereoisomers that are not enantiomers.

18.5   (a) Stereoisomers   (b) Constitutional

18.6   Each unique substance must have a unique molecular structure.

18.7

(a) 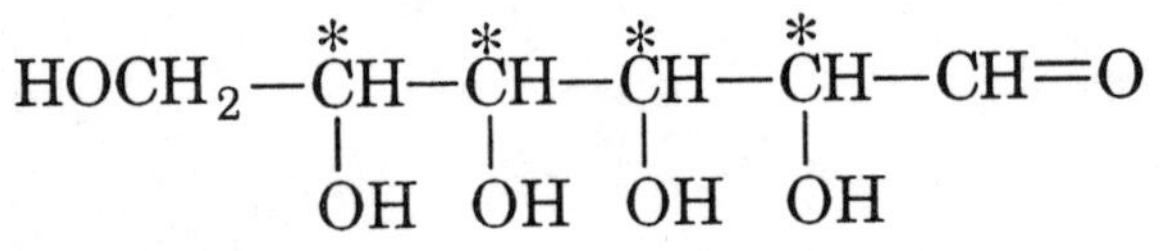 $\text{HOCH}_2-\overset{*}{\text{C}}\text{H}-\overset{*}{\text{C}}\text{H}-\overset{*}{\text{C}}\text{H}-\overset{*}{\text{C}}\text{H}-\text{CH}=\text{O}$
with OH, OH, OH, OH substituents

(b)   All are different.

(c)   16

(d)   8

18.8   No; glycine has no tetrahedral stereocenter.

18.9   (a) No; citric acid has no tetrahedral stereocenter.

(b)

$$CH_2CO_2CH_3$$
$$|$$
$$HO\overset{*}{C}CO_2H$$
$$|$$
$$CH_2CO_2H$$

(The bottom carboxyl group, but not the middle one, might also have been chosen for showing it as a methyl ester.)

18.10   148.5 °C. The designations (+) and (−) placed before otherwise identical names tell us that the two compounds are enantiomers, and enantiomers have identical physical properties.

18.11   They have identical constitutions, bond lengths, and bond angles and so must have identical polarities and identical London forces between molecules. Because the factors that determine physical properties are identical, the properties must be identical.

18.12   The ability of the molecules of enantiomers to be approached by and fit to an *achiral* molecule must be identical in the same way that either hand can "react" with an achiral water glass or broom handle.

18.13   In the same way that one hand fits best to its matching glove, both hand and glove being chiral, so must one enantiomer interact differently than the other with a chiral ion or molecule.

18.14   −0.375°

18.15   −21°

18.16   The amount of rotation is directly proportional to the actual population of chiral molecules encountered by the polarized light. This population increases directlyi with concentration or with path length.

18.17   The optical activity is lost. The effect on the polarized light by the chiral molecules of one enantiomer is cancelled by the opposite effect exerted by the molecules of the other enantiomer.

18.18   3.01 g/100 mL

18.19   4.86 g/100 mL

18.20   Strychnine. The calculated specific rotation for the sample is −139°, which corresponds to the value for strychnine, not for brucine.

18.21   Cortisone. The calculated specific rotation for the sample is +209, which corresponds to cortisone, not corticosterone.

18.22   (a)   They are not related as object to mirror image.
        (b)   Because they are stereoisomers of each other.
        (c)   What makes them different is not a lack of free rotation.
        (d)   Diastereomers

18.23   Methane lacks a tetrahedral stereocenter and is not a member of a *set* of stereoisomers.

18.24   It has tetrahedral stereocenters and is a member of a set of stereoisomers some of which are chiral and optically active.

18.25   A 50:50 mixture of enantiomers consists of chiral molecules but the mixture as a whole is optically inactive.

18.26   (a)   2-Butanol
        (b)   3-Methylhexane

18.27   The cis isomer exists as a pair of enantiomers involving the tetrahedral stereocenter (with the OH group), and the trans isomer likewise exists a a pair of enantiomers.

Chapter 19

Practice Exercises, Chapter 19

1.   (a)   a = b
              c = e
        (b)   Compounds a and d are enantiomers.
        (c)   Compound c (or e) is a meso compound.

2.

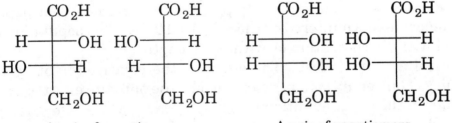

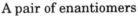

A pair of enantiomers   A pair of enantiomers

Review Exercises, Chapter 19

19.1   Materials, energy, and information.
19.2   Carbohydrates, lipids, and proteins.
19.3   Nucleic acids.
19.4   Organization.
19.5   (a) C   (b) D
       (c) A   (d) B and D

19.6

(a)

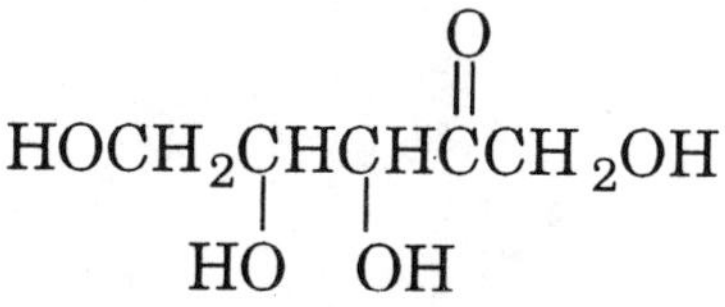

$$HOCH_2CHCHCCH_2OH$$
          $$|$$ $$|$$ $$||$$
          HO OH   O

(b)

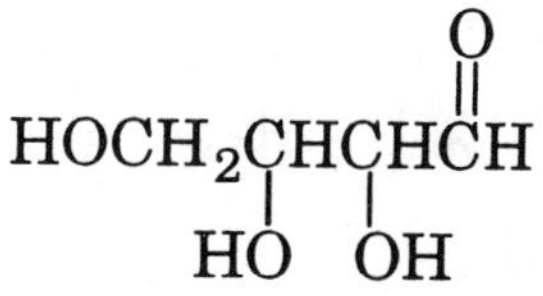

$$HOCH_2CHCHCH$$
          $$|$$ $$|$$ $$||$$
          HO OH   O

19.7

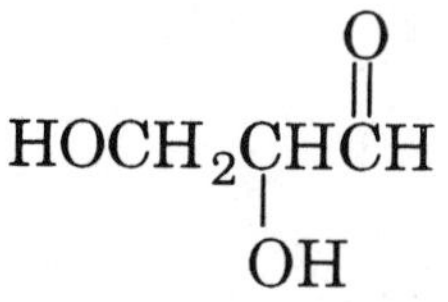

$$HOCH_2CHCH$$
          $$|$$ $$||$$
          OH   O

Glyceraldehyde

19.8

$$HOCH_2CCH_2OH$$
          $$||$$
          O

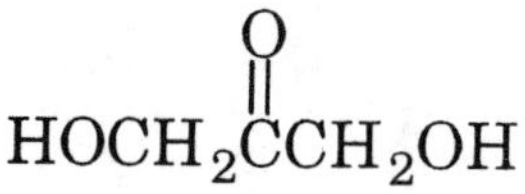

Dihydroxyacetone

19.9   Polysaccharide.
19.10   Reducing carbohydrate.
19.11   (a) 2   (b) Trisaccharide
19.12   Because the formula mass of CH_2O is 30, the unknown must have 5 CH_2O units
        and be a pentose, $C_5H_{10}O_5$. The change to $C_{13}H_{18}O_9$ signifies a gain of 4 O atoms;
        thus 4OH groups have been acetylated. Gentle oxidation *without loss of carbon*
        signifies an aldehyde; the unknown is an aldopentose. Its reduction to pentane
        means a *straight chain*. So, write the structure of an aldopentose with a
        straight chain.

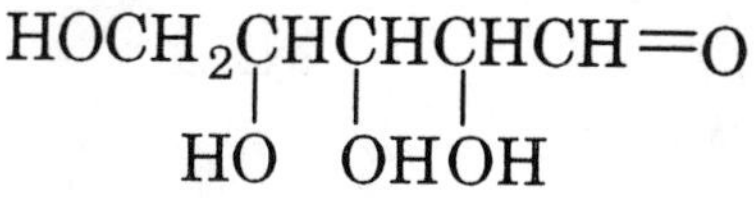

$$HOCH_2CHCHCHCH=O$$
          $$|$$ $$|$$ $$|$$
          HO OH OH

19.13

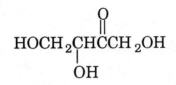

19.14   **A** is ruled out because it has one carbon holding two OH groups, an unstable
         system.
19.15   Glucose
19.16   (a)   2

(b)
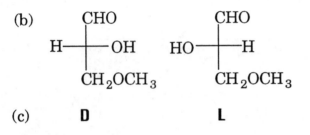

(c)   **D**   **L**

19.17   It has no tetrahedral stereocenter
19.18

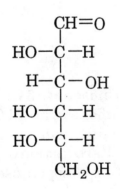

19.19

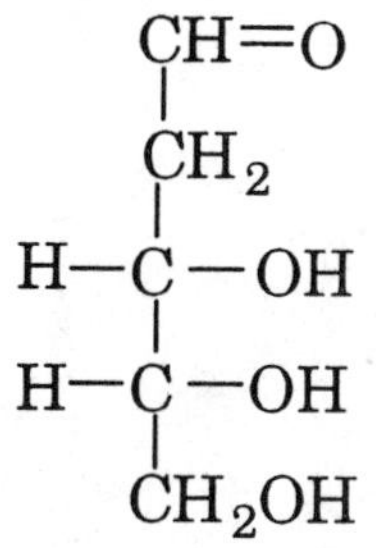

$$CH=O$$
$$CH_2$$
$$H-C-OH$$
$$H-C-OH$$
$$CH_2OH$$

19.20

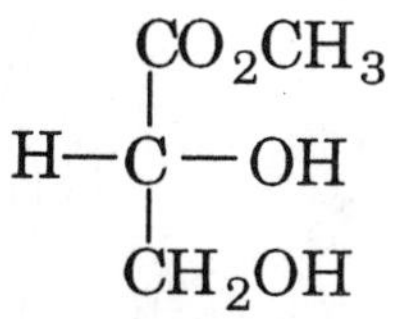

$$CO_2CH_3$$
$$H-C-OH$$
$$CH_2OH$$
$$\mathbf{D}$$

It must be in the same configurational family as **D**-glyceraldehyde because no bonds to the tetrahedral stereocenter are broken during its synthesis from **D**-glyceraldehyde.

19.21   (a)   **L** family

(b)
$$CH_2OH$$
$$C=O$$
$$H-OH$$
$$HO-H$$
$$H-OH$$
$$CH_2OH$$

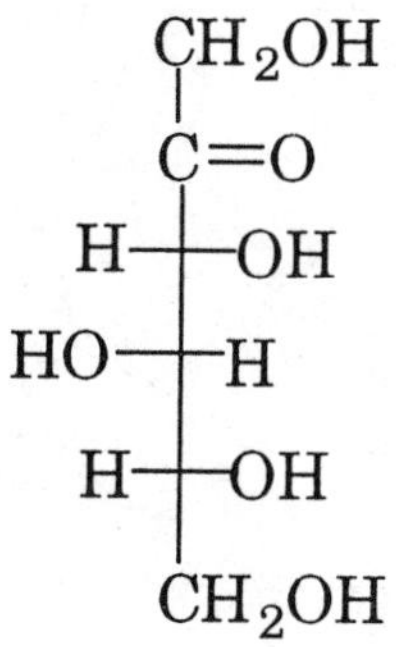

(c)

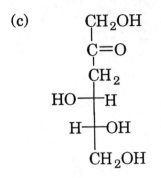

$$
\begin{array}{c}
CH_2OH \\
| \\
C=O \\
| \\
CH_2 \\
HO{-}\!\!|{-}H \\
H{-}\!\!|{-}OH \\
| \\
CH_2OH
\end{array}
$$

19.22

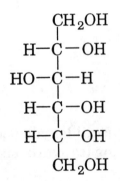

$$
\begin{array}{c}
CH_2OH \\
| \\
H{-}C{-}OH \\
| \\
HO{-}C{-}H \\
| \\
H{-}C{-}OH \\
| \\
H{-}C{-}OH \\
| \\
CH_2OH
\end{array}
$$

19.23

$$
\begin{array}{c}
CO_2H \\
| \\
H{-}C{-}OH \\
| \\
HO{-}C{-}H \\
| \\
H{-}C{-}OH \\
| \\
H{-}C{-}OH \\
| \\
CH_2OH
\end{array}
$$

19.24

(a)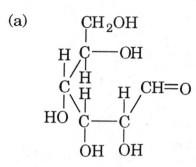

(b)   At carbon 3.

(c)   **D**-family. The relative positions of the CH_2OH group and the O atom of the ring tell us that the compound is in the **D**-family.

(d)   **D**-allose

(e)   An epimer

19.25

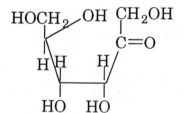

19.26

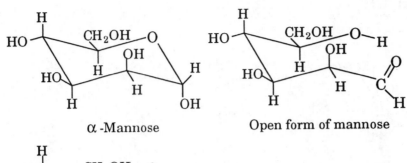

α-Mannose

Open form of mannose

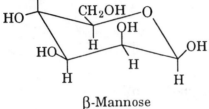

β-Mannose

19.27

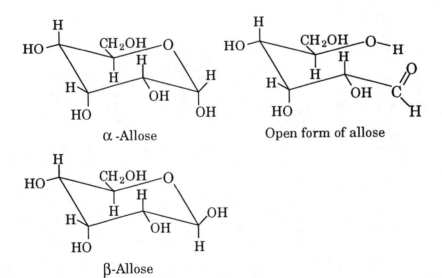

α-Allose

Open form of allose

β-Allose

19.28   As molecules of the open-chain form are oxidized, the equilibrium continuously shifts to make more of the open chain form from the cyclic forms.

19.29   As the beta form is used, molecules of the other forms continuously change into it as the equilibria shift.

19.30

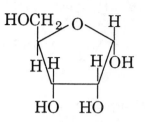

19.31   Something else: β-2-deoxyfructose

19.32

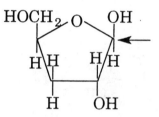

19.33   No, an OH group is required at position 4 to make possible the formation of the five-membered ring.

19.34   Sorbose is epimeric with fructose at positions 3 and 4.

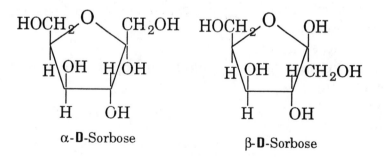

19.35

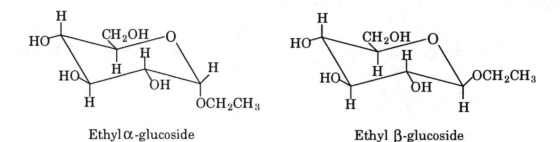

Ethyl α-glucoside   Ethyl β-glucoside

Another kind (diastereomers, Special Topic 18.1).

19.36

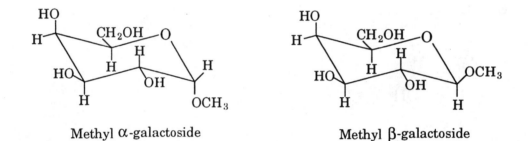

Methyl α-galactoside   Methyl β-galactoside

These are cis-trans isomers in the sense that we have used this concept, because the OCH$_3$ group is on opposite sides of the rings. However, the term is just not used in connection with glycosides.

19.37   Maltose, lactose, and sucrose.

19.38   A 50 : 50 mixture of glucose and fructose.

19.39   Its molecules have no hemiacetal or hemiketal group at which ring-opening and ring-closing can occur.

19.40   (a)   Yes, see arrow
        (b)   Yes, see enclosure

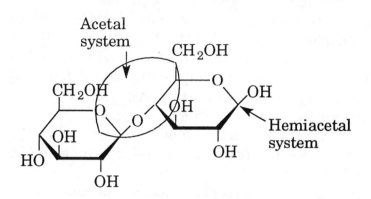

(c)   A β(1→4) bridge

(d)   Yes, it has the hemiacetal system so the open form of the corresponding ring (on the right) has an aldehyde group.

(e)   Maltose has an α(1→4) bridge between the two rings.

(f)   Two glucose molecules

19.41   (a)   No, it has no hemiacetal or hemiketal system and so cannot give a Tollens' or a Benedict's test.

(b)   No, for the same reason given in (a).

(c)   Two molecules of glucose

19.42

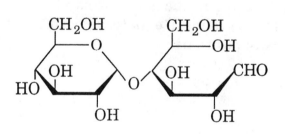

19.43

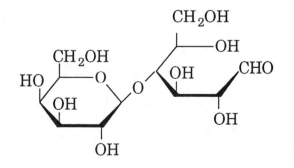

19.44   Amylose and amylopectin in starch; glycogen; cellulose

19.45   The oxygen bridges in amylose are $\alpha(1\rightarrow4)$ and in cellulose they are $\beta(1\rightarrow4)$.

19.46   They are polymers of α-glucose and have $\alpha(1\rightarrow4)$ bridges.

19.47   Amylose is an entirely linear polymer of α-glucose in which all of the oxygen bridges are $\alpha(1\rightarrow4)$, and amylopectin has branching in which $\alpha(1\rightarrow6)$ bridges link amylose-like strands to other amylose strands.

19.48   Humans lack the enzyme for catalyzing this reaction.

19.49   A test for starch. The reagent is a solution of iodine in aqueous potassium iodide. It is used to test for starch, and a positive test is the immediate appearance of a blue-black color.

19.50   They are very similar except that glycogen is more branched.

19.51   To store glucose units.

19.52   Solar energy is the energy that makes possible the synthesis of glucose from low-energy, simple molecules.

19.53 $n\mathrm{CO_2} + n\mathrm{H_2O} + \text{solar energy} \xrightarrow[\text{plant enzymes}]{\text{chlorophyll}} (\mathrm{CH_2O})_n + n\mathrm{O_2}$

19.54   Chlorophyll. Green

19.55   The oceans. By algae and phytoplankton

19.56   Oxygen is synthesized by photosynthesis and then consumed by the animals and plants that use the products of photosynthesis. As the living systems use these products, they release $\mathrm{CO_2}$ and $\mathrm{H_2O}$ (and minerals), which is again re-used in photosynthesis.

19.57   Less nudging of electron-clouds occurs in the chair forms.

19.58   The electron clouds associated with groups in equatorial positions are farther apart than when they are in axial positions.

19.59

(a)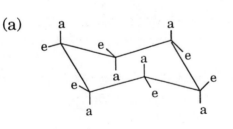

(b)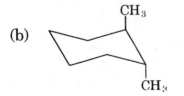

(c)

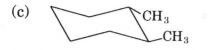

(d)

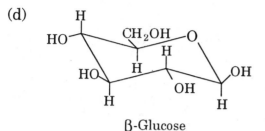

β-Glucose
(all substituents are equatorial)

(e)

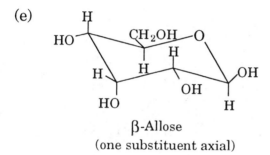

β-Allose
(one substituent axial)

19.60   Over a period of a week some of the sucrose (a nonreducing sugar) hydrolyzes to give glucose and fructose, both being reducing sugars that give a positive Tollens' test.

19.61   An enzyme (amylase) in the saliva catalyzes the hydrolysis of enough of the starch so that the resulting solution fails to give the iodine test.

19.62   5

19.63   To form a cyclic hemiacetal, the ring would be limited to four atoms. Although four-membered rings are known, they are difficult to form because of the unfavorable bond angle (90° as compared to the normal angle of 109.5°).

Chapter 20

Practice Exercises, Chapter 20

1.

$$CH_3(CH_2)_7 \quad (CH_2)_7CO_2H$$
$$\diagdown C=C \diagup$$
$$H \diagup \qquad \diagdown H$$

2. $CH_3(CH_2)_{26}CO_2(CH_2)_{25}CH_3$

3.

$$I + 3NaOH \longrightarrow$$

$$\underset{\text{Glycerol}}{\begin{array}{l} CH_2OH \\ | \\ CHOH \\ | \\ CH_2OH \end{array}} \quad \begin{array}{l} + \ Na^+ \ ^-O\overset{\displaystyle O}{\overset{\|}{C}}(CH_2)_7CH=CH(CH_2)_7CH_3 \\[2mm] + \ Na^+ \ ^-O\overset{\displaystyle O}{\overset{\|}{C}}(CH_2)_{16}CH_3 \\[2mm] + \ Na^+ \ ^-O\overset{\displaystyle O}{\overset{\|}{C}}(CH_2)_7CH=CHCH_2CH=CH(CH_2)_4CH_3 \end{array}$$

4.

$$I + 3H_2 \xrightarrow{\text{catalyst}}$$

$$\begin{array}{l} CH_2-O-\overset{\displaystyle O}{\overset{\|}{C}}(CH_2)_{16}CH_3 \\ | \qquad\qquad\quad O \\ CH-O-\overset{\displaystyle\ }{\overset{\|}{C}}(CH_2)_{16}CH_3 \\ | \qquad\qquad\quad O \\ CH_2-O-\overset{\displaystyle\ }{\overset{\|}{C}}(CH_2)_{16}CH_3 \end{array}$$

Review Exercises, Chapter 20

20.1   It is not obtainable from living plants or animals.

20.2   It is extractable from animal and plant sources by relatively nonpolar solvents.

20.3   It is soluble in water, and it isn't present in plant or animal sources.

20.4   It is present in undecomposed plant or animal materials and is extractable by relatively nonpolar solvents.

20.5   Palmitic acid, $CH_3(CH_2)_{14}CO_2H$

Stearic acid, $CH_3(CH_2)_{16}CO_2H$

20.6

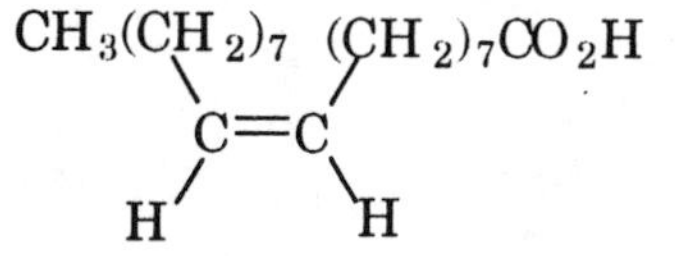

$CH_3(CH_2)_7$ $(CH_2)_7CO_2H$

$$C=C$$

H   H

Oleic acid

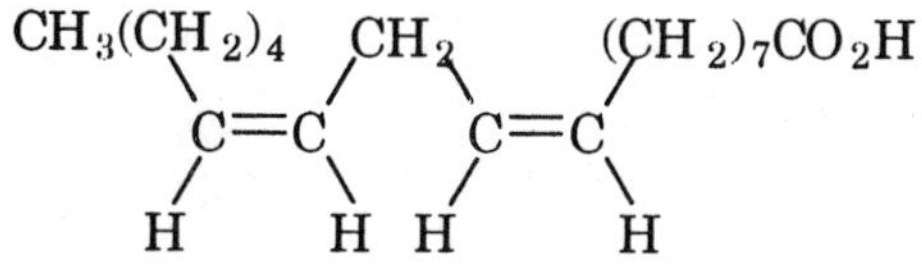

$CH_3(CH_2)_4$ CH_2 $(CH_2)_7CO_2H$

$$C=C \quad C=C$$

H   H H   H

Linoleic acid

CH_3CH_2 CH_2 CH_2 $(CH_2)_7CO_2H$

$$C=C \quad C=C \quad C=C$$

H   H H   H H   H

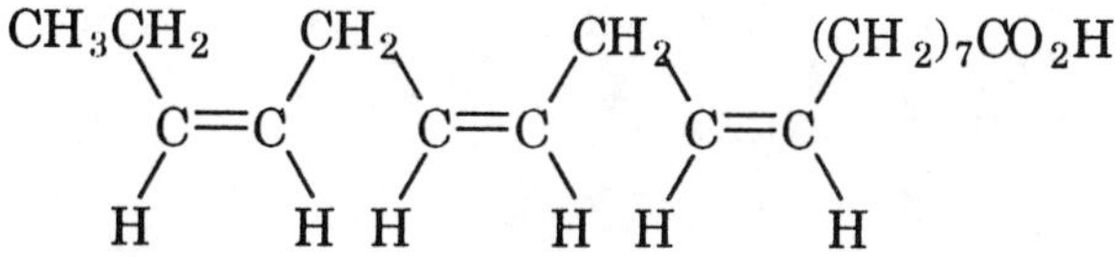

Linolenic acid

20.7   (a) $CH_3(CH_2)_{14}CO_2H + NaOH \rightarrow CH_3(CH_2)_{14}CO_2^-Na^+ + H_2O$

(b) $CH_3(CH_2)_{14}CO_2H + CH_3OH \xrightarrow{HCl} CH_3(CH_2)_{14}CO_2CH_3 + H_2O$

20.8   The organic products of the reactions are the following.

(a) 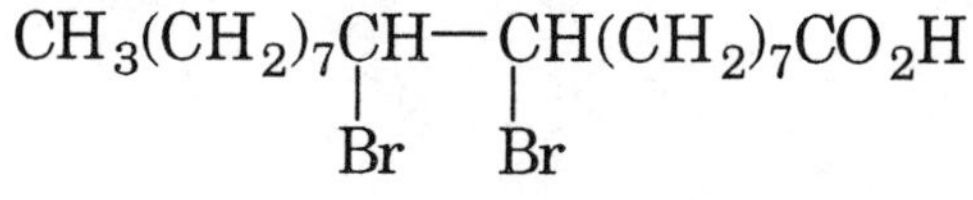 $CH_3(CH_2)_7CH-CH(CH_2)_7CO_2H$

          Br   Br

(b) $CH_3(CH_2)_7CH=CH(CH_2)_7CO_2^-K^+$

(c) $CH_3(CH_2)_{16}CO_2H$

(d) $CH_3(CH_2)_7CH=CH(CH_2)_7CO_2CH_2CH_3$

20.9   **A**. **B** is branched and has an uneven number of carbon atoms.

20.10   They are fatty acids with 20 carbons per molecule, including five-membered rings.

20.11

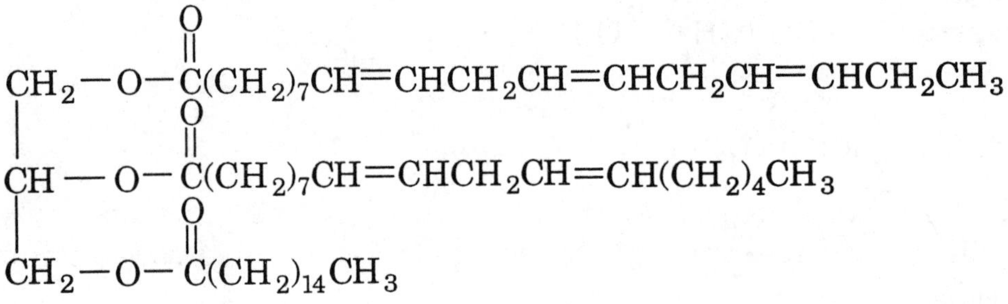

$$CH_2-O-\overset{\overset{\displaystyle O}{\|}}{C}(CH_2)_7CH=CHCH_2CH=CHCH_2CH=CHCH_2CH_3$$
$$CH-O-\overset{\overset{\displaystyle O}{\|}}{C}(CH_2)_7CH=CHCH_2CH=CH(CH_2)_4CH_3$$
$$CH_2-O-\overset{\overset{\displaystyle O}{\|}}{C}(CH_2)_{14}CH_3$$

20.12

$$CH_2-O-\overset{\overset{\displaystyle O}{\|}}{C}(CH_2)_{16}CH_3$$
$$CH-O-\overset{\overset{\displaystyle O}{\|}}{C}(CH_2)_7CH=CH(CH_2)_7CH_3$$
$$CH_2-O-\overset{\overset{\displaystyle O}{\|}}{C}(CH_2)_{14}CH_3$$

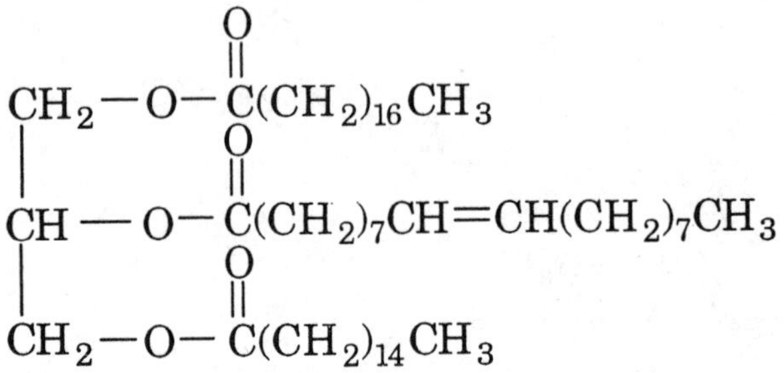

20.13

$$HOCH_2\underset{\underset{\displaystyle OH}{|}}{C}HCH_2OH + HO_2C(CH_2)_7CH=CHCH_2CH=CH(CH_2)_4CH_3$$

$$+ \ HO_2C(CH_2)_{12}CH_3 \ + \ HO_2C(CH_2)_7CH=CH(CH_2)_7CH_3$$

20.14

$$HOCH_2\underset{\underset{\textstyle OH}{|}}{CH}CH_2OH + Na^{+\,-}O_2C(CH_2)_7CH=CHCH_2CH=CH(CH_2)_4CH_3$$

$$+\ Na^{+\,-}O_2C(CH_2)_{12}CH_3 + Na^{+\,-}O_2C(CH_2)_7CH=CH(CH_2)_7CH_3$$

20.15   More than one structure is possible because the three different acyl groups can be joined in different orders to the glycerol unit. One possible structure is the following.

$$
\begin{aligned}
&\qquad\qquad\ \ \overset{\textstyle O}{\overset{\textstyle\|}{}} \\
&CH_2-O-C(CH_2)_{10}CH_3 \\
&|\qquad\qquad\ \ \overset{\textstyle O}{\overset{\textstyle\|}{}} \\
&CH\ -O-C(CH_2)_7CH=CHCH_2CH=CH(CH_2)_4CH_3 \\
&|\qquad\qquad\ \ \overset{\textstyle O}{\overset{\textstyle\|}{}} \\
&CH_2-O-C(CH_2)_7CH=CH(CH_2)_7CH_3
\end{aligned}
$$

20.16   Only one structure is possible if the molecule is to be chiral (have a tetrahedral stereocenter indicated by the asterisk).

$$
\begin{aligned}
&\qquad\qquad\ \ \overset{\textstyle O}{\overset{\textstyle\|}{}} \\
&CH_2-O-C(CH_2)_7CH=CH(CH_2)_7CH_3 \\
&|\qquad\qquad\ \ \overset{\textstyle O}{\overset{\textstyle\|}{}} \\
&\overset{*}{CH}\ -O-C(CH_2)_{10}CH_3 \\
&|\qquad\qquad\ \ \overset{\textstyle O}{\overset{\textstyle\|}{}} \\
&CH_2-O-C(CH_2)_{10}CH_3
\end{aligned}
$$

20.17   There are more alkene double bonds per molecule in vegetable oils than in animal fats.

20.18   The triacylglycerol molecules that are present have several alkene units per molecule, so the substances are more "polyunsaturated" than the animal fats.

20.19   Hydrogenation.

20.20   Butter melts on the tongue:, lard and tallow do not.

20.21 $CH_3(CH_2)_{16}CO_2(CH_2)_{17}CH_3$

20.22   **C.** **A** is ruled out because *both* the acid and alcohol portions of the wax molecule are usually long-chain. **B** is ruled out because *both* of these portions are likely to have an even number of carbons.

20.23   The molecules of both types give glycerol and phosphoric acid plus a fatty acid when fully hydrolyzed.

20.24   The phosphate ester unit; the negative charge is on oxygen. A nitrogen atom carries the positive charge.

20.25   Molecules of both types are derivatives of sphingosine (rather than glycerol). Sphingomyelin molecules have a phosphate ester unit but those of the cerebrosides have a monosaccharide unit instead.

20.26   The OH (alcohol) groups on the sugar unit.

20.27   Their molecules bear electrical charges at different locations.

20.28   Cell membranes.

20.29   Sphingomyelins and cerebrosides

20.30   Glycosidic links. The linkage involves the hemiacetal carbon of the sugar ring. The glycosidic link is more easily hydrolyzed (being an acetal, not an ordinary ether).

20.31

(a)

$$CH_2-O-\overset{\overset{O}{\|}}{C}(CH_2)_7CH=CHCH_2CH=CHCH_2CH=CHCH_2CH_3$$

$$\overset{*}{C}H-O-\overset{\overset{O}{\|}}{C}(CH_2)_7CH=CH(CH_2)_7CH_3$$

$$CH_2-O-\underset{\underset{O^-}{|}}{\overset{\overset{O}{\|}}{P}}OCH_2CH_2\overset{+}{N}(CH_3)_3$$

(b)   A glycerophospholipid, because it is based on glycerol, not sphingosine.

(c)   Yes, the asterisk in the structure of part (a) marks the tetrahedral stereocenter.

(d)   A lecithin, because its hydrolysis would give 2-(trimethylamino)ethanol.

20.32

(a)

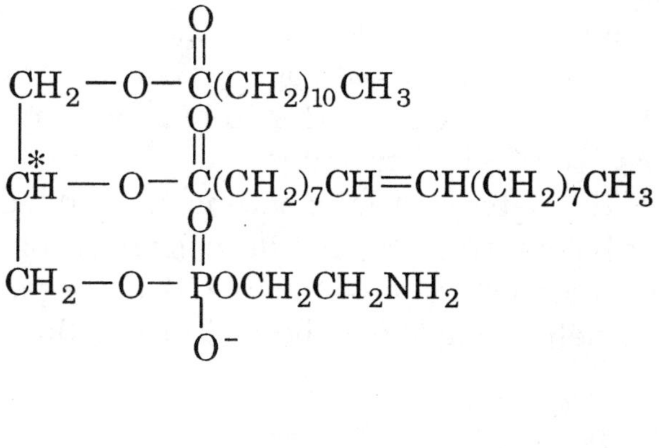

$$CH_2-O-\overset{\overset{O}{\|}}{C}(CH_2)_{10}CH_3$$

$$\overset{*}{C}H-O-\overset{\overset{O}{\|}}{C}(CH_2)_7CH=CH(CH_2)_7CH_3$$

$$CH_2-O-\underset{\underset{O^-}{|}}{\overset{\overset{O}{\|}}{P}}OCH_2CH_2NH_2$$

(b)   A phosphoglyceride, because it is based on glycerol.

(c)   Yes, the asterisk marks a tetrahedral stereocenter.

(d)   A cephalin, because its hydrolysis would give ethanolamine.

20.33   The anion of cholic acid.

20.34   Vitamin D_3.

20.35   Estradiol, progesterone, testosterone, and androsterone are four.

20.36   Cholesterol.

20.37   Cholesterol. As surface-active agents (detergents) to aid in the digestion of lipids and the absorption of hydrophobic molecules from the digestive tract.

20.38   In various lipoprotein complexes.

20.39   The membrane consists mostly of two layers of phospholipid molecules whose hydrophobic parts intermingle with each other between the layers and whose hydrophilic parts face toward aqueous solutions whether they are inside the cell or outside.

20.40   The hydrophobic tails intermesh with each other between the two layers of the bilayer.

20.41   Proteins

20.42   The water-avoiding properties of the hydrophobic units and the water-attracting properties of the hydrophilic units.

20.43   The provide conduits for the movements of small ions and molecules and they furnish recognition sites for hormones.

20.44   Arachidonic acid

20.45   Aspirin inhibits the synthesis of prostaglandins. Since prostaglandins enhance a fever, aspirin reduces a fever by this action.

20.46   It has a double bond at the third carbon counting from the ω-carbon, the one most remote from the carboxyl group.

20.47   Marine oils

20.48   Some evidence suggests that they protect one against the heart disease associated with elevated cholesterol levels.

20.49   Detergent. Soap is just one example of a detergent.

20.50   A mixture of the sodium or potassium salts of long-chain fatty acids.

20.51   A synthetic detergent, because it works better in hard water.

20.52   The detergent properties are those of an anion.

20.53   The hydrophobic tails of the detergent ions become embedded in the grease layer and the hydrophilic heads stick out into the wash solution. As the grease breaks up, its tiny globules become pincushioned with detergent ions, and the effect of the charges is to help bring the globules into a colloidal dispersion.

20.54   (a)   Yes

(b)   Yes

(c)   Ester groups

(d)

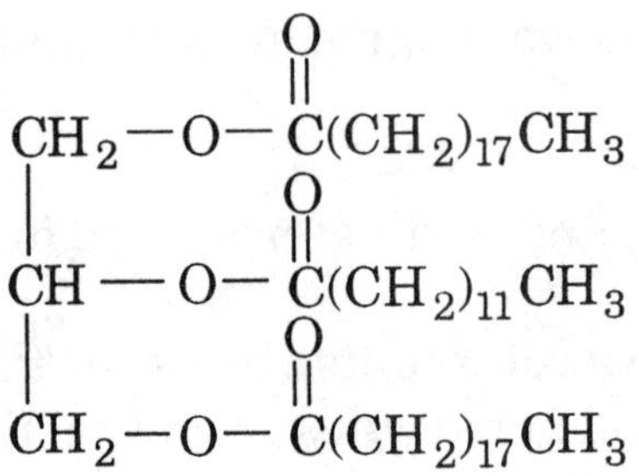

$$
\begin{array}{l}
CH_2-O-\overset{\displaystyle O}{\overset{\displaystyle \|}{C}}(CH_2)_{17}CH_3 \\
\mid \qquad\quad\; \overset{\displaystyle O}{} \\
CH-O-\overset{\displaystyle O}{\overset{\displaystyle \|}{C}}(CH_2)_{11}CH_3 \\
\mid \qquad\quad\; \overset{\displaystyle O}{} \\
CH_2-O-\overset{\displaystyle O}{\overset{\displaystyle \|}{C}}(CH_2)_{17}CH_3
\end{array}
$$

(e)   No. Its fatty acid units have odd numbers of carbon atoms.

20.55   (a)   Yes; it has both hydrophobic sections and polar groups (OH).

(b)   No, steroids have *three* six-membered rings plus a five-membered ring.

Chapter 21

Practice Exercises, Chapter 21

1.

Glycine	$^+NH_3CH_2CO_2^-$
Alanine	$^+NH_3CHCO_2^-$ $\underset{\displaystyle CH_3}{\vert}$
Lysine	$^+NH_3CHCO_2^-$ $\underset{\displaystyle CH_2CH_2CH_2CH_2NH_2}{\vert}$
Glutamic acid	$^+NH_3CHCO_2^-$ $\underset{\displaystyle CH_2CH_2CO_2H}{\vert}$

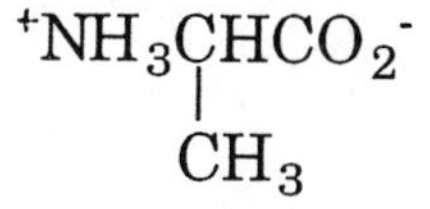

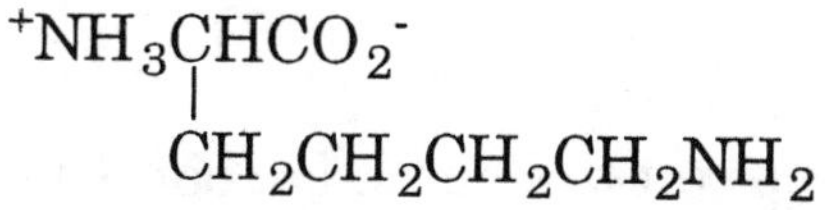

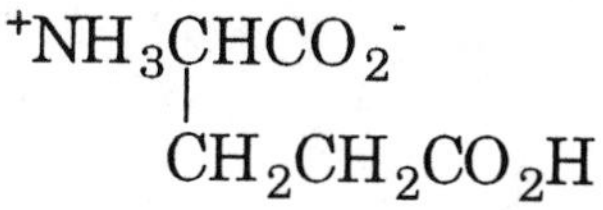

2.

(a)

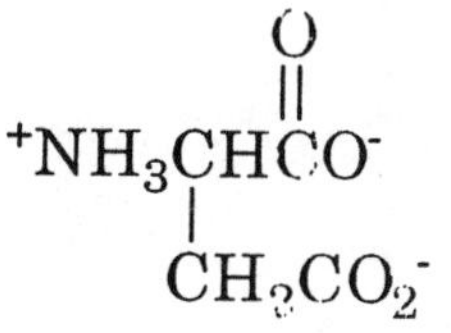

$$\underset{\displaystyle CH_2CO_2^-}{\overset{\displaystyle \overset{O}{\overset{\|}{}}}{^+NH_3CHCO^-}}$$

(b)

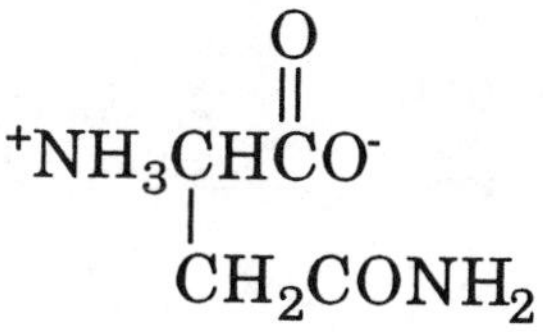

$$\underset{\displaystyle CH_2CONH_2}{\overset{\displaystyle \overset{O}{\overset{\|}{}}}{^+NH_3CHCO^-}}$$

3.

$$\underset{\displaystyle CH_2CH_2CH_2NHCNH_2}{\overset{\displaystyle \overset{O}{\overset{\|}{}}}{^+NH_3CHCO^-}} \quad \overset{\displaystyle \overset{+NH_2}{\overset{\|}{}}}{}$$

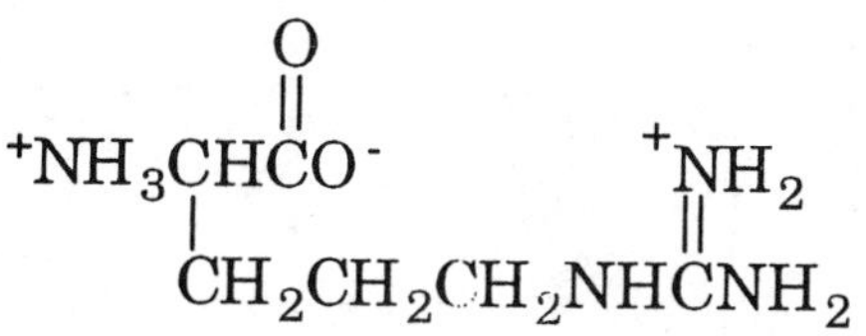

4. Hydrophilic; neutral. (The side chain has an amide group, not an amino group.)

5.

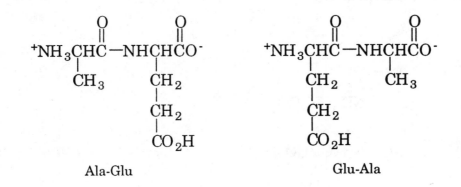

Ala-Glu   Glu-Ala

Review Exercises, Chapter 21

21.1   **B**. Its NH₃⁺ group is not on the same carbon that holds the CO_2^- group.
21.2

(a)

$$-NHCHC-$$
$$\overset{|}{CH_2CH(CH_3)_2}$$

(b) Leucine, Leu
(c) Hydrophobic
21.3 $^+NH_3CH_2CO_2H$
21.4

$$NH_2\underset{\overset{|}{CH_3}}{C}HCO_2^-$$

21.5

$$NH_2\underset{\overset{|}{CH_3}}{C}HCO_2CH_2CH_3$$

The polarity of this molecule is much, much less than the polarity of the dipolar ionic form of alanine. Thus, the ester molecules stick together with weaker forces than present between alanine molecules, and the ester has a lower melting point than alanine.

21.6   The ester has an NH_2 group as the proton acceptor, whereas alanine itself has the CO_2^- group as the acceptor. The CO_2^- group in alanine is made a weak acceptor by the electron withdrawal of the adjacent NH_3^+ group of the dipolar ion. (The withdrawal of electron density from a proton-accepting site renders this site less able to take and hold a proton.)

21.7   **A**. It has amine-like groups that can both donate hydrogen bonds to water molecules and accept them. (**B** has an alkyl group side chain, which is hydrophobic.)

21.8   **B**. Its side chain is hydrocarbon-like, whereas **A** has an OH group.

21.9   (a)   At a pH of 10.   At the more basic pH, all protons that can be donated to base from the amino acid have left the molecule leaving it with a net charge of 1−.

(b)   To the anode.

21.10   Hydrophobic groups in the water-insoluble compound are unable to establish hydrogen bonds to water molecules. Thus the water molecules continue to "stick" to each other forcing the hydrophobic molecule to stay gathered together and insoluble.

21.11   Oxidizing agent

21.12   In the presence of additional acid, the following equilibrium shifts to the right in accordance with Le Châtelier's principle. This neutralizes the extra acid.

$$^+NH_3CH_2CO_2^- + H^+ \rightleftharpoons {}^+NH_3CH_2CO_2H$$

In the presence of additional base, the following equilibrium shifts to the right in accordance with Le Châtelier's principle. This neutralizes the extra base.

$$^+NH_3CH_2CO_2^- + OH^- \rightleftharpoons NH_2CH_2CO_2^- + H_2O$$

21.13

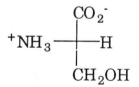

21.14   **A** has an amide bond not to the amino group of the α–position of an amino acid unit but to an amino group of a side chain (that of lysine). **B** has a proper peptide bond.

21.15

21.16

21.17	Lys-Glu-Cys	Glu-Cys-Lys Cys-Lys-Glu
	Lys-Cys-Glu	Glu-Lys-Cys Cys-Glu-Lys
21.18	Gly-Cys-Ala	Cys-Ala-Gly Ala-Gly-Cys
	Gly-Ala-Cys	Cys-Gly-Ala Ala-Cys-Gly

21.19

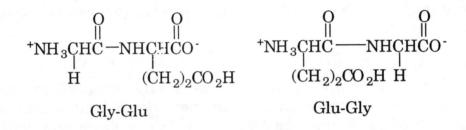

21.20

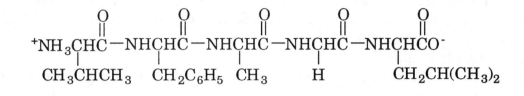

21.21

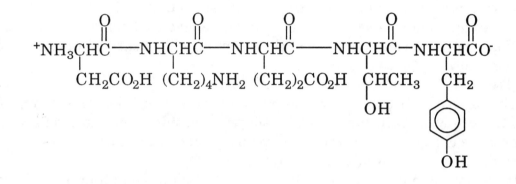

21.22   (a)   **A**
        (b)   **B**; it has only hydrophilic side chains. All those in **A** are hydrophobic.
21.23   (a)   **D**; its side chains are hydrophobic whereas those of **C** are hydrophilic.
21.24

        Gly-Cys-Ala
            |
        Gly-Cys-Ala

21.25   It is the sequence of four atoms of the polypeptide "backbone" that starts with
        an α-carbon and goes through the carbonyl carbon and its attached nitrogen
        to the next α-position (see Figure 21.3). These four atoms lie in the same plane.
21.26   The side chain on the first α-position of the peptide group is cis to the H atom
        on the N atom and trans to the side chain on the second α-position.
21.27   Primary structure
21.28   A protein with the overall structure and shape as it is found in the living
        system.
21.29   Tertiary
21.30   It forms *after* a polypeptide with a cysteine side chain has been put together,
        so it forms after the primary structure has become set.

21.31   Quaternary

21.32   Reduce

21.33   It is a right-handed helix stabilized by hydrogen bonds between carbonyl oxygen atoms and H atoms on N atoms farther down the helix. The side chains project to the outside of the helix.

21.34   A left-handed helix structure.

21.35   It aids in the hydroxylation of proline and lysine residues without which collagen is not adequately made.

21.36   It consists of three left-handed collagen helices wound together as a right-handed, cable-like triple helix. Between the strands occur molecular "bridges." A fibril forms when individual triple helices overlap lengthwise.

21.37   Covalent linkages fashioned from lysine side chains.

21.38   Hydrogen bonds. The side chains project above and below the "sheets."

21.39   No, they represents portions of the secondary structure of a polypeptide and often both features are present.

21.40   Hydrophobic and hydrophilic interactions.

21.41   The force of attraction between a site bearing a full negative charge (e,g., a CO_2^- group on a glutamic acid or aspartic acid side chain) and a site with a full positive charge (e.g., a NH_3^+ group on a lysine side chain).

21.42   In the development of tertiary structure.

21.43   It consists of more than two polypeptides associated together in a specific way, each with primary, secondary, and tertiary structure.

21.44   (a)   Myoglobin is single stranded; hemoglobin has four subunits.
        (b)   Myoglobin is in muscle tissue; hemoglobin is in red cells.
        (c)   Both have the heme unit.
        (d)   Myoglobin accepts and stores O_2 molecules carried into tissue by hemoglobin molecules.

21.45

$$\overset{+}{N}H_3CH\overset{\overset{\displaystyle O}{\|}}{C}O^- + \overset{+}{N}H_3CH\overset{\overset{\displaystyle O}{\|}}{C}O^- + \overset{+}{N}H_3CH\overset{\overset{\displaystyle O}{\|}}{C}O^-$$

$$\underset{CH_2OH}{} \qquad \underset{CH_3}{} \qquad \underset{CH_3CHCH_3}{}$$

$$+ \ \overset{+}{N}H_3CH\overset{\overset{\displaystyle O}{\|}}{C}O^- + \overset{+}{N}H_3CH_2CO_2^-$$

$$\underset{(CH_2)_4NH_2}{}$$

21.46   When pH = pI, the protein molecules carry equal numbers of opposite charges and so have net charges of 0. The oppositely charged sites of separate molecules are able to attract each other and form huge clusters of protein molecules that drop out of solution.

21.47   Digestion is the hydrolysis of peptide bonds to give a mixture of amino acids. Denaturation is the disorganization of the overall shape of a protein without necessarily the breakup of peptide bonds.

21.48   The reducing agent cleaves disulfide groups to SH units, and on renaturation by oxidation the same disulfide groups form again.

21.49   A change in the value of something, like concentration, from one place to another.

21.50   Plasma

21.51   Cell fluid

21.52   Cell fluid

21.53   It moves sodium and potassium ions through membranes against their concentration gradients in order to reestablish these gradients.

21.54   Metabolic, energy-consuming reactions involving membrane components drive the transport of substances through membranes.

21.55   Gap junctions are tubules made of proteins and fastened between cells that provide avenues for the direct movements of ions and molecules from one cell to another.

21.56 Ca^{2+}

21.57   A unit of a carbohydrate molecule.

21.58   An oligosaccharide is made from more than two monosaccharide units, and it never has the thousands of such units commonly present in polysaccharide molecules.

21.59   It is the generic name of all polysaccharides.

21.60   D-glucosamine

21.61   A shock-absorbing gel-like material made of glycosaminoglycans and found in cartilage and other extracellular spaces that hold fibrous proteins.

21.62   The molecules of fibrous proteins (collagen and elastin) give tensile strength; ground substance provides resiliency and shock-absorbancy.

21.63   The resiliency of ground substance depends on the hydrogen bonds increasing the "stickiness" of the molecules of ground substance and their abilities to hold large amounts of water as water of hydration.

21.64   Because of the several OH groups per monosaccharide unit, the oxygen bridges between monosaccharide units can be formed in a large number of ways.

21.65   Fibrous proteins are insoluble in water; globular proteins are more soluble.

21.66   Collagen changes to gelatin when boiled in water.

21.67   They both have strengthening functions in tissue; both are fibrous proteins.

The action of hot water on collagen turns it to gelatin, but elastin is unaffected in this way.

21.68   The globulins are less soluble in water than the albumins and they need the presence of dissolved salts to dissolve.

21.69   Fibrin is the protein that forms a blood clot. Fibrinogen is changed to fibrin by the clotting mechanism.

21.70   A lipoprotein

21.71   In a β-subunit, a valine residue with an isopropyl side chain has replaced a glutamic acid residue with a $CH_2CH_2CO_2H$ side chain. This affects the shape of the hemoglobin molecule.

21.72   Deoxygenated hemoglobin precipitates inside the red cell.

21.73   The distorted red cells are harder to pump and they can clump together to plug capillaries.

21.74   A membrane-bound protein to which a hormone (or neurotransmitter) molecule can bind and thus initiate some action in the cell.

21.75   RU 486 prevents the implantation of a fertilized ovum in the uterus by blocking the action of progesterone, a hormone needed to prepare the uterus for the implantation.

21.76   The linkages of oligosaccharide unit occur largely at protein surfaces, not in their interiors. Loss of the oligosaccharide thus leaves the protein shape intact.

21.77

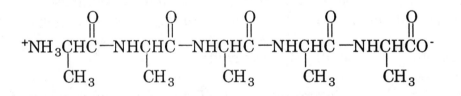

21.78   (a)   Yes. What is shown is a tripeptide written backwards from the conventional way.
   (b)   Phe
   (c)   Phe-Ala-Cys (N-terminus to C-terminus)
   (d)   No effect

Chapter 22

Practice Exercises, Chapter 22

1.   (a)   sucrose   (b)   glucose   (c)   protein   (d)   an ester

2.   Feedback inhibition

Review Exercises, Chapter 22

22.1   (a)   A catalyst.
        (b)   It consists of a protein.
22.2   Each enzyme catalyzes a reaction for a specific substrate or a specific kind of reaction.
22.3   (a)   An apoenzyme is the wholly polypeptide part of the enzyme.
        (b)   A cofactor is a non-polypeptide molecule or ion needed to make the complete enzyme.
        (c)   A coenzyme is one kind of cofactor, an organic molecule.
22.4 $CO_2 + H_2O \rightleftharpoons HCO_3^- + H^+$
        Carbonic anhydrase provides one of the greatest rate enhancements of all enzymes.
22.5   It catalyzes the rapid reestablishment of the equilibrium after it has been disturbed.
22.6   Nicotinamide.
22.7   Riboflavin.
22.8

$$\underset{\text{OH}}{CH_3CHCH_3} + NAD^+ \longrightarrow \underset{O}{CH_3CCH_3} + NAD{:}H + H^+$$

22.9 $H^+ + NADH + FAD \rightarrow NAD^+ + FADH_2$
22.10   By a phosphate ester unit. NADPH
22.11   (a)   An oxidation   (b)   The transfer of a methyl group
        (c)   A reaction with water   (d)   An oxidation-reduction equilibrium
22.12   Lactose is a disaccharide and the substrate for the enzyme, lactase.
22.13   Hydrolysis is a kind of reaction catalyzed by a hydrolase enzyme.
22.14   Enzymes of identical function but with slight differences in structure.
22.15   CK(MM) in skeletal muscle; CK(BB) in brain; and CK(MB) in heart muscle.
22.16   Active site.
22.17   By the necessity of the fitting of the substrate molecule to the surface of the enzyme much as a key must fit to a particular lock.
22.18   During the formation of the enzyme-substrate complex, the substrate induces modifications in the enzyme's shape to enable a better fit .
22.19   One
22.20   (a) $V \propto [E_0]$
        (b) $V \propto [S]$

22.21 The value of $[S]$ at which the reaction rate is one-half of the maximum rate.

22.22 At the another site. *Allosteric* describes an action induced at a site on an enzyme molecule at some distance from the active site.

22.23 The enzyme has more than one active site and that the (slower) activation of one site automatically causes the activation of the other(s).

22.24 As the substrate binds to one active site it induces changes in the shape of the enzyme that enable all active sites to become active, so the rate of the reaction suddenly increases rapidly.

22.25 An effector binds allosterically to the enzyme (by binding at a place other than any of the catalytically active sites) and induces changes in shape that activate these sites.

22.26 Calmodulin and troponin, the latter being in muscle cells.

22.27 In the cytosol: 10^{-7} mol/L; in the fluid just outside the cell: 10^{-3} mol/L. Ca^{2+} ions that enter the cell are pumped back out after their work is over. The calcium channels through the membrane are kept shut until an appropriate signal arrives.

22.28 At higher Ca^{2+} concentration, $Ca_3(PO_4)_2$ would precipitate.

22.29 No, most Ca^{2+} is held by calmodulin or troponin.

22.30 Ca^{2+} converts them to activated effectors.

22.31 An enzyme might be activated or a muscle might be induced to contract. After such action, Ca^{2+} is pumped back out of the cell.

22.32 When a zymogen is cleaved properly, an active enzyme emerges. Trypsinogen is the zymogen for trypsin.

22.33 It is a compound released from cells of the small intestine when food material moves into this part of the intestinal tract. Enteropeptidase converts trypsinogen to trypsin, a protease.

22.34 A proteolytic, blood-clot dissolving enzyme. It normally circulates in its inactive form, plasminogen.

22.35 The activation of certain enzymes.

22.36 The inhibitor is a non-substrate molecule resembling the true substrate enough to enable the binding of the inhibitor to the enzyme. By thus occupying the active site, the enzyme's work is inhibited.

22.37 Molecules of the product of enzyme action take up active sites on one of the enzymes used to make it and thus inhibit further enzyme action.

22.38 Because it shuts down a pathway when it is no longer needed but lets the pathway occur when it is needed.

22.39 Competitive inhibition involves blocking an active site; allosteric inhibition involves blocking the site where an effector normally works to activate the enzyme.

22.40 (a) It binds to a metal ion cofactor and so deactivates the enzyme.
　　　(b) It denatures enzymes by combining with their SH groups.

(c)   They deactivate enzymes of the nervous system

22.41   Antimetabolites are compounds that interfere with the metabolism of disease-causing bacteria. Antibiotics are those antimetabolites that are made by microorganisms.

22.42   It inhibits an enzyme needed for the growth of bacteria.

22.43   The levels of these enzymes increase in blood as the result of a disease or injury to particular tissues, which causes tissue cells to release their enzymes.

22.44   The CK(MB) band originates in the leakage of this isoenzyme only from damaged heart muscle.

22.45   CK(MM).

22.46   Of the five LD isoenzymes, LD_1 normally is less concentrated than LD_2. The "flip" is the reversal of this relationship. LD_1 shows up as *more* concentrated than LD_2. This flip is observed in patients who have suffered a myocardial infarction.

22.47   Urease is immobilized on an electrode used to determine the concentration of urea in some fluid. The urease catalyzes the hydrolysis of urea to the ammonium ion, the species actually measured.

22.48   To catalyze the breakdown of heparin that is used to prevent blood clots during hemodialysis.

22.49   Urease immobilized on an electrode for urea in blood catalyzes the hydrolysis of the urea, and the electrode picks up the change in concentration of NH_4^+.

22.50   APSAC, streptokinase, and tissue plasminogen activator (rtPA). rtPA occurs in human blood and it can be manufactured by recombinant DNA technology.

22.51   Fibrin, which dissolves as a result of catalysis by rtPA.

22.52   (a) Adrenal glands   (b) Nerve cells

22.53   These concepts describe how receptors recognize molecules of hormones or neurotransmitters.

22.54   They are primary chemical messengers.

22.55   Receptor

22.56   Cyclic AMP and inositol phosphate

22.57   G-protein

22.58   When activated, adenylate cyclase catalyzes the formation of cyclic AMP (from ATP), which then activates an enzyme inside the target cell.

22.59   It is an enzyme activator.

22.60   The cyclic AMP is hydrolyzed to AMP.

22.61   It is started in the same general way, up to and including the step in which the G-protein does its work.

22.62   One helps keep the cellular glucose level high and the other helps to bring the Ca^{2+} level of the cytosol up.

22.63   Steroids, polypeptides, simple amino compounds, and local hormones (prostaglandins).

22.64   They are hydrocarbon-like and so slip through a hydrocarbon-like lipid bilayer.

22.65   (a) Glucose (b) amino acids (c) metal ions

22.66   The work where they are made or very close by.

22.67   It is hydrolyzed back to acetic acid and choline. The enzyme is cholinesterase. Nerve poisons inactivate this enzyme.

22.68   It inactivates the receptor protein for acetylcholine.

22.69   It blocks the receptor protein for acetylcholine.

22.70   It prevents the synthesis of acetylcholine.

22.71   They catalyze the deactivation of neurotransmitters such as norepinephrine and thus reduce the level of signal-sending activity that depends on such neurotransmitters.

22.72   Iproniazid inhibits the monoamine oxidases and thus lets norepinephrine work at a higher level of activity.

22.73   They inhibit the reabsorption of norepinephrine by the presynaptic neuron and thus reduce the rate of its deactivation by the monoamine oxidases.

22.74   Norepinephrine, acting as a hormone, serves as a backup to its acting as a neurotransmitter should some injury disrupt the latter action.

22.75   Dopamine.

22.76   They bind to dopamine receptors in the postsynaptic nerve and inhibit the action of dopamine.

22.77   They accelerate the release of dopamine from the presynaptic neuron.

22.78   Degenerated neurons can use L-DOPA to make dopamine.

22.79   BDNF protects those cells that make dopamine from further degeneration, stimulates the cells to recover, and protects susceptible cells (at least in animal studies).

22.80   GABA (gamma-aminobutyric acid), whose signal-inhibiting activity is enhanced by Valium and Librium.

22.81   Enkephalin molecules enter pain-signalling neurons and inhibit the release of substance P, a neurotransmitter that helps to send pain signals. Thus enkephalin, like an opium-drug, inhibits pain.

22.82   It moderates pain signals.

22.83   By reducing the flow of Ca^{2+} into cells of heart muscles, the heart beats with reduced vigor.

22.84   A substance made by a signal-receiving nerve cell that moves back to the signal-sending cell to strengthen the connection between the two cells.

22.85   They consist of very tiny, gaseous molecules that easily slip through cell membranes.

22.86 $H:^-$ and H^+. $H:^-$ goes to NAD^+. H^+ is handled by the buffer.

22.87 $H:^-$ and H^+. Both go to FMN or FAD to form $FMNH_2$ or $FADH_2$.

22.88   The positive charge on the nicotinamide ring (the "N" of NAD).

22.89 H_2O

22.90   A disease-causing microorganism or virus.

22.91   Cellular immunity uses T lymphocytes or T cells to handle viruses that have entered cells as well as parasites, fungi, and foreign tissue. Humoral immunity uses B lymphocytes or B cells to handle bacterial infections and viral agents while they are at work outside cells.

22.92   Cellular immunity, by attacking the helper T cells.

22.93   An antigen is any molecular species or any pathogen that induces the immune system to make antibodies and to give the immune system a molecular-cellular memory for the antigen. An antibody is a glycoprotein that is able to take antigen molecules out of circulation enabling white cells to destroy the antigens.

22.94   The presence of glycoproteins with highly individual oligosaccharide units. This enables a lock-and-key kind of specificity between antibody and antigen.

22.95   Humoral immunity; antibodies.

22.96   It works to generate an antibody when introduced into the presence of type B blood.

22.97   In the specific structures of the oligosaccharide units on the glycolipids of red blood cell membranes.

22.98   A red cell with an oligosaccharide that functions as an antibody in the presence of the introduced type B blood.

22.99   Type O red cells carry the H antigens and the blood carries both anti-A and anti-B antibodies, so only type O blood can be received. But type O blood can be donated to people of any type because the H antigen has no enemies in other types of blood.

22.100 (a)   Ess shape (cf. Figure 22.5)

         (b)   See Figure 22.4.

22.101 Competitive inhibition.

22.102 (a)   The lock-and-key theory, perhaps as modified by induced fit.

         (b)   Add water to the alkene group and then oxidize the resulting 2° alcohol to a ketone. (An enzyme would have to guide the addition of the water molecule to give the specific 2° alcohol needed.)

22.103

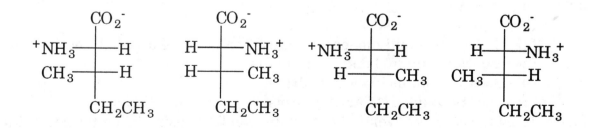

22.104   165.1 mg of isoleucine

Chapter 23

Review Exercises, Chapter 23

23.1   Interstitial fluid and blood.

23.2   Saliva, gastric juice, pancreatic juice, and intestinal juice.

23.3   The distension of the stomach caused by entering food causes the hormone gastrin to be secreted from cells of the gastric lining of the stomach. Gastrin stimulates the release of gastric juice.

23.4   Molecules of a competitive inhibitor occupy the active sites of an enzyme. Cimetidine shuts down the K^+–H^+ pump and prevents the secretion of gastric juice, which gives the ulcer time to heal in a relatively acid-free environment.

23.5   Cholecystokinin modulates the release of food materials from the stomach into the upper intestinal tract. Secretin causes the pancreas to release bicarbonate ion for the neutralization of the gastric juice that accompanies food matter into the upper intestinal tract.

23.6   (a)   α-Amylase.
(b)   Pepsinogen and gastric lipase.
(c)   α-Amylase, lipase, nuclease, trypsinogen, chymotrypsinogen, pro-carboxypeptidase, and proelastase
(d)   No enzymes.
(e)   Amylase, aminopeptidase, sucrase, lactase, maltase, lipase, nucleases, enteropeptidase.

23.7   (a)   Pepsin from its zymogen in gastric juice:, trypsin, chymotrypsin, and elastase from zymogens in pancreatic juice.
(b)   Lipases provided in gastric juice, pancreatic juice, and intestinal juice.
(c)   Amylases in saliva, pancreatic juice, and intestinal juice.
(d)   Sucrase in intestinal juice.
(e)   Carboxypeptidase from its zymogen in pancreatic juice; aminopeptidase from its zymogen in intestinal juice.
(f)   Nucleases in pancreatic juice and intestinal juice.

23.8   (a)   Amino acids.
(b)   Glucose, fructose, and galactose.
(c)   Fatty acids and monoacylglycerols (plus some diacylglycerols).

23.9   (a)   Peptide (amide) bonds in proteins.
(b)   Acetal systems in carbohydrates.
(c)   Ester groups in triacylglycerols.

23.10   It catalyzes the conversion of trypsinogen to trypsin. Then trypsin catalyzes the conversion of other zymogens to chymotrypsin, carboxypeptidase, and elastin. Thus enteropeptidase turns on enzyme activity for three major protein-digesting enzymes.

23.11 They would catalyze the digestion of proteins that make up part of the pancreas to the serious harm of this organ.

23.12 They are surface active agents that help to break up lipid globules, wash lipids from the particles of food, and aid in the absorption of fat-soluble vitamins.

23.13 (a) Lubricates the food.
(b) Protects the stomach lining from gastric acid and pepsin.

23.14 (a) HCl   (b) Enteropeptidase
(c) Trypsin   (d) Trypsin
(e) Trypsin

23.15 It helps to coagulate the protein in milk so that this protein stays longer in the stomach where it can be digested with the aid of pepsin.

23.16 This enzyme is inactive at the high acidity of the digesting mixture in the adult stomach, but the acidity of this mixture in the infant's stomach is less.

23.17 Pancreatic juice delivers its zymogens and enzymes into the duodenum, whereas the enzymes of the intestinal juice work within cells of the intestinal wall.

23.18 Dilute sodium bicarbonate released from the pancreas. This raises the pH of the chyme to the optimum pH for the action of the enzymes that will function in the duodenum.

23.19 They recombine to molecules of triacylglycerol during their migration from the intestinal tract toward the lymph ducts.

23.20 The flow of bile normally delivers colored breakdown products from hemoglobin in the blood, and these products give the normal color to feces. When no bile flows, no colored products are available to the feces.

23.21 Cholesterol has no hydrolyzable groups.

23.22 The concentration of soluble proteins is greater in blood.

23.23 The serum-soluble proteins (albumins, mostly).

23.24 Fibrinogen is a protein in blood that is changed to fibrin, the insoluble protein of a blood clot, by the clotting mechanism.

23.25 Albumin molecules transport hydrophobic molecules such as fatty acids and cholesterol, and albumins contribute as much as 75-80% of the osmotic effect of the blood.

23.26 Na^+ is in blood plasma and other extracellular fluids; K^+ is chiefly in intracellular fluids. The two ions help to maintain osmotic pressure relationships; be part of the regulatory mechanisms for acid-base balance; and participate in the smooth working of the muscles and the nervous system.

23.27 145 meq/L

23.28 135 meq/L

23.29   Such injuries allow the contents of cells to spill out and enter circulation.

23.30   5.0 meq/L

23.31   Hyponatremia.

23.32   Hypermagnesemia and cardiac arrest.

23.33   The activation of several enzymes.

23.34   In bones and teeth

23.35   Activates enzymes and initiates muscle contraction

23.36   Hypercalcemia.

23.37   Hypomagnesemia.

23.38   Chloride ion, Cl^-.

23.39   100-106 meq/l. Loss of Cl^- causes retention of HCO_3^-, a base.

23.40   Blood pressure and osmotic pressure. Blood pressure tends to force blood fluids out of the blood vesseland osmotic pressure tends to force fluids back. The return of fluids to the blood from the interstitial compartment on the arterial side is overbalanced by the blood pressure. The net effect on the arterial side is a diffusion of fluids from the blood.

23.41   Blood pressure and osmotic pressure. The natural return of fluids to the blood on the venous side from the interstitial compartment is not balanced by the now reduced blood pressure on the venous side, so fluids return to the blood from which they left on the arterial side.

23.42   Serum proteins are lost from the blood, which upsets the osmotic pressure of the blood. Water leaves the blood for the interstitial compartment, and the blood volume drops. Loss of blood delivery to the brain leads to the symptoms of shock.

23.43   (a)   Blood proteins leak out which allows water to leave the blood and enter interstitial spaces throughout various tissues.
(b)   Blood proteins are lost to the blood by being consumed which also leads to the loss of water from the blood and its appearance in interstitial compartments.
(c)   Capillaries are blocked at the injured site reducing the return of blood in the veins, so fluids accumulate at the site.

23.44   Oxygen and carbon dioxide.

23.45   Hemoglobin.

23.46   The first oxygen molecule to bind changes the shapes of other parts of the hemoglobin molecule and makes it much easier for the remaining three oxygen molecules to bind. This ensures that all four oxygen-binding sites of each hemoglobin molecule will leave the lungs fully loaded with oxygen.

23.47 $HHb + O_2 \rightleftharpoons HbO_2^- + H^+$
(a) To the left.   (b) To the left.
(c) To the right.   d) To the left.
(e) To the left.   (f) To the right.

23.48

(a) $HHb + O_2 \longleftarrow HbO_2^- + H^+$

$CO_2 + H_2O \longrightarrow HCO_3^- + H^+$

Isohydric shift in metabolizing tissue

(b) $HHb + O_2 \longrightarrow HbO_2^- + H^+$

$CO_2 + H_2O \longleftarrow HCO_3^- + H^+$

Isohydric shift in alveolus

23.49   It generates H^+ needed to convert HCO_3^- to CO_2 and H_2O and to convert $HbCO_2^-$ to HHb and CO_2.

23.50   Waste CO_2 combines with water to give HCO_3^- and the H^+ that is needed to react with HbO_2^- to form HHb and release O_2.

23.51   It helps to shift the following equilibrium to the left:

$$HHb + O_2 \rightleftharpoons HbO_2^- + H^+$$

23.52   It is found in red cells.
(a)   It catalyzes the conversion of HCO_3^- and H^+ to CO_2 and H_2O.
(b)   It catalyzes the conversion of CO_2 and H_2O to HCO_3^- and H^+.
   It can do both because it accelerates *both* the forward and the reverse reactions in the equilibrium:

$$CO_2 + H_2O \rightleftharpoons HCO_3^- + H^+$$

Other factors, such as the value of the partial pressure of carbon dioxide, determine whether the forward or the reverse reaction is favored.

23.53   The migration of BPG molecules out of hemoglobin molecules as the first oxygen molecules enter the hemoglobin helps the remaining oxygen molecules to bind more readily.

23.54   It migrates into a cavity within the hemoglobin molecule and helps to change the shapes of subunits so that oxygen molecules are more easily ejected.

23.55   The body makes more hemoglobin and red cells. This allows the body to pick up oxygen more readily. The body also makes more BPG, which helps the system release oxygen where needed.

23.56   For oxygenation:
$HHb\text{-}BPG + O_2 + HCO_3^- \rightarrow HbO_2^- + BPG + CO_2 + H_2O$

For deoxygenation:

$$HbO_2^- + BPG + CO_2 + H_2O \rightarrow HHb\text{-}BPG + O_2 + HCO_3^-$$

23.57   As HCO_3^- in the serum and as $HbCO_2^-$ (carbaminohemoglobin) in red cells.

23.58   Oxygen affinity is lowered. Where the partial pressure of CO_2 is relatively high (as in actively metabolizing tissue) there is a need for oxygen, so the lowering effect of CO_2 on oxygen affinity helps to release O_2 precisely where O_2 is most needed.

23.59   The exchange of a chloride ion for a bicarbonate ion between a red blood cell and blood serum. This brings Cl^- inside the red cell when it is needed to help deoxygenate HbO_2^-.

23.60   Myoglobin can take oxygen from oxyhemoglobin and thus ensure that the oxygen needs of myoglobin-containing tissue are met.

23.61   Fetal hemoglobin can take oxygen from the oxyhemoglobin of the mother's blood and thus ensure that the fetus gets needed oxygen.

23.62

Condition	pH	pCO_2	$[HCO_3^-]$
Normal	7.35-7.45	35-40 mm Hg	25-30 meq/L
Metabolic acidosis	↓ 7.20	↓ 30 mm Hg	↓ 14 meq/L
Metabolic alkalosis	↑ 7.45	↑ >45 mm Hg	↑ >29 meq/L
Respiratory acidosis	↓ 7.10	↑ 68 mm Hg	↑ 40 meq/L
Respiratory alkalosis	↑ 7.54	↓ 32 mm Hg	↓ 20 meq/L

23.63   The pH of the blood decreases in both but both pCO_2 and $[HCO_3^-]$ increase in respiratory acidosis and both decrease in metabolic acidosis.

23.64   Hyperventilation is observed in metabolic acidosis, and HCO_3^- can be given intravenously to neutralize excess acid. Hyperventilation is also observed in respiratory alkalosis (because the patient can't help hyperventilating), and CO_2 is given (by rebreathing one's own air) to keep up the supply of H_2CO_3, which can neutralize excess base.

23.65   Hypoventilation is observed in metabolic alkalosis, and isotonic ammonium chloride can be given to neutralize the excess base. Involuntary hypoventilation is observed in respiratory acidosis, and isotonic sodium bicarbonate might be given to neutralize excess acid.

23.66   In metabolic acidosis, because it helps to blow out CO_2 and thereby to reduce the level of H_2CO_3 in the blood and simultaneously raise the pH.

23.67   In respiratory alkalosis. The involuntary loss of CO_2 reduces the level of H_2CO_3 in the blood and thereby reduces the level of H^+.

23.68   In metabolic alkalosis.

23.69   In respiratory acidosis.

23.70   The kidneys work to remove acids from the blood, but to remove them they must also remove water from the blood. If too much water is taken in this way, then the blood obtains more water by taking it from interstitial and intracellular compartments.

23.71	(a) Respiratory alkalosis	(b)	Metabolic alkalosis
	(c) Respiratory acidosis	(d)	Respiratory acidosis
	(e) Metabolic acidosis	(f)	Respiratory alkalosis
	(g) Metabolic acidosis	(h)	Metabolic alkalosis
	(i) Respiratory acidosis	(j)	Respiratory acidosis
23.72	(a) Hyperventilation	(b)	Hypoventilation
	(c) Hypoventilation	(d)	Hypoventilation
	(e) Hyperventilation	(f)	Hyperventilation
	(g) Hyperventilation	(h)	Hypoventilation
	(i) Hypoventilation	(j)	Hypoventilation

23.73 CO_2 is removed at an excessive rate, which removes carbonic acid, so the blood becomes more alkaline and the pH of the blood rises (alkalosis).

23.74 Hypoventilation in emphysema lets the blood retain carbonic acid, and the pH decreases.

23.75 The loss of acid with the loss of the stomach contents results in a loss of acid from the blood, which means an increase in the blood's pH and alkalosis.

23.76 The loss of alkaline fluids from the duodenum and lower intestinal tract leads to a loss of base from the bloodstream, too. The result is a decrease in the blood's pH and thus acidosis.

23.77 Hypocapnia

23.78 Hypercapnia

23.79 The blood has become more concentrated in solutes.

23.80 It acts to prevent the loss of water via the urine by letting the hypophysis secrete vasopressin whose target cells are in the kidneys. The retention of water helps to keep the blood's osmotic pressure from increasing further. The thirst mechanism is also activated to bring in more water to dilute the blood.

23.81 Aldosterone is secreted from the adrenal cortex, and it instructs the kidneys to retain sodium ion in the blood.

23.82 The kidneys secrete a trace of renin into the blood. This catalyzes the conversion of angiotensinogen into angiotensin I, which catalyzes the formation of angiotensin II, a neurotransmitter and powerful vasoconstrictor. With constricting of the capillaries, the blood pressure has to increase to keep the delivery of blood going.

23.83 The rate of diuresis increases.

23.84 They transfer hydrogen ions into the urine and put bicarbonate ions into the bloodstream.

23.85 A molecule of a monoacylglycerol retains a considerable hydrophobic unit (the fatty acyl "tail") and so enters the hydrophobic region of a membrane more easily than a molecule like glycerol with three hydrophilic OH groups.

23.86   Without the bile salts in the bile, normally obtained from the gall bladder, there is less emulsifying action to aid in the digestion of triacylglycerols with the usual long fatty acyl side chains. The shorter chain molecules are a little more soluble in the digestive medium.

23.87   The blood produced while at a high altitude has a higher concentration of hemoglobin and of BPG. This aids in their ability to use oxygen during a race.

23.88   These animals can store more oxygen in heart muscle, which helps them to go longer without breathing.

Chapter 24

Practice Exercises, Chapter 24

1.   (a)   Proline   (b)   Arginine
      (c)   Glutamic acid   (d)   Lysine
2.   (a)   Serine   (b)   CT (chain termination)
      (c)   Glutamic acid   (d)   Isoleucine

Review Exercises, Chapter 24

24.1   (a)   Cytosol   (b)   Protoplasm
        (c)   Cytoplasm   (d)   Ribosome
        (e)   Mitochondrion   (f)   Deoxyribonucleic acid
        (g)   Chromatin   (h)   Histone
        (i)   Gene

24.2   *Chromatin* is a substance made up of nucleosomes—complexes of proteins (called histones) around which are wrapped coiled molecules of DNA—connected by DNA strands. *Chromosomes* are rod-like bodies made microscopically observable when chromatin thickens at the onset of the process that leads to cell division.

24.3   The cell nucleus.

24.4   Duplicate copies of DNA are made.

24.5   Nucleic acids

24.6   Nucleotides

24.7   Ribose and deoxyribose.

24.8   (a) Adenine, A. Thymine, T. Guanine, G. Cytosine, C.
        (b) Adenine, A. Uracil, U. Guanine, G. Cytosine, C.

24.9   The main chains all have the same phosphate-deoxyribose-phosphate-deoxyribose repeating system.

24.10   In the sequence of bases attached to the deoxyribose units of the main chain.

24.11   The main chains all have the same phosphate-ribose-phosphate-ribose repeating system.

24.12 DNA occurs as a double helix, and it alone has the base thymine (T). RNA alone has the base uracil (U). (The remaining three bases, A, G, and C, are the same in both DNA and RNA.) DNA molecules have one less OH group per pentose unit than RNA molecules.

24.13 A and T pair to each other, so they must be in a 1:1 ratio regardless of the species. Similarly, G and C pair and so must be in a 1:1 ratio.

24.14 Bases that project from the twin spirals of DNA chains fit to each other on opposite strands by hydrogen bonds. The geometries and functional groups are such that only A and T can pair (or only A and U can pair when RNA is involved), and only G and C can pair.

24.15 Hydrophobic interactions stabilize the helices. (Hydrogen bonds hold two helices together.)

24.16

$$5' \rightarrow 3'$$

Given segment: AGGCTGA

Opposite segment: TCCGACT

$$3' \leftarrow 5'$$

24.17 The base pairings of A with T and G with C.

24.18 In cells of higher animals, a series of separated segments of a DNA molecule comprise one gene, each segment called an *exon* and each separated by DNA segments called *introns*.

24.19 The introns are b, d, and f, because they are the longer segments.

24.20 A sequence of base triplets comprising a gene corresponds to and specifies a sequence of amino acid residues of a polypeptide.

24.21 It consists of several proteins plus rRNA, and it serves as the assembly area for the synthesis of polypeptides.

24.22 It is heterogeneous nuclear RNA. Its sequence of bases is complementary to a sequence of bases on DNA, those of both the exons and introns. It is processed to make mRNA whose base sequence is complementary only to the exons of the DNA.

24.23 Heterogeneous nuclear RNA (hnRNA)

24.24 A codon is a specific triplet of bases that corresponds to a specific amino acid residue in a polypeptide, and mRNA consists of a continuous sequence of codons.

24.25 A triplet of bases found on tRNA and which is complementary to a codon found on mRNA.

24.26 ATA. A codon is RNA material, and T does not occur in RNA.

24.27 (a) Phenylalanine   (b)   Serine
     (c)   Threonine   (d)   Aspartic acid

24.28   Writing them in the 5' to 3' direction:
    (a)   AAA   (b)   GGA
    (c)   UGU   (d)   AUC

24.29   (a)   5'→ 3'
        UUUCUUAUAGAGUCCCCAACAGAU
    (b)   5'→ 3'
        UUUUCCACAGAU
    (c)   Phe-Ser-Thr-Asp

24.30   B < A < D < C

24.31   Translation is the mRNA-directed synthesis of a polypeptide. Transcription is the DNA-directed synthesis of mRNA.

24.32   (a)   A large number of sequences are possible because three of the specific amino acid residues are coded by more than one codon. The possibilities are indicated by:

         Met—Ala—Trp—Ser—Tyr
        AUG GCU UGG UCU UAU   (5' → 3')
            GCC   UCC UAC
            GCA   UCA
            GCG   UCG

    (b)   CAU (5'→ 3') or if (3' → 5'), then UAC

24.33   The starting point is a specific triplet that forces the acceptance of all remaining sets of three, in order, to be seen as specific codons.

24.34   How polypeptide synthesis can be controlled by the use of repressors.

24.35   Structural gene. The *regulator gene* is coded to direct the synthesis of a polypeptide repressor. The *operator gene* is the site at which the repressor binds and blocks the operation of the strutural gene.

24.36   A substance whose molecules can block DNA-directed polypeptide synthesis.

24.37   It cancels the effect of a repressor.

24.38   Some block the expression of a gene by interfering with DNA-directed polypeptide synthesis.

24.39   The four-letter DNA language and the twenty-letter amino acid language.

24.40   The codons specify the same amino acids in all organisms.   No.

24.41   By causing chemical changes in the substances involved with the genetic apparatus so that cell division is no longer controlled.

24.42   At high enough, well-focused doses they destroy the genetic apparatus of a cancer cell and render it incapable of dividing.

24.43   A substance that mimics the effects of radiations in cells.

24.44   All viruses have nucleic acid, and many also contain a protein.

24.45   A molecular feature on the surface of a virus particle fits by a flexible lock-and-key mechanism to a specific glycoprotein on the membrane of one specific kind of host cell.

24.46   A protein part of a virus catalyzes the digestion of part of the cell's membrane. This opens a hole for the virus particle or its nucleic acid to enter the cell.

24.47   RNA replicase is able to direct the synthesis of RNA from the "directions" encoded on RNA. A normal host cell does not contain RNA replicase, so the virus either must bring it along or it must direct its synthesis inside the host cell.

24.48   Reverse transcriptase, a DNA polymerase enzyme, directs the synthesis of viral DNA that subsequently is used to code for the synthesis of more viral RNA. Reverse transcriptase is able to use RNA information to make DNA.

24.49   (+)mRNA

24.50   It must not only make (+) RNA to direct multiplication, it must also make the (–)RNA that new virus particles require.

24.51   RNA replicase

24.52   That the cell is able to move information backward, from RNA to DNA. (Normally information always flows from DNA to RNA.)

24.53   A silent gene is a unit provided by a virus particle to a host cell but which does not take over the genetic apparatus of the cell until activated.

24.54   Cancer-causing

24.55   Human immunodeficiency virus

24.56   The T-lymphocyte. It's part of the body's immune system, so when it is destroyed, the body has no defense against infectious diseases and certain kinds of cancer.

24.57   The theory is that AZT molecules will bind to reverse transcriptase and inhibit the work of this enzyme in HIV.

24.58   A circular molecule of super-coiled DNA found in bacteria.

24.59   Restriction enzyme

24.60   One source is the plasmid and another is new material added to the bacterium or yeast.

24.61   Polypeptides of critical value to human medicine or technology.

24.62   The use of recombinant DNA to make genes and the products of genes.

24.63   A defect in a gene.

24.64   The synthesis of a transmembrane protein that lets chloride ion pass through the membranes of mucous cells in the lungs and the digestive tract. The reduced movement of Cl^- out of the cell means that less water is outside of the cell, and the mucous is thereby thickened and made more viscous. Breathing is thereby impaired.

24.65   To insert correct DNA by some mechanism into cells lacking such DNA and so to repair the defect.

24.66   Retroviruses can bring about the insertion of DNA into a chromosome of a host cell.

24.67   The surface carries the recognition molecules needed to find the appropriate host cells.

24.68   A gene needed for the metabolism of phenylalanine is defective. This leads to an increase in the level of phenylpyruvic acid in the blood, which causes brain damage. A diet very low in phenylalanine is prescribed.

24.69   All of the cells of an individual have the entire genome.

24.70   It is the synthesis of clones of DNA. DNA samples at crime scenes generally involve tiny amounts of DNA, and DNA typing depends on making enough cloned DNA for the next steps of the procedure.

24.71   The common core segments of minisatellites. These DNA segments can be picked up by radioactively labeled and complementary DNA segments. Then the patterns of dark lines or spots—the "bar code"—produced on X ray film by the radiations are obtained.

24.72   A family of proteins (small glycoproteins) that inhibit viruses.

24.73   People do not develop a second viral infection when another is in progress, suggesting that the first infection produces something that provides the protection against another infection at the same time.

24.74   Viruses.

24.75   By recombinant DNA technology

24.76   (a)   By one methyl group

(b)   No

(c)   Both uracil and thymine can form a base pair with adenine.

24.77

(a)

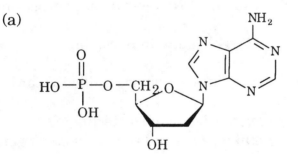

(b)

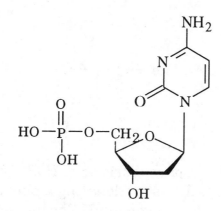

24.78   (a)   A dinucleotide; it has two side chain bases and two ribose units.
        (b)   Of RNA, because the sugar units are those of ribose.
        (c)   At the top.
        (d)   AC

Chapter 25

Practice Exercise, Chapter 25

1.   (a) Yes (b) Yes (c) No

Review Exercises, Chapter 25

25.1   All of them, but chiefly fatty acids and carbohydrates.
25.2   Carbon dioxide and water.
25.3   Combustion produces just heat. The catabolism of glucose uses about half of
        the energy to make ATP and the remainder appears as heat.
25.4   Carbon dioxide and water.
25.5

Adenosine $-\text{O}-\overset{\overset{\text{O}}{\|}}{\underset{\underset{\sigma}{|}}{\text{P}}}-\text{O}-\overset{\overset{\text{O}}{\|}}{\underset{\underset{\sigma}{|}}{\text{P}}}-\text{O}-\overset{\overset{\text{O}}{\|}}{\underset{\underset{\sigma}{|}}{\text{P}}}-\sigma$

25.6

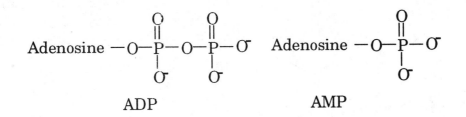

ADP   AMP

25.7   The singly and doubly ionized forms of phosphoric acid, $H_2PO_4^- + HPO_4^{2-}$.
25.8   The relative potential that phosphate X has for donating a phosphate unit in the synthesis of another organophosphate compound. The higher the number is in a negative sense, the higher is this potential.
25.9   The first two have phosphate group transfer potentials equal to or higher than that of ATP, whereas this potential is lower than that of ATP for glycerol-3-phosphate.
25.10 The left.
25.11 (a) Yes   (b) Yes   (c) No   (d) No
25.12 The substrate is directly phosphorylated by the *transfer* of a phosphate group from an organic donor.
25.13 It stores phosphate group energy and transfers phosphate to ADP to remake the ATP consumed by muscular work.
25.14 As the supply of ATP decreases, the supplies of ADP and P_i increase, and this development launches events that make creatine phosphate so that more ATP can be made.
25.15 (a)   The aerobic synthesis of ATP.
       (b)   The synthesis of ATP when a tissue operates anaerobically.
       (c)   The supply of metabolites for the respiratory chain.
       (d)   The supply of metabolites for the respiratory chain and for the citric acid cycle.
25.16 The disappearance of ATP by some energy-demanding process and the simultaneous appearance of ADP + P_i.
25.17 An increase in its supply of ADP. The need to convert ADP back to ATP is met by metabolism, which requires oxygen.
25.18 The citric acid cycle.
25.19 (a) $E < B < C < A < D$
       (b) $B < C < A < D$
25.20 It starts with glycolysis and since this is aerobic as stated, it ends with the respiratory chain.

25.21   A fatty acid

25.22   It starts with glucose and ends with lactate.

25.23   When a cell is temporarily low on O_2 for running the respiratory chain (as a source of ATP), the cell can continue to make ATP anyway.

25.24   When the respiratory chain starts up, the citric acid cycle must start up to keep the chain going.

25.25

An acetyl unit:

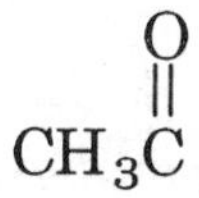

$$\underset{CH_3C}{\overset{\overset{\displaystyle O}{\|}}{}}$$

25.26   Two

25.27   Two

25.28   ADP. The cycle helps the cell make ATP from ADP, so activation by ADP is logical.

25.29   (a) 15   (b) 12

25.30   9

25.31   An oxidation; the reactant loses hydrogen.

25.32   An enzyme like isocitrate dehydrogenase, because the reaction is a dehydrogenation (not an addition of water to a double bond, catalyzed by an enzyme like aconitase).

25.33   A pair of electrons on the left of the arrow.

25.34   Respiratory chain.

25.35

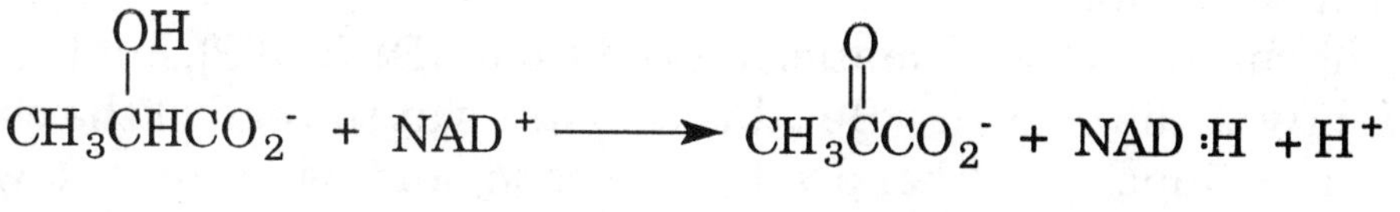

$$\underset{CH_3CHCO_2^-}{\overset{\overset{\displaystyle OH}{|}}{}} + NAD^+ \longrightarrow \underset{CH_3CCO_2^-}{\overset{\overset{\displaystyle O}{\|}}{}} + NAD\!:\!H + H^+$$

(a) $\underset{CH_3CHCO_2^-}{\overset{\overset{\displaystyle OH}{|}}{}}$

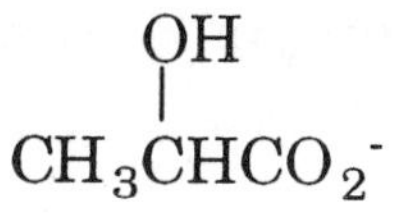

(b) NAD^+

25.36

$$^-O_2CH_2CH_2CO_2^-$$ FAD

$$^-O_2CCH=CHCO_2^-$$ FADH$_2$

25.37   NAD$^+$ < FMN < FeSP < CoQ

25.38   It catalyzes the reduction of oxygen to water.

25.39   It is a riboflavin-containing coenzyme that in its reduced form, FADH$_2$, passes electrons and H$^+$ into the respiratory chain.

25.40   Across the inner membrane of the mitochondrion. The value of [H$^+$] is higher on the outer side of the innermembrane than in the mitochondrial matrix.

25.41   The flow of protons across the inner mitochondrial membrane.

25.42   If the membrane is broken, then the simple process of diffusion defeats any mitochondrial effort to set up a gradient of H$^+$ ions across the membrane, but the chain itself can still operate.

25.43 $MH_2 + nH^+ + f_{(1,2)}O_2 \rightarrow$
$M + H_2O + nH^+$ (outside the inner mitochondrial membrane)

25.44   Oxidative phosphorylation is the kind made possible by the energy released from the operation of the respiratory chain. Substrate phosphorylation arises from the direct transfer of a phosphate unit from a higher to a lower energy phosphate.

25.45   A gradient of positive charge. The migration of *any* cation away from the region of higher positive charge density or the migration of *any* anion toward this region will be spontaneous.

25.46   An enzyme catalyzes the formation of ATP from ADP and P$_i$, but the new ATP sticks tightly to the enzyme. But this enzyme is at the end of the channel for protons in the inner mitochondrial membrane, and as protons flow through they change the enzyme so that it expels ATP.

25.47   Acetone. Unlike propane, acetone has an electronegative oxygen that causes electron density to shift out of C–H bonds tending to make the H atom more acidic.

25.48

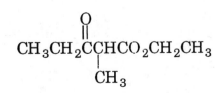

25.49 $[H^+] = 1.0 \times 10^{-7}$ mol/L (instead of 1.0 mol/L) and 25 °C. In living cells, a molar concentration of H^+ of 1.0 M is simply unrealistic.

25.50 $C_2H_3O_2^- + 3H^+ + 2e^- \rightleftharpoons CH_3CH{=}O + H_2O$ $E^\circ = -0.60$ V.

25.51 $CH_3CH{=}O + NAD^+ + H_2O \rightarrow C_2H_3O_2^- + NADH + 2H^+$ $ES_{(\omega,cell)} = +0.28$ V
The spontaneous reaction is the oxidation of ethanal.

25.52 $CH_3CH{=}O + (1/2)O_2 \rightarrow C_2H_3O_2^- + H^+$ $ES_{(\omega,cell)} = +1.42$ V
The spontaneous reaction is the oxidation of ethanal.

25.53   Reactions in a chain of reactions that follow an unfavorable step may be able to force this step to go anyway.

25.54   The overall rate of the series of steps is more easily controlled and certain individual steps can be used to run energy-consuming reactions.

25.55   (a) $CH_3CH{=}O$
(b)   Acetic acid, CH_3CO_2H (or acetate ion, $CH_3CO_2^-$)
(c)   α-Ketoglutarate

25.56   Pyruvate

25.57   (a)   4
(b)   The nucleus of a hydrogen atom, because $H{:}^-$ transfers.
(c)   Dehydrogenase

Chapter 26

Review Exercises, Chapter 26

26.1   Glucose, fructose, and galactose.

26.2   After a few steps, the metabolic pathways of galactose and fructose merge with the pathway of glucose.

26.3   The concentration of reducing monosaccharides, chiefly glucose, in the blood is called the blood sugar level. The normal fasting level is the blood sugar level after several hours of fasting.

26.4   70-110 mg/dL (3.9-6.1 mmol/L). (Note. Various references give slightly different ranges of values.)

26.5   99 mg/dL

26.6   (a)   Glucose in urine.
(b)   A low blood sugar level.
(c)   A high blood sugar level.
(d)   The conversion of glycogen to glucose.
(e)   The concentration of something (e.g., glucose) in blood above which that solute appears in the urine.
(f)   The synthesis of glycogen from glucose.

26.7   The synthesis of glucose in the body from smaller molecules. Hypoglycemia normally activates gluconeogenesis.

26.8   The lack of glucose means the lack of the one nutrient most needed by the brain.

26.9   It increases.

26.10   Muscle tissue.

26.11   The enzyme adenylate cyclase.

26.12 $D < C < E < A < B$

26.13 10^4

26.14   Glucose might be changed back to glycogen as rapidly as it is released from glycogen, and no glucose would be made available to the cell.

26.15   The activated form of protein kinase.

26.16   Glucose-1-phosphate is the end product and phosphoglucomutase catalyzes its change to glucose-6-phosphate.

26.17   Liver, but not muscles, has the enzyme glucose-6-phosphatase that catalyzes the hydrolysis of glucose-6-phosphate. This frees glucose for release from the liver to the bloodstream.

26.18   It is a polypeptide hormone made in the alpha cells of the pancreas and released into circulation when the blood sugar level drops. At the liver it activates adenylate cyclase, which leads to glycogenolysis and the release of glucose into circulation.

26.19   Glucagon, because it works better at the liver than epinephrine in initiating glycogenolysis, and when glycogenolysis occurs at the liver there is a mechanism for releasing glucose into circulation.

26.20   It stimulates the release of glucagon, which leads to the release of glucose into circulation.

26.21   It is a polypeptide hormone released from the beta cells of the pancreas in response to an increase in the blood sugar level, and it acts most effectively at adipose tissue.

26.22   An increase in the blood sugar level.

26.23   Too much insulin leads to a sharp decrease in the blood sugar level and therefore a decrease in the supply of glucose, the chief nutrient for the brain.

26.24   Somatostatin is a polypeptide hormone released by the hypothalamus, and it acts at the pancreas to inhibit the release of glucagon and slow down the release of insulin.

26.25   The body's ability to manage dietary glucose without letting the blood sugar level swing too widely from its normal fasting level.

26.26   By its conversion to glucose-6-phosphate, which either enters a pathway that makes ATP or is converted to glycogen for storage.

26.27   Glucose absorbed from the blood stream circulates and some is removed by muscle tissue, some by the liver. As needed, glucose is catabolized by glycolysis, which generates ATP and pyruvate (in an aerobic situation) or lactate (in an anaerobic situation). When excess lactate is made, some lactate is further catabolized in the liver to provide the energy to convert the remaining lactate back to glucose. This may be stored as liver glycogen or it may reenter circulation, be removed at muscles, and thus replenish glycogen reserves in muscle tissue.

26.28 Some is catabolized in the liver to provide the energy to convert the rest, via gluconeogenesis, to glucose.

26.29 To test for the possibility of diabetes mellitus. An adult patient is given a drink that has 75 g of glucose. For children, 1.75 g of glucose per kilogram of body weight is given. Then the blood sugar level is measured at regular intervals.

26.30 (a)   The blood sugar level initially rises rapidly, but then drops sharply and slowly levels back to normal.
(b)   The blood sugar level, already high to start, rises much higher and never sharply drops. It only very slowly comes back down.

26.31 An over-release of epinephrine (as in a stressful situation) that induces an over-release of glucose.

26.32 $C_6H_{12}O_6 + 2\ ADP + 2P_i \rightarrow 2C_3H_5O_3^- + 2H^+ + 2ATP$

26.33 Glycolysis can operate and make ATP even when the oxygen supply is low, so a tissue in oxygen debt can continue to function.

26.34 Glyceraldehyde-3-phosphate is in the direct pathway of glycolysis, so changing dihydroxyacetone phosphate into it ensures that all parts of the original glucose molecule are used in glycolysis.

26.35 (a)   It undergoes oxidative decarboxylation and becomes the acetyl group in acetyl CoA.
(b)   Its keto group is reduced by NADH to a 2° alcohol group in lactate, which enables the NADH to be reoxidized to NAD+ and then reused for more glycolysis.

26.36 It is reoxidized to pyruvate, which undergoes oxidative decarboxylation to the acetyl group in acetyl CoA. This enters the citric acid cycle.

26.37 (a)   17 ATP   (b)   18 ATP

26.38 PH forms; the body uses this reducing agent to make fatty acids.

26.39 It makes glucose out of smaller molecules obtained by the catabolism of fatty acids and amino acids.

26.40 All are catabolized, and parts of some of their molecules are used to make fatty acids and, thence, fat.

26.41 (a)   Alanine   (b   Aspartic acid

26.42 α-Ketoglutarate is an intermediate in the citric acid cycle (Figure 25.2) and so is changed eventually to oxaloacetate (normally the acceptor of acetyl units at the start of the citric acid cycle). Gluconeogenesis also can use oxaloacetate to make "new" glucose.

26.43   Succinyl units are in the citric acid cycle, which ends with the formation of oxaloacetate. and the later can be used in gluconeogenesis.

26.44   (a) Glucose 6-phosphatase. Glucose cannot leave the liver, so the liver enlarges as glycogen reserves become high. The blood sugar level decreases, and the blood levels of pyruvate and lactate increase.
(b) An enzyme for breaking 1,6-glycosidic bonds. Not as much glycogen can be used. Symptoms develop like those of Von Gierke's disease, but milder.
(c) Phosphorylase. Glucose-1-phosphate cannot bes obtained from glycogen. Reduced physical activity follows.
(d) Enzymes for making the branches in glycogen. Liver failure occurs.

26.45   Type I diabetics cannot make insulin.

26.46   Type I

26.47   Type II

26.48   1. Presence of genetic defects.
2. Some triggering incident occurs, like a viral infection.
3. Particular antibodies associated with diabetes appear in the blood.
4. Gradual loss of ability to secrete insulin.
5. Full-fledged diabetes. Hyperglycemia.
6. Destruction of β-cells is complete.

26.49   The β-cells of the pancreas.

26.50   Changes occur in body molecules that the immune system reads as new antigens. The antibodies then made destroy body tissue.

26.51   One explanation: insulin receptors "wear out." Another: the β-cells of the pancreas "wear out." Still another: amylin (a recently discovered protein component of what is released by the β-cells) suppresses glucose uptake.

26.52   The basement membrane of capillaries.

26.53   Its aldehyde group reacts with amino groups on proteins and genes to form C=N systems by means of which the glucose units are tied to other molecules.

26.54   It decreases. The equilibrium involving glucose, an amino group, and glucosylated hemoglobin shifts back to regenerate glucose.

26.55   They change to more permanent Amadori compounds, which constitute more permanent changes in cell molecules.

26.56   The sorbitol made by the hydrogenation of glucose stays inside the eye lens where it draws water osmotically. This produces a swelling of the lens, pressure, glaucoma, and eventually blindness.

26.57

(a)

$$\underset{\displaystyle CH_3CHCH_2CH}{\overset{\displaystyle \overset{OH}{|} \qquad \overset{O}{\|}}{}}$$

(b)

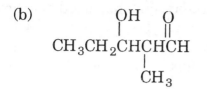

$$CH_3CH_2\overset{\overset{\displaystyle OH}{|}}{C}H\overset{\overset{\displaystyle O}{\|}}{C}HCH$$
$$\quad\quad\quad\quad\underset{\underset{\displaystyle CH_3}{|}}{}$$

(c)

$$CH_3\overset{\overset{\displaystyle OH}{|}}{\underset{\underset{\displaystyle CH_3}{|}}{C}}CH_2\overset{\overset{\displaystyle O}{\|}}{C}CH_3$$

26.58

$$C_6H_5CH_2\overset{\overset{\displaystyle O}{\|}}{C}H$$

26.59   (a)   Yes, either pyruvate or lactate containing carbon-13 may reentercirculation.

(b)   Yes, either pyruvate or lactate containing carbon-13 might be absorbed by the liver from the blood stream.

(c)   Yes, glucose with carbon-13 atoms might be made via gluconeogenesis from either pyruvate or lactate containing carbon-13.

26.60   (a)   15 ATP

(b)   3 ATP

(c)   3 Glucose, (because 6 ATP are needed to make each molecule of glucose by gluconeogenesis).

Chapter 27

Review Exercises, Chapter 27

27.1   Fatty acids and monoacylglycerols (plus some diacylglycerols).
27.2   They become reconstituted into triacylglycerols.
27.3   They transport lipids received from the digestive tract to the liver.
27.4   They unload some of their triacylglycerol.

27.5   They are absorbed.

27.6   Some cholesterol has originated in the diet and some has been synthesized in the liver.

27.7   (a)   Very low density lipoprotein complex.
         (b)   Intermediate density lipoprotein complex.
         (c)   Low density lipoprotein complex.
         (d)   High density lipoprotein complex.

27.8   Triacylglycerol.

27.9   The loss of the less dense triacylglycerol leaves a higher concentration of the more dense cholesterol.

27.10   The liver.

27.11   Cholesterol.

27.12   The synthesis of steroids and the fabrication of cell membranes.

27.13   IDL and LDL.

27.14   When the receptor proteins are reduced in number, the liver cannot remove cholesterol from the blood, so the blood cholesterol level increases.

27.15   Return to the liver any cholesterol that extrahepatic tissue cannot use.

27.16   The concentration of the higher density cholesterol is greater in HDL

27.17   The grams of a particular tissue or fluid needed to store one kilocalorie of reserve energy.

27.18 $3 < 1 < 2$

27.19   Fasting and diabetes.

27.20   Insulin suppresses the lipase needed to hydrolyze triacylglycerols in storage prior to the release of their fatty acids into circulation.

27.21 $E < D < A < C < B$

27.22   The operation of the β-oxidation pathway feeds electrons and protons directly to the respiratory chain, and it makes acetyl CoA that the citric acid cycle catabolizes as it also sends electrons and protons into the respiratory chain.

27.23   The citric acid cycle processes the acetyl units manufactured by the β-oxidation pathway and so fuels the respiratory chain.

27.24   Epinephrine and glucagon. They help keep a normal blood sugar level.

27.25   An increase in the blood sugar level triggers the release of insulin which inhibits the release of fatty acids from adipose fat.

27.26   It is changed to dihydroxyacetone phosphate, which enters the pathway of glycolysis.

27.27   They are joined to coenzyme A as fatty acyl CoA.

27.28

$$CH_3CH_2CH_2\overset{O}{\underset{\|}{C}}SCoA + FAD \longrightarrow CH_3CH{=}CH\overset{O}{\underset{\|}{C}}SCoA + FADH_2$$

$$CH_3CH{=}CHCSCoA + H_2O \longrightarrow CH_3CHCH_2CSCoA$$
(with O above the first structure's carbonyl and OH, O above the product)

$$CH_3CHCH_2CSCoA + NAD^+ \longrightarrow CH_3CCH_2CSCoA + NAD{\cdot}H + H^+$$
(with OH, O above reactant and O, O above product)

$$CH_3CCH_2CSCoA + CoASH \longrightarrow 2CH_3CSCoA$$
(with O, O above reactant and O above product)

No more turns of the β-oxidation pathway are possible.

27.29   FADH2 passes its hydrogen into the respiratory chain and is changed back to FAD.

27.30   NADH passes its hydrogen into the respiratory chain and is changed back to NAD⁺.

27.31   Steps 1-3 succeed in oxidizing the beta position of the fatty acyl unit to a ketone group.

27.32   (a)   Inside mitochondria.
        (b)   Cytosol.

27.33   An acetyl unit in acetyl CoA is activated for the overall synthesis.

$$CH_3CSCoA + HCO_3^- + ATP \longrightarrow {}^-OCCH_2CSCoA + 2H^+ + ADP + P_i$$
(with O above reactant and O, O above product)

The malonyl unit is transferred to the acyl carrier protein, ACP.

$${}^-OCCH_2CSCoA + ACP \longrightarrow {}^-OCCH_2CS{-}ACP + CoA$$
(with O, O above reactant and O above product)

Acetyl E is made by attaching acetyl CoA to the E unit of the enzyme.

$$CH_3\overset{O}{\overset{\|}{C}}SCoA + E \longrightarrow CH_3\overset{O}{\overset{\|}{C}}S\text{—}E + CoA$$

The acetyl group transfers from acetyl E to malonyl ACP.

$$CH_3\overset{O}{\overset{\|}{C}}S\text{—}E + {}^{-}O\overset{O}{\overset{\|}{C}}CH_2\overset{O}{\overset{\|}{C}}S\text{—}ACP \rightarrow CH_3\overset{O}{\overset{\|}{C}}CH_2\overset{O}{\overset{\|}{C}}S\text{—}ACP + CO_2 + E$$

The keto group of acetoacetyl ACP is reduced.

$$CH_3\overset{O}{\overset{\|}{C}}CH_2\overset{O}{\overset{\|}{C}}S\text{—}ACP + NADPH + H^+ \longrightarrow$$

$$CH_3\overset{OH}{\overset{|}{C}}HCH_2\overset{O}{\overset{\|}{C}}S\text{—}ACP + NADP^+$$

The 2° alcohol group is removed by dehydration.

$$CH_3\overset{OH}{\overset{|}{C}}HCH_2\overset{O}{\overset{\|}{C}}S\text{—}ACP \longrightarrow CH_3CH{=}CH\overset{O}{\overset{\|}{C}}S\text{—}ACP + H_2O$$

The alkene group is reduced by NADPH.

$$CH_3CH{=}CH\overset{O}{\overset{\|}{C}}S\text{—}ACP + NADPH + H^+ \rightarrow$$

$$CH_3CH_2CH_2\overset{O}{\overset{\|}{C}}S\text{—}ACP + NADP^+$$

27.34   The pentose phosphate pathway of glucose catabolism.
27.35   Mevalonate.
27.36   Cholesterol inhibits the synthesis of HMG-CoA reductase.
27.37   Oxaloacetate
27.38   Oxaloacetate is the carrier of acetyl groups in the citric acid cycle, so its loss means that the acetyl CoA level increases.
27.39

$$CH_3\overset{\text{O}}{\overset{||}{C}}CH_2\overset{\text{O}}{\overset{||}{C}}SCoA$$

27.40   A proton or hydrogen ion, H^+. If the level of hydrogen ion increases, the problem is acidosis.
27.41

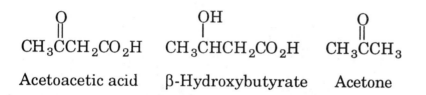

$$CH_3\overset{\text{O}}{\overset{||}{C}}CH_2CO_2H \qquad CH_3\overset{\text{OH}}{\overset{|}{C}}HCH_2CO_2H \qquad CH_3\overset{\text{O}}{\overset{||}{C}}CH_3$$

Acetoacetic acid   β-Hydroxybutyrate   Acetone

27.42   An above normal concentration of the ketone bodies in the blood.
27.43   An above normal concentration of the ketone bodies in the urine.
27.44   Enough acetone vapor in exhaled air to be detected by its odor.
27.45   Ketonemia + ketonuria + acetone breath.
27.46   Metabolic acidosis brought on by an increase in the level of the ketone bodies in the blood.
27.47   Acetoacetic acid.
27.48   Diuresis is accelerated to remove ketone bodies from the blood, and their removal requires the simultaneous removal of water, so the urine volume increases.
27.49   Their *over*-production leads to acidosis.
27.50   Amino acids are catabolized at a faster than normal rate to participate in gluconeogenesis, and their nitrogen is excreted largely as urea.
27.51   Each Na^+ ion that leaves corresponds to the loss of one HCO_3^- ion, the true base, because HCO_3^- neutralizes acid generated as the ketone bodies are made. And for every negative ion that leaves with the urine a positive ion, mostly Na^+, has to leave to ensure electrical neutrality.
27.52   A disease in which arterial walls become clogged by plaques—mixtures of collagen, elastic fibers, triacylglycerols, cholesterol and cholesterol esters.

27.53   A genetically caused sharply elevated level of blood cholesterol for which both parents bore the defective genes.

27.54   LDL, because its cholesterol contributes significantly to plaque deposits.

27.55   HDL

27.56   A low level of HDL means that cholesterol is not being returned to the liver in significant amounts.

27.57   Apolipoprotein(a)

27.58   Brown cells carry out fatty acid catabolism within themselves. White cells send the fatty acids to the liver.

27.59   The inner mitochondrial membrane permits a flow of protons across it only at those sites that connect to the enzyme responsible for making and releasing ATP.

27.60   It becomes heat.

27.61   The generation of body heat by catabolism.

27.62

(a) $CH_3CH_2CH_2CH_2CH_2\overset{\overset{\displaystyle O}{\|}}{C}SCoA$ + FAD $\longrightarrow$

$CH_3CH_2CH_2CH=CH\overset{\overset{\displaystyle O}{\|}}{C}SCoA$

(b) $CH_3CH_2CH_2CH=CH\overset{\overset{\displaystyle O}{\|}}{C}SCoA + H_2O \rightarrow$

$CH_3CH_2CH_2\overset{\overset{\displaystyle OH}{|}}{C}HCH_2\overset{\overset{\displaystyle O}{\|}}{C}SCoA$

(c) $CH_3CH_2CH_2\overset{\overset{\displaystyle OH}{|}}{C}HCH_2\overset{\overset{\displaystyle O}{\|}}{C}SCoA + NAD^+ \longrightarrow$

$CH_3CH_2CH_2\overset{\overset{\displaystyle O}{\|}}{C}CH_2\overset{\overset{\displaystyle O}{\|}}{C}SCoA + NADH + H^+$

(d) $CH_3CH_2CH_2\overset{O}{\overset{||}{C}}CH_2\overset{O}{\overset{||}{C}}SCoA$ + CoASH $\longrightarrow$

$CH_3CH_2CH_2\overset{O}{\overset{||}{C}}SCoA$ + $CH_3\overset{O}{\overset{||}{C}}SCoA$

27.63   (a)   7
      (b)   6
      (c)   6
      (d)   112. A table like Table 27.2 would be the following.

Intermediate	Maximum No. of ATP from Each	Total No. of ATP Possible fromEach Intermediate as Acetyl CoA Forms
6 FADH$_2$	2	12
6 NADH	3	18
7 CH$_3$COSCoA	12	84
	Sum	114
Deduct 2 high-energy phosphate bonds for activating the myristyl group		−2
Net ATP produced for each myristyl group as it changes to acetyl CoA		112

Chapter 28

Review Exercises, Chapter 28

28.1   The entire collection of nitrogen compounds found anywhere in the body.
28.2   To synthesize protein.
      To synthesize nonprotein compounds of nitrogen.
      To synthesize nonessential amino acids.
      To contribute to the synthesis of ATP.
28.3   Infancy.

28.4   They are catabolized. Some are converted to fatty acids.

28.5   Glutamic acid (glutamate)

28.6

$$\text{}^-O_2CCH_2CH_2\overset{\displaystyle O}{\overset{\displaystyle \|}{C}}CO_2^- + NH_4^+ + NADPH + H^+ \rightleftharpoons$$

$$\text{}^-O_2CCH_2CH_2\overset{\displaystyle NH_3^+}{\overset{\displaystyle |}{C}H}CO_2^- + NADP^+ + H_2O$$

28.7

$$C_6H_5CH_2\overset{\displaystyle O}{\overset{\displaystyle \|}{C}}CO_2H$$

28.8

$$(CH_3)_2CH\overset{\displaystyle O}{\overset{\displaystyle \|}{C}}CO_2H$$

28.9   The body can use it to make glucose by gluconeogenesis.

28.10 Lysine can be used to make fatty acids but not glucose.

28.11 Ketogenic

28.12

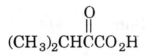

$$CH_3\overset{\displaystyle NH_3^+}{\overset{\displaystyle |}{C}H}CO_2^- + \text{}^-O_2CCH_2CH_2\overset{\displaystyle O}{\overset{\displaystyle \|}{C}}CO_2^- \longrightarrow$$

$$CH_3\overset{\displaystyle O}{\overset{\displaystyle \|}{C}}CO_2^- + \text{}^-O_2CCH_2CH_2\overset{\displaystyle NH_3^+}{\overset{\displaystyle |}{C}H}CO_2^-$$

$$\overset{\overset{\displaystyle NH_3^+}{|}}{^-O_2CCH_2CH_2CHCO_2^-} + NAD^+ + H_2O \longrightarrow$$

$$^-O_2CCH_2CH_2\overset{\overset{\displaystyle O}{||}}{C}CO_2^- + NADH + H^+ + NH_4^+$$

28.13 $4 < 1 < 5 < 2 < 3$

28.14 $5 < 2 < 1 < 3 < 4$

28.15   Yes: glucose $\dfrac{\text{aerobic}}{\text{glycolysis}} >$ pyruvate $\dfrac{\text{transa min ation}}{} >$ alanine

28.16

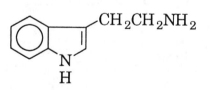

$$CH_3CH_2\overset{\overset{\displaystyle O}{||}}{C}CO_2^-$$

28.17

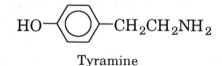

Tyramine

28.18

28.19   To synthesize glucose by means of gluconeogenesis

28.20   (a)   Originally, the amino groups of amino acids.
(b)   Carbon dioxide.

28.21   An above normal concentration of ammonium ion in the blood. Infants improve on a low-protein diet.

28.22 $2NH_3 + H_2CO_3 \rightarrow NH_2CONH_2 + 2H_2O$

28.23   Hyperammonemia. Step 2 consumes carbamoyl phosphate, which is made using ammonia. If carbamoyl phosphate levels rise, a backup occurs to cause ammonia levels to increase.

28.24   The purine bases of nucleic acids, adenine and guanine.

28.25   Sodium urate.

28.26 $3 < 2 < 1 < 4 < 5 < 7 < 6$

28.27   It gives the skin a yellowish color.

28.28   (a)   Bile pigments form faster than the liver can clear them.
(b)   Hepatic disease can prevent the liver from removing bilirubin from the blood.

28.29   Bile, carrying bile pigments, moves through the bile ducts. If it cannot move, the pigments back up into the blood.

28.30   Serine $\rightarrow$ pyruvate $\rightarrow$ acetyl CoA $\rightarrow$ (fatty acid synthesis)
$\rightarrow$ palmitic acid

28.31   The exclusively ketogenic amino acids, those not also glucogenic, cannot produce net extra oxaloacetate.

Chapter 29

Review Exercises, Chapter 29

29.1   It identifies the nutrients needed for health, determines the amounts required, and finds foods that are good sources of the nutrients.

29.2   It is any compound needed for health.

29.3   Foods are complex mixtures of nutrients.

29.4   Dietetics is the application of the findings of nutrition to the feeding of individuals whether ill or well.

29.5   To allow for individual differences among people and to ensure that practically all people can thrive.

29.6   1.   People with chronic diseases.
2.   People who must take special medications.
3.   Prematurely born infants.
4.   Pregnant women.
5.   Lactating women.
6.   People involved in strenuous physical activity.
7.   People exposed for prolonged periods to high temperatures.

29.7   No food contains all of the essential nutrients, and there might still be nutrients yet to be discovered but which are routinely provided by a varied diet.

29.8   (a)   The body must make its own glucose, which can lead to a buildup of harmful substances.

(b)   It lacks the essential fatty acids and it makes the absorption of the fat-soluble vitamins more difficult.

29.9   Linoleic acid. "Essential" means that it must be provided in the diet. If linoleic acid is absent in the diet, the prostaglandins are not made at a sufficient rate.

29.10   Linolenic acid and arachidonic acid.

29.11   Arachidonic acid

29.12   The body can make several amino acids itself.

29.13   Not all of the protein is digested, and of what is digested, not all is absorbed into circulation.

29.14   It breaks them down and eliminates the products.

29.15   Coefficient of digestibility $= \dfrac{(N\ in\ food\ eaten - N\ in\ feces)}{N\ in\ food\ eaten}$

The numerator, (N in food eaten − N in feces), is the food nitrogen that is actually absorbed into circulation.

29.16   From an animal source.

29.17   Mill them into flour, but this also lowers their vitamin and mineral content.

29.18   The proportions of essential amino acids available from it.

29.19   Human milk protein is the best, but whole egg protein is very close.

29.20   The essential amino acid most poorly supplied by the protein.

29.21   Corn protein is low in tryptophan and lysine.

29.22   (a) 1.3×10^2 g
        (b) 1.7×10^3 g
        (c) 6.1×10^3 kcal
        (d)   Very likely not, since 1.7×10^3 g is nearly 3 lb.

29.23

Vitamin	Source(s)	Problem(s) If Deficient
A	carrots	night blindness, deterioration of mucous membranes, blindness
D	dairy products, fatty fish	poor bone development, rickets
E	vegetable oils	edema and anemia (in infants), accelerated hemolysis, possible heart disease
K	green leafy vegetables	increased susceptibility to hemorrhages
C	citrus fruits, potatoes, leafy vegetables, tomatoes	scurvy, possibly increased susceptibility to colds
Choline	meats, egg yolk, cereals, legumes	none known in humans; fatty liver and kidney disease in animals
Thiamine	lean meats, legumes whole grains	beri beri

Vitamin	Source(s)	Problem(s) If Deficient
Riboflavin	milk, meat	problems with tissue around the mouth, nose and tongue; skin scaling; impaired wound healing
Niacin	meat, whole grains	pellagra
Folate	green, leafy vegetables:, liver, kidneys	megaloblastic anemia
B6	meat, wheat, yeast	possibly disturbances in the central nervous system; hyperchromic microcytic anemia
B12	meat and dairy products	pernicious anemia
Pantothenic acid milk	not observed clinically	liver, kidney, egg yolk, skim in humans
Biotin	egg yolk, liver, tomatoes, yeast	seldom observed; anorexia, nausea, pallor, dermatitis, depression

29.24   They are needed in much more than trace amounts, and they come from proteins.

29.25   Vitamin B_{12}

29.26   No single vegetable source has a balanced supply of essential amino acids.

29.27   Vitamins A, D, E, and K.

29.28   Vitamin D.

29.29   Vitamin D.

29.30   Vitamin A.

29.31   Vitamin A.

29.32   Vitamin K

29.33   A species that has an unpaired electron in the valence shell of one of its atoms. Free radicals attack essential components of cells and they accelerate the aging process.

29.34   Vitamins C and E

29.35   Partially oxidized cholesterol, produced by the action of free radicals, attracts white blood cells, and this can cause the buildup of plaque.

29.36   Vitamin C.

29.37   Vitamin C, choline, thiamin, riboflavin, niacin, folate, vitamin B_6, vitamin B_{12}, pantothenic acid, and biotin

29.38   Vitamin C

29.39   Vitamin C, thiamin, riboflavin, niacin, and folate.

29.40   Thiamin

29.41   Niacin

29.42   Folate

29.43   The quantity needed per day. Minerals are needed in the amount of more than 100 mg/day and trace elements in the amount of less than 20 mg/day.

29.44   Calcium, Ca^{2+}; phosphorus, P_i (Chiefly, the mix of HPO_4^{2-} and $H_2PO_4^-$ plus some PO_4^{3-} that exists at body pH and in bone.); magnesium, Mg^{2+}; sodium, Na^+; potassium, K^+; and chloride, Cl^-.

29.38

Trace Element	Functions
Fluorine (F^-)	sound teeth
Chromium (Cr^{3+})	glucose metabolism; work of insulin
Manganese (Mn^{2+})	nerve function, sound bones, reproduction
Iron (Fe^{2+})	heme, many enzyme
Cobalt (Co^{2+})	vitamin B_{12}
Copper (Cu^{2+})	in proteins and enzymes
Zinc (Zn^{2+})	enzymes, nucleic acids, bones; prevention of dwarfism; possible protection against heart disease
Selenium	possible protection against heart disease
Molybdenum	nucleic acid metabolism
Iodine (I^-)	synthesis of thyroid hormones

29.46   Goiter

29.47 2.13×10^3 L air

29.48   (a)   79 g

(b) 3.0×10^2 g

(c) 8.5×10^2 kcal

(d)   Because 3.0×10^2 g of peanuts is about 2/3 lb, a child could probably get this much down.